Birkhäuser Verlag
Basel · Boston · Berlin

ISNM 99:
International Series of Numerical Mathematics
Internationale Schriftenreihe zur Numerischen Mathematik
Série Internationale d'Analyse Numérique
Vol. 99

Edited by
K.-H. Hoffmann, Augsburg; H. D. Mittelmann, Tempe;
J. Todd, Pasadena

Birkhäuser Verlag
Basel · Boston · Berlin

Numerical Methods for Free Boundary Problems

Proceedings of a Conference held at the Department of Mathematics, University of Jyväskylä, Finland, July 23–27, 1990

Edited by

P. Neittaanmäki

1991

Birkhäuser Verlag
Basel · Boston · Berlin

Editor

P. Neittaanmäki
University of Jyväskylä
Department of Mathematics
P.O. Box 35
SF–40351 Jyväskylä
Finland

Deutsche Bibliothek Cataloging-in-Publication Data

Numerical methods for free boundary problems: proceeding of a conference held at the Department of Mathematics, University of Jyväskylä, Finland, July 23–27, 1990 / ed. by P. Neittaanmäki. – Basel ; Boston ; Berlin : Birkhäuser, 1991
(International series of numerical mathematics ; Vol. 99)
ISBN 3-7643-2641-7 (Basel ...)
ISBN 0-8176-2641-7 (Boston)
NE: Neittaanmäki, Pekka [Hrsg.]; Matematiikan Laitos <Jyväskylä>; GT

Printed from the authors' camera-ready manuscripts on acid-free paper in Germany
ISBN 3-7643-2641-7
ISBN 0-8176-2641-7

Preface

About 80 participants from 16 countries attended the Conference on Numerical Methods for Free Boundary Problems, held at the University of Jyväskylä, Finland, July 23–27, 1990. The main purpose of this conference was to provide up-to-date information on important directions of research in the field of free boundary problems and their numerical solutions.

The contributions contained in this volume cover the lectures given in the conference. The invited lectures were given by H.W. Alt, V. Barbu, K.-H. Hoffmann, H. Mittelmann and V. Rivkind. In his lecture H.W. Alt considered a mathematical model and existence theory for non-isothermal phase separations in binary systems. The lecture of V. Barbu was on the approximate solvability of the inverse one phase Stefan problem. K.-H. Hoffmann gave an up-to-date survey of several directions in free boundary problems and listed several applications, but the material of his lecture is not included in this proceedings. H.D. Mittelmann handled the stability of thermocapillary convection in float-zone crystal growth. V. Rivkind considered numerical methods for solving coupled Navier-Stokes and Stefan equations.

Besides of those invited lectures mentioned above there were 37 contributed papers presented. We shall briefly outline the topics of the contributed papers:

Stefan like problems. *Modelling, existence and uniqueness.*
In the contribution of I.G. Götz a nonuniqueness theorem for a self-similar solution in a model for phase transitions in binary mixtures is proved. Moreover, the existence of the generalized solution and the stability criterion are studied. In a joint paper of I. Götz and B.B. Zaltzman the disappearance of the mushy region in the multidimensional Stefan problem is discussed. N.V. Shemetov considers the Stefan problem with the time relaxation of Cattaneo, proves the existence of the weak solution of the relaxed Cattaneo-Stefan problem and shows that the weak solution of this problem converges to the weak solution of the Stefan problem. In the contribution of A.M. Maximov and G.G. Tsypkin a mathematical model of phase transition in frozen soil containing unfrozen water is proposed.

Modelling and numerical methods.
Z. Chen presents a numerical scheme to solve the continuous casting problem. The scheme is based on the nonequilibrium phase relaxation to smooth the enthalpy and the characteristic finite element method to treat the convection term. D.A. Kurtze presents a fixed grid finite element method for solidification. The method is intended for problems in which supercooling (and possibly superheating) occurs, and in which the effects of nonequilibrium interface kinetics and surface tension at the front are important. R.H. Nochetto, M. Paolini and C. Verdi study the mesh adaptation for the two phase Stefan problem in 2D domains and consider the efficient implementation of an adaptive FEM for parabolic free boundary problems. A. Bossavit considers a two-phase free boundary problem in magnetostatics and introduces special "mixed" finite elements for its numerical solution. K.-H. Hoffmann and K. Liu treat a thermodynamical model of ferromagnetism and its numerical simulation.

Concerning front-tracking there were two contributions. G. Bellettini, M. Paolini and C. Verdi consider front-tracking and variational methods to approximate interfaces with prescribed mean curvature and G.H. Meyer handles front-tracking of free boundaries with curvature terms and among others presents numerical results of front-tracking for 3D Stefan problem with Gibbs-Thomson interface condition.

A. Lapin proposes domain decomposition method to realize implicit mesh schemes for a class of singular parabolic equations including, among others, one-phase and two-phase Stefan problems. S. Jensen, E. Laitinen, P. Neittaanmäki and T. Seidman handle a free boundary problem modelling the growth/dissolution of a crystal and study the question of stability of a radially symmetric solution in two dimensions. The contribution of J. Steinbach is devoted to the numerical solutions of variational inequalities which are used to model the injection moulding process of a plastic melt into a mould cavity. S. Mazzullo, M. Paolini and C. Verdi give an analysis of thermal effects during the cementation of femoral prosthesis and present several numerical simulations to illustrate critical aspects of this implant.

Optimal control, optimal shape design, identification, applications.
V. Arnăutu considers approximation of the inverse one-phase Stefan problem in terms of an optimal control problem.

J. Haslinger and P.D. Panagiotopoulos study the approximation of the optimal control problem coverned by hemivariational inequalities. A.M. Khludnev considers the convergence of the solutions into problem of optimal control of the fourth order variational inequality (contact problem). T. Männikkö and M.M. Mäkelä apply a nonsmooth optimization technique (Proximal Bundle method) to solve control problems arising from the continuous casting process. M. Trigub considers numerical solutions of optimal control problems for a dynamical system described by ordinary differential equations. The proposed approach combines analytical expansions of nonlinear functions with error evaluation by Krotov's formula. V.N. Phat studies the control problem of nonlinear dynamical systems with phase constraints and gives some controllability criterion for discrete time systems. A. Kadoya and N. Kenmochi consider problems of shape optimization in which the driving actions are performed by geometry of the domain. V. Daněk and R. Mäkinen study the feasibility of finite element and mathematical programming methods for finding an optimal shape for a symmetric airfoil in the case of transonic flow. A. Mysklinski proposes a mixed variational approach for shape optimization in contact problem with prescribed friction. X.-C. Tai and P. Neittaanmäki present a linearization method concerning a nonlinear distributed parameter identification problem in which one recovers the nonlinear parameters from the identified linear parameters. Ch. Grossmann considers the numerical methods for solving variational inequality and proposes an iteration process for solving the discrete problems (obtained by mixed finite element method) and also investigates the selection rules for penalty parameters.

Dam, fluid flow and free boundary problems
N. Van Luoc deals with a free boundary problem of systems for earth dams with unknown intermediate water levels and separated variable filtration coefficients. C.A. Papadopoulos, J.M. Sloss and J.C. Bruch Jr. apply a domain decomposition to a free surface seepage problem. E.A. Karabut gives a semi-analytical investigation of unsteady free boundary

flows and presents the solution in the form of a power series in time, the coefficients for which have been computed. V.M. Teshukov considers long wave approximation for vortex free boundary flows. The work of B.E. Protopopov is devoted to numerical investigation of the process of soliton generation by a moving disturbance.

P.J. Shopov presents a numerical method for free surface hydrodynamical problems. With the contribution of C. Cuvelier and R.M.S.M. Schulkes the authors consider numerical methods for capillary free boundaries governed by the Navier-Stokes equations and in the contribution of R.M.S.M. Schulkes and C. Cuvelier eigenfrequencies of a viscous, imcompressible fluid with a capillary free boundary are studied.

The organizers are grateful to the participants, and especially to the speakers who made this meeting an important scientific event. We are indebted to the Administration of the Faculty of Mathematics, to the younger members of the numerical analysis group and to the secretatiat of the Department of Mathematics whose support was an indispensable contribution to the success of this conference. We also acknowledge the financial support for this meeting given by Academy of Finland, Research Council of Technology and Rolf Nevanlinna Institute.

Jyväskylä, April 1991 P. Neittaanmäki

CONTENTS

LIST OF CONTRIBUTORS

Alt, Hans Wilhelm
Institut für Angewandte Mathematik
Universität Bonn
Wegelerstr.6, D-5300 Bonn 1
Germany

Arnăutu, Viorel
Faculty of Mathematics
University of Iaşi
6600 Iaşi, Romania

Barbu, Viorel
Faculty of Mathematics
University of Iaşi
6600 Iaşi, Romania

Bellettini, G.
International School for Advanced Studies SISSA/ISAS
34014 Trieste, Italy

Bossavit, A.
Electricité de France
1 Avenue du Général de Gaulle
92141 Clamart, France

Bruch Jr, J.C.
Department of Mechanical and Environmental Engineering
University of California
Santa Barbara, CA 93106, USA

Chen, Zhiming
Institut für Mathematik
Universität Augsburg
Universitätstr. 8,D-8900 Augsburg
Germany

Cuvelier, C.
Joint Research Centre CEC
21020 Ispra (Va), Italy

Daněk, Vladimír
Institute of Thermomechanics
Czechoslovak Academy of Sciences
Prague, Czechoslovakia

Grossmann, Christian
Department of Mathematics
Dresden University of Technology
Mommsenstr.13,Dresden, Germany–8027

Götz, I.G.
Lavrentyev Insitute of Hydrodynamics
Siberian Division of the USSR
Academy of Science
Novosibirsk 630090, USSR

Haslinger, Jaroslav
Faculty of Mathematics and Physics
Charles University
KFK MFF UK KE Karlovu 5
12000 Praha 2, Czechoslovakia

Hoffmann, Karl-Heinz
Institut für Mathematik
Universität Augsburg
Universitätsstrasse D 8900, Augsburg
Germany

Jankowski, D.F.
Department of Mechanical and Aerospace Engineering
Arizona State University
Tempe, AZ 85287-6106 USA

Jensen, S.
Department of Mathematics and Statistics
University of Maryland, Baltimore Country
Baltimore, MD 21228, USA

Kadoya, Atsushi
Department of Mathematics
Graduate School of Science and Technology
Chiba University, Chiba-shi, 260 Japan

Karabut, E.A.
Lavrentyev Institute of Hydrodynamics
Siberian Division of the USSR
Academy of Science
Novosibirsk 630090, USSR

Kenmochi, Nobuyuki
Department of Mathematics
Faculty of Education
Chiba University, Chiba-shi 26,Japan

Khludnev, A.M.
Lavrentyev Institute of Hydrodynamics
Siberian Division of the USSR
Academy of Science
Novosibirsk 630090, USSR

Kunkun Liu
Institut für Mathematik
Universität Augsburg
Universitätsstrasse D 8900, Augsburg
Germany

Kurtze, Douglas A.
Department of Physics
North Dakota State University
Fargo, North Dakota 58105-5566
USA

Laitinen, Erkki
Department of Mathematics
University of Jyväskylä
Seminaarinkatu 15
40100 Jyväskylä, Finland

Lapin, Alexandre
Department of Numerical Mathematics
Kazan University
Lenin street 18, Kazan 420008,USSR

Law, Cindy C.
Department of Mechanical and
Aerospace Engineering
Arizona State University
Tempe, AZ 85287-6106 USA

Maximov, Alexej, M.
Institute for problems in mechanics
The USSR Academy of Science
Prospect Vernadskogo, 101
Moscow, 117526, USSR

Mazzullo, S.
HIMONT Italy
Centro Ricerche "G. Natta"
44100 Ferrara, Italy

Meyer, Gunter H.
School of Mathematics
Georgia Insitute of Technology
Atlanta, Georgia 30332, USA

Mittelmann, Hans.D.
Department of Mathematics
Arizona State University
Tempe, Arizona 85282, USA

Myslinski, Andrzej
System Research Institute
01–447 Warsaw, ul. Newelska 6
Poland

Mäkelä, Marko
Department of Mathematics
University of Jyväskylä
Seminaarinkatu 15
40100 Jyväskylä, Finland

Mäkinen, Raino
Department of Mathematics
University of Jyväskylä
Seminaarikatu 15,
40100 Jyväskylä, Finland

Männikkö, Timo
Department of Mathematics
University of Jyväskylä
Seminaarikatu 15,
40100 Jyväskylä, Finland

Neittaanmäki, Pekka
Department of Mathematics
University of Jyväskylä
Seminaarinkatu 15, 40100 Jyväskylä
Finland

Neitzel, G.P.
Department of Mechanical and
Aerospace Engineering
Arizona State University
Tempe, AZ 85287-6106 USA

Ngo Van Luoc
Institute of Mathematics
P.O.Box 631 Bo Ho 10000 Hanoi,
Vietnam

Nochetto, Ricardo H.
Department of Mathematics
University of Maryland
College Park, MD. 20742, USA

Panagiotopoulos, P.D.
Chair of Steel Structures
School of Technology of Aristotele
University
Thessaloniki, Greece

Paolini, Maurizio
Istituto di Analisi Numerica del CNR
Corso C. Alberto 5,I–27100 Pavia
Italy

Papadopoulos, C.A.
Department of Mathematics
University of California
Santa Barbara, CA 93106, USA

Pawlow, Irena
Systems Research Institute
Polish Academy of Science
Newelska 6, 01–447 Warsaw, Poland

Protopopov, Boris
Lavrentyev Insitute of Hydrodynamics
Siberian Division of the USSR
Academy of Science
Novosibirsk 630090, USSR

Rivkind, Vladimir
Department of Mathematics
University of Leningrad
Bibliotechnaya sg.2 Leningrad
Petrodvorets 198904 Leningrad, USSR

Schulkes, R.M.S.M.
Department of Mathematics
Delft University of Technology
P.O. Box 356, 2600 AJ Delft
The Netherlands

Seidman, T.I.
Department of Mathematics and Statistics
University of Maryland, Baltimore Country
Baltimore, MD 21228, USA

Shopov, Peter J.
Laboratory of Numerical Methods
Institute of Mathematics
acad. G. Bontchev str. bl. 8
1113 Sofia, P.O.Box 373, Bulgaria

Shemetov, N.V.
Lavrentyev Insitute of Hydrodynamics
Siberian Division of the USSR
Academy of Science
Novosibirsk 630090, USSR

Sloss, James M.
Department of Mathematics
University of California
Santa Barbara, CA 93106, USA

Steinbach, Jörg
Department of Mathematics
Technical University of Chemnitz
9010 Chemnitz, PSF 964, Germany

Tai, Xue–Cheng
Academia Sinica, Beijing, China
and Department of Mathematics
University of Jyväskylä
Seminaarinkatu 15, 40100 Jyväskylä
Finland

Teshukov, V.M.
Lavrentyev Institute of Hydrodynamics
Siperian Division of the USSR
Academy of Sciences
pr.Laventyeva 15,Novosibirsk 630090
USSR

Trigub, Maria
Kharkov Engineering Pedagogics Institute
Electromechanical Department
Kharkov 71, USSR
Moscow, 117526, USSR

Tsypkin, G.G.
Institute for problems in mechanics
The USSR Academy of Science
Prospect Vernadskogo, 101
Moscow, 117526, USSR

Verdi, Claudio
Dipartimento di Meccanica Strutturale
Universita di Pavia
Via Abbiategrasso, 27100 Pavia, Italy

Vu Ngoc Phat
Institute of Mathematics
P.O. Box 631, Bo Ho, 10.000 Hanoi
Vietnam

Zaltzman, B.B.
Institute of Water and Ecological
Problems, Siberian Division
Academy of Sciences of the USSR
Novosibirsk 630090, USSR

International Series of Numerical Mathematics, Vol. 99, © 1991 Birkhäuser Verlag Basel

A mathematical model and an existence theory for non-isothermal phase separation

HANS WILHELM ALT* AND IRENA PAWLOW**

Abstract. We present a mathematical model for non-isothermal phase separation in binary systems. The model is constructed within the Landau-Ginzburg theory of phase transitions and non-equilibrium thermodynamics. It consists of a system of nonlinear parabolic differential equations for the order parameter and the energy as conserved quantities. The model is conformable with the first principles of thermodynamics. Besides a description of the model we study the stability of stationary solutions, and give a survey of the existence theory for the system of governing differential equations.

AMS-Classification: 35K55, 35B40

1. The mathematical model

The process of spatial phase separation usually takes place in a multicomponent system which originally is in a thermodynamical equilibrium and then is rapidly cooled to a non-equilibrium state within the coexistence region of its phase diagram. Due to fluctuations of the initially homogeneous state the individual components locally separate and the system evolves to a new equilibrium with a spatially inhomogeneous structure. The phenomenon of phase separation appears in various physical systems, e.g., in metallic alloys, glasses, polymers, magnets, and liquid mixtures, see [11] and [12].

A commonly used phenomenological approach to formulate dynamical equations for phase transitions, in particular for phase separation, is based on the Landau-Ginzburg free energy functional

$$F_\Omega(c) := \int_\Omega F(c) \tag{1.1}$$

where $\Omega \subset \mathbb{R}^n$ is the region occupied by the system, and c is the order parameter which at each time instant t is a function over Ω. For binary systems $c(t)$ is the local concentration of either of the two components. The free energy density $F(c)$ has the form

$$F(c) = f(c) + \frac{\kappa}{2}|\nabla c|^2 \quad , \tag{1.2}$$

*supported by SFB 256, University of Bonn

**partially supported by the Research Program RP.I.02 of Ministry of National Education, Warsaw, and by SFB 256, University of Bonn where $f(c)$ is the local Helmholtz free energy density at constant concentration c , and the gradient term with a positive coefficient κ represents the surface energy between the two phases for a spatially non-constant distribution of c. The qualitative behavior of f as a function of c depends on the temperature. Typically, below a critical temperature f is a double-well function, see Fig.1a, that gives rise to thermodynamically unstable states, whereas above this temperature f is a convex function, what means that all homogeneous states are stable.

It is assumed that the dynamics of the system is governed by the first variation $\frac{\delta}{\delta c}F_\Omega$ of the free energy function F_Ω, which for a perturbation of c in the direction of a test function ζ is defined by

$$\langle \zeta, \frac{\delta}{\delta c}F_\Omega(c)\rangle := \frac{d}{d\epsilon}F_\Omega(c+\epsilon\zeta)|_{\epsilon=0} \quad .$$

For local perturbations ζ we have

(1.3) $$\langle \zeta, \frac{\delta}{\delta c}F_\Omega(c)\rangle := \int_\Omega \zeta \frac{\delta}{\delta c}F(c) \quad ,$$

where

(1.4) $$\frac{\delta}{\delta c}F(c) = f_{,c}(c) + \frac{\kappa_{,c}}{2}|\nabla c|^2 - \nabla\cdot(\kappa\nabla c) \quad \text{in} \quad \Omega \quad .$$

The representation (1.3), (1.4) also holds for perturbations near the boundary $\partial\Omega$, provided the natural condition

(1.5) $$\vec{n}\cdot\nabla c = 0 \quad \text{on} \quad \partial\Omega$$

is satisfied, where $\vec{n}$ denotes the outward unit normal to $\partial\Omega$.

Cahn and Hilliard, see [5], [6] and [7], have proposed an isothermal model for the dynamics of phase separation, based on the equation of continuity for the concentration c,

(1.6) $$\partial_t c + \nabla\cdot\vec{j} = 0 \quad \text{in} \quad \Omega, \quad \vec{n}\cdot\vec{j} = 0 \quad \text{on} \quad \partial\Omega \quad ,$$

with the generalized Fick's law

$$\vec{j} = -M\nabla\mu$$

for the mass flux $\vec{j}$, and mass isolation at the boundary. Here μ is the chemical potential difference between the two components, and the positive factor M represents the diffusive mobility. It has been assumed that the chemical potential difference μ is given by

(1.7) $$\mu = \frac{\delta}{\delta c}F(c) \quad .$$

Then equations (1.4) - (1.7) define a parabolic fourth order boundary value problem for c.

The postulate about the isothermal character of the process is justified in situations where thermal effects can be neglected. This applies in particular to metallic alloys with a large heat conduction. For materials with smaller heat conduction it is necessary to account for the temperature distribution as well. In [2] (see also [1]) we have proposed a mathematical model for non-isothermal phase separation. The model is constructed within the Landau-Ginzburg framework and non-equilibrium thermodynamics. In the case of an infinitely large heat conduction coefficient that model reduce to the Cahn-Hilliard equation.

The system of partial differential equations we consider consists of the mass conservation equation (1.6) coupled with the balance equation for the internal energy density E, given by

$$\partial_t E + \nabla \cdot \vec{q} = g \quad \text{in} \quad \Omega, \quad \vec{n} \cdot \vec{q} + p = 0 \quad \text{on} \quad \partial\Omega \quad , \tag{1.8}$$

where $\vec{q}$ is the energy flux, g is a given heat source density, and p is the heat exchange rate at the boundary. It follows from (1.8) that the total internal energy $\int_\Omega E$, up to the g and p terms, is conserved in time. We note that by (1.6) the total concentration $\int_\Omega c$ is also a conserved quantity.

The constitutive relations for the mass and energy fluxes are postulated according to the non-equilibrium thermodynamics (see [9]) in the form

$$\begin{aligned} \vec{j} &= -l_{11}\nabla(\frac{\mu}{\theta}) + l_{12}\nabla(\frac{1}{\theta}) \quad , \\ \vec{q} &= -l_{21}\nabla(\frac{\mu}{\theta}) + l_{22}\nabla(\frac{1}{\theta}) \end{aligned} \tag{1.9}$$

with a positive definite matrix $(l_{ij})_{ij}$. Here θ denotes the Kelvin temperature, and μ as before is the chemical potential difference. We remark that such approach has been used in [10] and [13].

The main postulate underlying the construction of our model concernes the non-isothermal version of the relation (1.7) between the chemical potential μ and the free energy F. The Landau-Ginzburg free energy potential now has the form

$$F(c,\theta) = f(c,\theta) + \frac{\kappa}{2}|\nabla c|^2 \quad , \tag{1.10}$$

where κ may depend on c and on θ as well.

In the case of homogeneous temperature distributions $\theta = const.$, the energy density

$$\frac{F(c,\theta)}{\theta}$$

rather then $F(c,\theta)$ itself is more relevant for the total free energy. For our further considerations we therefore stipulate that such potential is also adequate in the case of a non-homogeneous temperature distribution θ. To this purpose we introduce the reduced free energy potential

(1.11) $$\Phi(c,\theta) := \frac{F(c,\theta)}{\theta} \quad ,$$

and replace (1.1) by

(1.12) $$\Phi_\Omega(c,\theta) = \int_\Omega \Phi(c,\theta) \quad .$$

The corresponding non-isothermal version of relation (1.7) is then

(1.13) $$\frac{\mu}{\theta} = \frac{\delta}{\delta c}\Phi(c,\theta) = \frac{\delta}{\delta c}(\frac{F(c,\theta)}{\theta}) \quad .$$

By (1.10) and (1.5) the latter expression gives

(1.14) $$\frac{\mu}{\theta} = \frac{f_{,c}(c,\theta)}{\theta} + \frac{\kappa_{,c}}{2\theta}|\nabla c|^2 - \nabla\cdot(\frac{\kappa}{\theta}\nabla c) \quad \text{in} \quad \Omega, \quad \vec{n}\cdot\nabla c = 0 \quad \text{on} \quad \partial\Omega \quad .$$

Together with the balance equations (1.6) and (1.8) this provides the system of governing equations which consists of two parabolic and one elliptic equation of second order of the triple (c,μ,θ).

It is to be mentioned that the particular form of definition (1.13) of the chemical potential difference μ is important for the properties of this system. The divergence structure provided by (1.13) is essentially used to show that the model is conformable with the second law of thermodynamics (see section 3).

The model is to be completed by a constitutive relation between the free energy F and the internal energy E. This is postulated in the form of Gibbs relation

(1.15) $$F = E - \theta S, \quad \text{where} \quad S = -F_{,\theta}$$

is the entropy density of the system. According to the representation (1.10) we split E and S into volumetric and surface energy parts,

(1.16) $$E = e + \frac{\kappa - \theta\kappa_{,\theta}}{2}|\nabla c|^2 \quad \text{with} \quad e = f - \theta f_{,\theta} \quad ,$$

$$S = s - \frac{\kappa_{,\theta}}{2}|\nabla c|^2 \quad \text{with} \quad s = -f_{,\theta} \quad .$$

Let us now discuss properties and particular examples of the volumetric part $f(c,\theta)$ of the free energy density. It exhibits the standard different qualitative behavior as a function of c at various ranges of θ. At high temperatures f is a convex function of c whereas below a critical temperature θ_c it contains a non-convex part, e.g., assumes a characteristic double-well form, see Fig. 1a. We thus split f into $f = f^0 + f^1$, where f^0 denotes the convexification of f with respect to c, and therefore $f^1 \geq 0$. The region of states (c, θ) in the phase diagram in Fig. 1b where $f^1(c,\theta) > 0$ is thermodynamically unstable and, according to the classical mean field description, can be splitted into a region of metastability where $f_{,cc}(c,\theta) > 0$, and a region of instability where $f_{,cc}(c,\theta) < 0$. The curve separating these regions is termed spinodal, and the curve separating the unstable region from the stable one is termed binodal.

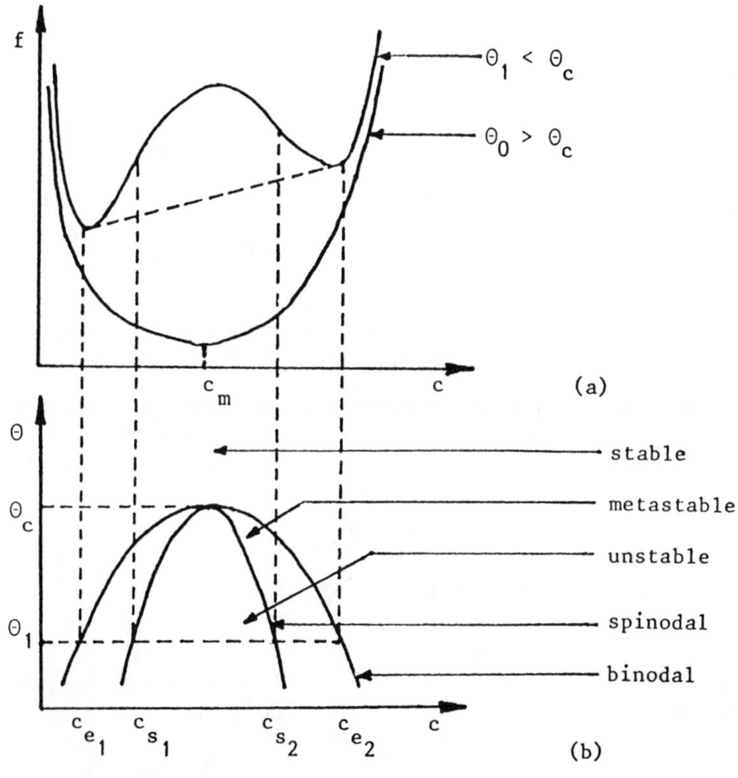

Fig.1 (a) Free energy f as a function of c at temperatures $\theta_0 > \theta_c$ and $\theta_1 < \theta_c$. (b) Phase diagram of f as a function of c and θ.

Explicit expressions for f, phenomenologically justified for various solid solutions, are usually fourth or sixth order polynomials in c, see [14], [15] and [16]. As a standard example for our model we take

$$f(c,\theta) = \alpha_0 f_*(\theta) + \alpha_1(\theta - \theta_c)c^2 + \alpha_2|c|^\nu \quad , \tag{1.17}$$

where $\nu > 2$ and $\alpha_i > 0$ are constants, and

$$f_*(\theta) = -\theta \log \theta, \quad \text{or} \quad f_*(\theta) = -\theta \log(1+\theta) \quad .$$

Correspondingly,

$$e(c,\theta) = \alpha_0 e_*(\theta) - \alpha_1 \theta_c c^2 + \alpha_2 |c|^\nu \quad ,$$
$$s(c,\theta) = \alpha_0 s_*(\theta) - \alpha_1 c^2 \quad ,$$

where for the first form of f_*

$$e_*(\theta) = \theta, \quad \text{and} \quad s_*(\theta)) = 1 + \log\theta \quad .$$

Therefore the internal energy e has physically realistic properties; it is bounded from below and linear in temperature, see e.g. the discussion in [17]. As a general postulate we assume that f is concave in temperature,

$$f_{,\theta\theta} < 0 \quad , \tag{1.18}$$

which means that the specific heat coefficient

$$C_V := e_{,\theta} = -\theta f_{,\theta\theta} > 0 \quad .$$

In the case of the first formula for f_* the specific heat coefficient is constant whereas for the second formula the entropy has the physically justified property $s_*(\theta) \to 0$ as $\theta \to 0$.

We remark that as a consequence of the concavity assumption (1.18) the free energy and entropy density obey the Legendre transform relations, see e.g. [17],

$$s(c,\theta) = \inf_{\tilde\theta > 0} \Big(\frac{e(c,\theta)}{\tilde\theta} - \frac{f(c,\tilde\theta)}{\tilde\theta} \Big) \quad ,$$

$$f(c,\theta) = \inf_{\tilde\theta > 0} \Big(e(c,\tilde\theta) - \theta s(c,\tilde\theta) \Big) \quad .$$

For the theoretical and numerical treatment we rewrite the system in terms of a concentration perturbation, the reduced chemical potiential, and the inverse temperature respectively, i.e.,

$$u := c - c_r, \quad v := \frac{\mu}{\theta}, \quad w := \frac{1}{\theta} \quad ,$$

where c_r is a given reference value. Noticing that

$$\theta f_{,\theta} + w f_{,w} = 0 \quad ,$$

we obtain

$$\Phi(u,w) = \varphi(u,w) + \frac{\kappa}{2} w |\nabla u|^2 \quad , \tag{1.19}$$

where $\varphi := wf$, and the Gibbs relation (1.15) reads as

$$E = \Phi_{,w} \quad \text{and} \quad S = w\Phi_{,w} - \Phi \quad . \tag{1.20}$$

Hence,

$$(1.21)\qquad E(u,w)=e(u,w)+\frac{(w\kappa)_{,w}}{2}|\nabla u|^2 \quad\text{with}\quad e(u,w)=\varphi_{,w}(u,w)\quad ,$$

$$(1.22)\qquad S(u,w)=s(u,w)+\frac{w^2\kappa_{,w}}{2}|\nabla u|^2 \quad\text{with}\quad s(u,w)=w\varphi_{,w}(u,w)-\varphi(u,w)\quad .$$

The example (1.17) now reads, with $c_r=0$,

$$\varphi(u,w)=\alpha_0\varphi_*(w)+\alpha_1(1-w\theta_c)u^2+\alpha_2 w|u|^\nu \quad ,$$

$$\varphi_*(w)=\log w,\quad\text{or}\quad \varphi_*(w)=-\log(1+\frac{1}{w})\quad .$$

From now on we assume that

$$\kappa=const.>0\quad .$$

Then (1.21) and (1.22) become

$$E(u,w)=e(u,w)+\frac{\kappa}{2}|\nabla u|^2 \quad\text{and}\quad S(u,w)=s(u,w)\quad ,$$

that is, the internal energy contains the whole surface energy term of the potential F whereas the entropy is purely volumetric. For constant κ the system of differential equations in terms of (u,v,w) is as follows

$$(1.23)\qquad -v+\varphi_{,u}(u,w)-\nabla\cdot(\kappa w\nabla u)=0\quad\text{in}\quad\Omega,\quad \vec{n}\cdot\nabla u=0\quad\text{on}\quad\partial\Omega\quad ,$$

$$(1.24)\quad \partial_t u-\nabla\cdot(l_{11}\nabla v-l_{12}\nabla w)=0\quad\text{in}\quad\Omega,\quad \vec{n}\cdot(l_{11}\nabla v-l_{12}\nabla w)=0\quad\text{on}\quad\partial\Omega\quad ,$$

$$(1.25)\qquad -\partial_t\Big(\varphi_{,w}(u,w)+\frac{\kappa}{2}|\nabla u|^2\Big)-\nabla\cdot(l_{22}\nabla w-l_{21}\nabla v)+g=0\quad\text{in}\quad\Omega,$$

$$\vec{n}\cdot(l_{22}\nabla w-l_{21}\nabla v)+p=0\quad\text{on}\quad\partial\Omega\quad .$$

From now on we shall consider this parabolic system. By a solution to this system we understand a weak solution (u,v,w) for which ∇u, ∇v and ∇w belong to $L^2_{loc}([0,\infty[;L^2(\Omega))$.

In order to give a perspicuous presentation of the existence theory for this system we restrict ourselves here to formal proofs (see section 3). For details we refer to [3], in particular for a-priori estimates on the nonlinear terms in the system which are consequences of the imposed structural assumptions.

The structural assumptions on the potential $\varphi:\mathbf{R}\times\mathbf{R}_+\to\mathbf{R}$ are the following. It admits a splitting $\varphi=\varphi^0+\varphi^1$ with C^2 - functions φ^0 and φ^1 such that φ^0 is convex in u, i.e.,

$$(1.26)\qquad \varphi^0_{,uu}(u,w)\geq 0\quad ,$$

and $u\varphi^0_{,u}(u,w) > 0$ for large $|u|$ uniformly in w. The remainder φ^1 is small compared to φ^0 in the sense that

$$(1.27) \qquad |\varphi^1_{,u}(u,w)| + |\varphi^1_{,uu}(u,w)| + (1+w)|\varphi^1_{,uw}(u,w)| \le C(1+w) \quad \text{for} \quad u \in \mathbf{R} \quad ,$$

$$|\varphi^0_{,u}(u,w)| \le C_\delta(1+w) \quad \text{for} \quad |u| \le \frac{1}{\delta} \quad .$$

For φ as a function of w we impose the concavity condition

$$(1.28) \qquad -\varphi_{,ww}(u,w) \ge \omega_0(w) > 0$$

with a continuous function $\omega_0 : \mathbf{R}_+ \to \mathbf{R}_+$.

For the energy we assume that for every $\alpha \ge 0$

$$(1.29) \qquad e(u,w) - \alpha s(u,w) \ge -C(\alpha)$$

with a constant $C(\alpha)$, and that for some small $\alpha_0 > 0$

$$(1.30) \qquad e(u,w) - \alpha_0 s(u,w) \ge c(\psi_0(u) + \psi_1(w)) - C \quad .$$

Here ψ_0, ψ_1 are positive continuous functions satisfying

$$(1.31) \qquad \frac{\psi_0(u)}{|u|} \to \infty \quad \text{as} \quad |u| \to \infty \quad ,$$

$$(1.32) \qquad \psi_1(w) \to \infty \quad \text{as} \quad w \to 0 \quad .$$

We assume that $u \mapsto \psi_0(u)$ is monotone for large values of $|u|$.

2. Stationary solutions

In this section we discuss the stability of stationary solutions to the system (1.23) - (1.25). We perform a nonlinear stability analysis based on a Liapunov functional which is non-increasing on solution paths. Besides we extend to our case the well-known linear stability analysis for the Cahn-Hilliard equation developed in [5].

Let $(\bar{u}, \bar{v}, \bar{w})$ be a stationary solution in the particular case $\kappa = const.$, $l_{ij} = \delta_{ij}$ (no cross effects), and $p = p(w)$ strictly monotone increasing in w. Then $\bar{v} =: \sigma = const.$, and

$$\varphi_{,u}(\bar{u},\bar{w}) - \kappa\nabla\cdot(\bar{w}\nabla\bar{u}) = \sigma \quad \text{in} \quad \Omega, \quad \vec{n}\cdot\nabla\bar{u} = 0 \quad \text{on} \quad \partial\Omega \quad ,$$

$$-\Delta\bar{w} + g = 0 \quad \text{in} \quad \Omega, \quad \vec{n}\cdot\nabla\bar{w} + p(\bar{w}) = 0 \quad \text{on} \quad \partial\Omega \quad .$$

We define the functional Q by

$$Q(u,w) := \int_\Omega \Big(\bar{w} E(u,w) - S(u,w) \Big) \quad . \tag{2.1}$$

Note that Q depends on the inverse temperature $\bar{w}$. We show

2.1 Proposition. For any solution (u,v,w) of (1.23) - (1.25) the function $t \mapsto Q(u(t),w(t))$ is non-increasing in t.

Proof. We prove that

$$\frac{d}{dt}Q(u,w) + \int_\Omega (|\nabla(v-\bar{v})|^2 + |\nabla(w-\bar{w})|^2) + \int_{\partial\Omega} (w-\bar{w})(p(w)-p(\bar{w}))d\mathcal{H}^{n-1} = 0 \quad . \tag{2.2}$$

This identity follows from the equations

$$v - \bar{v} = \varphi_{,u}(u,w) - \kappa\nabla\cdot(w\nabla u) - \sigma \quad \text{in} \quad \Omega, \quad \vec{n}\cdot\nabla(u-\bar{u}) = 0 \quad \text{on} \quad \partial\Omega \quad ,$$

$$\partial_t(u-\bar{u}) - \Delta(v-\bar{v}) = 0 \quad \text{in} \quad \Omega, \quad \vec{n}\cdot\nabla(v-\bar{v}) = 0 \quad \text{on} \quad \partial\Omega \quad ,$$

$$-\partial_t(E(u,w)-E(\bar{u},\bar{w})) - \Delta(w-\bar{w}) = 0 \quad \text{in} \quad \Omega, \quad \vec{n}\cdot\nabla(w-\bar{w}) + p(w) - p(\bar{w}) = 0 \quad \text{on} \quad \partial\Omega \quad .$$

In fact, multiplying the second differential operator above by $v-\bar{v}$ and the third one by $w-\bar{w}$ we obtain the integrals in (2.2) and

$$\int_\Omega \Big((v-\bar{v})\partial_t(u-\bar{u}) - (w-\bar{w})\partial_t(E(u,w)-E(\bar{u},\bar{w})) \Big) \quad . \tag{2.3}$$

The potential terms in this expression are

$$\int_\Omega \Big((\varphi_{,u}(u,w)-\sigma)\partial_t(u-\bar{u}) - (w-\bar{w})\partial_t(\varphi_{,w}(u,w)-\varphi_{,w}(\bar{u},\bar{w})) \Big) \quad .$$

Since $\int_\Omega u$ is time independent the σ-term vanishes, and we are left with

$$\int_\Omega \Big(\varphi_{,u}(u,w)\partial_t u - (w-\bar{w})\partial_t\varphi_{,w}(u,w) \Big)$$

$$= \int_\Omega \Big(\partial_t\varphi(u,w) - \partial_t((w-\bar{w})\varphi_{,w}(u,w)) \Big) = \partial_t \int_\Omega \Big(\bar{w}e(u,w) - s(u,w) \Big) \quad .$$

The surface energy terms in (2.3) are

$$\int_\Omega \Big(\kappa w\nabla u\cdot\partial_t\nabla(u-\bar{u}) - \frac{\kappa}{2}(w-\bar{w})\partial_t(|\nabla u|^2 - |\nabla\bar{u}|^2) \Big)$$

$$= \int_\Omega \left(\kappa w \partial_t (\frac{|\nabla u|^2}{2}) - \frac{\kappa}{2}(w - \bar{w})\partial_t |\nabla u|^2\right) = \partial_t \int_\Omega \frac{\kappa}{2}\bar{w}|\nabla u|^2 \quad .$$

By definition of Q this proves (2.2). □

2.2 Remark. The Liapunov functional Q can be written as

$$Q(u,w) = Q^0(u) + Q^1(u,w) \quad , \tag{2.4}$$

where $Q^0(u) := \Phi_\Omega(u,\bar{w}) = Q(u,\bar{w})$ is the Liapunov functional for the Cahn-Hilliard equation with a given temperature distribution $\bar{w}$, which is constant if $p = 0$ and $g = 0$. The contribution

$$Q^1(u,w) := \int_\Omega \Big(\varphi(u,w) - \varphi(u,\bar{w}) - (w - \bar{w})\varphi_{,w}(u,w)\Big)$$

with $Q^1(u,\bar{w}) = 0$ corresponds to the coupled mass and heat diffusion, and is non-negative by assumption (1.28). The differential equation for $\bar{u}$ implies that

$$\frac{\delta}{\delta u} Q(\bar{u},\bar{w}) = \sigma, \quad \text{moreover} \quad \frac{\delta}{\delta w} Q(\bar{u},\bar{w}) = 0 \quad .$$

This means that $(\bar{u},\bar{w})$ is a critical point for $Q(u,w)$ as a functional of (u,w) under the mean value constraint

$$⨍_\Omega (u - \bar{u}) = 0 \quad . \tag{2.5}$$

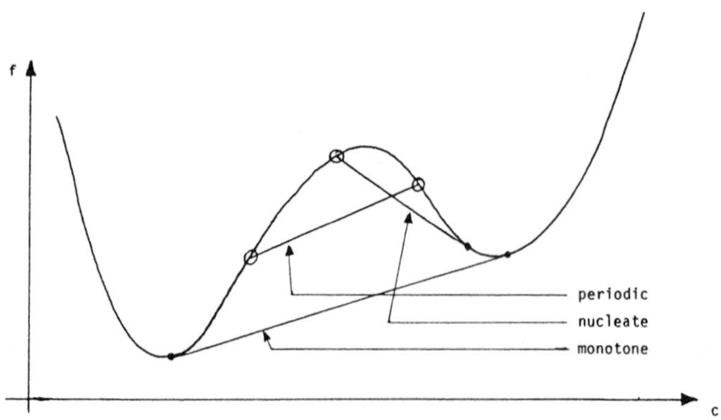

Fig.2. Illustration of one-dimensional periodic solutions.

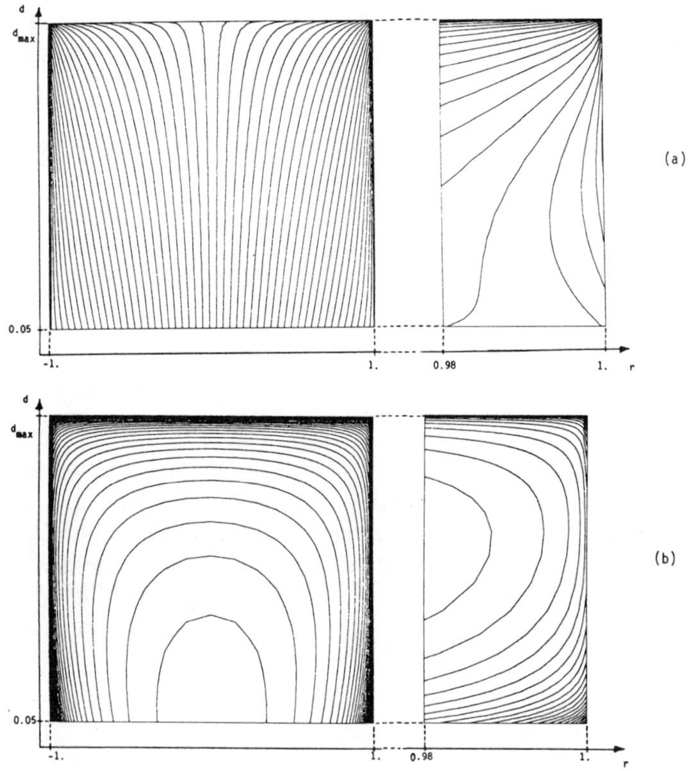

Fig.3. Mean value (a) and wave length (b) of periodic solutions as a function of a scaled middle value and oscillation.

We recall that in the one-dimensional case, and if $\bar{w} = const.$, the stationary solution $\bar{u}$ satisfies

$$\frac{\kappa\bar{w}}{2}|\bar{u}'|^2 = \varphi(\bar{u},\bar{w}) - l(\bar{u}) \geq 0 \quad ,$$

where $l(\bar{u}) = \sigma\bar{u} + \tau$ for some constant τ. It is well-known (see [16]) that for standard double-well potentials and on the entire real axis there are three classes of stationary solutions: periodic solutions, nucleate solutions with one extremum, and monotone van der Waal's solution. Periodic solutions correspond to the situation in which the line l intersects $\varphi(\cdot,\bar{w})$ with two positive angles, see Fig. 2. Nucleate solutions are related to the case in which l is tangential on one side. Van der Waal's solution refers to the situation in which l is the supporting tangent to the potential. Each of these solutions has a range $[u_-, u_+]$, and the set of all periodic solutions is a two parameter family with $\frac{1}{2}(u_+ - u_-) = d$ and $\frac{1}{2}(u_+ + u_-) = \frac{1-r}{2}u_{min}(d) + \frac{1+r}{2}u_{max}(d)$, where $|r| \leq 1$ and $0 < d < d_{max}$. Fig. 3a shows curves in the (r,d) plane which correspond to solutions with a given mean value;

solutions with equal wave length are shown in Fig. 3b. This illustrates the well-known fact (see [18]) that on a finite interval the number of stationary solutions of the Cahn-Hilliard equation with a prescribed mean value is finite. Moreover, as proved in [8], among all critical points of Q^0 non-monotone solutions cannot be even local minimizers of Q^0. The unique absolute minimum is van der Waal's solution.

For the subsequent (in part n-dimensional) stability considerations we need to introduce a family of neighborhoods of $(\bar{u}, \bar{w})$. For this purpose we replace Q^0 by

$$d^0(u) := \int_\Omega \Big(\varphi^0(u,\bar{w}) - \varphi^0(\bar{u},\bar{w}) - (u-\bar{u})\varphi^0_{,u}(\bar{u},\bar{w})\Big) + \frac{\kappa}{2}\int_\Omega \bar{w}|\nabla(u-\bar{u})|^2 \quad ,$$

which is non-negative by assumption (1.26). The distance of a pair (u, w) from $(\bar{u}, \bar{w})$ is then defined by

$$d(u,w) := d^0(u) + Q^1(u,w) \quad . \tag{2.6}$$

Since Q serves as the Liapunov functional the stability of $(\bar{u}, \bar{w})$ depends on the behavior of Q near $(\bar{u}, \bar{w})$. In the case of linear stability analysis we look at the behavior of a quadratic expansion of Q. To perform nonlinear stability analysis we compare Q with the distance function d in (2.6).

2.3 Proposition. For (u, w) satisfying (2.5) we have

$$|Q(u,w) - Q(\bar{u},\bar{w}) - d(u,w)| \le C\int_\Omega (1+\bar{w})|u-\bar{u}|^2 \quad . \tag{2.7}$$

Proof. Applying the differential equation for $\bar{u}$ and the equality (2.5) we have

$$Q(u,w) - Q(\bar{u},\bar{w}) = Q(u,\bar{w}) - Q(\bar{u},\bar{w}) + Q^1(u,w)$$

$$= \int_\Omega \Big(\varphi(u,\bar{w}) - \varphi(\bar{u},\bar{w}) - (u-\bar{u})\varphi_{,u}(\bar{u},\bar{w})) + \frac{\kappa}{2}\int_\Omega \bar{w}|\nabla(u-\bar{u})|^2 + Q^1(u,w) \quad .$$

Hence, using growth condition (1.27) for $\varphi^1_{,uu}$ the assertion follows. □

2.4 Corollary. If $\bar{w}$ is bounded and strictly positive then for any solution (u, v, w) of (1.23) - (1.25) the function $Q(u(t), w(t))$ is bounded for $t \geq 0$. Moreover, this function as well as $d(u(t), w(t))$ are continuous in t.

Proof. Let $\omega(t)$ denote the integrals in the identity (2.2) at time t, so that

$$Q(u(t),w(t)) + \int_0^t \omega(t')dt' = Q(u(0),w(0)) \quad . \tag{2.8}$$

Hence $Q(u,w)$ coincides almost everywhere with a continuous function. Moreover, since $\omega \geq 0$ it follows that $Q(u,w)$ is bounded from above. By assumption, $\frac{1}{\alpha} \leq \bar{w} \leq \alpha$ for some $\alpha > 0$. Therefore using (1.29) we have

$$\bar{w}e(u,w) - s(u,w) \geq \frac{1}{\alpha}e(u,w) - s(u,w) + \alpha \min(e(u,w),0) \geq -\frac{1}{\alpha}C(\alpha) - \alpha C(0) \quad .$$

This estimate implies that $Q(u,w)$ is also bounded from below. Note that employing this to (2.8) we obtain that $\omega \in L^1(]0,\infty[)$.

To prove the continuity of $d(u,w)$ we use the representation

$$d(u(t),w(t)) = Q(u(t),w(t)) - Q(\bar{u},\bar{w}) - \int_\Omega \gamma(x,u(t,x))dx$$

from the previous proof, where γ is a Caratheodory function with

$$|\gamma(\cdot,u)| \leq C_\alpha |u-\bar{u}|^2 \quad .$$

Since it follows from (1.24) that $u \in C^0_{loc}([0,\infty[;L^2(\Omega))$, we infer that $\gamma(\cdot,u) \in C^0_{loc}([0,\infty[;L^1(\Omega))$. This shows the continuity of $d(u,w)$. □

We are now concerned with the nonlinear stability.

2.5 Definition. We say that $(\bar{u},\bar{w})$ is stable if and only if for all solutions (u,v,w) of (1.23) - (1.25) for which $u(0)$ satisfies (2.5) and for which $d(u(0),w(0))$ is small enough, it follows that

$$d(u(t),w(t)) \to 0 \quad \text{as} \quad t \to \infty \quad .$$

The following holds in the one-dimensional case.

2.6 Proposition. Assume that $\bar{w}$ is bounded and strictly positive, and that $\bar{u}$ is an isolated stationary point of the Cahn-Hilliard equation with a prescribed inverse temperature $\bar{w}$. Moreover, suppose that φ satisfies the growth condition

$$|\varphi_{,w}(u,w)| + (1+|u|)|\varphi_{,u}(u,w)| \leq \gamma(w)(1+|u|^\nu)$$

for some $\nu \geq 0$ and with a continuous function $\gamma : \mathbf{R}_+ \to \mathbf{R}_+$. For $0 < \alpha < 1$ and $\rho > 0$ define

$$\lambda_{\alpha,\rho} := \inf\{Q(u,w) - Q(\bar{u},\bar{w}); \quad \alpha\rho \leq d(u,w) \leq \rho \quad \text{and} \quad u \quad \text{satisfies} \quad (2.5)\} \quad .$$

Then the following holds. If

$$\lambda_{\alpha,\rho} < 0 \quad \text{for some} \quad \alpha \quad \text{and a sequence} \quad \rho \to 0 \quad , \tag{2.9}$$

then $(\bar{u}, \bar{w})$ is unstable. On the other hand, if

$$\lambda_{\alpha,\rho} > 0 \quad \text{for some} \quad \alpha \quad \text{and a sequence} \quad \rho \to 0 \quad , \tag{2.10}$$

then $(\bar{u}, \bar{w})$ is stable.

Remark. The assumption on $\bar{u}$ is satisfied in the one-dimensional case provided $\bar{w}$ is constant. This follows from [18].

Proof. We work in the class of functions satisfying (2.5). Fix $\rho > 0$ in (2.9) and choose (u_0, w_0) with $d(u_0, w_0) \leq \rho$ so that $Q(u_0, w_0) < Q(\bar{u}, \bar{w})$, and let (u, v, w) be the solution with $u(0) = u_0, w(0) = w_0$. Integrating (2.2) in time we obtain for $t \geq 0$

$$Q(u(t), w(t)) \leq Q(u_0, w_0) < Q(\bar{u}, \bar{w}) \quad . \tag{2.11}$$

By contradiction assume that $d(u(t), w(t)) \to 0$ for a sequence $t \to \infty$. Then by definition (2.6) of d it follows that $\nabla u(t) \to \nabla \bar{u}$ in $L^2(\Omega)$. Thus the right-hand side of (2.7) converges to zero what contradicts (2.11).

Now assume that (2.10) holds. Choose $\rho_0 > 0$ sufficiently small to assure that $\{u; \quad d(u, \bar{w}) \leq \rho_0\}$ contains $\bar{u}$ as the only stationary solution of the Cahn-Hilliard equation with given inverse temperature $\bar{w}$. Take (u_0, w_0) with $d(u_0, w_0) \leq \delta_0 < \rho_0$. Then by (2.7)

$$Q(u_0, w_0) - Q(\bar{u}, \bar{w}) \leq d(u_0, w_0) + C \int_\Omega |u_0 - \bar{u}|^2 \quad ,$$

and using Poincare's inequality this is estimated by

$$\leq C d(u_0, w_0) \leq C\delta_0 < \lambda_{\alpha,\rho_0} \quad ,$$

provided δ_0 is small enough. Then it follows from the monotonicity of $Q(u, w)$ in Proposition 2.1 and the continuity of $d(u, w)$ in Corollary 2.4 that

$$d(u(t), w(t)) < \alpha\rho_0 \quad \text{for all} \quad t \geq 0. \tag{2.12}$$

Now consider any sequence $t_i \to \infty$ as $i \to \infty$ so that $[t_i - 1, t_i + 1]$ are disjoint, and define

$$u_i(t) := u(t_i - 1 + t) \quad .$$

Similarly define v_i and w_i. Since the function ω in (2.8) belongs to $L^1(]0, \infty[)$ as shown in the proof Corollary 2.4, we have

$$\epsilon_i := \int_0^2 \omega(t_i - 1 + t) dt \to 0 \quad \text{as} \quad i \to \infty \quad . \tag{2.13}$$

Therefore,

$$\mathcal{L}^1(\{t \in]0, 2[; \quad \omega(t_i - 1 + t) \geq \sqrt{\epsilon_i}\}) \leq \sqrt{\epsilon_i} \to 0 \quad .$$

Consequently, we can choose values $s_i \in [0,2]$, so that $\omega(t_i - 1 + s_i) < \sqrt{\epsilon_i} \to 0$ as $i \to \infty$. It follows that the functions $\bar{u}_i := u_i(s_i)$ etc., satisfy

$$\bar{w}_i \to \bar{w} \quad \text{in} \quad H^{1,2}(\Omega), \quad \nabla \bar{v}_i \to 0 \quad \text{in} \quad L^2(\Omega) \quad .$$

Since we restrict ourselves to the one-dimensional case only it follows that $w_i \to \bar{w}$ uniformly. Now we have $||\nabla(\bar{u}_i - \bar{u})||^2_{L^2(\Omega)} \leq Cd(\bar{u}_i, \bar{w}_i)$, which is bounded by (2.12). Hence, using (2.5) we conclude that

$$\bar{u}_i \to \bar{u}_\infty \quad \text{weakly in} \quad H^{1,2}(\Omega) \quad ,$$

and in the one-dimensional case, strongly in $L^q(\Omega)$ for $q < \infty$. Our purpose is to pass to the limit in the equation for $\bar{u}_i$

$$-\bar{v}_i + \varphi_{,u}(\bar{u}_i, \bar{w}_i) - \nabla \cdot (\kappa \bar{w}_i \nabla \bar{u}_i) = 0 \quad . \tag{2.14}$$

The polynomial growth of $\varphi_{,u}$ implies that $\varphi_{,u}(\bar{u}_i, \bar{w}_i) \to \varphi_{,u}(\bar{u}_\infty, \bar{w})$ in $L^q(\Omega)$. Multiplying (2.14) by 1 we derive that the mean value of $\bar{v}_i$ is bounded, consequently for a subsequence $i \to \infty$ and some $\bar{\sigma} \in \mathbf{R}$

$$\bar{v}_i \to \bar{v} := \bar{\sigma} \quad \text{in} \quad H^{1,2}(\Omega) \quad .$$

Thus we obtain as a weak limit of (2.14)

$$-\bar{\sigma} + \varphi_{,u}(\bar{u}_\infty, \bar{w}) - \nabla \cdot (\kappa \bar{w} \nabla \bar{u}_\infty) = 0 \quad , \tag{2.15}$$

that is, $\bar{u}_\infty$ is a stationary solution of the Cahn-Hilliard equation. By the imposed assumption on $\bar{u}$ it follows that $\bar{u}_\infty = \bar{u}$. Then multiplying the difference of (2.14) and (2.15) by the difference $\bar{u}_i - \bar{u}$ we obtain as $i \to \infty$

$$0 \leftarrow \int_\Omega \nabla(\bar{u}_i - \bar{u})(\bar{w}_i \nabla \bar{u}_i - \bar{w} \nabla \bar{u}) \geq \frac{1}{2} \int_\Omega \bar{w}_i |\nabla(\bar{u}_i - \bar{u})|^2 - \frac{1}{2} \int_\Omega \frac{(\bar{w}_i - \bar{w})^2}{\bar{w}_i} |\nabla \bar{u}|^2 \quad .$$

Since $\bar{w}_i \to \bar{w}$ uniformly, we conclude that $\nabla \bar{u}_i \to \nabla \bar{u}$ strongly in $L^2(\Omega)$. Using similar arguments and the growth condition on $\varphi_{,w}$ we derive that

$$d(\bar{u}_i, \bar{w}_i) \to 0 \quad \text{as} \quad i \to \infty \quad . \tag{2.16}$$

To get the desired stability statement we still have to show that

$$\sup_{[0,2]} d(u_i, w_i) \to 0 \quad \text{as} \quad i \to \infty \quad . \tag{2.17}$$

To this purpose, first note that such convergence holds for the functional Q. In fact, we see from (2.16) and (2.7) that $Q(\bar{u}_i, \bar{w}_i) - Q(\bar{u}, \bar{w}) \to 0$ as $i \to \infty$, therefore it follows from (2.8) and (2.13) that

$$\sup_{[0,2]} |Q(u_i, w_i) - Q(\bar{u}, \bar{w})| \to 0 \quad \text{as} \quad i \to \infty \quad .$$

Now let $\rho \to 0$ be a sequence for which $\lambda_{\alpha,\rho} > 0$. For any such ρ we have for large i

$$d(\bar{u}_i, \bar{w}_i) < \rho \quad \text{and} \quad \sup_{[0,2]} |Q(u_i, w_i) - Q(\bar{u}, \bar{w})| < \lambda_{\alpha,\rho} \quad .$$

Then the continuity of $d(u_i, w_i)$ in time and the definition of $\lambda_{\alpha,\rho}$ imply that $d(u_i, w_i) < \alpha\rho$ on $[0,2]$. This proves (2.17). □

We discuss the relationship between the stability criteria for the system (1.23) - (1.25) and for the single Cahn-Hilliard equation, (1.23) - (1.24) with given $\bar{w}$. To this purpose we introduce the corresponding quantity

$$\lambda^0_{\alpha,\rho} := \inf\{Q^0(u) - Q^0(\bar{u}); \quad \alpha\rho \le d^0(u) \le \rho \quad \text{and} \quad u \quad \text{satisfies} \quad (2.5)\} \quad .$$

Since $Q^0(u) = Q(u, \bar{w})$ and $d^0(u) = d(u, \bar{w})$ we see that

$$\lambda^0_{\alpha,\rho} \ge \lambda_{\alpha,\rho} \quad .$$

Now note that the above stability considerations hold also for the Cahn-Hilliard equation, that is, formally we set everywhere $w = \bar{w}$ and neglect all terms coming from (1.25). In particular, we can apply the criteria (2.9), (2.10) to λ^0 instead of λ. We conclude the following. If the stability criterion (2.10) is satisfied for the system then also for the Cahn-Hilliard equation. Conversely, if the instability criterion is satisfied for the Cahn-Hilliard equation then also for our system.

To show the equivalance between the stability criteria (2.9), (2.10) for the system and for the Cahn-Hilliard equation we need to estimate $\lambda_{\alpha,\rho}$ from below. To do this let us choose a sufficiently small $\delta_0 > 0$, and consider two situations for (u, w) in the definition of $\lambda_{\alpha,\rho}$. If $d(u, \bar{w}) \ge \delta_0\alpha\rho$ then

$$Q(u,w) - Q(\bar{u}, \bar{w}) \ge Q(u, \bar{w}) - Q(\bar{u}, \bar{w}) \ge \lambda^0_{\delta_0\alpha,\rho} \quad .$$

Otherwise $d(u, \bar{w}) \le \delta_0\alpha\rho$. Then by (2.7), provided $\bar{w}$ is bounded, we have

$$Q(u,w) - Q(\bar{u}, \bar{w}) \ge d(u,w) - C\int_\Omega |u - \bar{u}|^2 \quad ,$$

and using Poincare's inequality

$$\ge d(u,w) - C_0 d(u, \bar{w}) \ge \alpha\rho - C_0\delta_0\alpha\rho \ge \frac{1}{2}\alpha\rho \quad ,$$

provided δ_0 is chosen sufficiently small. Simultaneously, by similar arguments,

$$\lambda^0_{\delta_0\alpha,\rho} \le \inf\{Q(u, \bar{w})) - Q(\bar{u}, \bar{w}); \quad d(u, \bar{w}) = \delta_0\alpha\rho\}$$

$$\leq \inf\{(1+C_0)d(u,\bar{w});\quad d(u,\bar{w}) = \delta_0\alpha\rho\} = (1+C_0)\delta_0\alpha\rho \leq \frac{1}{2}\alpha\rho \quad ,$$

provided δ_0 is chosen small enough. Combining the considerations we conclude that for a sufficiently small $\delta_0 > 0$, independent of α and ρ,

$$\lambda_{\alpha,\rho} \geq \lambda^0_{\delta_0\alpha,\rho} \quad .$$

Hence, the following conclusions follow. If the stability criterion (2.10) with $\alpha < \delta_0$ is satisfied for the Cahn-Hilliard equation with given $\bar{w}$ then this criterion with $\frac{\alpha}{\delta_0}$ holds also for the system. Besides, if the instability criterion (2.9) with $\alpha > 0$ is satisfied for the system then it is also satisfied with $\delta_0\alpha$ for the Cahn-Hilliard equation.

Now we shall present briefly the main results that follow from the linear stability analysis of the system (1.23) - (1.25) (for details we refer to [2]). The linearized equations for perturbations $\tilde{u} := u - \bar{u}$,
$\tilde{v} := v - \bar{v}, \tilde{w} := w - \bar{w}$ of the stationary solution $(\bar{u}, \bar{v}, \bar{w})$ are

$$\tilde{v} = \bar{\varphi}_{,uu}\tilde{u} + \bar{\varphi}_{,uw}\tilde{w} - \kappa\bar{w}\Delta\tilde{u} - \kappa\nabla\cdot(\tilde{w}\nabla\bar{u}) \quad \text{in} \quad \Omega, \quad \vec{n}\cdot\nabla\tilde{u} = 0 \quad \text{on} \quad \partial\Omega \quad ,$$

$$\partial_t\tilde{u} - \Delta\tilde{v} = 0 \quad \text{in} \quad \Omega, \quad \vec{n}\cdot\nabla\tilde{v} = 0 \quad \text{on} \quad \partial\Omega \quad ,$$

$$-\partial_t\tilde{E} - \Delta\tilde{w} = 0 \quad \text{in} \quad \Omega, \quad \vec{n}\cdot\nabla\tilde{w} + \bar{p}'\tilde{w} = 0 \quad \text{on} \quad \partial\Omega \quad ,$$

where

$$\tilde{E} = \bar{\varphi}_{,ww}\tilde{w} + \bar{\varphi}_{,wu}\tilde{u} + \kappa\nabla\bar{u}\cdot\nabla\tilde{u}$$

and, according to (2.5), the mass constraint is

$$\int_\Omega \tilde{u} = 0 \quad .$$

Here the notation $\bar{\varphi} = \varphi(\bar{u}, \bar{w})$, etc. is used. The Liapunov functional that corresponds to this system (representing a quadratic expansion of Q) is

$$\tilde{Q}(\tilde{u}, \tilde{w}) = \frac{1}{2}\int_\Omega (\bar{\varphi}_{,uu}\tilde{u}^2 + \kappa\bar{w}|\nabla\tilde{u}|^2 - \bar{\varphi}_{,ww}\tilde{w}^2) \quad .$$

We consider the eigenvalue problem associated with the above system. In the case $\bar{u}=const.$ and $\bar{w} = const. > 0$ this system reads

$$\partial_t\tilde{u} - a\Delta\tilde{u} + b\Delta^2\tilde{u} - c\Delta\tilde{w} = 0 \quad , \tag{2.18}$$

$$d\partial_t\tilde{w} - \Delta\tilde{w} - c\partial_t\tilde{u} = 0 \quad , \tag{2.19}$$

where

$$a := \bar{\varphi}_{,uu}, \quad b := \kappa\bar{w} > 0, \quad c := \bar{\varphi}_{,uw}, \quad d := -\bar{\varphi}_{,ww} > 0 \quad .$$

In the one-dimenional case solution of (2.18), (2.19) admits the representation

$$\tilde{u}(x,t) = A(\beta,t)\cos\beta x, \quad \tilde{w}(t,x) = B(\beta,t)\cos\beta x$$

with A, B satisfying

$$\frac{d}{dt}\begin{bmatrix} A(\beta,t) \\ B(\beta,t) \end{bmatrix} + \beta^2 \begin{bmatrix} a+b\beta^2 & c \\ \frac{c}{d}(a+b\beta^2) & \frac{1+c^2}{d} \end{bmatrix} \begin{bmatrix} A(\beta,t) \\ B(\beta,t) \end{bmatrix} = 0 \quad .$$

The corresponding eigenvalues λ_+ and λ_- are then given by (we assume that $\lambda_- \leq \lambda_+$) :

$$\text{(2.20)} \qquad \mu_\pm := \frac{2\lambda_\pm}{\beta^2} = W \pm \sqrt{Z^2 + \frac{4c^2}{d}(a+b\beta^2)} = W \pm \sqrt{W^2 - \frac{4}{d}(a+b\beta^2)} \quad ,$$

where

$$W := (a+b\beta^2) + (\frac{1+c^2}{d}), \quad Z := (a+b\beta^2) - (\frac{1+c^2}{d}) \quad ,$$

$$W + Z = 2(a+b\beta^2) =: \mu_{CH} \quad , \quad \mu_{CH} = \frac{2\lambda_{CH}}{\beta^2}, \quad \lambda_{CH} := \beta^2(a+b\beta^2) \quad .$$

λ_{CH} is the eigenvalue that corresponds to the linearized Cahn-Hilliard equation, i.e., equation (2.18) with $c = 0$. If follows from the representation of $\mu_\pm$ in (2.20) that if $a + b\beta^2 > 0$ then $0 < \mu_- < \mu_{CH}$. In turn, if $a + b\beta^2 < 0$ then $\mu_{CH} < \mu_- < 0$. With this we arrive at the following conclusions. The instability condition for the system (2.18), (2.19), i.e., $\mu_- < 0$, is satisfied if and only if it is satisfied for the Cahn-Hilliard equation (2.18), i.e., $\mu_{CH} < 0$. Moreover, if the Cahn-Hilliard equation is stable, i.e., $\mu_{CH} > 0$, then the system is less stable, $0 < \mu_- < \mu_{CH}$. On the contrary, if the Cahn-Hilliard equation is unstable, i.e., $\mu_{CH} < 0$, then the system is less unstable, $\mu_{CH} < \mu_- < 0$.

3. Existence theory

We give a survey of the existence proof developed in [3] for the initial boundary value problem (1.23) - (1.25). The main difficulty which arises in the existence theory for weak solutions is the lack of maximum principles for the temperature. As a consequence, the coefficient κw in the highest order term of (1.23)-(1.24) can degenerate or explode. We solve this difficulty by a variational inequality approximation with constraint $\epsilon \leq w \leq \frac{1}{\epsilon}$. This is applied to the time-discrete approximation of the system, defined as follows.

3.1 Time discretization. For small time steps $\tau > 0$ we replace ∂_t in (1.24) and (1.25) by the backward difference quotient $\partial_t^{-\tau}$, and shall denote by (u_τ, v_τ, w_τ) the time-discrete solution which has the form

$$u_\tau(t) = u^i \quad \text{for} \quad (i-1)\tau < t \leq i\tau, \quad \text{etc.} \ ,$$

that is, (u^i, v^i, w^i) represents the solution at time $i\tau$ and will be element of the cone

(3.1)
$$\mathcal{M} := \{(u,v,w) \in V \quad ; \quad w > 0 \quad \text{almost everywhere in } \Omega\} \text{ with } V := H^{1,2}(\Omega; \mathbb{R}^3) \quad .$$

3.2 Time-discrete operators. To solve the time-discrete equation at time $i\tau$, we introduce

$$\langle \zeta, \mathcal{F}_0^i(u,v,w) \rangle := \int_\Omega \Big(\zeta(-v + \varphi^0_{,u}(u,w) + \frac{\varphi^1(u,w) - \varphi^1(u^{i-1},w)}{u - u^{i-1}}) + \kappa w \nabla\zeta \cdot \nabla u \Big) \quad ,$$

$$\langle \xi, \mathcal{F}_1^i(u,v,w) \rangle := \int_\Omega \Big(\xi(u - u^{i-1}) + \tau \nabla\xi \cdot (l_{11}\nabla v - l_{12}\nabla w) \Big) \quad ,$$

$$\langle \eta, \mathcal{F}_2^i(u,v,w) \rangle := -\int_\Omega \eta \Big(E(u,w) - E(u^{i-1}, w^{i-1}) \Big)$$

$$+\tau \int_\Omega \Big(\nabla\eta \cdot (l_{22}\nabla w - l_{21}\nabla v) + \eta g^i \Big) + \tau \int_{\partial\Omega} \eta p d\mathcal{H}^{n-1} \quad ,$$

where $l_{ij} = l_{ij}(u,v,w), p = p(w)$, and

$$g^i(x) := \int_{(i-1)\tau}^{i\tau} g(t,x)dt \quad .$$

It is a part of the existence theory to specify minimal conditions on the solution $(u^i, v^i, w^i) \in \mathcal{M}$ and the test triple $(\zeta, \xi, \eta) \in V$ so that the operators $\mathcal{F}_k^i, k = 0,1,2$, are well-defined on these triples. Before we go into this theory let us first summarize the assumptions on the data.

3.3 Assumptions. In addition to the structural assumptions (1.26) - (1.32) we assume that $(l_{ij})_{ij}$ is uniformly bounded and strictly positive, and that p is continuous with

(3.2)
$$p(w) \to \infty \quad \text{as} \quad w \to \infty \quad .$$

As growth conditions we assume

(3.3)
$$-C \le p(w) \le Cw, \quad 0 \le wp_{,w}(w) \le C(p(w)_+ + 1) \quad .$$

Further we assume $g \in L^\infty(\Omega_{t_0})$ with $\Omega_{t_0} :=]0, t_0[\times \Omega$, and that the initial data $u_0, w_0 \in H^{1,2}(\Omega)$ satisfy

(3.4)
$$\psi_0(u_0) \in L^1(\Omega), \quad \psi_1(w_0) \in L^1(\Omega) \quad .$$

We postulate the growth conditions

(3.5)
$$-C \le e(u,w) \le C(\Psi(u,w) + 1) \quad ,$$

(3.6) $$|\varphi(0,w)| + |s(u,w)| \le \delta\Psi(u,w) + C\delta$$

for $\delta > 0$, where

$$\Psi(u,w) := \psi_0(u) + |u|^{q_n} + \psi_1(w) + (1+|u|^{q_n-1})w \quad ,$$

and q_n is the exponent for which the Sobolev embedding from $H^{1,2}(\Omega)$ to $L^{q_n}(\Omega)$ is continuous. The dual exponent of q_n we denote by q_n^*. Moreover, we assume that

(3.7) $$l := \frac{l_{12}}{l_{22}} \quad \text{is globally bounded and Lipschitz continuous} \quad .$$

To explain the existence proof for the time-discrete problem we derive formally estimates for solutions of this problem. The proof is based on the identity

$$\frac{d}{dt}\int_\Omega S(u,w) = \int_\Omega \nabla\begin{pmatrix} v \\ w \end{pmatrix} \cdot (l_{ij})\nabla\begin{pmatrix} v \\ w \end{pmatrix} + \int_\Omega wg + \int_{\partial\Omega} wp(w)$$

which formally follows by multiplying equation (1.24) by v and (1.25) by w, then integrating over Ω and using boundary conditions. Since by assumption the matrix $(l_{ij})_{ij}$ is positive definite, and $\vec{n}\cdot\vec{j} = 0, \quad \vec{n}\cdot\vec{q} + p(w) = 0$ on $\partial\Omega$, the above identity implies the inequality

$$\frac{d}{dt}\int_\Omega S(u,w) + \int_\Omega \nabla\cdot(w\vec{q} - v\vec{j}) - \int_\Omega wg \ge 0 \quad .$$

The latter is known as Clausius-Duhem inequality for the entropy production and represents one of possible formulations of the second principle of thermodynamics.

In the following proof we derive a discrete version of the Clausius-Duhem inequality. We use the notation in 3.1.

3.4 Lemma. The discrete solution $(u,v,w) := (u_\tau, v_\tau, w_\tau)$ with initial data $(u^0, w^0) = (u_0, w_0)$ and with

$$\mathcal{F}_k^i(u^i, v^i, w^i) = 0 \quad \text{for} \quad k = 0,1,2 \quad \text{and} \quad i \ge 1$$

satisfies the following a-priori estimates with a constant C depending on the data and t_0, but independent of τ:

(1) $$\int_0^{t_0} \left(||\nabla v(t)||^2_{L^2(\Omega)} + ||\nabla w(t)||^2_{L^2(\Omega)}\right) dt \le C \quad ,$$

(2) $$\sup_{0<t<t_0} \left(||\nabla u(t)||_{L^2(\Omega)} + ||\psi_0(u(t))||_{L^1(\Omega)} + ||\psi_1(w(t))||_{L^1(\Omega)}\right) \le C \quad ,$$

$$\text{(3)} \qquad \int_0^{t_0} \|(1+w(t))p(w(t))\|_{L^1(\partial\Omega)} \leq C \quad .$$

Proof. We consider for $\alpha > 0$ and $i_0 \geq 1$

$$0 = \sum_{i=1}^{i_0} \Big(\langle u^i - u^{i-1}, \mathcal{F}_0^i(u^i, v^i, w^i) \rangle + \langle v^i, \mathcal{F}_1^i(u^i, v^i, w^i) \rangle + \langle w^i - \alpha, \mathcal{F}_2^i(u^i, v^i, w^i) \rangle \Big) \quad .$$

The terms containing the coefficients $(l_{ij})_{ij}$ will give (1). The potential terms not containing α are

$$\sum_{i=1}^{i_0} \int_\Omega \Big((u^i - u^{i-1}) \varphi^0_{,u}(u^i, w^i) + \varphi^1(u^i, w^i) - \varphi^1(u^{i-1}, w^i) - w^i(\varphi_{,w}(u^i, w^i) - \varphi_{,w}(u^{i-1}, w^{i-1})) \Big) \quad .$$

By the convexity (1.26) and the concavity (1.28) this is

$$\geq \sum_{i=1}^{i_0} \int_\Omega (-s(u^i, w^i) + s(u^{i-1}, w^{i-1})) = -\int_\Omega s(u^{i_0}, w^{i_0}) + \int_\Omega s(u_0, w_0) \quad .$$

Adding the α-terms we arrive at

$$\int_\Omega \Big(\alpha E(u^{i_0}, w^{i_0}) - S(u^{i_0}, w^{i_0}) \Big) - \int_\Omega \Big(\alpha E(u_0, w_0) - S(u_0, w_0) \Big) \quad .$$

Then using (1.30) with $\alpha = \alpha_0^{-1}$ we will obtain the left-hand side of (2) at time $i_0\tau$. The κ-terms not containing α are

$$\sum_{i=1}^{i_0} \kappa \int_\Omega \Big(w^i \nabla(u^i - u^{i-1}) \cdot \nabla u^i - \frac{1}{2} w^i (|\nabla u^i|^2 - |\nabla u^{i-1}|^2) \Big)$$

$$= \sum_{i=1}^{i_0} \frac{\kappa}{2} \int_\Omega w^i |\nabla(u^i - u^{i-1})|^2 \geq 0 \quad .$$

Thus we obtain the inequality

$$\int_\Omega \Big(\alpha E(u^{i_0}, w^{i_0}) - S(u^{i_0}, w^{i_0}) \Big) + c \sum_{i=1}^{i_0} \tau \int_\Omega (|\nabla v^i|^2 + |\nabla w^i|^2)$$

$$+ \sum_{i=1}^{i_0} \tau \Big(\int_\Omega (w^i - \alpha) g^i + \int_{\partial\Omega} (w^i - \alpha) p(w^i) d\mathcal{H}^{n-1} \Big)$$

$$\leq \int_\Omega \Big(\alpha E(u_0, w_0) - S(u_0, w_0) \Big) \quad .$$

The source terms are estimated by

$$\geq \sum_{i=1}^{i_0} \tau \Big(\int_{\partial\Omega} (w^i - \alpha) p(w^i) d\mathcal{H}^{n-1} - C \int_\Omega |w^i - \alpha| \Big)$$

$$\geq -C \sum_{i=1}^{i_0} \tau \int_\Omega |\nabla w^i| + \sum_{i=1}^{i_0} \tau \int_{\partial\Omega} \Big((w^i - \alpha) p(w^i) - C |w^i - \alpha| \Big) d\mathcal{H}^{n-1} \quad .$$

The first term is absorbed by (1), and using (3.2) and (3.3) the second term is

$$\geq \sum_{i=1}^{i_0} \tau \Big(\int_{\partial\Omega} w^i p(w^i)_+ d\mathcal{H}^{n-1} - C(\alpha) \Big)$$

which gives (3) .

□

3.5 Lemma. In addition the discrete solution $(u, v, w) := (u_\tau, v_\tau, w_\tau)$ satisfies the following a–priori estimates:

(1) $$\sup_{0<t<t_0} ||u(t)||_{L^{q_n}(\Omega)} + \int_0^{t_0} \Big(||w(t)||_{L^{q_n}(\Omega)} + ||w(t) p(w(t))||_{L^1(\Omega)} \Big) dt \leq C \quad ,$$

(2) $$\int_0^{t_0} \Big(||v(t) - \nu(t)||^2_{L^{q_n}(\Omega)} + |\nu(t)| \Big) dt \leq C, \quad \text{where} \quad \nu(t) := \fint_\Omega v(t) \quad ,$$

(3) $$\int_0^{t_0} ||(1 + |u(t)|) \varphi^0_{,u}(u(t), w(t))||_{L^1(\Omega)} dt \leq C \quad , \int_0^{t_0} ||\sqrt{w(t)} \nabla u(t)||^2_{L^2(\Omega)} dt \leq C \quad ,$$

(4) $$\sup_{0<t<t_0} ||e(u(t), w(t))||_{L^1(\Omega)} \leq C \quad .$$

Proof. The L^{q_n}-estimates follow from Sobolev's embeddings using (1.31) for u and (3.2) for w. By (3.3)

$$|(wp(w))_{,w}|^2 \leq C(|p(w)| + 1)^2 \leq C(|wp(w)| + w + 1)$$

which implies

$$\int_\Omega |w^i p(w^i)| \leq C \Big(\int_\Omega |(w^i p(w^i))_{,w} \nabla w^i| + \int_{\partial\Omega} |w^i p(w^i)| d\mathcal{H}^{n-1} \Big)$$

$$\leq \delta \int_\Omega |w^i p(w^i)| + C_\delta \int_\Omega (1 + w^i + |\nabla w^i|^2) + C \int_{\partial\Omega} |w^i p(w^i)| d\mathcal{H}^{n-1} \quad ,$$

which gives the last estimate in (1). From $\langle 1, \mathcal{F}_0^i(u^i, v^i, w^i) \rangle = 0$ we derive, using (1.27)

$$|\int_\Omega v^i| = |\int_\Omega \varphi_{,u}(u^i, w^i)| \leq \delta \int_\Omega |u^i \varphi^0_{,u}(u^i, w^i)| + C_\delta(||w^i||_{L^1(\Omega)} + 1) \quad ,$$

and from $\langle u^i, \mathcal{F}_0^i(u^i, v^i, w^i) \rangle = 0$, using (1)

$$\int_\Omega \left(|u^i \varphi^0_{,u}(u^i, w^i)| + w^i |\nabla u^i|^2 \right) \leq C \int_\Omega |u^i| (|v^i| + |w^i| + 1) \leq C(||v^i||_{L^{q_n^*}(\Omega)} + ||w^i||_{L^{q_n^*}(\Omega)} + 1) \quad .$$

Applying Sobolev inequalities to v_i and using 3.4(1) these two inequalities give (2), and then the second inequality implies (3). Estimate (4) is a consequence of $\langle 1, \mathcal{F}_2^i(u^i, v^i, w^i) \rangle = 0$, by (3.4) and (3.5). □

With these estimates we are able to prove

3.6 Theorem. There exist (u_τ, v_τ, w_τ) satisfying the estimates in Lemma 3.4 and Lemma 3.5, such that for $i \geq 1$

$$\langle \zeta, \mathcal{F}_0^i(u^i, v^i, w^i) \rangle = 0, \quad \langle \xi, \mathcal{F}_1^i(u^i, v^i, w^i) \rangle = 0, \quad \langle \eta, \mathcal{F}_2^i(u^i, v^i, w^i) \rangle = 0$$

for test triples $(\zeta, \xi, \eta) \in V$ with $\zeta, \eta \in L^\infty(\Omega)$ and $\sqrt{w^i} \nabla \zeta \in L^2(\Omega)$.

Sketch of proof. We consider at time $i\tau$

$$\langle (\zeta, \xi, \eta), \mathcal{F}^i(u, v, w) \rangle := \langle \zeta, \mathcal{F}_0^i(u, v, w) \rangle + \langle \xi, \mathcal{F}_1^i(u, v, w) \rangle + \langle \eta, \mathcal{F}_2^i(u, v, w) \rangle$$

on the set $\mathcal{M}_\epsilon \cap V_m$, where

$$\mathcal{M}_\epsilon := \{(u, v, w) \in \mathcal{M}; \quad \epsilon \leq w \leq \frac{1}{\epsilon} \quad \text{almost everywhere and} \quad |\fint_\Omega v| \leq \frac{1}{\epsilon}\}$$

with $\epsilon > 0$, and $V_m \subset H^{1,\infty}(\Omega; \mathbf{R}^3)$ is a suitable Galerkin approximation of V. To be consistent with this approximation one has to replace u^{i-1} in the definitions of $\mathcal{F}_h^i$ by suitable approximations u_m^{i-1}. Then the inequality in the proof of Lemma 3.4, performed for a single time step, gives the coercivity of $\mathcal{F}^i$ on $\mathcal{M}_\epsilon \cap V_m$. This implies the existence of a triple $(u_{\epsilon m}^i, v_{\epsilon m}^i, w_{\epsilon m}^i)$ in this set so that

(3.8)

$$0 \geq \langle (u_{\epsilon m}^i, v_{\epsilon m}^i, w_{\epsilon m}^i) - (\tilde{u}, \tilde{v}, \tilde{w}), \mathcal{F}^i(u_{\epsilon m}^i, v_{\epsilon m}^i, w_{\epsilon m}^i) \rangle \quad \text{for all} \quad (\tilde{u}, \tilde{v}, \tilde{w}) \in \mathcal{M}_\epsilon \cap V_m \quad .$$

Moreover, the coercivity implies estimates as in Lemma 3.4 and Lemma 3.5, uniform in m and ϵ. Then we infer that the constraint for $v_{\epsilon m}^i$ in the definition of $\mathcal{M}_\epsilon$ is inactive for small ϵ. Thus we can pass to the limit with $m \to \infty$, and then $\epsilon \to 0$ to obtain a triple $(u^i, v^i, w^i) \in \mathcal{M}$ so that

$$0 \geq \langle (u^i, v^i, w^i)) - (\tilde{u}, \tilde{v}, \tilde{w}), \mathcal{F}^i(u^i, v^i, w^i)\rangle \tag{3.9}$$

for all $(\tilde{u}, \tilde{v}, \tilde{w}) \in \mathcal{M}$ satisfying

$$|\tilde{u}| \leq \frac{1}{\epsilon_0} \quad \text{and} \quad \epsilon_0 \leq \tilde{w} \leq \frac{1}{\epsilon_0} \quad \text{for some} \quad \epsilon_0 > 0, \quad \text{and} \quad \int_\Omega w^i |\nabla \tilde{u}|^2 < \infty \quad .$$

The last condition on $\tilde{u}$ is needed to handle, for $\epsilon \to 0$, the term

$$\kappa \int_\Omega (w^i_\epsilon \nabla (u^i_\epsilon - \tilde{u}) \cdot \nabla u^i_\epsilon - \frac{1}{2} w^i_\epsilon |\nabla u^i_\epsilon|^2)$$

in the variational inequality (3.8) for the m-limit $(u^i_\epsilon, v^i_\epsilon, w^i_\epsilon)$. Replacing $\tilde{u}$ by $\tilde{u}_{\delta\epsilon} := \eta_\delta(w^i_\epsilon)\tilde{u}$ with $\eta_\delta(w) := \min(1, (\delta w)^{-1/2})$ this term is

$$\frac{\kappa}{2} \int_\Omega w^i_\epsilon |\nabla u^i_\epsilon|^2 - \kappa \int_\Omega \sqrt{w^i_\epsilon} \eta_\delta(w^i_\epsilon) \nabla \tilde{u} \cdot (\sqrt{w^i_\epsilon} \nabla u^i_\epsilon) - \kappa \int_\Omega \sqrt{w^i_\epsilon} \eta_{\delta,w}(w^i_\epsilon) \tilde{u} \nabla w^i_\epsilon \cdot (\sqrt{w^i_\epsilon} \nabla u^i_\epsilon) \quad .$$

Since $\sqrt{w^i_\epsilon} \nabla u^i_\epsilon$ converges weakly in $L^2(\Omega)$ to $\sqrt{w^i} \nabla u^i$ the first term is lower semicontinuous, and since $w \mapsto \sqrt{w} \eta_\delta(w)$ is bounded the second term converges. The third term we estimate uniformly in ϵ by

$$|\sqrt{w} \eta_{\delta,w}(w)| \leq \frac{\sqrt{\delta}}{2} \to 0 \quad \text{as} \quad \delta \to 0 \quad .$$

Now let (ζ, ξ, η) be a test triple as in the statement of the theorem, and assume that $\eta \leq w$. For $\sigma > 0$ and $\rho > 0$ we set in (3.9)

$$\tilde{u} := \max(-\frac{1}{\sigma}, \min(\frac{1}{\sigma}, u^i)) - \zeta, \quad \tilde{v} := v^i - \xi, \quad \tilde{w} = \max(\rho, \min(\frac{1}{\rho}, w^i - \eta)) \quad .$$

Then letting $\sigma \to 0$ and $\rho \to 0$ we obtain

$$0 \geq \langle (\zeta, \xi, \eta), \mathcal{F}^i(u^i, v^i, w^i)\rangle \quad . \tag{3.10}$$

Since there are no inequality constraints on ζ and ξ this gives the first two equalities in the assertion. To derive the last equality, we apply (3.10) to the test triple $(0, 0, \min(w, \delta\eta))$ for a given $\eta \in H^{1,2}(\Omega) \cap L^\infty(\Omega)$, where $\delta > 0$, and divide (3.10) by δ. Then the critical term

$$\frac{1}{\delta} \int_{\{w < \delta\eta\}} \nabla w \cdot (l_{22} \nabla w - l_{21} \nabla v)$$

is non-negative if $l_{21} = 0$. Under assumption (3.7) one can show that this term is non-negative in the limit $\delta \to 0$, see [3] . □

The next step is to derive estimates for time differences of the solution (u_τ, v_τ, w_τ). These estimates give the compactness statements in Theorem 3.8 and imply, for a subsequence $\tau \to 0$, the pointwise convergence of the nonlinear coefficients in the system. Before presenting the compactness estimates let us define the weak differential operators which correspond to (1.23) - (1.25).

3.7 Differential operators. For triples $(u, v, w) \in L^2(]0, t_0[; \mathcal{M})$ satisfying the estimates in Lemma 3.4 and Lemma 3.5 define

$$\langle \zeta, \mathcal{F}_0(u, v, w) \rangle := \int_{\Omega_{t_0}} \Big(\zeta(-v + \varphi_{,u}(u, w)) + \kappa w \nabla\zeta \cdot \nabla u \Big) \quad , \tag{3.11}$$

$$\langle \xi, \mathcal{F}_1(u, v, w) \rangle := - \int_{\Omega_{t_0}} \partial_t \xi (u - u_0) + \int_{\Omega_{t_0}} \nabla\xi \cdot (l_{11} \nabla v - l_{12} \nabla w) \quad , \tag{3.12}$$

(3.13)

$$\langle \eta, \mathcal{F}_2(u, v, w) \rangle := \int_{\Omega_{t_0}} \partial_t \eta \Big(E(u, w) - E(u_0, w_0) \Big) + \int_{\Omega_{t_0}} \Big(\nabla\eta \cdot (l_{22} \nabla w - l_{21} \nabla v) + \eta g \Big) + \int_{(\partial\Omega)_{t_0}} \eta p \, d\mathcal{H}^n \ ,$$

where $l_{ij} = l_{ij}(u, v, w)$ and $p = p(w)$. These expressions are defined for arguments $(\zeta, \xi, \eta) \in L^2(]0, t_0[; V)$ satisfying

$$\zeta \in L^\infty(\Omega_{t_0}) \quad \text{and} \quad \sqrt{w} \nabla \zeta \in L^2(\Omega_{t_0}) \quad , \tag{3.14}$$

$$\partial_t \xi \in L^2(\Omega_{t_0}) \quad \text{with} \quad \xi(t_0) = 0 \quad , \tag{3.15}$$

$$\eta, \partial_t \eta \in L^\infty(\Omega_{t_0}) \quad \text{with} \quad \eta(t_0) = 0 \quad . \tag{3.16}$$

We call (u, v, w) a weak solution if $\mathcal{F}_k(u, v, w) = 0$ for $k = 0, 1, 2$, and arguments (ζ, ξ, η) as in (3.14) - (3.16).

3.8 Theorem. The following families of functions, for $0 < \tau \leq 1$, are precompact:

(1) $\quad u_\tau \ \text{ in } \ L^2(\Omega_{t_0}), \quad w_\tau \ \text{ in } \ L^1(\Omega_{t_0}) \quad ,$

(2) $\quad \varphi^0_{,u}(u_\tau, w_\tau) \ \text{ and } \ \varphi^1_{,u}(u_\tau, w_\tau) \ \text{ in } \ L^1(\Omega_{t_0}), \quad \nu_\tau \ \text{ in } \ L^1(]0, t_0[) \quad ,$

(3) $\quad \sqrt{w}_\tau \nabla u_\tau \ \text{ in } \ L^2(\Omega_{t_0}), \quad u_\tau \varphi^0_{,u}(u_\tau, w_\tau) \ \text{ in } \ L^1(\Omega_{t_0}) \quad ,$

(4) $$v_\tau \quad \text{in} \quad L^1(\Omega_{t_0}) \quad .$$

Sketch of proof. We give a formal proof using the differential operators (3.11) - (3.13) for weak solutions rather than the time-discrete version in Theorem 3.6. Let us write (u,v,w) instead of (u_τ, v_τ, w_τ).

For $h > 0$ define $u_h(t) := u(t-h)$, etc. First set $\xi = \chi_{[t-h,t]} \cdot (u(t) - u_h(t))$ in (3.12), where the first factor in this definition of ξ is a function of time, and the second factor a function of space. After integration over t we obtain

$$\int_h^{t_0} \int_\Omega |u - u_h|^2 = R \quad ,$$

where R comes from the flux term with an estimate $|R| \le C \cdot h$. Together with 3.4(2) and 3.5(1) this implies that the precompactness condition for subsets in $L^2(\Omega_{t_0})$ is satisfied, which gives the first statement in (1).

Similarly, setting $\zeta = -\partial_t \chi_{[t-h,t]} \cdot (u(t) - u_h(t))$ in (3.11) we obtain

$$0 = -\int_h^{t_0} \int_\Omega (u - u_h)(v - v_h) + \int_h^{t_0} \int_\Omega (u - u_h)(\varphi_{,u}(u,w) - \varphi_{,u}(u_h, w_h)) + \kappa \int_h^{t_0} \int_\Omega (\nabla u - \nabla u_h) \cdot (w \nabla u - w_h \nabla u_h) \quad .$$

With $\xi = \chi_{[t-h,t]} \cdot (v(t) - v_h(t))$ in (3.12) we see that

$$0 = \int_h^{t_0} \int_\Omega (v - v_h)(u - u_h) + R_1 \quad ,$$

where again R_1 consists of the flux term. Finally, setting $\eta = \chi_{[t-h,t]} \cdot (w(t) - w_h(t))$ in (3.13) we derive

$$0 = -\int_h^{t_0} \int_\Omega (w - w_h)(E(u,w) - E(u_h, w_h)) + \int_h^{t_0} \Big(\int_{\partial\Omega} (w - w_h)(p(w) - p(w_h)) d\mathcal{H}^{n-1} \Big) + R_2 \quad ,$$

where R_2 contains the flux and g-term. Adding up these identities we obtain as κ-terms

(3.17) $$\kappa \int_h^{t_0} \int_\Omega \Big((\nabla u - \nabla u_h) \cdot (w \nabla u - w_h \nabla u_h) - \frac{1}{2}(w - w_h)(|\nabla u|^2 - |\nabla u_h|^2) \Big)$$

$$= \kappa \int_h^{t_0} \int_\Omega \frac{w + w_h}{2} |\nabla (u - u_h)|^2 \quad ,$$

which provides an estimate for time differences of ∇u. With the notation

$$\omega(f) := \int_0^1 f((1-\alpha)(u,w) + \alpha(u_h, w_h)) d\alpha \quad ,$$

the potential terms can be expressed as

$$\int_h^{t_0}\int_\Omega \Big((u-u_h)(\varphi_{,u}(u,w)-\varphi_{,u}(u_h,w_h))-(w-w_h)(\varphi_{,w}(u,w)-\varphi_{,w}(u_h,w_h))\Big)$$

$$=\int_h^{t_0}\int_\Omega \Big((u-u_h)^2\omega(\varphi_{,uu})+(w-w_h)^2\omega(-\varphi_{,ww})\Big) \quad .$$

By (1.26) - (1.28) and the above estimate for $u-u_h$ this is

$$\geq \int_h^{t_0}\int_\Omega (w-w_h)^2\int_0^1 \omega_0((1-\alpha)w+\alpha w_h)d\alpha - C\cdot h \quad .$$

Together with 3.4(1) and 3.5(1) this implies the precompactness condition for w in $L^1(\Omega_{t_0})$, hence the second statement in (1) is proved. Then (2) follows from 3.5(3) and (1.27), and from (3.11) by setting $\zeta=\chi_{[t_1,t_2]}$, which gives

$$\nu(t)=\fint_\Omega v(t)=\fint_\Omega \varphi_{,u}(u(t),w(t))$$

for almost all t.

To prove (3) we use (3.11) and show sequential compactness. In fact, every sequence (u_k,v_k,w_k) of weak solutions has a subsequence such that $v_k-\nu_k\to v-\nu$, $\nabla v_k\to\nabla v$, and $\nabla u_k\to\nabla u$ weakly in $L^2(\Omega_{t_0})$. Moreover, by (1) and (2) we can assume that $u_k\to u, \nu_k\to\nu$, and $w_k\to w$ almost everywhere. Then consider

$$0=\langle u_k-\tilde u, \mathcal{F}_0(u_k,v_k,w_k)\rangle$$

with $\tilde u$ as in (3.14). The terms with $u_k\varphi_{,u}(u_k,w_k)$ and $w_k|\nabla u_k|^2$ are lower semicontinous with a possible jump I. We obtain

$$0=I+\langle u-\tilde u,\mathcal{F}_0(u,v,w)\rangle \quad .$$

Letting $\tilde u\to u$ we see that $I=0$, which proves (3).

To prove (4) let $v^0:=v-\nu$ and $v^0_\delta:=\max(-\frac{1}{\delta},\min(\frac{1}{\delta},v^0))$. Setting $\zeta=-\partial_t\chi_{[t-h,t]}\cdot\rho\cdot(v^0_\delta(t)-v^0_{\delta h}(t))$ in (3.11) with weight function $\rho:=(1+w+w_h)^{-1/2}$ we obtain

$$\int_h^{t_0}\int_\Omega \rho(v^0_\delta-v^0_{\delta h})(v^0-v^0_h)=\int_h^{t_0}\int_\Omega \zeta(\psi-\psi_h)+\kappa\int_h^{t_0}\int_\Omega \nabla\zeta\cdot(w\nabla u-w_h\nabla u_h) \quad ,$$

where $\psi:=-\nu+\varphi_{,u}(u,w)$. Since $\rho^{-1}\nabla\zeta$ is estimated in $L^2(\Omega_{t_0})$ by $\frac{C}{\delta}$ using 3.4(1), and since

$$\rho^2|w\nabla u-w_h\nabla u_h|^2=\rho^2ww_h|\nabla(u-u_h)|^2+\rho^2(w-w_h)(w|\nabla u|^2-w_h|\nabla u_h|^2)$$

$$\leq \frac{1}{4}(w+w_h)|\nabla(u-u_h)|^2 + |w|\nabla u|^2 - w_h|\nabla u_h|^2|$$

we see that

$$\int_h^{t_0}\int_\Omega \rho|v_\delta^0 - v_{\delta h}^0|^2 \leq \frac{C}{\delta}\Big(||\psi-\psi_h||_{L^1(\Omega)} + ||w|\nabla u|^2 - w_h|\nabla u_h|^2||_{L^1(\Omega)}^{1/2} + ||\sqrt{w+w_h}\nabla(u-u_h)||_{L^2(\Omega)}\Big).$$

The first two norms are small in h by (2) and (3), whereas the last one is small by the proof of (1), see (3.17). Using 3.5(1) we see that the left–hand side dominates

$$\int_h^{t_0}\int_\Omega |v_\delta^0 - v_{\delta h}^0|^{4/3} \quad .$$

Together with the estimate for v^0 in 3.5(2) this proves (4). □

As a consequence we obtain

3.9 Theorem. There exists $(u,v,w) \in L^2(]0,t_0[;\mathcal{M})$ satisfying the estimates in Lemma 3.4 and Lemma 3.5, and a non-negative $\lambda \in C^0(\bar{\Omega}_{t_0})^*$ so that for (ζ,ξ,η) as in (3.14) - (3.16) with $\partial_t\eta \in C^0(\bar{\Omega}_{t_0})$

$$0 = \langle\zeta, \mathcal{F}_0(u,v,w)\rangle, \quad 0 = \langle\xi, \mathcal{F}_1(u,v,w)\rangle, \quad 0 = \langle\eta, \mathcal{F}_2(u,v,w)\rangle + \int_{\bar{\Omega}_{t_0}} \partial_t\eta d\lambda \quad .$$

Proof. From Lemma 3.4 and Lemma 3.5 we obtain the weak convergences $\nabla u_\tau \to \nabla u, \nabla v_\tau \to \nabla v$, and $\nabla w_\tau \to \nabla w$ in $L^2(\Omega_{t_0})$, and 3.8(1) and 3.8(4) imply that $u_\tau \to u$ strongly in $L^2(\Omega_{t_0})$, and $v_\tau \to v, w_\tau \to w$ strongly in $L^1(\Omega_{t_0})$. Together with 3.8(2) and 3.8(3) we see that all terms in the time-discrete equations converge to the desired limit except the energy $E(u_\tau,w_\tau)$. It follows from 3.4(2) and 3.5(4) that

$$E(u_\tau,w_\tau) \to E(u,w) + \lambda \quad \text{weakly star in} \quad C^0(\Omega_{t_0})^* \quad ,$$

and since E is essentially nonnegative by (3.5), we see that $\lambda \geq 0$. □

Therefore, in order to prove the existence of a weak solution, it remains to investigate conditions under which the internal energy $E(u_\tau,w_\tau)$ is precompact in $L^1(\Omega_{t_0})$. In [3] this has been proved under the following additional

3.10 Assumptions.

(1) $\quad l_{22} = 1, \quad l_{21} = 0 \quad .$

(2) $\quad p(w) \leq 0$ for $w \leq \alpha_1$ with some $\alpha_1 > 0$.

(3) $\frac{|(w\varphi_{,w})_{,w}(u,w)|^2}{1-\varphi_{,ww}(u,w)} + \frac{|(w\varphi_{,w})_{,u}(u,w)|^2}{1+w+\varphi^0_{,uu}(u,w)} \leq C\cdot\Big((u\varphi^0_{,u}(u,w))_+ + (\varphi_{,w}(u,w))^2_+ + \Psi(u,w)+1\Big)$

(4) $e(u,w) \geq \frac{c}{w} - C.$

(5) $|e(u,w)| + \frac{1}{\sqrt{w}}|\varphi^0_{,u}(u,w)| \leq \omega_1(\frac{1+u^2}{w})(1+w^{\frac{\nu}{2}})$ with a continuous function ω_1 and $\nu < q_n$.

(6) $\Gamma \in C^{1,1}$ for $n=2$, and $\Gamma \in C^{2,1}$ for $n=3$.

(7) $u_0, w_0, \frac{1}{w_0} \in L^\infty(\Omega), \nabla u_0 \in L^{p_0}(\Omega)$ with $p_0 > 2\max(n,2)$.

3.11 Theorem. Under the additional assumptions in 3.10 it follows, for $n \leq 3$, that $\lambda = 0$ in 3.9, that is, (u,v,w) is a weak solution in the sense of 3.7.

Remark. In [3] the compactness of $E(u_\tau, w_\tau)$ is a consequence of an a-priori estimate for E in $L^2(\Omega_{t_0})$. This estimate requires regularity properties for solutions of the time-discrete system, namely, $u_\tau(t), w_\tau(t) \in H^{2,2}(\Omega)\cap L^\infty(\Omega)$, $\nabla u_\tau(t), \nabla w_\tau(t) \in L^4(\Omega)$, and $\frac{1}{w_\tau(t)} \in L^\infty(\Omega)$. To achieve this, a regularity theory for the corresponding elliptic system has been developed in [3]. For this theory some of the assumptions in 3.10 are needed, and the restriction $n \leq 3$ on the dimension.

Sketch of proof. We give a formal proof of the L^2-estimate for E, assuming that $l_{ij} = \delta_{ij}$. In deriving the Clausius-Duhem inequality we have multiplied the system (1.24) - (1.25) by the elliptic variables (v,w). Now multiplying it by the parabolic variables $(u,-E)$ we obtain at time t

$$\int_\Omega (u\partial_t u + E\partial_t E) + \int_\Omega (\nabla u\cdot\nabla v - \nabla E\cdot\nabla w) = \int_\Omega Eg + \int_{\partial\Omega} Ep\, d\mathcal{H}^{n-1} \quad . \tag{3.18}$$

The first integral on the left equals

$$\frac{1}{2}\partial_t \int_\Omega (u^2+E^2)$$

and will provide the desired estimate for E in $L^\infty(]0,t_0[;L^2(\Omega))$. The first term on the right is

$$\leq \frac{1}{2}\int_\Omega E^2 + C$$

which is a corresponding Gronwall term. The potential terms on the left-hand side of (3.18) are

$$\int_\Omega (\nabla u\cdot\nabla\varphi_{,u} - \nabla\varphi_{,w}\cdot\nabla w) = \int_\Omega (\varphi_{,uu}|\nabla u|^2 - \varphi_{,ww}|\nabla w|^2) \tag{3.19}$$

$$= \int_\Omega \Big(\varphi^0_{,uu}|\nabla u|^2 + (-\varphi_{,ww})|\nabla w|^2\Big) - C(t) \quad ,$$

where $t \mapsto C(t)$ is integrable by previous estimates, and the integrand on the right is non-negative. The potential term on the right-hand side of (3.18) is, using 3.10(2),

$$\int_{\partial\Omega} \varphi_{,w} p \, d\mathcal{H}^{n-1} \leq \int_{\partial\Omega} |w\varphi_{,w}| d\mathcal{H}^{n-1} + C(t)$$

$$\leq C\Big(\int_\Omega |w\varphi_{,w}| + \int_\Omega |\nabla(w\varphi_{,w})|\Big) + C(t) \quad .$$

By the structural pointwise inequality

$$(w\varphi_{,w}(u,w))_+ \leq (u\varphi^0_{,u}(u,w))_+ + C(\Psi(u,w)+1)$$

with Ψ as in (3.5), the first integral on the right is controlled by 3.5(3). The purpose of assumption 3.10(3) is to estimate the second integral by

$$\delta \int_\Omega \Big(\varphi^0_{,uu}|\nabla u|^2 - \varphi_{,ww}|\nabla w|^2\Big) + C_\delta(t) + C_\delta \int_\Omega E^2 \quad .$$

Now the first term of the latter expression is absorbed by (3.19), and the last term is controlled again by Gronwall's lemma.

The remaining, and most interesting part of (3.18) is the contribution from the surface energy. On the left side the κ-terms are

$$\sum_{ij} \int_\Omega \Big(-\partial_i u \partial_{ij}(w\partial_j u) - \partial_i(\frac{|\partial_j u|^2}{2})\partial_i w\Big)$$

$$= -\sum_{ij} \int_{\partial\Omega} \partial_i u \partial_i(w\partial_j u) n_j d\mathcal{H}^{n-1} + \sum_{ij} \int_\Omega \Big(\partial_{ij} u \partial_i(w\partial_j u) - \partial_{ij} u \partial_j u \partial_i w\Big) \quad ,$$

where n_j is the j-th component of the outer normal $\vec{n}$. The integral over Ω reduces to the positive term

$$\sum_{ij} \int_\Omega w(\partial_{ij} u)^2 \quad . \tag{3.20}$$

The boundary integral we write as

$$-\sum_i \int_{\partial\Omega} \partial_i u \partial_i(w\nabla u \cdot \vec{n}) d\mathcal{H}^{n-1} + \sum_{ij} \int_{\partial\Omega} \partial_i n_j w \partial_i u \partial_j u \, d\mathcal{H}^{n-1} \quad .$$

In the first term $\partial_i u = 0$ if i corresponds to the direction of $\vec{n}$, and $\partial_i(w\nabla u \cdot \vec{n}) = 0$ for tangential directions. The second term is

$$\geq -C \int_{\partial\Omega} w|\nabla u|^2 d\mathcal{H}^{n-1} \quad .$$

The same contribution comes from the κ-term on the right side of (3.18). Thus we have to estimate

$$\begin{aligned}\int_{\partial\Omega} w|\nabla u|^2 d\mathcal{H}^{n-1} &\leq C\Big(\int_\Omega w|\nabla u|^2 + \int_\Omega |\nabla(w|\nabla u|^2)|\Big)\\ &\leq C\int_\Omega \Big(|\nabla w||\nabla u|^2 + w|\nabla u||D^2 u|\Big) + C(t)\\ &\leq \delta\int_\Omega |\nabla u|^4 + \delta\int_\Omega w|D^2 u|^2 + C_\delta(t) \quad .\end{aligned}$$

Now observe that the second term is absorbed by (3.20) and concerning the first, note that $|\nabla u|^4$ is part of E^2, that is, this is another Gronwall term. □

References:

[1] H.W. Alt, I. Pawlow, Dynamics of non-isothermal phase separation, in: "Free Boundary Problems", K.-H. Hoffmann, J. Sprekels (Eds.),International Series of Numerical Mathematics, Vol. 95, Birkhäuser-Verlag, Basel, 1990.

[2] H.W. Alt, I. Pawlow, A mathematical model of dynamics of non-isothermal phase separation, SFB 256 University Bonn, Preprint, 1990.

[3] H.W. Alt, I. Pawlow, Existence of solutions for non-isothermal phase separation, SFB 256 University Bonn, Preprint, 1990.

[4] G. Caginalp, The dynamics of a conserved phase field system: Stefan-like, Hele-Shaw, and Cahn-Hilliard models as asymptotic limits. IMA J. Appl. Math. **44** (1990), 77-94.

[5] J.W. Cahn, On spinodal decomposition, Acta Metall. **9** (1961),795-801.

[6] J.W. Cahn, J.E. Hilliard, Free energy of a nonuniform system. I. Interfacial free energy, J. Chem. Physics **28** (1958), No. 2, 258-267.

[7] J.W. Cahn, J.E. Hilliard, Spinodal decomposition: -a reprise, Acta Metall. **19** (1971), 151-161.

[8] J. Carr, M.E. Gurtin, M. Slemrod, Structural phase transition on a finite interval, Arch. Rat. Mech. Anal. **86** (1984), 317-351.

[9] S.R. de Groot, P. Mazur, Non-equilibrium thermodynamics, Dover Pub., New York 1984.

[10] J.D.P. Donnelly, A model for non-equilibrium thermodynamic processes involving phase change. J. Inst. Maths. Applics **24** (1979), 425-438.

[11] J.D. Gunton, M. San Miguel, P.S. Sahni, The dynamics of first-order phase transitions, in: "Phase Transitions and Critical Phenomena", C. Domb. J.L. Lebowitz (Eds.), Academic Press, London, 1983, 267-482.

[12] S. Komura, H. Furukawa (Eds), Dynamics of Ordering Processes in Condensed Matter, Plenum Press, New York, 1988.

[13] S. Luckhaus, A. Visintin, Phase transition in Multicomponent systems. Manuscripta Math. **43** (1983), 261-288.

[14] T. Miyazaki, T. Kozakai, S. Mizuno, M. Doi, A theoretical analysis of the phase decompositions based upon the non-linear diffusion equation, Trans. Japan Inst. Metals **24** (1983), No. 4, 246-254.

[15] T. Miyazaki, T. Kozakai, S. Mizuno, M. Doi, A theoretical analysis of the phase decompositions based upon the two-dimensional non-linear diffusion equation, Trans. Japan Inst. Metals, **24** (1983), No. 12, 799-808.

[16] A. Novick-Cohen, L.A. Segel, Nonlinear aspects of the Cahn-Hilliard equation, Physica D **10** (1984) 277-298.

[17] O. Penrose, P.C. Fife, Thermodynamically consistent models of phase-field type for the kinetics of phase transition, Physica D **43** (1990), 44-62.

[18] Zheng Songmu, Asymptotic behaviour of the solution to the Cahn-Hilliard equation, Applic. Anal. **23** (1986), 165–184.

International Series of Numerical Mathematics, Vol. 99, © 1991 Birkhäuser Verlag Basel

The approximate solvability of the inverse one phase Stefan problem

VIOREL BARBU

Faculty of Mathematics
University of Iasi, Romania

1. INTRODUCTION

Let Ω be a bounded and open subset of $\mathbb{R}^N$ with a sufficiently smooth boundary Γ and let $\sigma \in C^2(\bar{D}_1)$ be given function on $D_1 \subset \Omega$ such that $D_t = \{x \in \Omega;\, \sigma(x) < t\}$ is increasing in t, $\sigma(x) = 0$ for $x \in D_0$, $D_T = D_1$ (Fig.1 below).

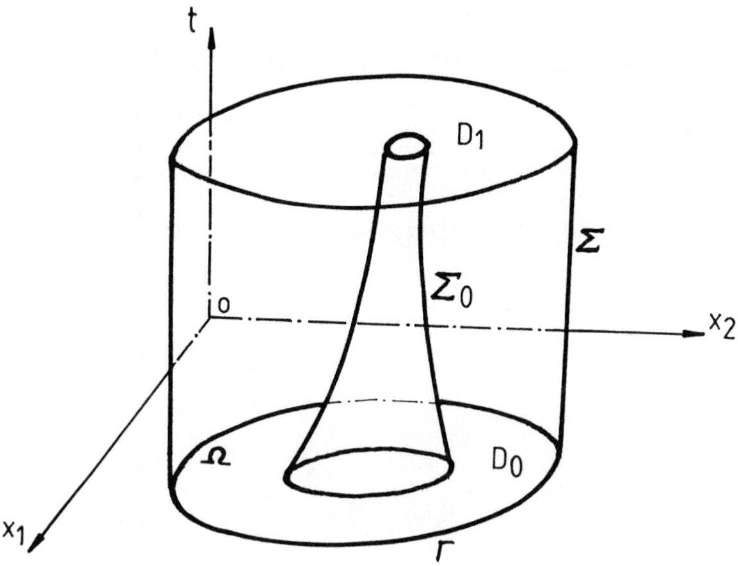

Fig. 1.

We will study here the following inverse problem: Given σ find $u \in H^1(0,T; L^2(\Gamma))$ such that

$$(1.1)\qquad \begin{aligned} &y_t - \Delta y = 0 \text{ in } Q = \{(x,t) \in \Omega \times (0,T);\, \sigma(x) < t < T\} \\ &(\nabla_x y(x,\sigma(x)), \nabla\sigma(x)) = \rho;\ y(x,\sigma(x)) = 0\ (\forall)\, x \in D_1 \setminus D_0 \\ &\frac{\partial y}{\partial \nu} + \alpha y = u \text{ in } \Sigma = \Gamma \times (0,T), \\ &y(x,t) \le 0\ (\forall)(x,t) \in Q,\ \ y(x,0) = y_0(x)\ (\forall) x \in D_0. \end{aligned}$$

Here $\alpha \geq 0,\ \rho > 0$ and

$$H_0^1(0,T;L^2(\Gamma)) = \{u \in L^2(0,T;L^2(\Gamma)); \\ \frac{\partial u}{\partial t} \in L^2(0,T;L^2(\Gamma)), u(0) = u(T) = 0\}.$$

It is well known that for $N = 1,2,3$ Eqns. (1.1) describe a solidification process having $\Sigma_0 = \{(x,t); t = \sigma(x)\}$ as the interface on which solidification occurs.

The main result of this work, Theorem 1 below, amounts to saying that under appropriate conditions the above inverse problem is approximately solvable in a sense to be precised. This result could be viewed as a controllability result for the free boundary of the one phase Stefan problem by boundary inputs $u \in H^1(0,T;L^2(\Gamma))$. The one dimensional case of this problem has been studied in [2].

The idea of the proof is to approximate the inverse problem by the optimal control problem: Minimize

$$(P_h)\quad \frac{1}{2}\int_{D_1\setminus D_0}((\nabla_x y(x,\sigma(x)),\nabla\sigma) - \rho)^2 + \frac{1}{2n}\|u\|^2_{H_0^1(0,T;L^2(\Gamma))}$$

on all (y,u) subject to

$$(1.2)\qquad \begin{aligned} & y_t - \Delta y = 0 \text{ in } Q \\ & y = 0 \text{ in } \Sigma_0 = \{(x,t); t = \sigma(x),\ x \in D_1\setminus D_0\} \\ & \frac{\partial y}{\partial \nu} + \alpha y = u \text{ in } \Sigma;\ y(x,0) = y_0(x)\ (\forall)\, x \in D_0. \end{aligned}$$

$$(1.3)\qquad y \leq 0 \text{ in } Q_\varepsilon$$

where

$$(1.4)\qquad Q_\varepsilon = \{(x,t) \in Q;\ \sigma(x) + \varepsilon < t < T - \varepsilon\}.$$

The control system (1.2) is a parabolic boundary value problem in the noncylindarical domain Q which will be studied in some details in Section 3. We shall denote by $H^1(Q)$, $H^1(D_0)$, $H^m(\Gamma)$ usual Sobolev spaces on Q and D_0, Γ; $C^{2,\alpha}$ the classical space of $\{u \in C^2; u_{x_i x_j}\ \alpha -$ Hölder continuos $\}$.

2. The main result

The following hypotheses will be in effect.

(i)
$\sigma \in C^2(\bar{D}_1)$, $\sigma(x) = 0\ (\forall)\ x \in D_0$; $\Delta\sigma(x) \geq 0\ \ (\forall)\ x \in D_1\setminus D_0$; $D_t \subset D_s$ for $t < s$, $|\nabla\sigma(x)| \neq 0 (\forall) x \in D_1\setminus D_0$.

The boundary Γ is of class $C^{2,\alpha}$, $0 < \alpha < 1$.
(ii)

$y_0 \in C^{2,\alpha}(\bar{\Omega}_0)$, $0 < \alpha < 1$; $y_0(x) < 0$ for $x \in D_0 \bigcup \Gamma$, $y_0 = 0$ on $\partial D_0 = \{x;\ \sigma(x) = 0\}$.

THEOREM 2.1. *Under hypotheses (i), (ii) for every $\varepsilon > 0$ there are the sequences $\{u_n\} \subset H_0^1(0,T;L^2(\Gamma))$, $\{y_n\} \subset H^1(Q)$ such that*

$$\begin{aligned} &(y_n)_t - \Delta y_n = 0 && \text{in } Q \\ &y_n = 0 && \text{in } \Sigma_0 \\ &\frac{\partial y_n}{\partial \nu} + \alpha y_n = u_n && \text{in } \Sigma \\ &y_n(x,0) = y_0(x) && (\forall) x \in D_0 \end{aligned} \tag{2.1}$$

$$y_n(x,t) \le 0 \qquad (\forall)\,(x,t) \in Q_\varepsilon \tag{2.2}$$

$$(\nabla_x y_n(x,\sigma(x)), \nabla\sigma(x)) \to \rho \text{ weakly in } L^2(D_1 \backslash D_0) \text{ for } n \to \infty. \tag{2.3}$$

As noticed earlier, this theorem may be interpreted as a controllability result for the free boundary of the one phase Stefan problem. For other results concerned with the control of free boundary we refer the reader to [1], [3], [4], [5].

3. Existence for control system (1.2)

We shall study here the problem

$$\begin{aligned} &y_t - \Delta y = f \text{ in } Q \\ &y = 0 \text{ in } \Sigma_0 \\ &\frac{\partial y}{\partial \nu} + \alpha y = u \text{ in } \Sigma \\ &y(x,0) = y_0(x) \text{ in } D_0. \end{aligned} \tag{3.1}$$

DEFINITION 1. *By solution to problem (3.1) we mean a function $y \in V$ which satisfies the equation*

$$\begin{aligned} &\int_Q (y\varphi_t - \nabla y \cdot \nabla\varphi)dx\,dt + \int_\Sigma (u - \alpha y)\varphi\,dx\,dt = \\ &-\int_Q f\varphi\,dx\,dt + \int_{D_0} y_0\varphi(x,0)\,dx - \int_{D_1} y(x,T)\varphi(x,T)\,dx \end{aligned} \tag{3.2}$$

for all $\varphi \in V = \{z \in H^1(Q);\ z = 0 \text{ in } \Sigma_0\}$.

It is readily seen that the solution if exists is unique.

PROPOSITION 1. *Let* $u \in H^1(0,T;L^2(\Gamma))$, $y_0 \in H^1(D_0)$ *and* $f \in L^2(Q)$. *If* σ *satisfies hypothesis (i) then problem (3.1) has a unique solution* $y \in H^1(Q)$. *Moreover,* $\Delta y \in L^2(Q), \nabla y$ *is well defined on* Σ_0 , *the function* $x \to |\nabla_x y(x,\sigma(x))|$ *belongs to* $L^2(D_1 \setminus D_0)$ *and the following estimate holds*

$$\|y\|^2_{H^1(Q)} + \|\Delta y\|^2_{L^2(Q)} + \int_{D_1\setminus D_0} |\nabla y(x,\sigma(x))|^2\,dx \le C(\|y_0\|^2_{H^1(D_0)} + \|f\|^2_{L^2(Q)} + \|u\|^2_{H^1(0,T;L^2(\Gamma))}). \tag{3.3}$$

PROOF: Approximate problem (3.1) by the family of elliptic problems.

$$\begin{aligned} &-\varepsilon y_{tt} + y_t - \Delta y = f \quad \text{in } Q \\ &y_t(x,0) = \varepsilon^{-1}(y(x,0) - y_0(x)) \quad (\forall)x \in D_0 \\ &y_t(x,T) = 0 \quad (\forall)x \in D_1 \\ &\frac{\partial y}{\partial \nu} + \alpha y = u \quad \text{in } \Sigma \\ &y = 0 \quad \text{in } \Sigma_0. \end{aligned} \tag{3.4}$$

By the solution to problem (3.4) we mean a function $y \in V$ such that

$$\begin{aligned} &\int_Q (\varepsilon y_t\varphi_t - y\varphi_t + \nabla y\cdot\nabla\varphi)\,dxdt = \int_Q f\varphi\,dxdt \\ &+ \int_\Sigma (u - \alpha y)\,dxdt + \int_{D_0} y_0(x)\varphi(x,0)\,dx \\ &- \int_{D_1} y(x,T)\varphi(x,T)\,dx \quad (\forall)\varphi \in V. \end{aligned} \tag{3.5}$$

By the Lax-Milgram theorem we see that problem (3.5) has a unique solution $y_\varepsilon \in V$.

A priori estimates. In the following we shall simply write y instead of y_ε. Also by a smoothing process we may assume without loss of generality that $y \in C^2(\bar{Q})$. We will use the notations $\nabla y(x,t) = \nabla_x J(x,t)$ and $\nabla y = \nabla_x y$.

Multiplying Eqn. (3.4) by y_t and integrating on Q we get

$$\begin{aligned} &-\frac{\varepsilon}{2}\int_{D_1} dx \int_{\sigma(x)}^T ({y_t}^2)_t\,dt + \int_Q {y_t}^2\,dx\,dt - -\int_{D_1} dx \quad \operatorname{div}\,(\int_{\sigma(x)}^T y_t\nabla y \quad dt) - \\ &-\int_{D_1\setminus D_0} y_t(x,\sigma(x))(\nabla\mathcal{J}(x,\sigma(x)),\nabla\sigma(x))\,dx + \frac{1}{2}\int_{D_1} dx \int_{\sigma(x)}^T |\nabla y|_t{}^2\,dt = \int_Q f y_t\,dx\,dt \end{aligned}$$

and by the divergence formula one finally obtains

(3.6)
$$\frac{\varepsilon}{2}\int_{D_1\setminus D_0} y_t^2(x,\sigma(x))dx + \frac{\varepsilon}{2}\int_{D_0} y_t^2(x,0)dx + \int_Q y_t^2(x,t)dx\ dt +$$
$$+\frac{1}{2}\int_{D_1\setminus D_0} |\nabla y(x,\sigma(x))|^2 dx + \frac{1}{2}\int_{D_1} (|\nabla y(x,T)|^2 dx + \alpha\int_\Gamma y^2(x,T)dx \leq$$
$$\leq \frac{1}{2}\int_{D_0} |\nabla y(x,0)|^2 dx + \alpha\int_\Gamma y^2(x,0)dx + \int_Q f^2\ dx\ dt +$$
$$+2\int_\Sigma u_t y\ dx\ dt + 2\int_\Gamma (u(x,T)y(x,T) - u(x,0)y(x,0))dx.$$

Now we multiply Eqn. (3.4) by y to get after some calculation

(3.7)
$$\int_Q (\varepsilon y_t^2 + |\nabla y|^2)dx\ dt + \int_{D_0} (y(x,0) - y_0(x))y(x,0)dx + \frac{1}{2}\int_{D_1} y^2(x,T)dx =$$
$$= \int_\Sigma y(u - \alpha y)dx\ dt + \int_Q fy\ dx\ dt.$$

Next we multiply Eqn. (3.4) by Δy. This yields

(3.8)
$$\varepsilon\int_{D_1} dx\int_{\sigma(x)}^T y_{tt}\nabla y dx - \int_{D_1} dx\int_{\sigma(x)}^T y_t\nabla y dt + \int_Q |\nabla y|^2 + \int_Q f\nabla y dx\ dt = 0.$$

We have

$$\int_Q y_t\Delta y dx\ dt = \int_{D_1} dx(\ \mathrm{div}\ (\int_{\sigma(x)}^T y_t\nabla y dx) + \tag{3.9}$$
$$+ y_t(x,\sigma(x))(\nabla y(x,\sigma(x)),\nabla\sigma(x)) + \frac{1}{2}\int_{D_1\setminus D_0} |\nabla y(x,\sigma(x))|^2 dx +$$
$$+\frac{1}{2}\int_{D_1\setminus D_0} |\nabla y(x,0)|^2 dx - \frac{1}{2}\int_{D_1} |\nabla y(x,T)|^2 dx =$$
$$= -\frac{1}{2}\int_{D_1\setminus D_0} |\nabla y(x,\sigma(x))|^2 dx - \frac{1}{2}\int_{D_1} |\nabla y(x,T)|^2 dx +$$
$$+\frac{1}{2}\int_{D_0} |\nabla y(x,0)|^2 dx - \frac{\alpha}{2}\int_\Gamma ((y(x,T))^2 - (y(x,0))^2)dx +$$
$$+\int_\Gamma (u(x,T)y(x,T) - u(x,0)y(x,0))dx.$$

Similarly,

$$\int_{\sigma(x)}^T y_{tt}\Delta y dt = -y_t(x,\sigma(x))\Delta y(x,\sigma(x)) -\ \mathrm{div}\int_{\sigma(x)}^T y_t\nabla y_t dt +$$
$$+\int_{\sigma(x)}^T |\nabla y_t|^2\ dt - y_t(x,\sigma(x))(\nabla y(x,\sigma(x)),\nabla\sigma(x))$$

and therefore

(3.10)

$$\int_Q y_{tt}\Delta y\,dx\,dt = -\int_{D_1} y_t(x,\sigma(x))\Delta y(x,\sigma(x))\,dx + \int_Q |\nabla y_t|^2\,dx\,dt -$$
$$-\int_{D_1} y_t(x,\sigma(x))(\nabla y_t(x,\sigma(x)),\nabla\sigma(x))\,dx - \int_\Sigma y_t\frac{\partial y_t}{\partial\nu}\,dx\,dt =$$
$$= -\int_{D_1} y_t(x,\sigma(x))\ \mathrm{div}(\nabla y(x,\sigma(x)))\,dx + \int_Q |\nabla y_t|^2\,dx\,dt -$$
$$-\int_\Sigma y_t(u_t-\alpha y_t)\,dx\,dt = \frac{1}{2}\int_{D_1\setminus D_0} y_t^2(x,\sigma(x))\Delta\sigma(x)\,dx +$$
$$+\int_Q |\nabla y_t|^2\,dx\,dt + \int_\Sigma (\alpha y_t - u_t)y_t\,dx\,dt.$$

Combining (3.6)∼(3.10) we get

(3.11)

$$\int_Q (\varepsilon y_t^2 + \varepsilon|\nabla y_t|^2 + |\nabla y|^2 + y_t^2 + (\Delta y)^2)\,dx\,dt +$$
$$+\int_{D_1\setminus D_0} (\varepsilon y_t^2(x,\sigma(x)) + |\nabla y(x,\sigma(x))|^2)\,dx + \int_{D_0} (\varepsilon y_t^2(x,0) + y^2(x,0))\,dx +$$
$$+\int_{D_1} (|y(x,T)|^2 + |\nabla y(x,T)|^2)\,dx \le C(\int_\Gamma y^2(x,0)\,dx +$$
$$+\int_\Sigma (u_t y + \varepsilon y_t u_t + uy)\,dx\,dt + \int_\Gamma (|u(x,T)y(x,T)| +$$
$$+|u(x,0)y(x,0)|)\,dx + \int_Q (f^2 + fy)\,dx\,dt),$$

where C is independent of ε.

Then by the trace theorem we find the estimate

(3.12)

$$\int_Q (\varepsilon(y_t^2 + |\nabla y_t|^2) + y_t^2 + y^2 + (\Delta y)^2)\,dx\,dt +$$
$$+\int_{D_0} (\varepsilon y_t^2(x,0) + y^2(x,0)\,dx + \int_{D_1\setminus D_0} (\varepsilon y_t^2(x,\sigma(x)) + |\nabla y(x,\sigma(x))|^2)\,dx \le$$
$$\le C(\|u\|^2_{H^1(0,T;L^2(\Gamma))} + \|y_0\|^2_{H^1(D_0)} + \|f\|^2_{L^2(Q)}),$$

where C is independent of ε and u, y_0, f.

Then on a subsequence, again denoted ε, we have for $\varepsilon \to 0$

$$\begin{aligned} y_\varepsilon &\to y && \text{weakly in } H^1(Q) \text{ and strongly in } L^2(Q)\\ \Delta y_\varepsilon &\to \Delta y && \text{weakly in } L^2(Q)\\ y_\varepsilon(\cdot,0) &\to y_0 && \text{strongly in } L^2(D_0). \end{aligned}$$

Letting ε tend to zero in (3.5) we conclude that y is the solution to the problem (3.2). By (3.12) it follows estimate (3.3).

Let us show now that ∇y is well defined on Σ_0. To this end we will show that $\{\nabla y_\varepsilon(x,\sigma(x))\}$ is strongly convergent in $L^2(D_1\backslash D_0)$ for $\varepsilon \to 0$ and take by definition

(3.13) $$\nabla y = \lim_{\varepsilon\to 0} \nabla y_\varepsilon \quad \text{in } L^2(\Sigma_0).$$

For $\varepsilon, \lambda > 0$ we have

(3.14)
$$\begin{aligned}
&-\varepsilon(y_\varepsilon)_{tt} + \lambda(y_\lambda)_{tt} + (y_\varepsilon - y_\lambda)_t - \Delta(y_\varepsilon - y_\lambda) = 0 \text{ in } Q\\
&(y_\varepsilon)_t(x,0) - (y_\lambda)_t(x,0) = \varepsilon^{-1}(y_\varepsilon(x,0) - y_0(x)) - \lambda^{-1}(y_\lambda(x,0) - y_0(x))\\
&(y_\varepsilon - y_\lambda)_t(x,T) = 0\\
&\frac{\partial}{\partial\nu}(y_\varepsilon - y_\lambda) + \alpha(y_\varepsilon - y_\lambda) = 0 \text{ in } \Sigma; \quad y_\varepsilon - y_\lambda = 0 \text{ in } \Sigma_0.
\end{aligned}$$

Multiplying Eqn. (3.14) by $(y_\varepsilon - y_\lambda)_t$ and using estimate (3.12) we get

$$\int_{D_1\backslash D_0} |\nabla y_\varepsilon(x,\sigma(x)) - \nabla y_\lambda(x,\sigma(x))|^2\,dx < C(\varepsilon+\lambda)$$

where C is independent of ε, λ. Hence $\{\nabla y_\varepsilon(x,\sigma(x))\}$ is strongly convergent in $L^2(D_1\backslash D_0)$ as claimed.

4. Problem (P_n)

We shall study here the optimal control problem (P_n). By a standard device involving Proposition 1 it follows that this problem has a unique solution $(y_n, u_n) \in H^1(Q) \times H_0^1(0,T;L^2(\Gamma))$. Moreover, one has for $\lambda \to 0$

(4.1)
$$\begin{aligned}
&y_\lambda \to y_n \text{ strongly in } H^1(Q)\\
&u_\lambda \to u_n \text{ strongly in } H_0^1(0,T;L^2(\Gamma)),
\end{aligned}$$

where (y_λ, u_λ) is the solution to approximating problem

(4.2)
$$\underline{\text{Minimize}}\ \frac{1}{2}\int_{D_1\backslash D_0} ((\nabla y(x,\sigma(x)),\nabla\sigma(x)) - \rho)^2\,dx +$$
$$(2n)^{-1}\int_\Sigma (u^2 + u_t^2)\,dx\,dt + (2\lambda)^{-1}\int_{Q_\varepsilon} (y^+)^2\,dx\,dt$$

<u>subject to</u> (1.2).

PROPOSITION 2. *There are $p_n \in (L^\infty(Q))^\star$ and $\mu_n \in (L^\infty(Q))^\star$ such that $\mu_n = 0$ in $Q\backslash\bar{Q}_\varepsilon$ and*

(4.3)
$$\begin{aligned}
&(p_n)_t + \Delta p_n = \mu_n \ \text{in}\, Q\\
&p_n = (\nabla y_n, \nabla\sigma) - \rho \ \text{in}\, \Sigma_0\\
&\frac{\partial p_n}{\partial\nu} + \alpha p_n = 0 \ \text{in}\, \Sigma;\ p_n(x,T) = 0 \ \text{in}\, D_1.
\end{aligned}$$

$$(4.4) \qquad \begin{aligned} &n^{-1}(u_n - (u_n)_{tt}) = p_n \text{ in } \Sigma \\ &u_n(x,0) = u_n(x,T) = 0 \, \forall x \in \Gamma. \end{aligned}$$

Here $(L^\infty(Q))^\star$ is the dual space of $L^\infty(Q)$ and the solution p_n to problem (4.3) is taken in the following weak sense

$$(4.5) \qquad p_n(\psi) + \gamma_0 p_n(v) = -\mu_n(\varphi) - \int_{D_1 \setminus D_0} ((\nabla y_n(x,\sigma(x)), \nabla\sigma(x)) - \rho) \\ (\nabla\varphi(x,\sigma(x)), \nabla\sigma(x)) \, dx$$

for all $\psi \in L^\infty(Q)$, $v \in H_0^1(0,T;H^m(\Gamma))$, $m > \frac{N}{2}$ and $\varphi \in H^1(Q)$ solution to (see Proposition 1)

$$(4.6) \qquad \begin{aligned} &\varphi_t - \Delta\varphi = \psi \text{ in } Q \\ &\varphi(x,\sigma(x)) = 0 \text{ in } D_1 \setminus D_0 \\ &\frac{\partial\varphi}{\partial\nu} + \alpha\varphi = v \text{ in } \Sigma \\ &\varphi(x,0) = 0 \text{ in } D_0. \end{aligned}$$

Note that since ψ and v are in L^∞, by the maximum principle, $\varphi \in L^\infty(Q)$ and $\|\phi\|_{L^\infty(Q)} \le C\left(\|\psi\|_{L^\infty(Q)} + \|v\|_{H_0^1(0,T;H^m(\Gamma))}\right)$. Hence Eqn. (4.5) defines $p_n \in (L^\infty(Q))^\star$ and its trace $\gamma_0 p_n$ to Σ. As regards Eq. (4.4) it is considered in the sense of $L^2(\Gamma)$ -valued distributions on $(0,T)$. When there is no danger of confusion we shall simply write p_n instead of $\gamma_0 p_n$. In particular, it follows by Eq. (4.4) that $p_n \in H^{-1}(0,T;L^2(\Gamma))$.

Proof of Proposition 2: Let $p_\lambda \in L^2(Q)$ be the solution to boundary value problem

$$(4.7) \qquad \begin{aligned} &(p_\lambda)_t + \Delta p_\lambda = \chi_\varepsilon \beta_\lambda(y_\lambda) \text{ in } Q \\ &p_\lambda = (\nabla y_\lambda(x,\sigma(x)), \nabla\sigma(x)) - \rho \text{ in } \Sigma_0 \\ &\frac{\partial p_\lambda}{\partial\nu} + \alpha p_\lambda = 0 \text{ in } \Sigma;\; p_\lambda(\cdot,T) = 0 \text{ in } D_1 \end{aligned}$$

where $\beta_\lambda(r) = \lambda^{-1} r^+ \; \forall r \in \mathbf{R}$ and χ_ε is the characteristic function of Q_ε. Problem (4.7) is considered of course in the weak sense (4.5), i.e.

$$(4.8) \qquad \int_Q p_\lambda \psi \, dx\, dt = -\int_{Q_\varepsilon} \beta_\lambda(y_\lambda)\varphi \, dx\, dt - \\ \int_{D_1 \setminus D_0} ((\nabla y_\lambda(x,\sigma(x)), \nabla\sigma(x)) - \rho)(\nabla\varphi(x,\sigma(x)), \nabla\sigma(x)) \, dx - \\ \int_\Sigma pv \, dx\, dt$$

for all $\psi \in L^2(Q)$, $v \in H_0^1(0,T;L^2(\Gamma))$, $\varphi \in H^1(Q)$ satisfying (4.6).

If $z \in H^1(Q)$ is the solution to (4.6) with $\psi = 0$ we see by (4.2) that

$$\int_{D_1 \setminus D_0} ((\nabla y_\lambda(x,\sigma(x)), \nabla\sigma(x)) - \rho)(\nabla z(x,\sigma(x)), \nabla\sigma(x))\, dx +$$
$$\int_{Q_\varepsilon} \beta_\lambda(y_\lambda) z \, dx\, dt +$$
$$n^{-1} \int_\Sigma (u_\lambda v + (u_\lambda)_t v_t)\, dx\, dt \geq 0 \ \forall v \in H_0^1(0,T; H^m(\Gamma))$$

and by (4.8) it follows that

$$-\int_\Sigma v p_\lambda \, dx\, dt + n^{-1} \int_\Sigma (u_\lambda v + (u_\lambda)_t v_t)\, dx\, dt = 0 \ \forall v \in H_0^1(0,T; H^m(\Gamma))$$

i.e.,

(4.9)
$$n^{-1}(u_\lambda - (u_\lambda)_{tt}) = p_\lambda \ \text{ in } \Sigma$$
$$u_\lambda(0) = u_\lambda(T) = 0.$$

Now let $\Theta \in H^1(Q)$ be the solution to boundary value problem

(4.10)
$$\Theta_t - \Delta\Theta = 0 \ \text{ in } Q$$
$$\Theta = 0 \ \text{ in } \Sigma_0$$
$$\Theta(x,0) = y_0(x) \ \text{ in } D_0\,;\ \Theta = y_0 \ \text{ in } \Sigma_0.$$

(The existence follows as in Proposition 1.) By assumption (ii) and the classical interior and boundary regularity properties for parabolic equations we know that $\Theta \in C^\infty(Q) \cap C^{2+\alpha, 1+\frac{\alpha}{2}}(\bar{Q}_\varepsilon)$ and by the maximum principle

$$\Theta(x,t) < -\zeta < 0 \ \forall (x,t) \in \bar{Q}_\varepsilon.$$

This yields

$$\beta_\lambda(y_\lambda)(y_\lambda - \Theta - \zeta w) \geq (2\lambda)^{-1}((y_\lambda^+)^2 - ((\Theta + \zeta w)^+)^2) \geq 0 \ \text{ in } Q_\varepsilon$$

for $|w| = 1$. Hence

$$\zeta \int_{Q_\varepsilon} |\beta_\lambda(y_\lambda)|\, dx\, dt \leq \int_{Q_\varepsilon} \beta_\lambda(y_\lambda)(y_\lambda - \Theta)\, dx\, dt.$$

Substituting $\varphi = y_\lambda - \Theta$ in (4.8) we get

$$\int_{Q_\varepsilon} \beta_\lambda(y_\lambda)(y_\lambda - \Theta)\, dx\, dt$$
$$= -\int_{D_1 \setminus D_0} ((\nabla y_\lambda(x,\sigma(x)), \nabla\sigma(x)) - \rho)(\nabla(y_\lambda - \Theta)(x,\sigma(x)), \nabla\sigma(x))\, dx -$$
$$-\frac{1}{n}\int_\Sigma (u_\lambda(u_\lambda - u_0) + (u_\lambda)_t(u_\lambda - u_0)_t)\, dx\, dt \leq C \ \forall \lambda > 0$$

where $u_0 = \frac{\partial\Theta}{\partial\nu} + \alpha\Theta$. Hence

$$\|\beta_\lambda(y_\lambda)\|_{L^1(Q_\varepsilon)} \le C \ (\forall)\ \lambda > 0 \tag{4.11}$$

where C is independent of λ and n.

Then by Eqn. (4.8) and estimate (3.3) we infer that

$$\|p_\lambda\|_{L^1(Q)} \le C \ (\forall)\ \lambda \ge 0. \tag{4.12}$$

Then letting λ tend to zero (on a subnet) it follows that

$$\begin{aligned} &p_\lambda \to p_n \quad \text{weak star in} \quad (L^\infty(Q))^\star \\ &\chi_\varepsilon\beta_\lambda(y_\lambda) \to \mu_n \quad \text{weak star in } (L^\infty(Q))^\star \\ &\gamma_0 p_\lambda \to q_n \end{aligned}$$

where p_n, μ_n satisfy Eqn. (4.5),(4.4), $\gamma_0 p_n = q_n$. By (4.11) and (4.12) we see that

$$\|p_n\|_{(L^\infty(Q))^\star} + \|\mu_n\|_{L^\infty(Q))^\star} \le C \ \forall n. \tag{4.13}$$

5. Proof of Theorem 1

Let y_n, u_n, p_n and μ_n be as in Proposition 2. Extracting further subsequence (or a subnet) we have

$$\begin{aligned} &p_n \to p \quad \text{weak star in } (L^\infty(Q))^* \\ &\mu_n \to \mu \quad \text{weak star in } (L^\infty(Q))^* \\ &(\nabla y_n(x,\sigma(x)), \nabla\sigma(x)) \to g \quad \text{weakly in } L^2(D_1\backslash D_0), \end{aligned} \tag{5.1}$$

whilist by (4.4)

$$\gamma_0 p_n \to 0 \quad \text{weakly in } H^{-1}(0,T;L^2(\Gamma)). \tag{5.2}$$

By (4.5) we see that

$$p(\psi) = -\mu(\varphi) - \int_{D_1\backslash D_0} (g(x) - \rho)(\nabla\varphi(x,\sigma(x)), \nabla\sigma(x))\,dx \tag{5.3}$$

for all $\psi \in L^\infty(Q)$, $v \in H_0^1(0,T;H^m(\Gamma))$ and $\varphi \in H^1(Q) \cap L^\infty(Q)$ satisfying Eqns. (4.6).

Note that supp$\mu \subset \bar{Q}_\varepsilon$, i.e., $\mu(\varphi) = 0$ for all $\varphi \in L^\infty(Q)$ such that $\varphi = 0$ a.e. in $\bar{Q}_\varepsilon$. By (5.3) we see that

$$p_t + \Delta p = 0 \quad \text{in } \mathcal{D}'(Q\backslash\bar{Q}_\varepsilon).$$

Moreover, it follows that

$$p(\varphi_t - \Delta\varphi) = 0 \tag{5.4}$$

for all $\varphi \in C^2(E)$ with supp$\varphi \subset E$, where $E = (Q\backslash\bar{Q}_\varepsilon) \cup (\overline{(Q\backslash Q_\varepsilon)} \cap \Sigma)$.

Let V be a neighbourhood of $\overline{Q\backslash Q_\varepsilon} \cap \Sigma$ and extend p on $E \cup V$ by

$$\tilde{p}(\psi) = p(\psi) \quad \forall \psi \in L^\infty(E \cup V). \tag{5.5}$$

By (5.4) we see that

$$\tilde{p}_t - \Delta \tilde{p} = 0 \quad \text{in } \mathcal{D}'((Q\backslash \bar{Q}_\varepsilon) \cup V).$$

Since $\tilde{p}$ is infinitely differentiable in $(Q\backslash \bar{Q}_\varepsilon) \cup V$, analytic in x and t and by (5.5) $\tilde{p} = 0$ in $V\backslash E$ we infer that $p = \tilde{p} = 0$ in $Q\backslash \bar{Q}_\varepsilon$. Then by (5.3) we see that

$$\int_{D_1\backslash D_0} (g(x) - \rho)(\nabla\varphi(x, \sigma(x)), \nabla\sigma(x))\, dx = 0 \tag{5.6}$$

for all $\varphi \in C^2(\bar{Q})$ such that supp$\varphi \subset \bar{Q}\backslash \bar{Q}_\varepsilon$. It should be observed that (5.6) implies that $g(x) - \rho = 0$ a.e. in $D_1\backslash D_0$. Indeed it suffices to take φ of the form

$$\varphi(x, t) = w(x)v(t - \rho(x)),$$

where w is arbitrary in $C^2(\bar{Q})$ and $v \in C^2(\mathbf{R})$ is such that $v(r) = 0$ for $r \geq \varepsilon$ $v(0) = 0$ and $v'(0) \neq 0$.

References

1. V.Barbu, "Optimal Control of Variational Inequalities," Pitman, London, 1984.
2. V.Barbu, *The inverse one phase Stefan problem*, Differential and Integral Equations **3**, **2** (1990), 209–218.
3. K.H.Hoffman and N.Niezgodka, *Control of parabolic systems involving free boundaries*, in "Free Boundary Problems, Theory and Applications Vol.2," Fasano and Primicerio eds. Pitman, 1983, pp. 431–462.
4. P.Jochum, *The inverse Stefan problem as a problem of nonlinear approximation theory*, J.Approximation Theory **30** (1980), 81–98.
5. J.CH.Saguez, "Contrôle optimal de systèmes à frontière libre," Thèse d'Etat, l'Université de Technologie de Compiègne, 1980.

STABILITY OF THERMOCAPILLARY CONVECTION IN FLOAT-ZONE CRYSTAL GROWTH

HANS D. MITTELMANN
Department of Mathematics
Arizona State University
Tempe, AZ 85287–1804

CINDY C. LAW, DANIEL F. JANKOWSKI and G. PAUL NEITZEL
Department of Mechanical and Aerospace Engineering
Arizona State University
Tempe, AZ 85287–6106

Abstract. Energy stability theory is applied to a basic state of thermocapillary convection occurring in a cylindrical half-zone of finite length to determine conditions under which the flow will be stable under *arbitrary* perturbations. In earlier work axisymmetric disturbances have been considered while the onset of buoyancy-driven convection in a cylinder heated from below has served as a test case for the three-dimensional problem. Here, initial results will be reported for thermocapillary convection under zero gravity. A description of the numerical method used to compute the stability bounds will also be given.

1. Background and motivation

Hydrodynamic stability theory is concerned with determining the conditions under which a certain flow, called the *basic state*, will remain stable or unstable due to the inevitable presence of unknown perturbations (JOSEPH, 1976). In general, these perturbations are governed by nonlinear partial differential equations. Linear-stability theory assumes the perturbations to be infinitesimally small and neglects the nonlinear terms in comparison with their linear counterparts. This theory is local in nature and results in a criterion which guarantees growth of these small disturbances. Typically, an externally controllable dimensionless parameter, say R, is selected and linear theory yields a value R_L such that $R > R_L$ is a sufficient condition for instability.

Energy stability theory, on the other hand, adopts a global approach by examining the behavior of a generalized integral disturbance-energy. Unlike linear stability theory, energy–stability theory provides a value R_E such that $R < R_E$ is a sufficient condition for stability of a given basic state to disturbances of *arbitrary amplitude*. This technique is equivalent to a stability analysis utilizing a Lyapunov function [see SINHA & CARMI (1976) and the literature cited there]. The application of either theory gives rise, in general, to an eigenvalue problem.

If R_E and R_L should coincide, a rigorous stability bound is obtained. However, this is usually not the case and the proximity of R_E to R_L is a function of the physical mechanism which gives rise to the instability (DAVIS, 1971). Two such mechanisms for which R_E and R_L may be expected to be relatively close to each other are buoyancy and thermocapillarity. The former is responsible for the onset of convection in an initially quiescent fluid layer which is heated from below (cooled from above) under certain conditions. This is the classically termed *Bénard convection.* Thermocapillarity, which is the variation of a liquid's surface tension with temperature, can also result in the instability of a quiescent liquid layer with a free surface (liquid-gas interface) when heated from below. This is known as *Marangoni convection.*

Buoyancy and thermocapillarity are also mechanisms which can drive *dynamic* basic states which themselves can become unstable; for instance, the buoyancy boundary layer adjacent to a vertical heated surface and *thermocapillary convection* which results when a temperature gradient exists *along* a free surface. Problems of technological interest in which both of these mechanisms play an important role may be found in the field of materials processing. One problem in particular which has received a considerable amount of attention is the stability of thermocapillary convection associated with the *float-zone crystal-growth process.* This process has been identified as one which may benefit from a micro-gravity environment. Although buoyancy forces will be significantly reduced in such an environment, thermocapillary convection will persist. Since it has been conjectured that the instability of thermocapillary convection may be responsible for undesirable striations observed in material grown by this process, the stability properties of this basic state are of interest for both terrestrial and microgravity conditions.

Recent work on the stability of thermocapillary convection has been done by SHEN, NEITZEL, JANKOWSKI, & MITTELMANN (1990). They employed energy stability theory to obtain sufficient conditions for stability against *axisymmetric* disturbances. Comparisons with the experimental results of PREISSER, SCHWABE, & SCHARMANN (1983) have identified a need for corresponding results for non-axisymmetric disubtances. The present work is motivated by the need for obtaining such stability information.

The earlier work of SHEN *et al.* (1990) required the calculation of the smallest positive eigenvalue of a generalized eigenvalue problem of the form $\mathbf{Ax} = \rho\mathbf{Bx}$. Energy theory, since it has its basis in a variational problem, results in a differential eigenvalue problem which is self-adjoint. The direct discretization of the variational problem employed by SHEN *et al.* preserved this character and thus resulted in *real symmetric* matrices $\mathbf{A}$ and $\mathbf{B}$. There are several complicating features: i) both matrices are indefinite; ii) the basic-state quantities in $\mathbf{B}$ depend on the stability parameter; and iii) both $\mathbf{A}$ and $\mathbf{B}$ depend on a free coupling parameter λ. The later two complications are easily dealt with by iteration processes once a reliable procedure for calculating the eigenvalue of interest has been developed.

The standard algorithm for the solution of eigenvalue problems of the form $\mathbf{Ax} = \rho\mathbf{Bx}$, for general real or complex matrices $\mathbf{A}$ and $\mathbf{B}$, is the QZ algorithm. This method computes *all* of the eigenvalues of the system by means of orthogonal transformations. However, since it does not exploit either the sparsity or symmetry of $\mathbf{A}$ and $\mathbf{B}$, and only a single eigenvalue is desired, its use in the application of interest, where the system order is typically quite large, is extremely inefficient in terms of computer resources. In addition, it is possible that the calculation of the *single* eigenvalue of interest, which does not occur at any particular stage of the overall solution process, can be contaminated by earlier calculations. These factors motivated the development of the method that was successfully used by SHEN *et al.* (1990). The QZ algorithm was used solely to obtain some insight into the distribution of the complete family of eigenvalues for coarse discretizations (i.e., low system order) of the variational problem.

Theoretically, the inclusion of non-axisymmetric disturbances into the discretized functional is straightforward, involving only a normal-mode decomposition in the azimuthal coordinate. However, the corresponding computational problem is more difficult because the matrices in the algebraic eigenvalue problem become *complex* and *Hermitian*. The numerical procedure of SHEN *et al.* (1990) is unable to handle this case and some modification is necessary. Basically, their procedure is a form of inverse iteration. The modification to handle complex, Hermitian matrices uses a residual-based inverse iteration, which, in each step, computes an increment of the last iterate and employs additional orthogonal projections. The complex case is reduced to a real case of twice the dimension which is also symmetric. This permits a relatively efficient solution using preconditioned conjugate-gradient methods.

In order to test this new numerical approach we chose in MITTELMANN *et al.* (1990) to examine a related stability problem for which results are available. As in the code verification done in SHEN *et al.* (1990) we considered the onset of buoyant convection in a fluid-filled cylinder heated from below with either a conducting or insulating sidewall boundary. Linear-stability limits have been computed by CHARLSON & SANI (1970, 1971) for both axisymmetric and non-axisymmetric disturbances. These linear-theory results can be compared directly with those of energy theory since it can be shown for this problem that both limits coincide (JOSEPH, 1976). Although the heated-cylin problem is somewhat simpler than the float-zone problem for which first results will be presented below, it nevertheless served as an excellent test problem for the numerical procedure.

2. Basic state

The basic state of interest is one of swirl-free thermocapillary convection in a model half-zone of $O(1)$ aspect ratio. The flow and temperature fields are two-dimensional and must therefore be obtained numerically for the nonlinear cases of interest. We model the liquid zone as a Newtonian, Boussinesq fluid and choose sclase for length, velocity and pressure to be R, $\gamma(T_H - T_C)/\mu$, and $\gamma(T_H - T_C)/R$, respectively. The quantity μ is the dynamic viscosity coefficient and $\gamma > 0$ is the rate of decrease of surface tension σ with temperature as defined by $\sigma = \sigma_m - \gamma(T - T_m)$, where $T_m = \frac{1}{2}(T_H + T_C)$ is the mean temperature of the two solid cylinders and σ_m is the surface tension at temperature T_m. The velocity scale is the Marangoni velocity (SEN & DAVIS 1982) obtained by balancing the surface-tension gradient along the interface with the jump in shear stress. A dimensionless temperature is defined by

$$\Theta \equiv \frac{T - T_m}{T_H - T_C}.$$

The resulting dimensionless governing equations for the velocity $\mathbf{U} \equiv (U, V, W)$, pressure P and temperature fields are

$$\frac{1}{r}(rU)_r + \frac{1}{r}V_\theta + W_z = 0, \tag{2.1}$$

$$Re\,(UU_r + \frac{1}{r}VU_\theta + WU_z) - \frac{1}{r}V^2 = -P_r + \nabla^2 U - \frac{U}{r^2} - \frac{2}{r^2}V_\theta, \tag{2.2}$$

$$Re\,(UV_r + \frac{1}{r}VV_\theta + WV_z) + \frac{1}{r}UV = -\frac{1}{r}P_\theta + \nabla^2 V - \frac{V}{r^2} + \frac{2}{r^2}U_\theta \tag{2.3}$$

$$Re\,(UW_r + \frac{1}{r}VW_\theta + WW_z) = -P_z + \nabla^2 W + \frac{Gr}{Re}\Theta, \tag{2.4}$$

$$Ma(U\Theta_r + \frac{1}{r}V\Theta_\theta + W\Theta_z) = \nabla^2\Theta, \tag{2.5}$$

where

$$\nabla^2 \equiv \frac{1}{r}\frac{\partial}{\partial r}(r\frac{\partial}{\partial r}) + \frac{1}{r^2}\frac{\partial^2}{\partial\theta^2} + \frac{\partial^2}{\partial z^2}.$$

The basic state velocity of the axisymmetric basic state satisfies (2.1.-2), (2.4-5) with all terms involving V, θ omitted. The three dimensionless parameters which appear are:

$$\text{Reynolds number} \quad Re = \frac{\gamma(T_H - T_C)R}{\mu\nu},$$

$$\text{Grashof number} \quad Gr = \frac{g\alpha(T_H - T_C)R^3}{\nu^2},$$

$$\text{Marangoni number} \quad Ma = \frac{\gamma(T_H - T_C)R}{\mu\kappa},$$

where g is the gravitational acceleration, α is the coefficient of volumetric expansion and the conventional subscript notation has been used to denote partial differentiation. The Prandtl number is obtained from the quotient Ma/Re.

We assume, as a first approximation, that the free surface is not permitted to deform, and so is fixed at $r = 1$. This corresponds to requiring that the volume of liquid in the half zone is $\pi\Gamma$ and that the mean surface tension is asymptotically large. The boundary conditions applied to complete the problem specification are:

$$U = W = 0 \quad , \quad \Theta = -1/2; \qquad z = 0 \tag{2.6a-c}$$

$$U = W = 0 \quad , \quad \Theta = 1/2; \qquad z = \Gamma \tag{2.7a-c}$$

$$U = 0, \quad U_z + W_r = -\Theta_z \quad , \quad -P + 2U_r = \frac{-\sigma}{\sigma_m Ca}, \qquad \Theta_r = Bi[\Theta - \Theta_a(z)]; \qquad r = 1 \tag{2.8a-d}$$

$$U = W_r = \Theta_r = 0 \quad ; \quad r = 0. \tag{2.9a-c}$$

Equations (2.6) and (2.7) express the kinematic and no-slip conditions and the requirement of isothermal surfaces, while (2.8a) is the kinematic condition on the free surface. Equations (2.8b,c) represent the shear and normal-stress balances. Symmetry conditions at the axis of symmetry are given by (2.9). The additional parameter appearing in (2.8d), which models the heat-transfer mechanism at the free surface, is the Biot number, $Bi = hR/k$ where h is a heat-transfer coefficient and k is the thermal conductivity of the liquid. Since h may vary with z, in general, $Bi = Bi(z)$. This simple conductive mechanism for heat transfer between the liquid and the external environment (at specified temperature $\Theta_a(z)$) was adopted for consistency with the work of XU & DAVIS (1983, 1984, 1985). For the majority of the calculations $\Theta_a(z) = -1/2$, i.e., the environment was assumed to be at a constant temperature equal to that of the cold cylinder at $z = 0$. Condition (2.8c) contains the capillary number $Ca = \gamma(T_H - T_C)/\sigma_m$ which vanishes in the limit of a non-deformable free-surface. Hence, this condition is not required in the present analysis.

The numerical solution of this problem is accomplished by first transforming the axisymmetric equations to a *stream-function/vorticity* form, thereby eliminating the pressure. The stream function Ψ and vorticity ζ are defined by

$$U = \frac{1}{r}\Psi_z, \quad W = -\frac{1}{r}\Psi_r, \quad \zeta = U_z - W_r,$$

and the problem to be solved transforms to

$$\nabla^2\Psi - \frac{2}{r}\Psi_r = r\zeta, \tag{2.10}$$

$$Re\,(-\frac{\zeta}{r^2}\Psi_z + \frac{1}{r}\Psi_z\zeta_r - \frac{1}{r}\Psi_r\zeta_z) = \nabla^2\zeta - \frac{\zeta}{r^2} - \frac{Gr}{Re}\Theta_r, \tag{2.11}$$

$$Ma(\frac{1}{r}\Psi_z\Theta_r - \frac{1}{r}\Psi_r\Theta_z) = \nabla^2\Theta, \tag{2.12}$$

with boundary conditions

$$\Psi = 0, \quad \zeta = \frac{1}{r}\Psi_{zz}, \quad \Theta = \mp\frac{1}{2}; \quad z = 0, \Gamma, \tag{2.13a-f}$$

$$\Psi = \zeta = \Theta_r = 0; \quad r = 0, \tag{2.14a-c}$$

$$\Psi = 0, \quad \zeta = \Theta_z, \; \Theta_r = Bi[\Theta - \Theta_a(z)]; \quad r = 1. \tag{2.15a-c}$$

These equations are solved using a modification of the predictor-corrector multiple iteration (PCMI) technique employed successfully by NEITZEL & DAVIS (1981) and NEITZEL (1984) to study centrifugally unstable flows in cylindrical geometries; the reader is referred to these papers for details. For results of the basic state computations and comments, we refer to SHEN et al. (1990).

3. Energy-stability analysis

We begin the energy-theory analysis of the basic state in the usual fashion by deriving the energy identity. We assume there exists a solution $[\mathbf{u}, p, T]$ to the governing equations ((2.1), plus the unsteady analogs of (2.2)–(2.5)) which is a perturbation to the axisymmetric basic state, i.e.,

$$\begin{aligned}[\mathbf{u}, p, T] &= [U(r,z), 0, W(r,z), P(r,z), \Theta(r,z)] \\ &+ [u'(r,\theta,z,t), v'(r,\theta,z,t), w'(r,\theta,z,t), p'(r,\theta,z,t), T'(r,\theta,z,t)].\end{aligned} \tag{3.1}$$

Substitution of (3.1) into the governing equations and boundary conditions leads to a system of equations for the disturbance quantities. We then take the inner product of the disturbance momentum equation with $\mathbf{u}'$, add to this the disturbance energy equation multiplied by $\lambda PrT'$, and integrate over the volume

$$V = \{(r, \theta, z) \mid 0 \leq r \leq 1,\ 0 \leq \theta \leq 2\pi,\ 0 \leq z \leq \Gamma\}$$

occupied by the liquid, using the disturbance boundary conditions. The result is exact disturbance-energy evolution equation

$$\frac{dE}{dt} = -PrD - MaI + PrJ,\ E = \frac{1}{2}\int_V (\mathbf{u}' \cdot \mathbf{u}' + \lambda PrT'^2)\, dV, \tag{3.2}$$

where

$$I = \int_V (\mathbf{u}' \cdot \mathbf{D} \cdot \mathbf{u}' + \lambda PrT' \nabla\Theta \cdot \mathbf{u}' - \frac{Gr}{Re^2} w'T')\, dV,$$

$$D = \int_V (\nabla\mathbf{u}' : \nabla\mathbf{u}' + \lambda\nabla T' \cdot \nabla T')\, dV,\ J = \int_S (-v'T'_\theta + v'^2 - w'T'_z + \lambda BiT'^2)\, dS$$

and S is the free surface $r = 1$. The velocity and temperature disturbances have been joined by a positive *coupling parameter* λ (JOSEPH 1976) to form a generalized disturbance energy, E, and the quantity $\mathbf{D}$ in the production integral I is the *symmetric* basic-state deformation–rate tensor,

$$\mathbf{D} = \begin{bmatrix} U_r & 0 & \frac{1}{2}(U_z + W_r) \\ & U/r & 0 \\ & & W_z \end{bmatrix}.$$

Employing the re-formulated energy theory of DAVIS & VON KERCZEK (1973), (3.2) is divided by the positive-definite functional E and an upper bound is constructed for the resulting right-hand side, viz.,

$$\frac{1}{E}\frac{dE}{dt} \leq \nu = \max_H \left(\frac{-PrD - MaI + PrJ}{E}\right), \tag{3.3}$$

where the maximum is taken over the space of kinematically admissible functions,

$$H = \{\mathbf{u}', T' \mid \mathbf{u}' = T' = 0 \text{ at } z = 0, \Gamma;\ u' = 0 \text{ at } r = 0, 1;\ \nabla \cdot \mathbf{u}' = 0\}.$$

We choose to formulate the problem so that the Marangoni number is the stability parameter. For fixed values of the other parameters associated with the problem, the smallest value of Ma which corresponds to the condition $\nu = 0$ will be called $Ma^*(\lambda)$.

The cylindrical geometry allows a Fourier decomposition in the azimuthal coordinate of the form

$$u'(r, \theta, z, t) \to u(r, z, t)e^{in\theta} + u^*(r, z, t)e^{-in\theta},$$

where n is the azimuthal (integer) wavenumber and "$*$" denotes complex conjugation.

Since λ is a free parameter, the maximum value of Ma^* for positive values of λ is sought (JOSEPH 1976), while a minimization has to be carried out with respect to n. The resulting value is the energy-stability limit, Ma_E, defined as

$$Ma_E = \min_n \max_{\lambda>0} Ma^*. \tag{3.4}$$

In many analyses, the search for this maximum is not performed. Rather, the variable λ is arbitrarily set to some value, say $\lambda = 1$, and the result is accepted as a lower bound to the actual energy-stability limit. It will be seen that, for the problem of interest here, the effort necessary to determine Ma_E is extremely worthwhile.

3.1. Formulation of the discrete problem

Typically, Ma^* is calculated by treating the Euler-Lagrange system which arises from the maximum problem in (3.3). However, the basic state, which appears in the coefficients at these equations, is known only numerically. Thus, we choose to approach the calculation of Ma^* by directly treating the functional ν in (3.3). It is convenient to consider a slightly different functional which incorporates the divergence constraint by means of a Lagrange multiplier. Hence, the maximum problem to be solved is expressed as

$$\max_h[-PrD - MaI + PrJ + 2\int_V \pi\nabla\cdot\mathbf{u}'\,dV + \bar{\nu}(E-1)] = 0, \tag{3.5}$$

where $\bar{\nu}$ is a Lagrange multiplier expressing the arbitrary normalization $E = 1$, $\pi(r, z)$ is a Lagrange multiplier, and h is the extension of H obtained by removing the divergence constraint. It is easy to show that $\bar{\nu} = \nu$. Thus, since the stability condition is given by $\nu = 0$, we are interested in the variation of the quadratic functional

$$F = -PrD - MaI + PrJ + 2\int_V \pi\nabla\cdot\mathbf{u}'\,dV.$$

A discrete version of this functional follows in an obvious way. A grid system, which divides the flow region into N rectangular subdomains, is chosen. The *unknown* values of the disturbance velocity and temperature at the intersections of the grid are denoted by $u_{i,j}$, $v_{i,j}$, $w_{i,j}$ and $T_{i,j}$. Since the Lagrange multiplier π plays the same role as the fluid pressure, a staggered grid is employed for it; the *unknown* values of π at the intersections of its grid are denoted by $\pi_{k,l}$. The various derivatives in the integrals of F are replaced by finite differences. The integrals are approximated on each subdomain by finite summations using the disturbance boundary conditions, where applicable, and finally the discrete version of the functional F_D, is formed by summing over all N subdomains. We refer to SHEN *et al.* (1990) where details are given in the two-dimensional case.

A stationary value of F_D is located by differentiating it with respect to each unknown and setting each of these derivatives to zero, i.e.,

$$\frac{\partial F_D}{\partial q_n} = 0, \quad q_n = u_{i,j}, v_{ij}, w_{i,j}, \phi_{i,j} \text{ or } \pi_{k,l}. \tag{3.7}$$

This process yields a generalized algebraic eigenvalue problem. We seek the minimum positive eigenvalue of this system as the approximate (subject to discretization error) value of Ma^*. Calling the vector consisting of the unknowns on all grid points $\overline{\mathbf{X}}$, we rewrite (3.7) in the matrix form

$$\overline{\mathbf{A}}\mathbf{X} = \rho\overline{\mathbf{B}}(Ma)\overline{\mathbf{X}}, \tag{3.8}$$

where $\overline{\mathbf{A}}$ and $\overline{\mathbf{B}}$ are *indefinite, Hermitian* with $\overline{\mathbf{A}}$ having a banded structure and $\overline{\mathbf{B}}$ depending on the basic-state deformation-rate tensor $\mathbf{D}$. The fact that the matrices are Hermitian is due to the derivation from the variational problem (3.5). The dependence on the basic state, which depends in turn on the Marangoni number Ma, complicates the calculation of Ma^* (MUNSON & JOSEPH 1971). For a given value of Ma, denote the smallest positive eigenvalue of the generalized eigenvalue problem (3.8) by ρ^*. If $\rho^* \neq Ma$, then a new Ma is chosen, the basic state re-computed, and the eigenvalues re-calculated. This process is repeated until $\rho^* = Ma$, in which case, $Ma^* = \rho^*$. This, of course, assumes all other parameters, including the coupling parameter λ, are fixed, necessitating further computation to find Ma_E according to (3.4). The *numerical* problem associated with these eigenvalue computations is, like the approach to the stability problem, somewhat unconventional. For this reason, the procedure by which ρ^* and Ma_E are computed is described in some detail below.

3.2 Numerical procedure for finding Ma_E

Equation (3.8) represents a generalized eigenvalue problem. The matrices $\bar{\mathbf{A}}$ and $\overline{\mathbf{B}}$ are Hermitian and sparse, but, in general, indefinite. For the ultimate problem of interest, in addition to the basic-state dependence of $\overline{\mathbf{B}}$ mentioned above, $\bar{\mathbf{A}}$ and $\overline{\mathbf{B}}$ depend nonlinearly on the other parameters of the problem, namely, Pr, Gr, n, and the coupling parameter, λ. We refer to SHEN et al. (1990) for the solution of the problems associated with the other parameters and thus consider only fixed values of these parameters, reducing (3.8) to the generalized eigenvalue problem

$$\bar{\mathbf{A}}\overline{\mathbf{X}} = \rho\overline{\mathbf{B}}\,\overline{\mathbf{X}}, \quad \|\overline{\mathbf{X}}\| = 1, \tag{3.9}$$

where $\|\cdot\|$ denotes the Euclidean norm.

The eigenvalues ρ of (3.9) are, in general, complex. Null vectors of $\bar{\mathbf{A}}$ and $\overline{\mathbf{B}}$ correspond to zero and "infinite" eigenvalues, respectively. The method developed for the present computations makes use of the sparseness of $\bar{\mathbf{A}}$ and $\overline{\mathbf{B}}$, the fact that they are Hermitian, and computes only the eigenvalue of interest.

Since a real eigenvalue of (3.9) has to be computed it is convenient to transfor the problem so that only real arithmetic is needed. Let

$$\mathbf{A} = \begin{bmatrix} \mathrm{Re}(\overline{\mathbf{A}}) & -\mathrm{Im}(\overline{\mathbf{A}} \\ \mathrm{Im}(\overline{\mathbf{A}}) & \mathrm{Re}(\overline{\mathbf{A}}) \end{bmatrix},$$

where $\mathrm{Re}(\cdot)$, $\mathrm{Im}(\cdot)$ denote real and imaginary parts, and let $\mathbf{B}$ be defined in a similar way. A straightforward calculation shows that the eigenvalue problem

$$\mathbf{A}X = \rho\mathbf{B}X, \quad \mathbf{X} \neq 0 \tag{3.10}$$

has the eigenpairs $\rho, (\overline{\mathbf{X}}, -i\overline{\mathbf{X}})^T$, $\overline{\rho}, (\overline{\mathbf{X}}, i\overline{\mathbf{X}})^T$, where $\rho, \overline{\mathbf{X}}$ are the eigenpairs of (3.9) and $i = \sqrt{-1}$ is the imaginary unit. Thus, each eigenvalue of (3.9) corresponds to a pair of complex-conjugate eigenvalues of (3.10).

It is important to note that all eigenvalues of (3.10) have the same modulus as the corresponding eigenvalues of (3.9) and that a simple real eigenvalue of (3.9) corresponds to a double eigenvalue of (3.10), but that (3.10) has no other eigenvalue of the same modulus. Apart from the multiplicity of the eigenvalues, (3.10) is an eigenvalue problem of the form considered in SHEN *et al.* (1990).

The stability theory requires the computation of but a single eigenvalue of the problem (3.10), namely, ρ^*, the smallest positive one. The following observations from computations of the entire spectrum using the complex QZ algorithm led to the choice of a suitable form of inverse iteration for the solution of this problem. The problem specified in (3.10) has a spectrum which is roughly symmetrically distributed in the complex plane with respect to both the real and the imaginary axis. There are a number of *infinite* eigenvalues corresponding to null vectors of $\mathbf{B}$. The smallest positive eigenvalue ρ^* was, in general, also the smallest one in modulus. There were, however, several eigenvalues both in the negative and the positive half-plane that were not much greater in modulus than ρ^*. The nullspaces of $\mathbf{A}$ and $\mathbf{B}$ did not appear to have a nontrivial intersection. Thus, inverse iteration with an appropriately chosen shift of orig was selected for the solution of (3.10).

When the matrix $\mathbf{B}$ in (3.10) is positive-definite, *Rayleigh quotient* iteration, i.e., inverse iteration with a shift computed in each step from the Rayleigh quotient of the current eigenvector approximation, is known to exhibit very rapid convergence. This procedure cannot be applied here. The technique developed for the present case is a generalization of that employed by BANK & MITTELMANN (1986) in the program PLTMG for the simpler problem of finding the smallest eigenvalue of a positive-definite matrix. It cannot be expected to solve for any desired eigenvalue of (3.10), but the observations mentioned above justified the application of a suitably implemented version for the computation of ρ^*. The process is started with a random normalized vector $\mathbf{X}_0$ which is such that its Rayleigh-quotient $\rho_0 = \mathbf{X}_0\mathbf{A}X_0/\mathbf{X}_0^T\mathbf{B}X_0$ is well-defined. Given this initial pair $\rho_0, \mathbf{X}_0$, the inverse iteration procedure is performed as follows:

1. Solve $(\mathbf{A} - s\mathbf{B})\overline{\mathbf{Y}} = (\rho_k\mathbf{B} - \mathbf{A})\mathbf{X}_k$ and define $\mathbf{Y} = \dfrac{\overline{\mathbf{Y}} - \mathbf{X}_k^T\overline{\mathbf{Y}}\mathbf{X}_k}{\|\overline{\mathbf{Y}} - \mathbf{X}_k^T\overline{Y}\mathbf{X}_k\|}$.
2. Form $\mathbf{Q} = [\mathbf{X}_k|\mathbf{Y}]$ and solve the 2×2 problem $\mathbf{Q}^T\mathbf{AQZ} = \tau\mathbf{Q}^T\mathbf{BQZ}$ for the eigenvalues τ_1, τ_2 and associated normalized eigenvectors $\mathbf{Z}_1, \mathbf{Z}_2$. Without loss of generality let τ_1 be the *smallest positive* eigenvalue.
3. Set $\rho_{k+1} = \tau_1$, $\mathbf{X}_{k+1} = \mathbf{QZ}_1$ and check for convergence. If not converged, increment iteration index k and repeat.

While no analysis of this algorithm will be given here, a few remarks are in order. The shift s is chosen as a positive real number. From the well-known theory of inverse iteration s has to be closer to ρ^* than to any other eigenvalue of (3.10). Since ρ^* is unknown, this may require some adjustment of s during the iteration. Experience has shown, however, that a rough knowledge of the expected ρ^* and the facts observed above on the distribution of the other eigenvalues permitted the determination of a reasonable value for the shift.

The eigenvalue problem in step 2 is basically an orthogonal projection of the original problem into the subspace spanned by the columns of $\mathbf{Q}$. Simpler inverse iteration algorithms are indeed available; however, their application to the present problem did not yield satisfactory results. In general, of course, this 2×2 eigenvalue problem may have complex eigenvalues, as well as real ones. While several precautions for this and other cases were put into the program, they will not be described here, being a rather technical detail. Eventually τ_1 will be positive and approximate ρ^* while $\mathbf{QZ}_1$ approximates the associated eigenvector. The quantities $\mathbf{X}_{k+1}$ and ρ_{k+1} are related through the Rayleig quotient.

Due to the properties of $\mathbf{A}$ and $\mathbf{B}$, the matrix on the left-hand side of the linear system in step 1 is highly indefinite but symmetric. The latest version of the program SYMMLQ [PAIGE & SAUNDERS (1975)] was used for the solution of this system. It applies a conjugate-gradient method and provides for preconditioning by a positive-definite matrix. There is no complete theory available for the preconditioning of indefinite systems. The standard diagonal preconditioning for the associated normal equations led to the choice of the diagonal matrix with its i-th element equal to the Euclidean norm of the i-th column of the matrix $\mathbf{A} - s\mathbf{B}$.

The convergence of the above inverse iteration procedure is, in general, linear with a factor asymptotically equal to

$$\left|\frac{s-\rho^*}{s-\rho_n}\right| < 1,$$

where ρ_n is the next nearest eigenvalue of (3.10) to s and different from ρ^*. Choosing s close to ρ^* will thus speed up convergence of the inverse iteration while generally requiring more conjugate-gradient iterations for the nearly singular system matrix. The essential computational requirement per conjugate-gradient iteration is one matrix-vector multiplication with the system matrix. Since ρ^* is, in general, a double eigenvalue of (3.10), it is also important to note that inverse iteration exhibits the same convergence behavior for eigenvalues that are equal as opposed to those that are equal in modulus but different. Again, the observations on the distribution of the spectrum and the properties of (3.10) as a transformation of (3.9) are of relevance.

Finally, as a stopping criterion, a test on the relative decrease of the residual combined with one on the convergence of subsequent eigenvalue approximations was used. The resulting code never failed to solve the above eigenvalue problem and some information on its performance will be given in the following section. Again, we refer to SHEN et al. (1990) for the solution of the other problems inherent in (3.4), in particular, the fixed-point iteration for the Marangoni-number and the maximization of the stability bound with respect to λ.

4. Numerical Results

The energy stability analysis of section 3 was carried out for the case $Pr = 1$, $Gr = 0$ and two different aspect ratios Γ. The numerical method described in 3.2 was successfully used to compute the corresponding stability bounds Ma_E which are also identical to the Reynolds number due to $Pr = 1$. The interesting question is, of course, how much these bounds differ from those of the axisymmetric case in SHEN et al. (1990). As in that paper, a comparison with experimental results is desirable. For this we chose the appropriately transformed values in VELTEN et al. (1990).

The following table 4.1 lists the values $Ma^*(n)$. The minimum value of these with respect to n is Ma_E, i.e., 2633 (3524) for aspect ratio 1.0 (.7). The optimal values of λ were in the range 10^{-7} to 10^{-8}. In VELTEN et al. only the value Ma_{exp} for the observed onset of instability is given. A sharp drop in the computed values of Ma^* is observed for $n > 1$. There are several reasons why a close agreement is not expected, these include uncertainties in the physical properties of the fluids used in the experiment, the type of thermal boundary conditions on the free surface, and a possible contamination of the free surface in the experiments. Preliminary computations show that the computed values are indeed sensitive to the thermal boundary condition. In a relative way, however, the initial computations reported here show a very similar trend. They show that more extensive computations are justified. For the discretization (nearly) square grids with mesh width 1/69 were used in both cases. For aspect ratio 1.0 (.7) the orders of the matrices $\bar{\mathbf{A}}$, $\overline{\mathbf{B}}$ were 22597 (16331) while the number of elements in one half of the real parts for $\bar{\mathbf{A}}$ were 129265 (89556), for its imaginary part 59638 (41095) and for the real part of $\overline{\mathbf{B}}$ 191970 (132675).

Γ	1.0		.7	
n	Ma^*	Ma_{exp}	Ma^*	Ma_{exp}
0	6254		8008	
2	2633	1350	3524	
3	3545		3713	2275

Table 4.1 Computed Marangoni numbers for different aspect ratios and wavenumbers

Acknowledgement. This work was partially supported by the US Air Force Office of Scientific Research under grant AFOSR-90-0080 and by the Microgravity Science and Applications Division of NASA under grant NAG-3-1054.

REFERENCES

BANK, R. & MITTELMANN, H. D. (1986) Continuation and multigrid for nonlinear elliptic systems. In *Multigrid Methods II* (ed. W. Hackbusch & U. Trottenb *Lect. Notes Math.* **1228**, Springer.

CHARLSON, G. S. & SANI, R. L. (1970) Thermoconvective instability in a bounded cylindrical fluid layer. *Int. J. Heat Mass Trans.* **13**, 1479.

CHARLSON, G. S. & SANI, R. L. (1971) On thermoconvective instability in a bound cylindrical fluid layer, *Int. J. Heat Mass Trans.* **14**, 2157.

DAVIS, S. H. (1971) Energy stability of unsteady flows. *IUTAM Symposium on Unsteady Boundary Layers*, 206.

DAVIS, S. H. & von KERCZEK, C. (1973) A reformulation of energy stability theory. *Arch. Rat. Mech. Anal.* **52**, 112.

JOSEPH, D. D. (1976) *Stability of Fluid Motions I, II*, Springer-Verlag, Berlin.

MITTELMANN, H. D., LAW, C. C., JANKOWSKI, D. F. & NEITZEL, G. P. (1990) A large sparse and indefinite generalized eigenvalue problem from fluid mechanics. submitted to SIAM J. Sci. Stat. Comp.

MUNSON, B. R. & JOSEPH, D. D. (1971) Viscous incompressible flow between concentric rotating spheres. Part 2. Hydrodynamic stability. *J. Fluid Mech.* **49**, 305.

NEITZEL, G. P. (1984) Numerical computation of time-dependent Taylor-vortex flows in finite-length geometries. *J. Fluid Mech.* **141**, 51.

NEITZEL, G. P. & DAVIS, S. H. (1981) Centrifugal instabilities during spin-down to rest in finite cylinders. Numerical experiments. *J. Fluid Mech.* **102**, 329.

PAIGE, C. C. & SAUNDERS, M. A. (1975) Solution of sparse indefinite systems of linear equations. *SIAM J. Numer. Anal.* **12**, 617.

PREISSER, F., SCHWABE, P. & SHARMANN, A. (1983) Steady and oscillatory thermocapillary convection in liquid columns with free cylindrical surface. *J. Fluid Mech.* **126**, 545.

SEN, A. K. & DAVIS, S. H. (1982) Steady thermocapillary flow in two dimension slots. *J. Fluid Mech.* **121**, 163.

SHEN, Y., NEITZEL, G. P., JANKOWSKI, D. F. & MITTELMANN, H. D. (1990) Energy stability of thermocapillary convection in a model of the float-zone, crystal-growth process. *J. Fluid Mech.*, to appear.

SINHA, S. C. & CARMI, S. (1976) On the Liapunov-Movchan and the energy theories of stability. *J. Appl. Math. Phys.* **27**, 607–612.

VELTEN, R., SCHWABE, D. & SCHARMANN, A. (1990) The periodic instability of thermocapillary convection in cylindrical liquid bridges, submitted to Phys. Fluids.

XU, J.-J. & DAVIS, S. H. (1983) Liquid bridges with thermocapillarity. *Phys. Fluids* **26**, 2880.

XU, J.-J. & DAVIS, S. H. (1984) Convective thermocapillary instabilities in liquid bridges. *Phys. Fluids* **27**, 1102.

XU, J.-J. & DAVIS, S. H. (1985) Instability of capillary jets with thermocapillarity. *J. Fluid Mech.* **161**, 1.

Numerical solution of coupled Navier-Stokes and Stefan equations

V. RIVKIND
Department of Mathematics
University of Leningrad

Abstract. Problems of numerical solutions of coupled Stefan and Navier-Stokes equations are analysed. The solvability of stationary problems and the smoothness of their solutions are considered. An iterative method to solve nonlinear equation is proposed. In the method at each iteration step the solution of corresponding linear problem is obtained by means of finite element technique. Estimates for the rate of convergence of the approximate solution to the exact one are given. This method and the estimates are generalized to the case of quasistationary equations. Methods to solve nonstationary problems for Navier-Stokes and Stefan problem are given.

Keywords. Coupled Navier–Stokes and Stefan equations, numerical solutions.

1980 Mathematics subject classifications: 65N30, 76D05.

1. INTRODUCTION

We analyze problems of evaporation of drops, films, a liquid partially filling a vessel and similar problems formulated by means of coupled systems of Navier-Stokes and Stefan equations. There is a long history of theoretical as well as numerical analysis studying each of these problems. In this paper we use a decomposition method to split the initial nonlinear problem into an auxiliary problem with a fixed boundary and a boundary value problem for finding the unknown boundary.

Theoretical results of these problems for Navier-Stokes equations are given in article [8] for example. The problems in our consideration can be treated by similar methods. Numerical analogues of these results for stationary viscous free boundary flow problems are formulated in the papers [4], [7], [9], [11], [13] for example. The methods of these papers are usually based on a transformation and a linearization of the unknown domain to a standard one on every iterative step. The convergence of approximate methods for problems of this type is proved in [9], [16]. Proofs are based on the fact that an operator of the exact problem is contractive in a ball of the Banach space and that the approximate operator is also a contractive in the finite-dimensional space.

Also an estimate for the rate of convergence is obtained. The fact that both operators (for exact and approximate problems) are contractive allows us to make use of the method of succesive approximation, which can be realized in two different ways. In the first one the problem with fixed boundary is solved on each step of iterations. So we find the fields of velocities and pressures, as well as the normal stresses on a fixed boundary. After that a new approximation to the free boundary is found and the process is repeated.

In the other type of successive iterations method (see [4], [5], [7], [15], [16], [20]) the unknown boundary is chosen simultaneously with the determination of pressure fields. Here finite elements for solving Navier-Stokes equations are determined via the unknown coordinates of the boundary. A difficulty is that during the computation process the finite elements can be deformed significantly if the ratio between their sides becomes too large. Similar methods are developed for the stationary and quasistationary coupled problems of Navier-Stokes and Stefan equations. The unknown boundary is determined through a kinematical condition. It is necessary to overcome supplementary difficulties. Actually many authors use Lagrange and Euler-Lagrange coordinates to solve nonstationary problems.

2. Mathematical model for stationary problems

Let $\Omega \subset \mathbf{R}^n$ be a domain with a boundary Σ and with a free surface Γ (Fig. 2.1).

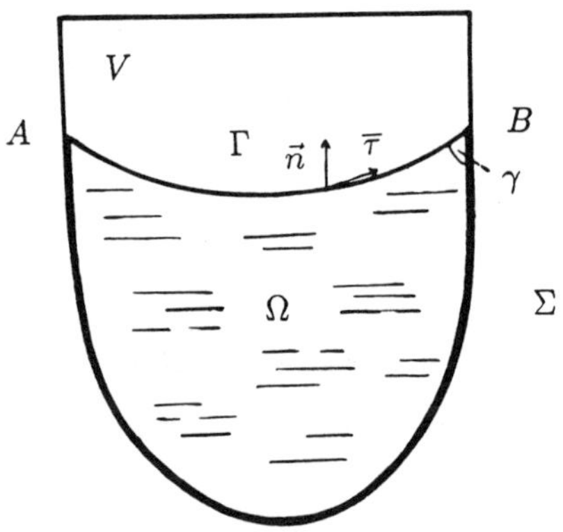

Fig. 2.1

We suppose that the velocity field $\vec{v}$ and the pressure p of the fluid in Ω are described by the full system of Navier-Stokes equations

$$\left.\begin{aligned} -\frac{1}{Re}\Delta\vec{v} + (\vec{v},\nabla)\,\vec{v} &= -\nabla p + Gr\vec{f} \quad \text{in } \Omega \\ \operatorname{div}\vec{v} &= 0 \quad \text{in } \Omega \end{aligned}\right\} \tag{2.1}$$

coupled with a Stefan equation for the temperature θ

$$-\frac{1}{Pr}\Delta\theta + \vec{v}\cdot\nabla\theta = Q \quad \text{in } \Omega \tag{2.2}$$

where Pr, Gr, Re are Prandtl, Grashof and Reynolds numbers and $\vec{f}$, Q are given.

The following boundary conditions mean that stresses at the free surface Γ are equal to the surface tension directed along the normal $\vec{n}(x)$ to Γ,

(2.3) $$\vec{\tau} \cdot S \cdot \vec{n}|_\Gamma = 0,$$

and moreover the stresses are proportional to the mean curvature:

(2.4) $$-We(\vec{n} \cdot S \cdot \vec{n})|_\Gamma = K$$

Above $\vec{n}$ is exterior normal, τ is tangent vector to Γ, We is the Weber number and

$$S(\vec{v}, p) = -pI + \frac{2}{Re} T(\vec{v})$$

is the strain tensor, whose elements $T_{ij}(\vec{v})$ are equal to $\frac{\partial v_i}{\partial x_j} + \frac{\partial v_j}{\partial x_i}$. Moreover, by $K(x)$ we denote the second mean curvature of Γ at the point x,

$$K\vec{n} = \Delta \vec{x},$$

where $\vec{x}$ is the radius vector corresponding to the point $x \in \Gamma$ and Δ is the Laplace-Beltrami operator on Γ.

The kinematic boundary conditions at the free surface are,

(2.5) $$\vec{v} \cdot \vec{n}\Big|_\Gamma = \lambda \frac{\partial \theta}{\partial n}\Big|_\Gamma$$

Finally we suppose that the temperature on the Γ satisfies the boundary condition

(2.6) $$\theta|_\Gamma = 0$$

In addition we have boundary conditions at the known boundary Σ. For example, we consider a problem of the evaporation of a liquid partially filling a vessel. Geometrically the vessel V is a semi-infinite cylinder in $\mathbf{R}^3$ and Ω is with the liquid domain. Thus,

$$\Gamma = \{x \mid \varphi(x) = 0\}$$

is the free boundary defined by a function φ and $\Sigma = \partial\Omega \backslash \Gamma$ is the boundary as indicated in Fig. 2.1 . The boundary conditions on Σ are following

(2.7) $$\vec{v}|_\Sigma = 0, \qquad \frac{\partial \theta}{\partial n} - \chi\theta|_\Sigma = 0$$

The angle γ between the free boundary Γ and boundary Σ is given.

To prove the unique solvability of the problem (2.1)–(2.7) in weighted Sobolev spaces we use a method of decomposition of the complete problem (2.1)–(2.7) into the auxiliary problem, (2.1)–(2.3), (2.5)–(2.7) with a fixed boundary and the equation (2.4) with boundary conditions $\sqrt{\gamma} = \gamma_0(x)$, see Fig.2.1, for finding the unknown boundary Γ ([1], [8], [10]–[13], [16]–[18], [21]). The analysis of solvability is carried out by a method proposed in [8], [13], [17], [18] and is based on the theorems of solvability for both the Stokes' problem and linearized problems for determining the temperature and the unknown boundary. This approach permits us to obtain the following theorem. We use standard notations for Hölder spaces $C^{k+\alpha}$, weighted Sobolev spaces $H_\mu^{(i)}$ $(k, i = 1, 2, \dots,\ 1 < \alpha < 2)$ and Slobodetski-Sobolev spaces $W_{k,\mu}^{l/2}$, $(l = 1, 3, 5)$ with a weight function μ.

THEOREM 2.1. *Let* $\Sigma \in C^{2+\alpha}$, $\alpha \in (\frac{1}{2}, 1)$, $f \in H_\mu^{(1)}(\Omega)$, $\theta_\Sigma \in H_\mu^{3/2}(\Sigma)$ *and let*

$$\chi \int_{\Sigma_1} \theta_\Sigma \, d\Sigma + \int_\Omega Q \, d\Omega = 0.$$

Then there exist values Re_1, Pr_1, λ_1, α_1 *such that for any* $Re < Re_1$, $Pr < Pr_1$, $\lambda < \lambda_1$, $\alpha < \alpha_1$ *the problem (2.1)–(2.7) has the unique solution*

$$(\Gamma, \vec{v}, p, \theta) \in W_{2,\mu}^{5/2}(\Gamma) \times H_\mu^{(2)}(\Omega) \times H_\mu^{(1)}(\Omega) \times H_\mu^{(2)}(\Omega),$$

where

$$\mu \in \left(\max \left(1 - S_0, \, 2 - \frac{\pi}{\max \gamma(x)} \right), \frac{1}{2} \right),$$

$$S_0 = \min \left(\min Re\, \xi(x), \, \frac{\pi}{2 \max \gamma(x)} \right)$$

and where $\xi(x)$ *is a root of the equation* $\sin 2\xi\gamma(x) = \xi(x) \sin 2\gamma(x)$.

PROOF: See [10], [21].

3. APPROXIMATION OF THE PROBLEM

Let us consider a problem of approximate determination of $(\varphi_t, \vec{v}, p, \theta)$, to solve system of equations (2.1)–(2.7) in the stationary case, for which the existence and uniqueness are stated in Theorem 2.1. .

Taking into account that the vessel V is rotating around the axis parallel to the direction of the force of gravity, we introduce a curvilinear coordinate system (q_1, q_2, q_3), such that velocity vector $\vec{v}$, pressure p and temperature θ would not depend upon the coordinate q_3 and $v_3 = 0$. On the rotation axis one has

$$\vec{v}|_{q_1=0} = 0 \tag{3.1}$$

We solve the problem (2.1)–(2.7), (3.1) by an iterative method. As an initial guess one can choose $\vec{v}^{(0)} = 0$, $p^{(0)} = \text{const}$, $\theta = \theta_1$ and let $\Gamma^{(0)}$ for the free boundary, i.e. the solution of the problem (2.1)–(2.7), (3.1) with $Re = 0$. If $(m-1)$-th approximation of the solution, i.e. $\vec{v}^{(m-1)}$, $p^{(m-1)}$, $\theta^{(m-1)}$, $\Gamma^{(m-1)}$ are known, then by solving the problem (2.1)–(2.3), (2.5)–(2.7), (3.1) with specified $\Gamma^{(m-1)}$ and $\theta^{(m-1)}$ we can find the values $\vec{v}^{(m)}$, $p^{(m)}$. Further, solving (2.2) with given $\vec{v}^{(m)}$ and with corresponding boundary condition we obtain the value of $\theta^{(m)}$. The next approximation $\varphi^{(m)}$ is found from the equations (2.4) using known $\vec{v}^{(m)}$, $p^{(m)}$, $\theta^{(m)}$.

The process described above is convergent with the rate of convergence of an infinitely decreasing geometric sequence [10]. In each iteration step the auxiliary problem (2.1)–(2.7), (3.1) and the problem of the surface reconstruction are solved by approximate methods. In accordance with the general theory of approximate methods [11] for solving equations (2.1)–(2.7), (3.1) it is sufficient to construct a sequence of finite-dimensional subspaces approximating the space $H^2_\mu \times H^1_\mu \times H^2_\mu \times W^{5/2}_{2,\mu}$ which contain the exact solution $(\vec{v}, p, \theta, \Gamma)$ by Theorem 2.1. .

By approximating the space $H^2_\mu(\Omega)$ by the set of solenoidal functions (which satisfy condition $\operatorname{div} \vec{v} = 0$) we can introduce the stream function ϕ related to the velocity components by equalities $v_1 = \frac{1}{H_2 H_3} \cdot \frac{\partial \phi}{\partial q_2}$ and $v_2 = -\frac{1}{H_1 H_3} \cdot \frac{\partial \phi}{\partial q_1}$ where H_i $(i = 1, 2, 3)$ are Lamé coefficients. For such an approximation it is advantageous to carry out the change of variables $\eta = Tq$, so that $T\Omega = \Omega^0$, Ω^0 being a domain where $\vec{v} = 0$, $p = \text{const}$, $\theta = \theta_1$, and $T\varphi = \varphi^0$ specifies a part of a circumference. In the region

$$\{(\eta_1, \eta_2) \mid \eta_1 \in (0,1); -1 \le \eta_2 \le \varphi^0(\eta_1)\}$$

a grid of triangles is introduced as follows. We draw the lines $r = (ih)^{1/\beta}$, $i = 1, \dots, n$, $h = \frac{1}{n}$, $0 < \beta < 1 - \mu$, where $r = \min(r_1, r_2)$, and r_1, r_2 are the distances to corner points M_1 and M_2, respectively. Now denote $h_i = (ih)^{1/\beta}$, $i = 1, \dots, n$ and construct a broken line Γ_h, approximating Γ_0 so that for all h less than a certain h_0, vertices of the broken line belonging to $\omega_i = \{h_{i-1} \le r \le h_i\}$, are no more than δh_i^2 away from Γ. The length of each section of the broken line with a vertex belonging to ω_i must be no less than $l_0 h_i$, where l_0 and δ do not depend on h. See Fig. 3.1 .

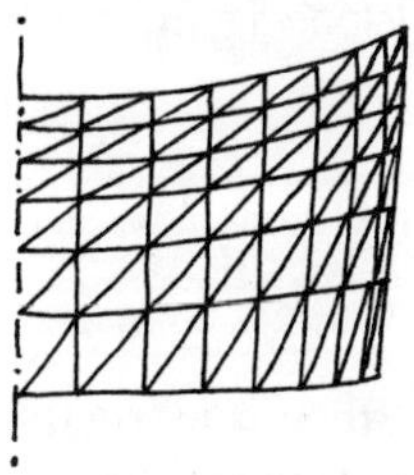

Fig. 3.1

Now triangulate the domain Ω_t bounded by Γ_h so that the following conditions are met:

1) the triangles do not intersect each other, or have only a common vertex or a common side, respectively;
2) if a triangle intersects ω_1, then its lateral lengths must be within the limits: $l_1 h_i < l < 2h_i$;
3) the angles of all the triangles must be not less than γ_0;
4) the number N of triangles that intersect ω must not exceed N_{0i}; the values of l_1, γ_0 and N_0 do not depend on h.

Nodal parameters for construction of the corresponding finite elements are chosen to be the values of the function ϕ averaged by Iljin-Golovkin procedure [3]

$$\phi_{\tau h} = \int_{\mathbf{R}^2} \phi(y)\, \tau_h(z - y) \frac{H_3(z)}{H_3(y)} I\, dy$$

and derivatives of (up to) the second order in vertices of triangles as well as normal derivatives at the mid-points of rectilinear sides, where I denotes the Jacobian.

The functions ϕ_h obtained with the help of these nodal parameters, for example, are polynomials of the fifth degree. Let V_h be the space of functions of the type

$$\vec{v}_h = \left\{ \frac{1}{H_2 H_3} \sum_{j=1}^{2} \frac{\partial \phi_h}{\partial \eta_j} \frac{\partial \eta_j}{\partial q_2}\bigg|_{Tq^{-1}}, \ -\frac{1}{H_1 H_3} \sum_{j=1}^{2} \frac{\partial \phi_h}{\partial \eta_j} \frac{\partial \eta_j}{\partial q_1}\bigg|_{Tq^{-1}} \right\}.$$

Then the following inequalities hold true [11]:

$$\|\vec{v} - \vec{v}_h\|_{W_2^s(\Omega)} \le ch^{2-s}, \quad 0 \le s \le 1, \tag{3.2}$$

$$\|\vec{v} - \vec{v}_h\|_{H_\mu^2(\Omega)} \le c. \tag{3.3}$$

For functions $\overline{p}_h \in \left(H_\mu^1(\Omega)\right)_h$ satisfying equations (2.1) with $\vec{v}_h$ instead of $\vec{v}$ and $\int_\Omega \overline{p}_h \, dq = 0$ we have

$$\|p - p_h\|_{L_2(\Omega)} \le ch, \tag{3.4}$$

$$\|p - p_h\|_{H_\mu^1(\Omega)} \le c. \tag{3.5}$$

To approximate the space $H_\mu^2(\Omega)$ when constructing the corresponding finite elements in Ω, as nodal parameters we choose values of the function θ averaged by Iljin-Golovkin procedure

$$\theta_{\tau h} = \int_{\mathbf{R}^2} \theta(y) \, \tau_h(p - y) \frac{H_3(p)}{H_3(y)} I \, dy$$

and their derivatives up to the second order in vertices of triangles as well as normal derivatives at the mid-points of rectilinear sides. For functions θ_h constructed by these nodal parameters which are polynomials of the fifth degree the following inequalities are valid :

$$\|\theta - \theta_h\|_{W_2^s(\Omega)} \le ch^{2-s} \quad 0 \le s \le 1, \tag{3.6}$$

$$\|\theta - \theta_h\|_{H_\mu^2(\Omega)} \le c \tag{3.7}$$

To reconstruct the form of the free surface we consider a grid of nodes the interval $[0\,,1]$ with coordinates $q_{1,j} = 1 - (jh)^{1/\beta}$, $j = 1, \ldots, n$, $h = 1/n$, $0 < \beta < 1 - 2\mu$. As nodal parameters averaging by Iljin-Golovkin procedure $\varphi_{\tau h}$, $i = 1, 2$, are chosen as well as their derivatives of (up to) the second order at the vertices of intervals. For extensions φ_h of the lattice function which are also polynomials of the fifth degree, the following inequality is true:

$$\|\varphi - \varphi_h\|_{W_2^s(\Omega)} \le ch^{3-s} \tag{3.8}$$

From the inequalities (3.2)–(3.8) it follows that the computed approximate solutions $(\vec{v}_h,\ p_h,\ \theta_h,\ \varphi_h)$ to the problems are bounded in the space $H_\mu^2 \times H_\mu^1 \times H_\mu^2 \times W_{2,\mu}^{5/2}$ and converge to the exact solution by the following law:

$$\|\vec{v} - \vec{v}_h\|_{W_2^1(\Omega)} + \|p - p_h\|_{L_2(\Omega)} + \|\theta - \theta_h\|_{W_2^1(\Omega)} + \|\Gamma - \Gamma_h\|_{W_2^{5/2}(\Gamma)} \le ch \tag{3.9}$$

The proofs of the error estimates (3.2)–(3.9) are omitted here. One can verify the validity of the estimates by applying the results obtained in [9,11].

4. Quasistationary and nonstationary problems

For solving the quasistationary problem we divide the time interval $[0\,,\,T]$ into N subintervals of leng Δt. On each subinterval $[t\,,\,t+\Delta t]$ we solve the system of equations in $\Omega = \Omega(t)$

$$\left.\begin{aligned} \frac{\partial\theta}{\partial t} + \vec{v}\cdot\nabla\theta &= +\frac{1}{Pr}\Delta\theta + Q && \text{in } \Omega \\ -\frac{1}{Re}\Delta\vec{v} + (\vec{v}, \nabla\vec{v}) &= -\nabla p + f && \text{in } \Omega \\ \operatorname{div}\vec{v} &= 0 && \text{in } \Omega \end{aligned}\right\} \tag{4.1}$$

with boundary conditions

$$\left.\begin{aligned} \vec{v}|_{\Sigma_t} &= \vec{v}_* & \left.\frac{\partial\theta}{\partial n}\right|_{\Sigma_t} &= \theta_* \\ \vec{\tau}\cdot S(\vec{v})\cdot\vec{n}|_{\Gamma_t} &= 0 & [\vec{v}]|_{\Gamma_t} &= 0 \\ \lambda\left.\frac{\partial\theta}{\partial n}\right|_{\Gamma_t} &= \vec{v}\cdot n|_{\Gamma_t} & \theta|_{\Gamma_t=t} &= \theta_t \end{aligned}\right\} \tag{4.2}$$

where Γ_t denotes the free boundary at time moment t.

The problems, which appear on each time subinterval can be solved by one of known methods. In particular it is possible to use the FEM, realized by the classic manner. One such possibility for the approximation by the space variables was noted earlier for the stationary problems. As for stationary problems we can use in quasistationary problems

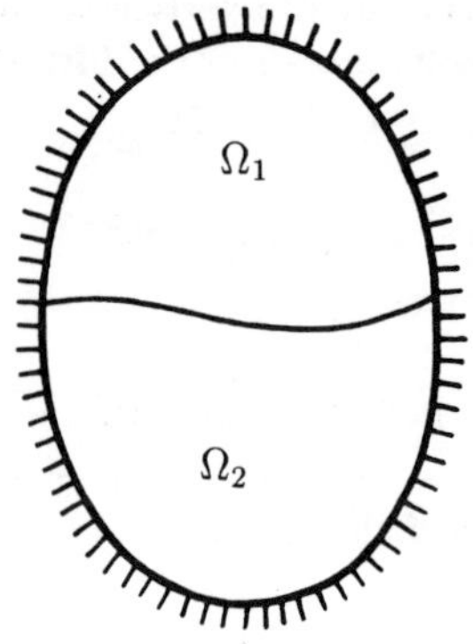

Fig. 4.1

the decomposition of domain method. We consider the problem of two media as an example of using this method.

Here the iterative process of the decomposition of domains can be realized by the rule [11]

$$\vec{\tau} S_1 \left(\vec{v}^{(k)}\right) \cdot \vec{n}\Big|_{\Gamma_t} = \vec{\tau} S_1 \left(\vec{v}^{(k-1)}\right) \cdot \vec{n}\Big|_{\Gamma_t} + \alpha \left[\vec{v}^{(k-1)}\right]\Big|_{\Gamma_t},$$
$$\left[\vec{\tau} \cdot S\left(v^{(k)}\right) \cdot \vec{n}\right]\Big|_{\Gamma_t} = 0,$$

where $v^{(k)}$ and $S(\vec{v}^{(k)})$ are the values of velocities and the stresses on domains Ω_1 and Ω_2 determined in the course of the "k"-th iteration (see Fig. 4.1). The rate of convergence for this method is the same as in the stationary case [11], namely

(4.3)
$$\left\| v^{(k)} - v \right\| \leq \frac{c}{k^N};\ N < \infty$$

In the nonstationary problems we construct an algoritm in another way. We find the boundary Γ at each step t using the kinematic compatibility condition:

(4.4)
$$\frac{\partial \Gamma}{\partial t} + \vec{v} \cdot \nabla \Gamma = \left[\lambda \frac{\partial \theta}{\partial n}\right]\Big|_{\Gamma},$$

where the values [ ] can be taken from the previous step. Then we solve the system of equations

(4.5)
$$\left.\begin{aligned} &\frac{\partial \vec{v}}{\partial t} + (\vec{v}, \nabla \vec{v}) = \frac{1}{Re} \Delta \vec{v} - \nabla p + \vec{f} && \text{in } \Omega \\ &\operatorname{div} \vec{v} = 0 && \text{in } \Omega \\ &\frac{\partial \theta}{\partial t} + (\vec{v}, \nabla \theta) = \frac{1}{Pr} \Delta \theta + Q && \text{in } \Omega \end{aligned}\right\}$$

with the boundary conditions

$$
(4.6)\qquad \left.\begin{array}{ll}
We\,[\vec{n}\cdot S(v)\cdot n]\big|_{\Gamma} = -\left(\dfrac{1}{R_1}+\dfrac{1}{R_2}\right) & [\vec{\tau}\cdot S(\vec{v})\cdot \vec{n}]\big|_{\Gamma} = 0 \\
\vec{v}\big|_{\Sigma_t} = \vec{v}_* & \left.\dfrac{\partial\theta}{\partial n}\right|_{\Sigma_t} = \theta_* \\
\vec{v}|_{\Gamma_t} = \vec{v}_t & \theta|_{\Gamma_t} = \theta_t
\end{array}\right\}
$$

At this point we divide the solution of (4.4) into three stages

1. Predictor: Here we consider an absolute, stable scheme with unilateral differences. From here we find $\check{\Gamma}(t)$
2. Corrector: Here we use an explicit scheme of higher exactness order. From this we find $\hat{\Gamma}(t)$
3. The filtering scheme: Here we project $\hat{\Gamma}$ onto the subspace of "permissible" boundaries. This can be done, in particular, by Fourier method, (deleting the high frequency)

Further we find the mean curvature of the boundary Γ and after substitute it into the equations. Here the decomposition process is constructed in such a way that both components of tension – the normal and tangent ones – take part in it. This process is continued until the jump becomes small.

In such a way were considered the representation of a rotating drop.

Fig. 4.2 (a) illustrates the shape of the rotating drop progressively moving in the flow. In Fig. 4.2 (b) we see the shape of the drop without rotation and in Fig. 4.2 (c) with rotation.

Here $Re = \frac{u_\infty a}{\nu}$, u_∞ velocity of the drop in a gravity force direction. $Ta = \frac{\omega a^2}{\nu_2}$, a-diametr of drop, ω-frequency of rotation of drop, $\kappa = \frac{\nu_1\rho_1}{\nu_2\rho_2}$, ν_i, ρ_i -kinematic viscosity and density of a fluid in a drop ($i = 1$) and out ($i = 2$).

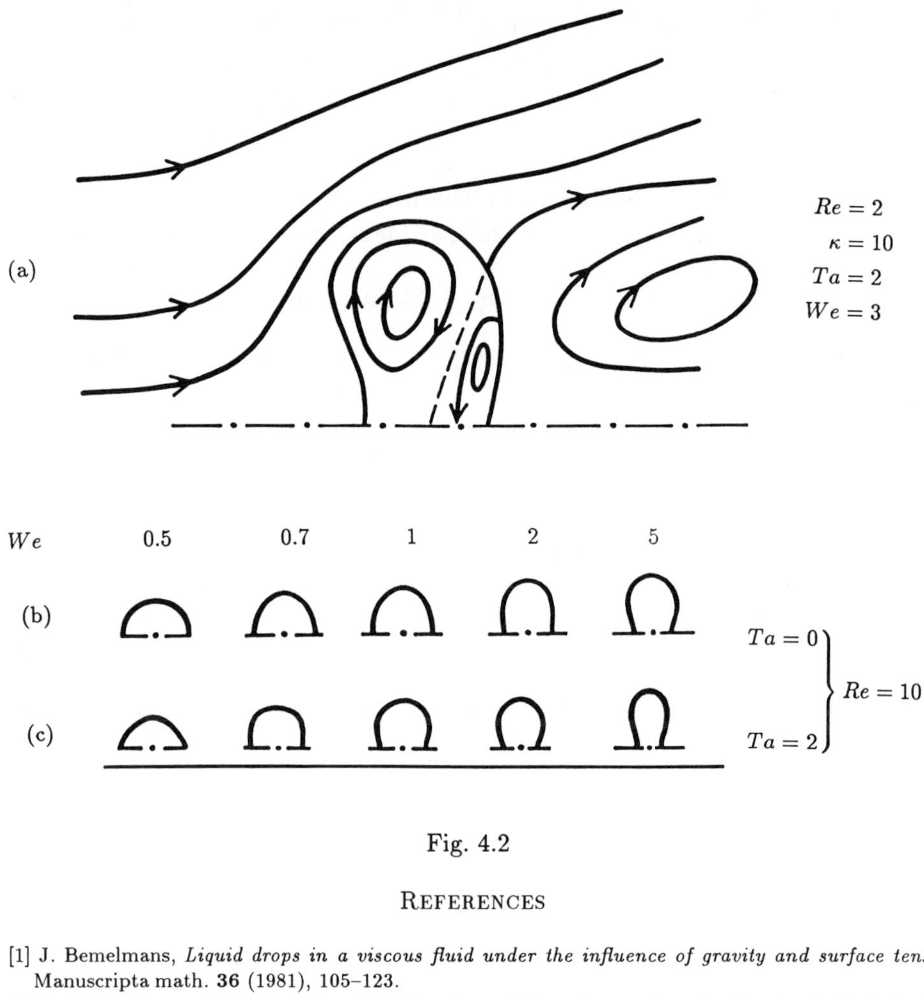

Fig. 4.2

References

[1] J. Bemelmans, *Liquid drops in a viscous fluid under the influence of gravity and surface tension*, Manuscripta math. **36** (1981), 105–123.

[2] V. P. Bushlanov, I. M. Vasenin, *Stability of a rotating viscous drop*, [in Russian], Teplofiz. i fiz. gidrodinamika (1978), 9–14, Novosibirsk.

[3] K. Golovkin, *Approximate of functions in arbitary norms*, Trudi Math. Steclov's Inst **70** (1964), 26–37.

[4] C. Cuvelier, A. Segal and A. A. Steenhoven, "Finite element methods and Navier-Stokes equations," Reidel publishing company, Dordrecht, 1986.

[5] A. V. Ilyin, "Numerical investigation of problems of thin fluid layers movements," [in Russian], Ph. D. Thesis, Leningrad, 1986.

[6] S. F. Kistler and L. E. Scriven, *Coating flow theory by finite element and asymptotic analyses of the Navier-Stokes system*, Inst. J. num. meth. fluids **4** (1984), 207–229.

[7] N. P. Kruyt, C. Cuvelier, A. Segal and I. Van Zanden, *A total linearization for solving viscous free boundary flow problems by the finite element method*, Int. J. Numer. Meth. Fluids **8** (1988), 351–363.

[8] V. V. Puchnachev, *A non-stationary problem for the Navier-Stokes equations with a free boundary in plane*, Appl. mathem. and techn. physik **3** (1973), no. 3, Novosibirsk.

[9] V. Ya. Rivkind, *Approximate Methods for solving problems of viscous fluid with a free boundary*, [in Russian], In the Proc.Numerical Methods and Applications (1985), 91–98, Sofia.

[10] V. Ya. Rivkind, *A study of the problem of the stationary motion of a drop in the flow of a viscous incompressible fluid*, [in Russian], Dokl. Akad. Nauk SSSR **227** (1976), no. 5, 1071–1073, Moscow.

[11] V. Ya. Rivkind, *Computational methods for fluid-flows of viscous incompressible fluids with free boundaries*, [in Russian], Chislenn. Meth. Meh. sploshnoi sredy **12** (1981), no. 4, 106–115, Novosibirsk.

[12] V. Ya. Rivkind, *Investigation of some problems of the flow of multi-layer viscous incompressible fluids*, [in Russian], Trudy Vsesoyuznoi konferencii o uravneniyam v chastnyh proizvodnyn Proceedings of the All-Union conference on partial differential equations, dedicated to the 5-th aniversary of I. G. Petrovskii (1978), Nauka, Moscow.

[13] V. Ya. Rivkind, N. B. Fridman, *The Navier-Stokes equations with discontinuous coefficients*, [in Russian], Zapiski nauchn. seminarov LOMI **38** (1973), 137–152, Leningrad.

[14] K. J. Ruschak, *A method for incorporating free boundaries with surface tension in finite-element fluid flow simulators*, Inst. J. Num. Meth. Engng. **15** (1980), no.5, 639–648.

[15] P. J. Shopov, *Numerical method for free surface hydrodynimical problems*, Comp. Rend. Acad. Bulg. Sci. **41** (1988).

[16] J. Socolovsky, *Eine verallgemeinerte Leitlinienmethode zur Berechnung mehrschichtiger Stromungen nichtlinearviskoser Fluide*, J. Appl. Maths and Phys. (ZAMP) **39** (Marz 1988), 221–233.

[17] V. A. Solonnikov, *Solvability of a problem on the motion of a viscous incompressible fluid bounded by a free surface*, Izv. Akad Nauk SSSR Ser. Mat. **41** (1977), 1388–1424; = Math. USSR Izv. **11** (1977), 1323–1358.

[18] V. A. Solonnikov, V. E. Shchadilov, *On one boundary value problem for the stationary NavierStokes equations system*, [in Russian], Trudy Mat. Inst. SSSR (1973), 125–137, Leningrad.

[19] T. G. Wang, M. M. Saffren and D. D. Elleman, *Drop dynamics in space*, In. Mater. Sci. Space Appl. Space Process (1977), 151–172, New York.

[20] W. J. Silliman, L. E. Scriven, *Separating flow near a static contact line: Slip at a wall and shape of a free surface*, J. Comp. Phys. **34** (1980), 287–313.

[21] I. B. Yerunova, *Investigation of a problem of the stationary movement of two fluids in a vessel*, Dokla Akad Nauk SSSR **279** (1984), no. 1, 55–58.

On approximation of the inverse one–phase Stefan problem

VIOREL ARNĂUTU

Faculty of Mathematics
University of Iasi
6600 Iasi, Romania

Abstract. The inverse one–dimensional one–phase Stefan problem is considered in terms of an optimal control problem. According to an idea of V. Barbu the state system is considered only on a domain delimited by the desired moving boundary. The necessary conditions for optimality are established and a descent algorithm is derived. Its numerical implementation for bang–bang suboptimal controls is presented; particular attention is devoted to find a starting control by a local variations method. Numerical tests are given.

Keywords. bang–bang control, descent method, local variations method.

1. INTRODUCTION

The inverse one–phase Stefan problem in one space dimension with flux boundary conditions is considered. There are different methods to treat it ([**8**], [**10**], [**7**], [**2**] and [**1**]). We consider here a new method introduced by V. Barbu in [**3**].

The control problem is presented in Section 2. The necessary optimality conditions and derived descent algorithms are given in Section 3. The numerical implementation of the algorithms together with numerical results are discussed in Section 4.

2. THE CONTROL PROBLEM

Denote $\Omega = (a, c)$, $\Gamma = \partial\Omega$ and $Q = \{(x,t) \in \Omega \times (0,T); \varrho(t) < x < c\}$. Consider the one–phase Stefan problem written in the equivalent form (e.q. [**10**], pp. 14–15):

(2.1) $$y_t(x,t) - y_{xx}(x,t) = 0 \quad \text{in } Q$$

(2.2) $$y_x(c,t) + \alpha y(c,t) = -v(t) \quad \text{for } t \in [0,T]$$

(2.3) $$y_x(\varrho(t),t) = \rho\varrho'(t) \quad \text{for } t \in [0,T]$$

(2.4) $$y(x,0) = y_0(x) \quad \text{for } x \in [b,c].$$

Here $x = \varrho(t)$ is a C^1–monotonically decreasing function on $[0,T]$ such that $\varrho(0) = b$ (see Figure 1). In terms of y the equation of the free surface separating the liquid and solid phase is given by $\{(x,t); y(x,t) = 0\}$.

Existence and regularity results for problem (2.1)–(2.4) are well known ([**4**], [**5**], [**10**]). For instance if $v \in H^1(0,T; L^2(\Gamma))$ and $y_0 \in H^1(\Omega)$, then the unique solution y is in $H^1(Q)$.

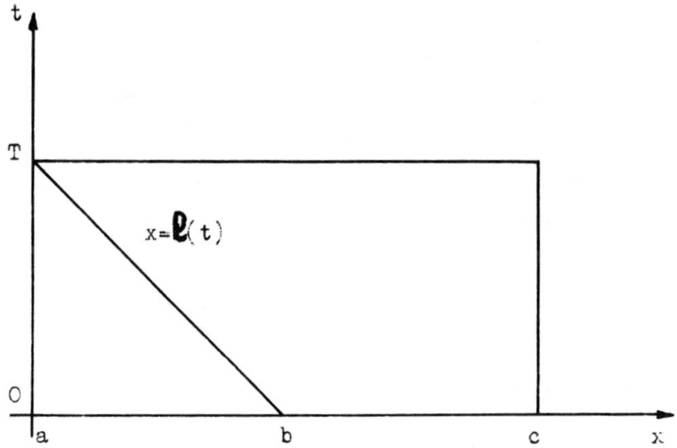

Figure 1.

The function v in (2.2) represents the temperature of the surrounding at $x = c$ and it is manipulated by a heating (cooling) system according to the equation

(2.5) $$v'(t) + \gamma v(t) = u(t) \quad \text{a.e. } t \in [0,T], v(0) = 0, u \in U,$$

where $u(t)$ is the fuel supply and

(2.6) $$U = \{u \in L^\infty(0,T); 0 \le u(t) \le R, \quad \text{a.e. } t \in [0,T]\}.$$

For every $u \in U$ we shall denote by y_u the solution to BVP (2.1)–(2.4) combined with (2.5). The inverse problem mentioned in Section 1 may be formulated in terms of y as follows:

Find $u \in U$ in such a way that

(2.7) $$y_u(\varrho(t), t) = 0 \quad \text{for every } t \in [0,T].$$

The least square approach to this problem leads to the optimal control problem

(P) $$\inf \left\{ \int_0^T y_u^2(\varrho(t), t)\, dt; u \in U \right\}.$$

We have

PROPOSITION 2.1. *The optimal control problem (P) admits at least one solution u^*. (e.g. [**10**], pp. 50–51, [**1**]).*

3. Descent Algorithms

We now establish the necessary conditions for optimality. Consider (u, v, y) from the control system and the corresponding variations $(u + \lambda w, v + \lambda\theta, y + \lambda z)$. Subtracting the corresponding equations (2.1)–(2.4) we obtain

(3.1) $$z_t(x,t) - z_{xx}(x,t) = 0 \quad \text{in } Q$$

(3.2) $$z_x(c,t) + \alpha z(c,t) = -\theta(t) \quad \text{for } t \in [0,T]$$

(3.3) $$z_x(\varrho(t),t) = 0 \quad \text{for } t \in [0,T]$$

(3.4) $$z(x,0) = 0 \quad \text{in } x \in [b,c].$$

From (2.5) we get

(3.5) $$\theta'(t) + \gamma\theta(t) = w(t) \quad \text{a.e. } t \in [0,T], \quad \theta(0) = 0.$$

Let us introduce the cost functional

(3.6) $$J(u) = \frac{1}{2}\int_0^T y_u^2(\varrho(t),t)\,dt + I_U(u),$$

where I_U is the indicator function of the set U. Consider u to be an optimal control for problem (P). Hence we have

$$(J(u+\lambda w) - J(u))/\lambda \geq 0 \quad \text{for } \lambda > 0.$$

We develope this formula according to (3.6) and let $\lambda \to 0$ to obtain

(3.7) $$\int_0^T y(\varrho(t),t)z(\varrho(t),t)\,dt + I'_U(u,w) \geq 0$$

for every $w \in L^2(0,T)$.

We now introduce the adjoint state system

(3.8) $$p_t(x,t) + p_{xx}(x,t) = 0 \quad \text{in } Q$$

(3.9) $$p_x(c,t) + \alpha p(c,t) = 0 \quad \text{for } t \in [0,T]$$

(3.10) $$p_x(\varrho(t),t) - p(\varrho(t),t)\varrho'(t) = y(\varrho(t),t) \text{ for } t \in [0,T]$$

(3.11) $$p(x,T) = 0 \text{ for } x \in [a,c].$$

The existence and uniqueness of the solution $p \in C([0,T]; L^2(\Omega))$ is straightforward.

We multiply (3.1) by p and integrate on Q. Using integration by parts formulas and (3.3) we get

(3.12) $$\begin{aligned}&\int_0^T\int_{\varrho(t)}^c z_t p\,dx\,dt - \int_0^T\int_{\varrho(t)}^c p_{xx} z\,dx\,dt - \\ &- \int_0^T (z_x(c,t)p(c,t) - z(c,t)p_x(c,t) + \\ &+ z(\varrho(t),t)p_x(\varrho(t),t))\,dt = 0.\end{aligned}$$

A simple calculation shows also that

$$\int_{\varrho(t)}^{c} z_t p\,dx = \frac{d}{dt}\left(\int_{\varrho(t)}^{c} zp\,dx\right) - \int_{\varrho(t)}^{c} zp_t\,dx + z(\varrho(t),t)p(\varrho(t),t)\varrho'(t).$$

Now using (3.4), (3.8) and (3.11) we evaluate the first two terms in the right–hand side of (3.12) to be $\int_0^T z(\varrho(t),t)p(\varrho(t),t)\varrho'(t)\,dt$. Finally (3.12) becomes

$$\begin{aligned}&\int_0^T (z(c,t)p_x(c,t) - z_x(c,t)p(c,t))\,dt-\\ &-\int_0^T z(\varrho(t),t)p_x(\varrho(t),t)\,dt+\\ &+\int_0^T z(\varrho(t),t)p(\varrho(t),t)\varrho'(t)\,dt = 0.\end{aligned} \tag{3.13}$$

Introducing (3.9), (3.2) and (3.10) yields

$$\int_0^T p(c,t)\theta(t)\,dt = \int_0^T y(\varrho(t),t)z(\varrho(t),t)\,dt. \tag{3.14}$$

From (3.14) and (3.7) we get

$$\int_0^T p(c,t)\theta(t)\,dt + I'_U(u,w) \geq 0 \quad \text{for every } w \in L^2(0,T). \tag{3.15}$$

Since the solution of (3.5) is $\theta(t) = \int_0^t \exp(\gamma(s-t))w(s)\,ds$, (3.15) becomes

$$\int_0^T q(s)w(s)\,ds + I'_U(u,w) \geq 0 \quad \text{for every } w \in L^2(0,T), \tag{3.16}$$

where

$$q(s) = \int_s^T \exp(\gamma(s-t))p(c,t)\,dt. \tag{3.17}$$

Hence we obtain from (3.16)

$$-q(s) \in \partial I_U(u(s)) \quad \text{a.e. } s \in (0,T), \tag{3.18}$$

where ∂ denotes the subdifferential, and

$$u(s) = \begin{cases} R & \text{if } q(s) < 0, \\ 0 & \text{if } q(s) > 0. \end{cases} \tag{3.19}$$

Using formula (3.19) we derive the descent method ALGC

S0: Choose $u^{(0)} \in U$; set $k := 0$.

S1: Compute $v^{(k)}$ from (2.5), i.e.

$$v_t^{(k)} + \gamma v^{(k)} = u^{(k)} \quad \text{on } [0,T], \quad v^{(k)}(0) = 0;$$

Compute $y^{(k)}$ from (2.1)–(2.4), i.e.

$$y_t^{(k)} - y_{xx}^{(k)} = 0 \quad \text{in } Q,$$
$$y_x^{(k)}(c,t) + \alpha y^{(k)}(c,t) = -v^{(k)}(t) \quad \text{for } t \in [0,T],$$
$$y_x^{(k)}(\varrho(t),t) = \rho\varrho'(t) \quad \text{for } t \in [0,T],$$
$$y^{(k)}(x,0) = y_0(x) \quad \text{for } x \in [b,c].$$

S2: Compute $p^{(k)}$ from (3.8)–(3.11), i.e.

$$p_t^{(k)} + p_{xx}^{(k)} = 0 \quad \text{in } Q,$$
$$p_x^{(k)}(c,t) + \alpha p^{(k)}(c,t) = 0 \quad \text{for } t \in [0,T],$$
$$p_x^{(k)}(\varrho(t),t) - p^{(k)}(\varrho(t),t)\varrho'(t) = y^{(k)}(\varrho(t),t) \quad \text{for } t \in [0,T],$$
$$p^{(k)}(x,T) = 0 \quad \text{for } x \in [a,c].$$

S3: Compute $q^{(k)}$ and $w^{(k)}$ given by

$$q^{(k)}(s) = \int_s^T \exp(\gamma(s-t))p^{(k)}(c,t)\,dt,$$

$$w^{(k)}(s) = \begin{cases} R & \text{if } q^{(k)}(s) < 0, \\ 0 & \text{if } q^{(k)}(s) \geq 0. \end{cases} \quad \text{for } s \in [0,T].$$

S4: Compute $\lambda_k \in [0,1]$ which is a solution of the minimization process

$$\min\left\{\Phi\left(\lambda u^{(k)} + (1-\lambda)w^{(k)}\right); \lambda \in [0,1]\right\},$$

where Φ is the cost functional of problem (P), i.e.

$$\Phi(u) = \int_0^T y_u^2(\varrho(t),t)\,dt,$$

y_u being the state corresponding to the control u.

Set $u^{(k+1)} := \lambda_k u^{(k)} + (1-\lambda_k)w^{(k)}$.

S5: (the 'Stopping Criterion'):

if $\|u^{(k+1)} - u^{(k)}\| \leq \epsilon$

then STOP

else $k := k+1$; GO TO S1.

Practically the norm used in S5 must be a discrete one corresponding to the discretization process of the numerical algorithm (we have used the l_∞ norm); $\epsilon > 0$ is a prescribed precision.

The 'Stopping Criterion' in S5 may be also

$$\text{S5': if } |\Phi(u^{(k+1)}) - \Phi(u^{(k)})| \le \epsilon' \ldots$$

We make now a very important remark. If we intend to compute a suboptimal bang–bang control then the step S4 of ALGC must be modified. It is easy to see that a convex combination of two bang–bang controls is not a bang–bang control. Hence we use in step S4 convex combinations of the switching points of $u^{(k)}$ and $w^{(k)}$. This idea and comments on the behaviour of such an algorithm can be found in [**6**]. For the convergence of the method see also [**3**].

A projected gradient algorithm can be faced out taking into account the formula (3.18). We derive ALGPG (steps S0–S3 and S5 are as in ALGC):

S0: Choose $u^{(0)} \in U$; set $k := 0$.

S1: Compute $v^{(k)}$ and $y^{(k)}$.

S2: Compute $p^{(k)}$.

S3: Compute $q^{(k)}$.

S4: $u^{(k+1)} := \Pr_U \left(u^{(k)} - \mu_k q^{(k)}\right)$,

where μ_k is an adaptive step of the gradient method and

$$\Pr_U(u) = \begin{cases} 0 & \text{if } u < 0, \\ u & \text{if } 0 \le u \le R, \\ R & \text{if } u > R. \end{cases}$$

S5: The 'Stopping Criterion'.

As we shall see in the next section a difficult problem is to find a good 'guess' for $u^{(0)}$ no matter which algorithm we use.

4. Numerical Implementation and Results

The problem considered for numerical tests is the following: $T = 1, a = 0, b = 1, c = 2, \varrho(t) = b - t, y_0(x) = (b - x)(c - x)$. Finite differences are used; the grids in effect with equidistant knots are:

$$a = x_1 < x_2 < \cdots < x_{2n+1} = c \quad \text{with } b = x_{n+1},$$
$$0 = t_1 < t_2 < \cdots < t_{m+1} = T.$$

Denote $Y(i,j) = y(x_i, t_j)$ and $U(j) = u(t_j)$ for all i and j.

The state system has been solved by a subroutine called STASYS:

– v from step S1 is computed by a numerical integration routine using the formula

$$v(t) = \int_0^t \exp\left(\gamma(s-t)\right) u(s)\, ds \tag{4.1}$$

derived from (2.5). We get $v_j = v(t_j)$ for $j = 1, \ldots, m+1$.

– using the values v_j we next solve the finite difference problem corresponding to the state system and we obtain the matrix Y. Its values are computed ascending with respect to levels of time, level by level. We have first

$$Y(i,1) = y_0(x_i), \ i = n+1, \ldots, 2n+1 \tag{4.2}$$

from the initial condition (2.4). To pass from level j to level $j+1$ the user may choose between the standard implicit scheme (SIS) and the Crank-Nicholson method (CNM).

In the case of SIS, Eqn. (2.1) is discretized as

$$\begin{gathered} cY(i-1,j+1) - (1+2c)Y(i,j+1) + cY(i+1,j+1) = -Y(i,j) \\ \text{for } i = IS(j+1), \ldots, 2n+1, \end{gathered} \tag{4.3}$$

where $IS(j) = \varrho(t_j)$ for $j = 1, \ldots, m+1$ and $c = \Delta t/(\Delta x)^2$. From (2.2) we obtain

$$Y(2n+1,j+1) = \left(Y(2n,j+1) - (\Delta x)v_{j+1}\right)/(1+\alpha(\Delta x)) \tag{4.4}$$

and from (2.3) we get

$$Y\left(IS(j+1),j+1\right) = Y\left(IS(j+1)+1,j+1\right) - \rho(\Delta x)\varrho'(t_{j+1}). \tag{4.5}$$

Now $Y(2n+1,j+1)$ and $Y(IS(j+1),j+1)$ are replaced in (4.3) which becomes a linear system with unknowns $Y(IS+1,j+1), \ldots, Y(2n,j+1)$. Its matrix is a band one (the bandwidth is 3) and the system is solved by a special Gauss routine. Next $Y(2n+1,j+1)$ and $Y(IS,j+1)$ are computed from (4.4) and (4.5) respectively. In the case of CNM formula (4.3) is different, but the structure of the linear system is the same.

The subroutine ADJSYS computes the matrix P solving the finite difference problem corresponding to the adjoint state system (step S2). We consider, of course, $P(i,j) = p(x_i,t_j)$. The values of this matrix are computed descending with respect to the levels of time, level by level. We have first

$$P(i,m+1) = 0 \text{ for } i = 1, \ldots, 2n+1 \tag{4.6}$$

from the final condition (3.11). Using SIS to pass from level $j+1$ to level j we get from (3.8)

$$\begin{gathered} cP(i-1,j) - (1+2c)P(i,j) + cP(i+1,j) = -P(i,j+1) \\ \text{for } i = IS(j)+1, \ldots, 2n. \end{gathered} \tag{4.7}$$

Formula (3.9) yields

$$P(2n+1,j) = P(2n,j)/(1+\alpha(\Delta x)) \tag{4.8}$$

```
T  |+++++++++++++++++++++++++++++++++++++++++
   |A++++++++++++++++++++++++++++++++++++++++
   |AA+++++++++++++++++++++++++++++++++++++++
   |AAA++++++++++++++++++++++++++++++++++++++
   |AAAA+++++++++++++++++++++++++++++++++++++
   |AAAAA++++++++++++++++++++++++++++++++++++
   |AAAAAA+++++++++++++++++++++++++++++++++++
   |AAAAAAA++++++++++++++++++++++++++++++++++
   |AAAAAAAA+++++++++++++++++++++++++++++++++
   |AAAAAAAAA++++++++++++++++++++++++++++++++
   |AAAAAAAAAA+++++++++++++++++++++++++++++++
   |AAAAAAAAAAA+++++++++++++++++++++++++++++-
   |AAAAAAAAAAAA+++++++++++++++++++++++++++--
   |AAAAAAAAAAAAA+++++++++++++++++++++++++---
   |AAAAAAAAAAAAAA++++++++++++++++++++++-----
   |AAAAAAAAAAAAAAA+++++++++++++++++++-------
   |AAAAAAAAAAAAAAAA+++++++++++++++----------
   |AAAAAAAAAAAAAAAAA++++++++++++------------
   |AAAAAAAAAAAAAAAAAA++++++++---------------
   |AAAAAAAAAAAAAAAAAAA++++------------------
0  |AAAAAAAAAAAAAAAAAAAAO-------------------O
   ------------------------------------------
    a                   b                   c
```

Figure 2. Constant control with $R = 1$; $\Phi = 1.73155$

and the unknown $P(2n+1, j)$ can be eliminated from (4.7). From (3.10) we get

$$P(IS(j)-1, j) = P(IS(j)+1, j) - \\ -2(\Delta x)(P(IS(j), j)\varrho'(t_j) + Y(IS(j), j)) \tag{4.9}$$

where $P(IS(j)-1, j)$ is a dummy variable. Hence (4.7) is written also for $i = IS(j)$ and replacing $P(IS(j)-1, j)$ from (4.9) we obtain a linear system with band matrix (the bandwidth is 3) with unknowns $P(IS(j), j), \ldots, P(2n, j)$. After solving this system (by a special Gauss routine) $P(2n+1, j)$ is computed from (4.8).

Step S3 is not complicated from the computational point of view. To fit λ_k in step S4 of ALGC we have used a carefully supervised loop of the form

$\Delta\lambda := 1/L$;
do – for $l = 0, 1, \ldots, L$
Try $\lambda := l \times \Delta\lambda$
end – do.

To fit μ_k in step S4 of ALGPG is a little more complicated and we refer to [**9**], pp. 14-15, where an interpolating procedure is presented.

A crucial point for every algorithm is to find a 'good' starting control $u^{(0)}$ in step S0. Our first try was made with $R = 1$ and $u^{(0)}(t) = 0$ for every t, giving $\Phi\left(u^{(0)}\right) = 1.8035$. After one iteration ALGC found the optimal control $u^{(1)} = w^{(1)} = 1$ from 0 to 0.975 and $= 0$ from 0.975 to 1, with $\Phi\left(u^{(1)}\right) = 1.73155$. The corresponding free boundary is shown in Figure 2.

A: the prescribed liquid phase;

+: a discretized position in which $Y(i,j) > 0$;
$-$: the same for $Y(i,j) < 0$;
0 : the same for $Y(i,j) = 0$.

Hence the desired interface between the two phases may be represented by "A+", "A–" or "A0", while the real interface may be represented by "+–" or "A–". It follows that the optimal solution obtained for $R = 1$ is far from the prescribed free boundary.

Two types of control have been involved in our strategy for finding a 'better' $u^{(0)}$:

i) constant controls (CC) of the form $u(t) = R$ for every $t \in [0, T]$;
ii) alternate controls (AC): we have considered an initial grid structure for the switching points given by $\zeta_1 = t_1$, $\zeta_i = (t_{i-1} + t_i)/2$ for $i = 2, \ldots, m+1$ and $\zeta_{m+2} = t_{m+1}$. An alternate control is defined by

$$u(t) = \begin{cases} R & \text{for } t \in [\zeta_i, \zeta_{i+1}), \\ 0 & \text{for } t \in [\zeta_{i+1}, \zeta_{i+2}) \end{cases} \quad \text{with } i = 1, 3, 5, \ldots$$

First of all the upper limit R has been increased 'quickly' by the following loop:

S01: do – for $l = 0, 1, \ldots, 10$
Try $R := 2^l$
end – do.

The corresponding values of the cost functional Φ are given in Table 1.

l	$R = 2^l$	Φ for CC	Φ for AC
0	1	1.7316	1.7695
1	2	1.6612	1.7359
2	4	1.5253	1.6698
3	8	1.2722	1.5418
4	16	0.8410	1.3024
5	32	0.2789	0.8899
6	64	0.3557	0.3312
7	128	5.3129	0.2779
8	256	34.4420	4.4283
9	512	169.5583	29.7568
10	1024	747.2270	148.5237

Table 1.

The evolution of the free boundary for different values of R is shown in Figures 3 and 4.

Let us observe that for increasing R the position of the moving boundary becomes 'better' in the sense that the "–" phase approaches the prescribed boundary. For $R = 1024$ the whole righthand side of the domain is "–" but we have to remember that we are working with only one phase. Moreover since along the prescribed boundary the "–" positions

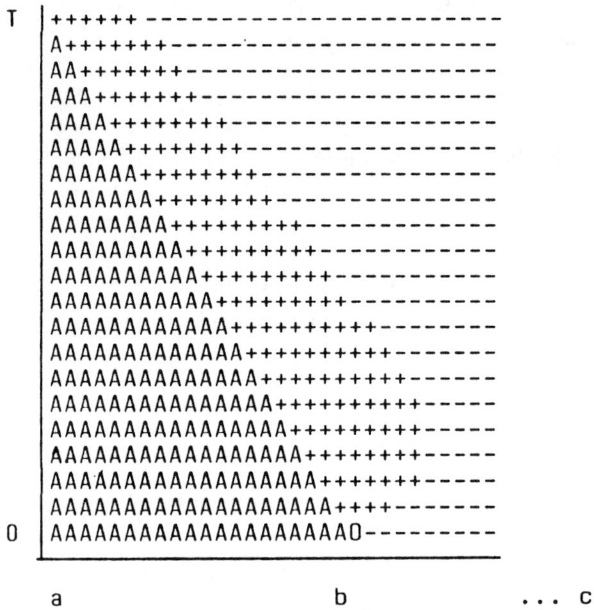

Figure 3: Alternate control with $R = 64$; $\Phi = 0.3312$

are advancing from the upper side of the domain to the lower one and since the values $|Y(IS(j),j)|$ are increasing for $Y(IS(j),j) < 0$ in the order $j = m+1, m, \ldots$ when R is increasing (compare Figures 3 and 4) it follows that the cost functional Φ will also increase (see Table 1).

Henceforth our effort was directed to find better values for Φ. We have used local variations method, namely the 'azimuth mark' method (AMM) involving R. For details concerning this algorithm we refer to [**11**]. Briefly for every column of Table 1 the following procedure has been applied: locate the best two values of Φ and denote the corresponding R-values by r_1 and r_2 (we have $r_1 = 32,\ r_2 = 64$ for CC and $r_1 = 64,\ r_2 = 128$ for AC). The starting azimuth mark contains the center $(r_1 + r_2)/2$ and the extremities r_1 and r_2. Its radius is equal to $|r_2 - r_1|/2$. So we have a new substep of S0, namely

S02: Find r_1 and r_2;
center := $(r_1 + r_2)/2$;
radius := $|r_2 - r_1|/2$;
Start the AMM.
. . . .

```
T |-------------------------------
  |A------------------------------
  |AA-----------------------------
  |AAA----------------------------
  |AAAA---------------------------
  |AAAAA--------------------------
  |AAAAAA-------------------------
  |AAAAAAA------------------------
  |AAAAAAAA-----------------------
  |AAAAAAAAA+---------------------
  |AAAAAAAAAA++-------------------
  |AAAAAAAAAAA++++----------------
  |AAAAAAAAAAAA+++++--------------
  |AAAAAAAAAAAAA+++++-------------
  |AAAAAAAAAAAAAA++++++-----------
  |AAAAAAAAAAAAAAA+++++++---------
  |AAAAAAAAAAAAAAAA+++++++--------
  |AAAAAAAAAAAAAAAAA+++++++-------
  |AAAAAAAAAAAAAAAAAA++++++-------
  |AAAAAAAAAAAAAAAAAAA++++--------
0 |AAAAAAAAAAAAAAAAAAAAA0---------
  +-------------------------------
   a                  b              ... c
```

Figure 4: Alternate control with $R = 128$; $\Phi = 0.2779$

We have obtained the following results:
– for CC: after 21 AMM iterations, $R = R_c = 46.453125$ and $\Phi\left(u^{(0)}\right) = 0.1153$;
– for AC: after 22 AMM iterations, $R = R_a = 90.40625$ and $\Phi\left(u^{(0)}\right) = 0.1262$ (compare now with Table 1).

The results obtained using ALGC are the following:
– for CC: after 3 iterations

$$u = \begin{cases} R_c & \text{from } 0 \text{ to } 0.4925, \\ 0 & \text{from } 0.4925 \text{ to } 1, \end{cases}$$

$$w = \begin{cases} R_c & \text{from } 0 \text{ to } 0.875, \\ 0 & \text{from } 0.875 \text{ to } 1. \end{cases}$$

The corresponding optimal values are $\lambda = 0.85$ and $\Phi^* = 0.102$.
– for AC: after 2 iterations the algorithm was giving two optimal controls

$$w^* = \begin{cases} R_a & \text{from } 0 \text{ to } 0.825, \\ 0 & \text{from } 0.825 \text{ to } 1, \end{cases}$$

$$u^* = \begin{cases} R_a & \text{from } 0 \text{ to } 0.115, \\ 0 & \text{from } 0.115 \text{ to } 0.49125, \\ \text{completely alternating from } 0.49125 \text{ to } 1. \end{cases}$$

```
T |------------------------------
  |A-----------------------------
  |AA----------------------------
  |AAA---------------------------
  |AAAA+-------------------------
  |AAAAA+------------------------
  |AAAAAA++----------------------
  |AAAAAAA+++--------------------
  |AAAAAAAA++++------------------
  |AAAAAAAAA++++-----------------
  |AAAAAAAAAA+++++---------------
  |AAAAAAAAAAA++++++-------------
  |AAAAAAAAAAAA++++++------------
  |AAAAAAAAAAAAA+++++++----------
  |AAAAAAAAAAAAAA+++++++---------
  |AAAAAAAAAAAAAAA+++++++--------
  |AAAAAAAAAAAAAAAA++++++++------
  |AAAAAAAAAAAAAAAAA++++++++-----
  |AAAAAAAAAAAAAAAAAA+++++++-----
  |AAAAAAAAAAAAAAAAAAA++++++-----
  |AAAAAAAAAAAAAAAAAAAA++++------
0 |AAAAAAAAAAAAAAAAAAAAAO--------
  +-------------------------------
   a                    b          ... c
```

Figure 5. Optimal solution for constant starting control; $\Phi = 0.102$

```
T |OO----------------------------
  |AO----------------------------
  |AA----------------------------
  |AAA+--------------------------
  |AAAA+-------------------------
  |AAAAA++-----------------------
  |AAAAAA++----------------------
  |AAAAAAA++---------------------
  |AAAAAAAA++--------------------
  |AAAAAAAAA+++------------------
  |AAAAAAAAAA+++-----------------
  |AAAAAAAAAAA+++----------------
  |AAAAAAAAAAAA++++--------------
  |AAAAAAAAAAAAA++++-------------
  |AAAAAAAAAAAAAA++++------------
  |AAAAAAAAAAAAAAA+++++----------
  |AAAAAAAAAAAAAAAA+++++---------
  |AAAAAAAAAAAAAAAAA+++++--------
  |AAAAAAAAAAAAAAAAAA+++++-------
  |AAAAAAAAAAAAAAAAAAA++++-------
0 |AAAAAAAAAAAAAAAAAAAAO---------
  +-------------------------------
   a                   b           ... c
```

Figure 6. Optimal solution for alternate starting control; $\Phi = 0.0383$

'Completely alternating' means changing the value from 0 to R_a and conversely at every switching point. The steplength of the switching-points grid is equal to 0.0275. The optimal value is $\Phi^* = 0.0383$.

Let us point out that the number of iterations for ALGC is very small thanks to the 'good' work made in step S0. Remark also that the structure of the starting control $u^{(0)}$ is changed by ALGC.

The above numerical results are synthesized in Table 2 and the moving boundary is shown in Figures 5 and 6.

Starting control	AMM no. of iterations	R	$\Phi(u^{(0)})$	ALGC no. of iterations	Φ^*
constant	21	46.453125	0.1153	3	0.102
alternate	22	90.40625	0.1262	2	0.0383

Table 2.

REFERENCES

1. Arnăutu, V. and Barbu, V., "Optimal control of the free boundary in a two-phase Stefan problem," Preprint Series in Mathematics, INCREST Bucharest, 11(1985).
2. Barbu, V., "Optimal Control of Variational Inequalities," Pitman, London, 1984.
3. Barbu, V., *The inverse one phase Stefan problem*, Differential and Integral Equations **3** (1990), 209–218.
4. Fasano, A. and Primicerio, M., *General free boundary problems for heat equation*, J.Math.Anal.Appl. **57, 58, 59** (1977), 694–723, 202–231, 1–14.
5. Friedman, A., "Variational principles and Free Boundary Problems," John Wiley & Sons, New York, 1983.
6. Glashoff, K. and Sachs, E., *On theoretical and numerical aspects of the bang-bang principle*, Numer.Math. **29** (1977), 93–113.
7. Hoffman, K.H. and Niezgodka, M., *Control of parabolic systems involving free boundaries*, in "Free Boundary Problems. Theory and Applications," Fasano, A. and Primicerio, M. eds., Pitman, London, 1983, pp. 431–462.
8. Jochum, P., *The inverse Stefan problem as a problem of nonlinear approximation theory*, J. Approx. Theory **30** (1980), 81–98.
9. Legras, J., "Algorithmes et programmes d'optimisation non linéaire avec contraintes. Application au contrôle optimal," Masson, Paris, 1980.
10. Saguez, Ch., "Contrôle optimal de systèmes à frontière libre," Thèse d'Etat de l'Universitè de Technologie de Compiègne, 1980.
11. Sibony, M., *Sur l'approximation d'équations et inéquations aux dérivées partielles non linéaires de type monotone*, J. Math. Anal. Appl. **34** (1971), 502–564.

FRONT-TRACKING AND VARIATIONAL METHODS TO APPROXIMATE INTERFACES WITH PRESCRIBED MEAN CURVATURE

G. BELLETTINI† M. PAOLINI‡ AND C. VERDI♯

Abstract. The numerical approximation of the minimum problem: $\min_{A\subseteq\Omega}\tilde{\mathcal{F}}(A)$, is considered, where $\tilde{\mathcal{F}}(A) := \mathcal{H}^{d-1}(\partial A\cap\Omega) + \cos(\theta)\mathcal{H}^{d-1}(\partial A\cap\partial\Omega) - \int_A \kappa\, dx$. The solution to this problem is a set $A\subseteq\Omega$ whose boundary has mean curvature κ and prescribed contact angle θ at $\partial\Omega$. A front-tracking algorithm and a variational algorithm are presented, and a few numerical experiments illustrate their behaviour.

1980 Mathematics subject classifications: 53A10,65K10,65N30

1. Introduction. The great attention paid lately to the analysis of systems involving a surface energy on unknown interfaces (see, for instance, [3]) led us to study the numerical minimization of a functional which gives rise to interfaces with prescribed mean curvature. This problem, so-called *prescribed mean curvature* problem, can be considered as a simple but effective model in this field.

More precisely, given an open bounded convex set $\Omega\subset\mathbf{R}^d$ $(d\geq 2)$ with piecewise C^2 boundary, a function $\kappa\in L^\infty(\Omega)$, and a constant $\mu\in[-1,1]$, we consider the minimum problem for the functional $\tilde{\mathcal{F}}(A)$ defined on the measurable sets $A\subseteq\Omega$ as follows:

$$\tilde{\mathcal{F}}(A) := \mathcal{H}^{d-1}(\partial A\cap\Omega) + \mu\mathcal{H}^{d-1}(\partial A\cap\partial\Omega) - \int_A \kappa\, dx,$$

where $\mathcal{H}^{d-1}$ denotes the $(d-1)$-dimensional Hausdorff measure [4]. Any (relative or absolute) minimum of $\tilde{\mathcal{F}}$ is a set whose boundary has mean curvature κ and contact angle $\theta = \arccos(\mu)$ at its intersection with $\partial\Omega$ [5].

Denoting by $BV(\Omega;\{-1,1\})$ the space of the functions of bounded variation on Ω with values in $\{-1,1\}$, by $\int_\Omega |Dv|$ the total variation on Ω of the Radon measure Dv, and by $\mathrm{tr}(v)$ the trace on $\partial\Omega$ of the BV function v, we can also define the following energy functional on the space $D(\mathcal{F}) := BV(\Omega;\{-1,1\})$:

$$\mathcal{F}(v) := \int_\Omega |Dv| + \int_{\partial\Omega} |\mathrm{tr}(v)+\mu|\, d\mathcal{H}^{d-1}(x) - \int_\Omega \kappa v\, dx.$$

Note that $\mathcal{F}(v) = 2\tilde{\mathcal{F}}(A_v) + (1-\mu)\mathcal{H}^{d-1}(\partial\Omega) + \int_\Omega\kappa$, for all $v\in D(\mathcal{F})$, where $A_v := \{x\in\Omega : v(x)=1\}$. As a generalization, μ should be considered to be a piecewise constant function $\mu\in BV(\partial\Omega;[-1,1])$.

†International School for Advanced Studies SISSA/ISAS, 34014 Trieste, Italy.
‡Istituto di Analisi Numerica del CNR, 27100 Pavia, Italy.
♯Dipartimento di Meccanica Strutturale, Università di Pavia, 27100 Pavia, Italy.

It is well known [5] that $\mathcal{F}$ admits at least a minimizer u, so that the set A_u minimizes $\tilde{\mathcal{F}}$, whereas uniqueness cannot be expected. In addition, the functionals $\tilde{\mathcal{F}}$ and $\mathcal{F}$ may exhibit many relative minima (the empty set is always a relative minimum).

In this paper, we shall describe and compare two different numerical approaches to this minimization problem, namely a front-tracking algorithm (FTA) and a variational algorithm (VA). FTA minimizes the functional $\tilde{\mathcal{F}}$ on polygonal subsets of Ω, whereas VA deals with the functional $\mathcal{F}$, where the unknown interface does not appear explicitly. It is to be stressed that, in general, both methods may converge to a *relative* minimum.

2. Front-Tracking Algorithm (FTA). Assuming that $\kappa \in C^0(\bar{\Omega})$, then any relative minimum of $\tilde{\mathcal{F}}$ has C^2 boundary; it can thus be approximated, with an L^∞-error of order $O(h^2)$, by polygons having edges $O(h)$-long. This remark leads us to minimize the functional $\tilde{\mathcal{F}}$ on the domain $D_h(\tilde{\mathcal{F}}) := \{A \subseteq \Omega : A \text{ is a polygon with edges of length } \geq h\}$.

FTA is presently implemented in 2-D. The 3-D case is considerably more complicated because of both the data structures for the representation of surfaces and the topological changes in the minimizing sequence of interfaces. An extra regularity for the curvature function, $\kappa \in C^{1,1}(\Omega)$, is required for using a Modified-Newton method [6] in the minimization process. The present version of the code does not deal with the boundary term $\mu\mathcal{H}^{d-1}(\partial A \cap \partial\Omega)$. Hence there must be no intersection of $\partial\Omega$ with the sets of the minimizing sequence. This is equivalent to require that $\Omega = \mathbf{R}^2$ and that any relative minimum of $\tilde{\mathcal{F}}$ is bounded, which is guaranteed if κ is negative outside a bounded set. The upgrading of the code to overcome this restriction is in progress. The convergence of FTA has not been proved yet; nonetheless, numerical experiments show very fast convergence and the iterative procedure seems to exhibit no oscillation phenomena, the relative minimum which is approximated just depending on the initial guess.

Let us now briefly describe the FTA code. Let $A_0 \in D_h(\tilde{\mathcal{F}})$ be the initial guess, for instance, $A_0 := \{x \in \Omega : \kappa(x) > 0\}$. We stress that any set A_0 so that $\mathrm{diam}(A_0) \sup_{x\in\Omega} \kappa(x) < 2$ evolves towards the empty set. Roughly speaking, FTA produces a minimizing sequence $\{A_n \in D_h(\tilde{\mathcal{F}})\}_n$ as follows: A_n has approximately the same number of vertices as A_{n-1} untill the value of the functional cannot be further lowered; in that case, the boundary Γ_n of A_n is enriched by adding intermediate vertices; the iterations stop when each edge of A_n has length $\simeq h$, so that A_n can approximate a C^2 curve with a prescribed error $O(h^2)$. We shall drop the subscript n whenever its presence is clear from the context. The FTA code can be summarized as follows:

(S0) Define A_0 and assign an iteration error threshold σ; $n = 0$.
(S1) $n = n + 1$; define A_n, moving the vertices of A_{n-1} along the "normals" to Γ_{n-1}, and using a Modified-Newton step in order to lower $\tilde{\mathcal{F}}$.
(S2) Perform a topological consistency test to check that the new Γ_n has no self-intersections. If this test fails, Γ_n must be suitably modified by changing its topology.
(S3) Redistribute the vertices of Γ_n, in order to avoid too near and too far adjacent vertices.
(S4) If the displacement between Γ_{n-1} and Γ_n is $< \sigma$, go to (S5). Otherwise, go to (S1).
(S5) If the length of the edges of Γ_n is $\simeq h$, stop. Otherwise, double the number of vertices by adding the midpoints of the edges of Γ_n and go to (S1).

2.1. Step (S1). At this stage, the connected components of ∂A can be treated independently from each other; hence, we can suppose that A has a connected boundary Γ. Let the vertices $P_1, \ldots, P_I$ of Γ be given in a counter-clockwise order. For any

P_i, let ν_i be the unit vector along the bisector of the inner angle of Γ at P_i; in addition, set $P_i(\lambda) := P_i + \lambda_i \nu_i$, where $\lambda_i \in \mathbf{R}$. Let $A(\lambda)$ and $\Gamma(\lambda)$ be the polygon defined by $P_1(\lambda), ..., P_I(\lambda)$ and its boundary, respectively. Clearly, $A(\mathbf{0}) = A$ and $\Gamma(\mathbf{0}) = \Gamma$. We are now in a position to define the finite dimensional functional $\mathcal{I} : \mathbf{R}^I \to \mathbf{R}$ as $\mathcal{I}(\lambda) := \tilde{\mathcal{F}}(A(\lambda)) - \tilde{\mathcal{F}}(A) = \text{length}(\Gamma(\lambda)) - \text{length}(\Gamma) - \int_{A(\lambda)\setminus A} \kappa\, dx + \int_{A\setminus A(\lambda)} \kappa\, dx$. Let P_i^- and P_i^+ denote the previous and the next vertex to P_i, respectively. Then, using the pointwise quadrature formula to approximate the integrals of κ on triangles, we have

$$\mathcal{I}(\lambda) \approx \sum_{i=1}^{I} \left[|P_i^+(\lambda) - P_i(\lambda)| - |P_i^+ - P_i| + T(\kappa; P_i^+(\lambda), P_i(\lambda), P_i^+) + T(\kappa; P_i(\lambda), P_i, P_i^+) \right],$$

where $T(\kappa; A, B, C) := \frac{1}{3}[\kappa(A) + \kappa(B) + \kappa(C)]\text{Area}(ABC)$; note that $\text{Area}(ABC) < 0$ if the vertices of the triangle ABC are in clockwise order. The components of $g := \nabla\mathcal{I}(\mathbf{0})$ are

$$\frac{\partial \mathcal{I}}{\partial \lambda_i}(0) = -\left(\frac{P_i^- - P_i}{|P_i^- - P_i|} + \frac{P_i^+ - P_i}{|P_i^+ - P_i|} \right) \cdot \nu_i + \frac{1}{2}\left[\kappa^-(P_i^- - P_i) - \kappa^+(P_i^+ - P_i) \right] \wedge \nu_i,$$

where

$$\kappa^- := 2\int_0^1 s\kappa(sP_i + (1-s)P_i^-)\, ds, \qquad \kappa^+ := 2\int_0^1 s\kappa(sP_i + (1-s)P_i^+)\, ds,$$

and $v \wedge w := v_2 w_1 - v_1 w_2$ is the usual external vector product in $\mathbf{R}^2$. The Hessian matrix $H := (\frac{\partial^2 \mathcal{I}}{\partial\lambda_i \partial\lambda_j}(\mathbf{0}))_{ij}$ has nonzero entries only if either $P_j = P_i$ or $P_j = P_i^+$ or $P_j = P_i^-$, namely, for adjacent vertices. Hence H is a symmetric, "almost" tridiagonal matrix (i.e., $H_{ij} = 0$ if $1 < |i - j| < I - 1$). We have

$$\frac{\partial^2 \mathcal{I}}{\partial \lambda_i^2}(0) = \frac{\left[(P_i^- - P_i) \wedge \nu_i \right]^2}{|P_i^- - P_i|^3} + \frac{\left[(P_i^+ - P_i) \wedge \nu_i \right]^2}{|P_i^+ - P_i|^3} + \frac{1}{3}(\nabla\kappa^- \cdot \nu_i)\left[(P_i^- - P_i) \wedge \nu_i \right] - \frac{1}{3}(\nabla\kappa^+ \cdot \nu_i)\left[(P_i^+ - P_i) \wedge \nu_i \right],$$

where

$$\nabla\kappa^- := 3\int_0^1 s^2 \nabla\kappa(sP_i + (1-s)P_i^-)\, ds, \qquad \nabla\kappa^+ := 3\int_0^1 s^2 \nabla\kappa(sP_i + (1-s)P_i^+)\, ds,$$

and, setting $P_j := P_i^+$,

$$\frac{\partial^2 \mathcal{I}}{\partial \lambda_i \partial \lambda_j}(0) = \frac{\left[(P_j - P_i) \cdot \nu_j \right]\left[(P_j - P_i) \cdot \nu_i \right]}{|P_j - P_i|^3} - \frac{\nu_j \cdot \nu_i}{|P_j - P_i|} + \frac{1}{6}(\nu_{ij} \nabla\kappa_{ij}) \wedge (P_j - P_i) - \frac{1}{2}\kappa_{ij}\nu_j \wedge \nu_i,$$

where $\nu_{ij} := \frac{1}{2}(\nu_j \otimes \nu_i + \nu_i \otimes \nu_j)$ is a 2 by 2 matrix, and

$$\kappa_{ij} := \int_0^1 \kappa(sP_i + (1-s)P_j)\, ds, \qquad \nabla\kappa_{ij} := 6\int_0^1 s(1-s)\nabla\kappa(sP_i + (1-s)P_j)\, ds.$$

The values κ^-, κ^+, κ_{ij}, $\nabla\kappa^-$, $\nabla\kappa^+$ and $\nabla\kappa_{ij}$ are approximated by using the linear interpolants of κ and $\nabla\kappa$ along the segments $P_iP_i^-$ and $P_iP_i^+$.

Since, in general, H is *not* positive definite, the standard Newton method for $\nabla\mathcal{I}(\lambda) = \mathbf{0}$ with initial point $\lambda = \mathbf{0}$ might not lower $\tilde{\mathcal{F}}$. Hence we define the first displacement vector λ using a Modified-Newton method [6], as follows:

$$\lambda := \begin{cases} -H^{-1}g, & \text{if } H \text{ is positive definite,} \\ -(H+E)^{-1}g, & \text{otherwise,} \end{cases}$$

where E is any diagonal positive matrix such that $H + E$ is positive definite. With this definition, λ is always a descent direction for $\mathcal{I}$. The matrix E can be generated during the Cholesky decomposition of the matrix H. Hence, taking advantage of the structure of H, we can factorize H (or $H + E$) $=: LDL^T$ with an optimal memory space and time usage. Here D is a positive diagonal matrix and L is a lower triangular matrix, with unitary diagonal entries and zero entries outside the codiagonal and the last row.

The set A_n is then defined from $A_{n-1} = A$ by

$$A_n := A_{n-1}(s\lambda),$$

for an appropriate value $s \in (0, \bar{s}]$, where $\bar{s}$ is given by local topological constraints. If $\bar{s} \geq 1$, $E = 0$, and $\mathcal{I}(\lambda) < 0$, then we take $s = 1$ (real Newton step); otherwise s is determined by a very few iterations of a one dimensional minimization technique.

2.2. Step (S2). A topological consistency test is performed to check that $\Gamma := \Gamma_n$ has no self-intersections. If this test fails, Γ is suitably modified. Since this test is performed at each iteration of FTA, its computational complexity (CC) is a crucial issue for the code efficiency. We stress that all the connected components of Γ must be taken into account simultaneously, because they might intersect each other. Testing for intersection every couple of edges has CC$= O(I^2)$, which slows down the whole algorithm. On the contrary, relating the existence of self-intersections to the existence of vertices of Γ which *cross* Γ_{n-1}, so-called *bad* vertices, reduces CC to $O(I \log I)$, which is nearly optimal. These *bad* vertices can be checked as follows. Let P_i be a vertex of Γ and $r_i(t) := P_i + t\mathbf{e}_1$, $t \geq 0$, be the half straight line from P_i in the direction of the vector $\mathbf{e}_1 := (1, 0)$. For the sake of simplicity, we suppose that P_i is not a self-intersection point and that r_i does not intersect any vertex of Γ as well as any self-intersection (these restrictions can be avoided by counting the intersections $r_i \cap \Gamma$ with the appropriate multiplicity). Let α (resp. β) denotes the angle between the vectors $\mathbf{e}_1$ and $P_i^- - P_i$ (resp. $P_i^+ - P_i$); $0 \leq \alpha, \beta < 2\pi$. Finally, let m_i be the number of intersections of r_i with Γ; the vertex P_i is counted only if $\beta > \alpha$ (i.e., if r_i belongs to the inner angle of Γ at P_i). We say that P_i is *bad*, if m_i is odd. Note that the values m_i, for $1 \leq i \leq I$, can be accumulated in parallel checking, for each edge s of Γ, the vertices P_i for which r_i intersects s. This operation can be performed in logarithmic time, if the vertices of Γ are organized in a binary tree, with the x_2 coordinate as the key.

If the consistency test fails (i.e., at least one *bad* vertex is found), a change of topology must be done. Recursively, for each self-intersection, a local change of topology is performed. To this end, their position must be exactly computed. Note that a self-intersection is present along an edge whenever only one of its vertices is *bad*. As a result, one or more small connected components of Γ are produced, with the vertices ordered in clockwise order. These small *negative* components are considered as spurious, and hence they are simply deleted. The change of topology should happen only sporadically, hence its computational complexity is not a critical issue.

3. Variational Algorithm (VA). The numerical minimization of the functional $\mathcal{F}$ by fixed domain methods is very difficult because of the lack of regularity and convexity of the problem at hand. Then, we first approximate $\mathcal{F}$ with a family $\{\mathcal{F}_\epsilon\}_{\epsilon>0}$ of regular nonconvex functionals defined in $H^1(\Omega)$ which, in turn, will be discretized by finite elements; ϵ is the *relaxation* parameter and h is the *meshsize*. The Γ-convergence of both the relaxed and discrete functionals has been proved in [7] and [1], respectively. In order to define the relaxed functionals $\mathcal{F}_\epsilon$ we need some preparation. Let $\omega, \beta : [-1,1] \to \mathbf{R}$ be defined by

$$\omega(t) := 1 - t^2, \qquad \beta(t) := \omega'(t).$$

Other choices for ω can be considered as well [1,2]. In addition, set $\varphi(t) := \int_0^t \sqrt{\omega(s)}\, ds$, for all $t \in [-1,1]$, and $c_0 := \int_{-1}^1 \sqrt{\omega(t)}\, dt$. Since $\varphi : [-1,1] \to [-\frac{c_0}{2}, \frac{c_0}{2}]$ is an (odd) strictly increasing function, the following piecewise constant function $g \in BV(\partial\Omega; [-1,1])$ is well defined: $g(x) := \varphi^{-1}\left(-\frac{c_0}{2}\mu(x)\right)$, for all $x \in \partial\Omega$. For any $\epsilon > 0$, let $g_\epsilon \in C^{0,1}(\partial\Omega; [-1,1])$ approximate g in the sense that $g_\epsilon(x) = g(x)$, if $\mathrm{dist}(x, S_g) \geq \epsilon$, and $\mathrm{Lip}(g_\epsilon) \leq \frac{L_g}{\epsilon}$, where S_g denotes the *jump* set of g and L_g is a constant independent of ϵ. We are now in a position to define the relaxed functionals:

$$\mathcal{F}_\epsilon(v) := \int_\Omega \left[\epsilon|\nabla v|^2 + \frac{1}{\epsilon}\omega(v) - c_0 \kappa v\right] dx, \qquad \text{if } v \in D(\mathcal{F}_\epsilon),$$

where $D(\mathcal{F}_\epsilon) := \{v \in H^1(\Omega; [-1,1]) : \ v = g_\epsilon \text{ on } \partial\Omega\}$. The existence of a solution u_ϵ to the minimum problem for $\mathcal{F}_\epsilon$ can be proven by direct methods. The nonconvexity of $\mathcal{F}_\epsilon$ allows, in general, the existence of more than one absolute or relative minima u_ϵ, which satisfy the following variational inequality (set $\langle u, v\rangle := \int_\Omega uv\, dx$):

$$2\epsilon\langle \nabla u_\epsilon, \nabla(v - u_\epsilon)\rangle + \frac{1}{\epsilon}\langle \beta(u_\epsilon), v - u_\epsilon\rangle - c_0\langle \kappa, v - u_\epsilon\rangle \geq 0, \qquad \forall\, v \in D(\mathcal{F}_\epsilon).$$

At this stage, we can introduce a discretization of the relaxed functional $\mathcal{F}_\epsilon$ by piecewise linear finite elements. Let us denote by $\{\mathcal{S}_h\}_{h>0}$ a regular and weakly acute family of partitions of Ω into simplices having diameter bounded by h. For the sake of simplicity we shall assume that Ω is a polyhedron, so that $\bar{\Omega} \equiv \Omega_h := \cup_{S \in \mathcal{S}_h} S$, for all $h > 0$. Let $\mathbf{V}_h \subset H^1(\Omega)$ indicate the usual piecewise linear finite element space over $\mathcal{S}_h$ and Π_h :

$C^0(\bar{\Omega}) \to \mathbf{V}_h$ the Lagrange interpolation operator. Let $\{a_j\}_{j=1}^J$ denote the nodes of $\mathcal{S}_h$ and $\{\chi_j\}_{j=1}^J$ the canonical basis of $\mathbf{V}_h$; we assume that $\{a_j\}_{j=1}^{J_0}$ are the internal nodes.

Finally, for any $\epsilon > 0$, let $\kappa_\epsilon \in C^{0,1}(\bar{\Omega})$ approximate the *curvature* function κ so that $\|\kappa_\epsilon\|_{L^\infty(\Omega)} \leq \|\kappa\|_{L^\infty(\Omega)}$, $\kappa_\epsilon \to \kappa$ in $L^1(\Omega)$, as $\epsilon \to 0$, and $\mathrm{Lip}(\kappa_\epsilon) \leq \frac{L_\kappa}{\epsilon}$, where L_κ is a constant independent of ϵ. We are now in a position to introduce the discrete functionals:

$$(3.1) \qquad \mathcal{F}_{\epsilon,h}(v) := \int_\Omega \left[\epsilon|\nabla v|^2 + \frac{1}{\epsilon}\Pi_h\omega(v) - c_0\Pi_h(\kappa_\epsilon v)\right] dx, \qquad \text{if } v \in D(\mathcal{F}_{\epsilon,h}),$$

where $D(\mathcal{F}_{\epsilon,h}) := \{v \in \mathbf{V}_h : \ |v| \leq 1 \text{ in } \Omega, \ v = \Pi_h g_\epsilon \text{ on } \partial\Omega\}$. The existence of a solution $u_{\epsilon,h}$ to the minimum problem for $\mathcal{F}_{\epsilon,h}$ is trivial. The integrals in (3.1) can be evaluated via the vertex quadrature rule, which is exact for piecewise linear functions, thus allowing the actual implementation of the discrete minimum problem on a computer.

A (relative) minimum $u_{\epsilon,h}$ for the functional $\mathcal{F}_{\epsilon,h}$ satisfies the variational inequality

$$(3.2) \quad 2\epsilon\langle\nabla u_{\epsilon,h}, \nabla(v-u_{\epsilon,h})\rangle + \frac{1}{\epsilon}\langle\beta(u_{\epsilon,h}), v-u_{\epsilon,h}\rangle_h - c_0\langle\kappa_\epsilon, v-u_{\epsilon,h}\rangle_h \geq 0, \quad \forall\, v \in D(\mathcal{F}_{\epsilon,h}),$$

where $\langle u,v\rangle_h := \int_\Omega \Pi_h(uv)dx$. Denoting by $M := \{\langle\chi_j,\chi_k\rangle_h\}_{j,k=1}^J$ the (diagonalized) mass matrix, by $A := \{\langle\nabla\chi_j,\nabla\chi_k\rangle\}_{j,k=1}^J$ the stiffness matrix, and by $D :=$ diagonal of A, $B := I - D^{-1}A$, the variational inequality (3.2) can then be written in matrix form as follows:

$$(3.3) \qquad \begin{cases} [2\epsilon AU + \frac{1}{\epsilon}M\beta(U) - c_0 MK]_j \in \psi(u_j), \quad u_j \in [-1,1], & j = 1,\dots,J_0, \\ u_j = g_\epsilon(a_j), & j = J_0+1,\dots,J. \end{cases}$$

Here $U = (u_1,\dots,u_J)^T$ represents the unknown solution $u_{\epsilon,h}$ (i.e., $u_j := u_{\epsilon,h}(a_j)$, $j = 1,\dots,J$), $K := (\kappa_\epsilon(a_1),\dots,\kappa_\epsilon(a_J))^T$, and $-\psi$ is the inverse of the *sgn* graph. In other words, $z \in \psi(u_j)$ means: $z = 0$, if $u_j \in (-1,1)$; $z \leq 0$, if $u_j = 1$; $z \geq 0$, if $u_j = -1$. A simple minded method for solving the nonlinear system (3.3) is the following Jacobi iterative scheme:

$$u_j^{k+1} := \Pi_{[-1,1]}\left(BU^k - \frac{1}{2\epsilon^2}D^{-1}M\beta(U^k) + \frac{c_0}{2\epsilon}D^{-1}MK\right)_j, \qquad j = 1,\dots,J_0,$$

where $\Pi_{[-1,1]}(s) := \min(1, \max(-1,s))$. A more effective iterative method can be easily obtained using an incomplete Cholesky factorization of the matrix A as a preconditioner.

Further details on VA can be found in [2].

4. Numerical Experiments. We present several numerical examples in order to show the behaviour of the algorithms FTA and VA.

4.1. Example I. Consider the cone-shaped curvature $\kappa_m(x,y) := -m\sqrt{x^2+y^2} + 2m + 0.5$. If $m > 0.25$, the circle $x^2+y^2 = 4$ is a relative minimum (with negative energy, if $m > 0.75$). In Fig. 5.1, we present the exact solution as well as the initial guess and the successive iterates generated by FTA, with $m = 1$. Fig. 5.2 shows two discrete interfaces obtained with VA; here $\Omega := (0,4)\times(0,4)$ and $\mu := 0$. Note the existence of a nonradially symmetric relative minimum, which is generated from the initial guess $A_0 := (0,4)\times(0,2)$. The interfaces produced by FTA and VA are compared in Fig. 5.3, whereas the performances of the two algorithms are summarized in Table 4.1 (DOF = degrees of freedom).

	L^∞-error	CPU (sec)	ϵ	h	iterates	DOF
FTA	0.002	6	—	~0.04	14	max 300
VA	0.15	735	0.14	0.1	~2000	~1500

TABLE 4.1. Comparison between FTA and VA.

4.2. Example II. Let $\kappa(x,y) := \lambda$ (positive constant) and $\mu := 1$. Note that, in this example, the boundary term plays an essential role. Fig. 5.4 illustrates the interfaces obtained with VA in two different domains Ω; the initial guess is $A_0 := \Omega$ for both.

4.3. Example III. Let $\kappa(x,y) := 2\sin x \sin y$. Fig. 5.5 shows four different relative minima of $\tilde{\mathcal{F}}$, obtained with FTA.

4.4. Example IV. Let $\kappa_t(x,y) := -40[x^2(x-1)(x+1)+y^2]+t$. Making use of FTA, we present the evolution of a relative minimum when the parameter t ranges from -1 to 3.6 (Fig. 5.6), from 3.6 to -3 (Fig. 5.7), and from -1 to 3.79 (Fig. 5.8). The results are obtained by choosing as initial guess the minimum computed for the previous value of t. Fig. 5.6 exhibits a jump at $t = 3.5$ when the two components touch, whereas Fig. 5.7 shows that, at $t = -3$, the previous relative minimum suddenly shrinks to the empty set; finally, Fig. 5.8 shows that the relative minimum becomes unstable at $t = 3.78$.

5. Comparison between FTA and VA. The two algorithms presented in this paper are based on substantially different approaches; this is reflected in their behaviour. The most evident difference between FTA and VA is their performances, as illustrated in Table 4.1 (in addition, note that, in Ex. I, VA exploits the symmetry of the problem at hand).

The slowness of VA is basically explainable as follows. In view of the Γ-convergence result proved in [1], VA requires the relation $h = o(\epsilon)$ to hold. Hence the meshsize has to be much smaller than the relaxation parameter, which then dictates the accuracy of the solution. Using a uniform mesh, we end up with $O(h^{-2})$ degrees of freedom for the nonlinear system to be solved. This concerns both the memory space and the cost of the nonlinear solver. Consequently, a possible remedy has to be be found in term of a suitable adaptive local refinement strategy, in order to concentrate the degrees of freedom near the developed interface. Moreover, as observed in [2], a number $O(h^{-2})$ of Jabobi iterations is espected for computing the discrete solution. The implementation of more efficient methods, such as nonlinear SORs, will probably reduce the number of iterations, but not its order of magnitude.

We also stress that the location of the relative minima might be very sensitive to the relaxation procedure or, even worse, that a relative minimum might disappears; this fact is reflected in Ex. I, for $m = 0.5$.

On the other hand, FTA has a number of restrictions. The data structure to describe the unknown interface is the major responsible for the difficulties in dealing with the 3-D case as well as with the boundary term $\mu\mathcal{H}^{d-1}(\partial A \cap \partial\Omega)$. Moreover, since the topological consistency test plays an essential role in FTA, it is another critical issue, in that it necessitates specific data structures (such as binary trees) and nontrivial algorithms to keep the CPU time under reasonable limits. On the contrary VA is completely unaware of the structure of the interface, which is defined implicitly as the zero level curve.

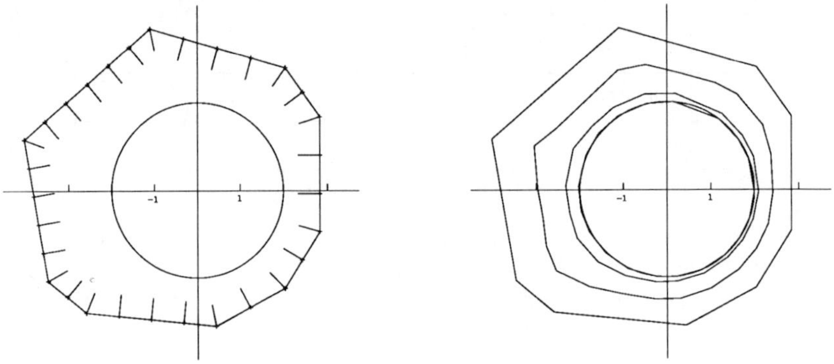

FIGURE 5.1. Ex. I: Initial guess with "normal" vectors and successive iterates (FTA).

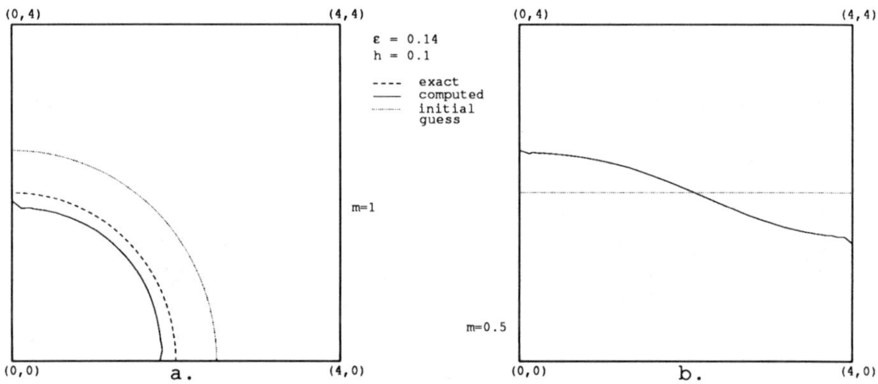

FIGURE 5.2. Ex. I: Exact and discrete relative minima (VA).

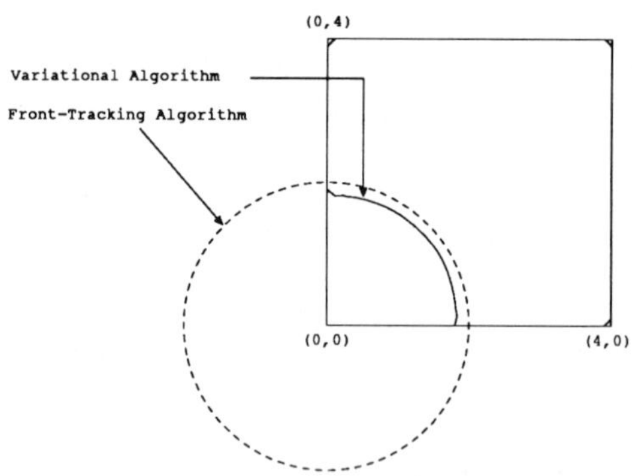

FIGURE 5.3. Ex. I: Comparison between FTA and VA.

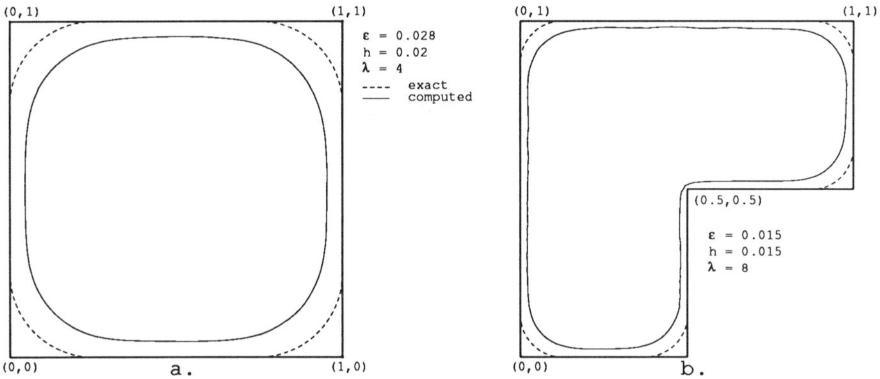

FIGURE 5.4. Ex. II: Exact and discrete relative minima (VA).

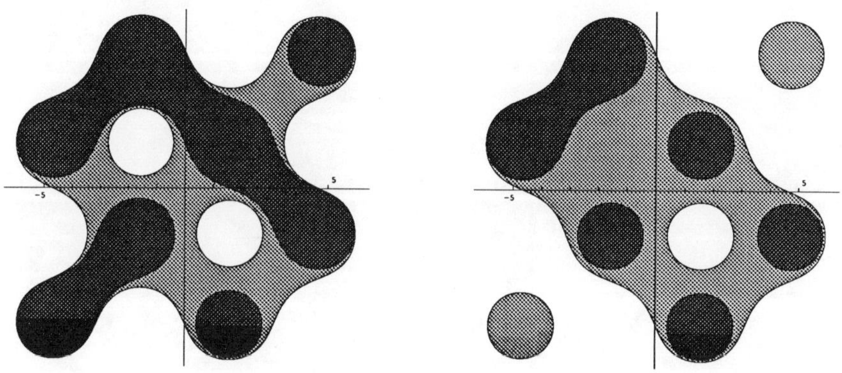

FIGURE 5.5. Ex. III: Some relative minima (FTA).

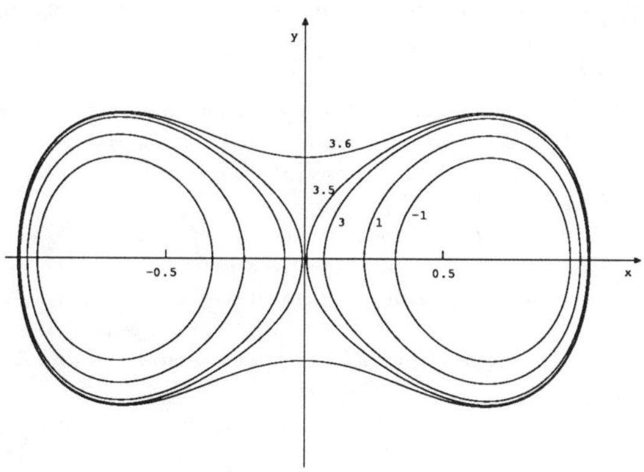

FIGURE 5.6. Ex. IV: Evolution of relative minima, $t = -1, 1, 3, 3.5, 3.6$.

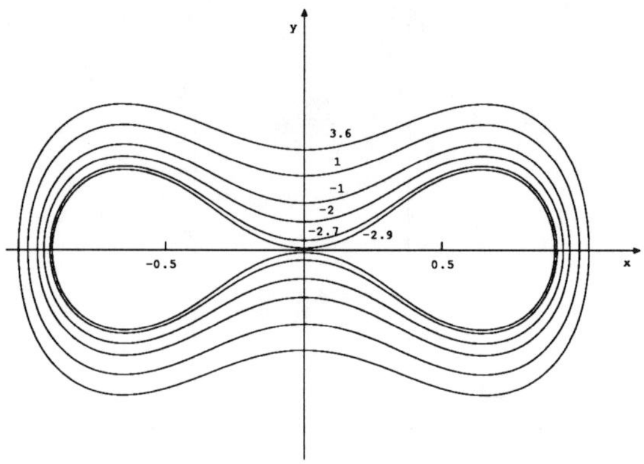

FIGURE 5.7. **Ex. IV: Evolution of relative minima, $t = 3.6, 1, -1, -2, -2.7, -2.9, -3$ (empty set).**

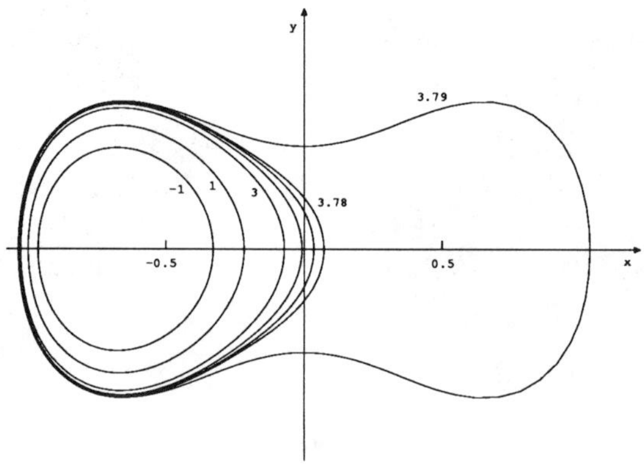

FIGURE 5.8. **Ex. IV: Evolution of relative minima, $t = -1, 1, 3, 3.5, 3.7, 3.78, 3.79$.**

References

1. G. Bellettini, M. Paolini, and C. Verdi, *Γ-convergence of discrete approximations to interfaces with prescribed mean curvature*, Atti Accad. Naz. Lincei Rend. Cl. Sci. Fis. Mat. Natur. (9) (to appear).
2. G. Bellettini, M. Paolini, and C. Verdi, *Numerical minimization of geometrical type problems related to calculus of variations*, Calcolo (to appear).
3. E. De Giorgi, *Free discontinuity problems in calculus of variations*, "in Proc. Meeting in honour of J.L. Lions," North-Holland, Amsterdam, 1988 (to appear).
4. H. Federer, "Geometric Measure Theory," Springer-Verlag, Berlin, 1968.
5. R. Finn, "Equilibrium Capillary Surfaces," Springer-Verlag, Berlin, 1986.
6. P.E. Gill and W. Murray, *Newton-type methods for unconstrained and linearly constrained optimization.*, Mathematical Programming **7** (1974), 311–350.
7. L. Modica and S. Mortola, *Un esempio di Γ-convergenza*, Boll. Un. Mat. Ital. (5) **14 B** (1977), 285–299.

International Series of Numerical Mathematics, Vol. 99, © 1991 Birkhäuser Verlag Basel

Mixed elements and a two-phase free-boundary problem in magnetostatics

A. Bossavit
Electricité de France, 1 Av. du Gal de Gaulle,
92141 Clamart

Abstract. Magnetostatics consists in finding vector fields b and h such that $\operatorname{div} b = 0, \operatorname{rot} h = j$ (j is given), and $b = \Gamma(h)$, where Γ is the subgradient of a convex functional U (the magnetic coenergy). When U is the sum of a quadratic functional and of a support functional, a 2–phase free-boundary problem results, a "vector" Stefan-like problem so to speak, because the unknown is a vector-field, not a function like e.g., temperature. The special structure of the equations calls for special "mixed" finite elements. We show how they help keep at the discrete level some interesting "complementarity" properties of the problem which are present at the continuous level.

Keywords. Mixed finite elements, magnetostatics, Stefan's problem.

1980 Mathematics subject classifications: 65N30

Introduction

Consider the following problem (Fig. 1) of non-linear magnetostatics. A current coil C drives a magnetic flux through a toroidal piece M, made of magnetizable material (mild iron). What is the relation between this flux and the total current, or *characteristic* of the circuit (to be defined with more precision below), and how is the magnetic field distributed?

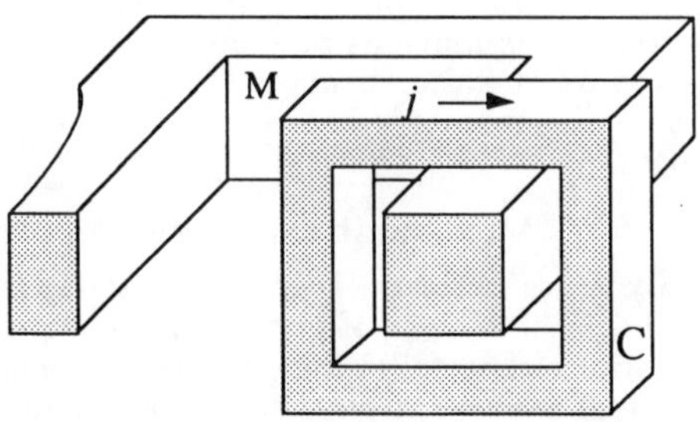

Figure 1. *The problem. Only one half of the system is shown. The other half is symmetrical with respect to the vertical plane. Currents in the coil C drive a magnetic flux in (the whole space but mainly in) the magnetic circuit M.*

The relevant equations are:

$$(1) \qquad \operatorname{rot} h = j, \quad (2) \quad b = \Gamma(h), \quad (3) \quad \operatorname{div} b = 0,$$

where b and h (vector fields, unknown) are the induction field and the magnetic field, and j (a vector field, given) is the current density in C. The crucial feature is the form of the non-linear behaviour law $b = \Gamma(h)$: at point x, the value of the field b is

$$(4) \qquad b(x) = \gamma_x(|h(x)|)\; h(x)/|h(x)|,$$

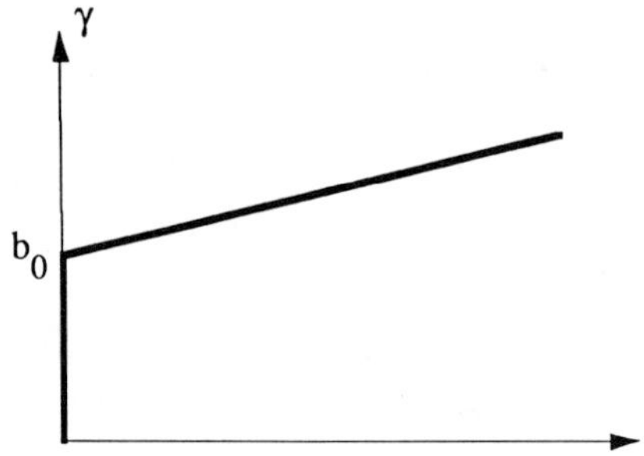

Figure 2. *Graph of γ_x, a maximal monotone graph of $\mathbb{R}^+ \times \mathbb{R}^+$ (not $\mathbb{R} \times \mathbb{R}$). The slope being μ_0 ($= 4\pi 10^{-7}$ MKSA), γ is the subdifferential of the function $f : \eta \mapsto b_0$ eta $+ \mu_0 \eta^2/2$. The "saturation threshold" b_0 is 0 in the air and may depend on position in the steel region (it depends on several factors, especially the temperature).*

with γ_x a maximal monotone graph as in Fig. 2. Due to the nature of this non-linearity, there are two regions in M, separated by a free boundary: the saturated region, where $|b(x)| > b_0(x)$ (cf. Fig. 2) and the non-saturated one, where $h(x) = 0$. An important part of the question is to locate this free boundary.

The γ of Fig. 2 is an idealization of the real b–h curve, which has a steep section near the origin, not a true discontinuity. So this is a toy problem, useful as a source of insight, as a benchmark for numerical methods, and perhaps interesting from the mathematical point of view, since it is the static case of a Stefan-like two-phase problem where the unknown field is *vectorial*, not scalar (the "eddy-currents problem", [9]).

As we shall see, the problem has a strong mathematical structure, including some "complementarity" properties (in the sense familiar to students of convex analysis; cf. e.g., [2, 16]). In particular, we show that *bilateral bounds* c an be computed for some parameters of interest. It is desirable to preserve as much as possible of this structure at the discrete level, and we shall introduce a family of finite elements ("Whitney elements" [6], an adaptation of classical objec ts of differential geometry known as "Whitney forms" [19, 1]), which seem well adapted to this purpose.

1. Mathematical modelling

The first formulation of a physics problem, even when largely mathematized, as above, is rarely the right one from the point of view of numerical simulation. This Section is devoted to the necessary reformulation. The following: rot for the curl operator, $\partial f(x)$ for the subgradient of a function f at point x, $\arg\inf\{f(x) : p(x)\}$ for the set which realizes the infimum of a real-valued function f over the set of points x f or which $p(x)$ is true, $L^2(D)$ [resp. $\mathbb{L}^2(D)$] for the Hilbert space of square-integrable functions [resp. vector fields] over domain D, $\mathbb{L}^2_{\text{div}}(D)$ [resp. $\mathbb{L}^2_{\text{rot}}(D)$] for elements of $\mathbb{L}^2$ whose divergence is in L^2 [resp. whose curl is in $\mathbb{L}^2$].

Starting from γ, let us define $f : \mathbb{R}^+ \mapsto \mathbb{R}^+$ by $f(\eta) = \int_0^\eta \gamma(s)ds$ and let $g(\beta) = \sup\{\eta \in \mathbb{R}^+ : \beta\eta - f(\eta)\}$ be its Fenchel conjugate. The inequality $f(\eta) + g(\beta) \geq \eta\beta$ holds, with equality iff the pair $\{\eta, \beta\}$ lies in the graph of γ. Given a vector field h [resp. b] over $\mathbb{R}^3$, let us set $U(h) = \int_{\mathbb{R}^3} f(|h(x)|)dx$ and $V(b) = \int_{\mathbb{R}^3} g(|b(x)|)dx$. Then U and V are convex, lower semi-continuous (l.s.c.) functionals, in duality. In the case under consideration, $U(h) = \int_{\mathbb{R}^3}(b_0(x)|h(x)| + \mu_0|h(x)|^2/2)\,dx$, and $V(b) = \mu_0^{-1}\int_{\mathbb{R}^3}((|b(x)| - b_0)^+)^2/2\,dx$. The

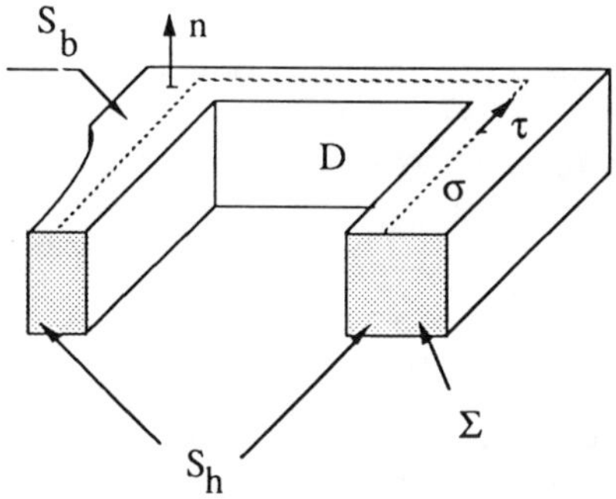

Figure 3. *The problem-domain, with its boundary S in two parts (S_h and S_b). The normal n, of length 1, is outward directed at all regular points of S, and τ is the unit tangent vector along path σ. The "cutting surface" Σ (which here is one of the connected components of S_h, but could be placed differently, provided it "cuts" the magnetic circuit) is in a kind of dual topological relationship with σ (cf. [1], p. 53).*

equality

$$U(h) + V(b) = \int_{\mathbb{R}^3} h(x) \cdot b(x)dx \tag{5}$$

means that relation (4) holds a.e. in x. (Note that if h and b are unrelated, the *inequality* $\geq$ holds in (5).) We may (according to an old idea, [14]) take advantage of this to consider other behaviour laws than (4): give a pair U and V of convex l.s.c. functions in duality on $\mathbb{L}^2(\mathbb{R}^3)$, then instead of (1), (2), (3), set the more general problem of finding h and b such that (1), (3) and (5) hold. What will be said below applies to this general situation. Note that anisotropy and non-homogeneity of the magnetic material may easily be taken into account this way, but not hysteresis.

As a function of h [resp. b], U [resp. V] is called the "magnetic coenergy" [resp. "magnetic energy"]. These are not arbitrary names: that V really is magnetic energy may be proven from first principles, but this appeals to the more general eddy-currents theory and will not be done here (cf. [8]).

So the problem is: given j (with $\operatorname{div} j = 0$), *find* a pair $\{h, b\}$ of vector fields over $\mathbb{R}^3$ *such that* (1), (3) and (5) *hold.* But leaving it in such form would be ignoring an essential aspect of the situation, which is physically intuitive, and could be established via an asymptotic analysis [5]: the field concentrates in M, and the air around contributes only a very small part of its total energy. So a computation which aims at finding the distribution of the field in M may ignore what happens in the air, and deal with (1), (3), (5) in M only. By using symmetry, one thus faces a boundary-value problem in the domain D of Fig. 3 (half of M). Now what about boundary conditions on the surface S of D? On the part S_h which belongs to the symmetry plane, $n \times h = 0$ by an easy symmetry argument. On the remaining part $S_b, n \cdot b = 0$, because the flux-lines of field b stay inside M. The initial problem has become: *find* $\{h, b\}$ *in* $\mathbb{L}^2_{\text{rot}}(D) \times \mathbb{L}^2_{\text{div}}(D)$ *such that*

$$\operatorname{rot} h = 0 \quad \text{in } D, \quad n \times h = 0 \quad \text{on } S_h, \tag{6}$$

$$\operatorname{div} b = 0 \quad \text{in } D, \quad n \cdot b = 0 \quad \text{on } S_b, \tag{7}$$

$$U(h) + V(b) = \int_D h \cdot b, \tag{8}$$

where U and V are as above, but defined as integrals over D, not over the whole space.

Fine, but where is the source of the field (which previously was in the right-hand side of eq. (1))? It now appears as a linear constraint on the circulation of field h along any path linking the two connected components of S_h, like σ on Fig. 3:

$$\int_\sigma \tau \cdot h = J, \tag{9}$$

where J is half the total intensity (intensity in the thread multiplied by half the number of turns) in the coil of Fig. 1. Note that (9) is a consequence of Stokes' theorem (known in electromagnetism as "Ampère's theorem") when applied to (1), and is valid for all paths similar to σ. It can be shown that problem (6), (7), (8), (9) is well-posed (at least as far as h is concerned; b can obviously be non-unique in the case of Fig. 2).

Condition (9) privileges h, because J is the source of the field in the present situation, but mathematically speaking a similar condition on b, that is

$$\int_S n \cdot b = F, \tag{10}$$

could be substituted for it (F is the flux of induction sustained by the magnetic circuit). This would make sense if the aim of the modelling was to answer the question: "which J should be applied in order to get the flux F?". One would then solve (6), (7), (8), (10), and obtain J by evaluating the line integral (9). The symmetry between these two formulations suggests a more general approach, which answers an enlarged family of questions: find the *pairs* $\{J, F\}$ of values which are compatible with (6), (7), (8). Taken all together, they form a graph in the J–F plane (whose right part is, like the graph of Fig. 2, a maximal monotone graph), which is called the *characteristic curve* of the circuit.

So we shall *set the determination of this characteristic curve as our objective.* Moreover, we shall be able to obtain, by a suitable a posteriori error analysis, unequivocal *information about the location of this graph* in the J–F plane: it will be shown that the graph lies inside a set that can be explicitly constructed (computed). This departs from classical error analysis, which, as criticized in [13], leans toward asymptotic error estimates, and goes in the direction of "useful error analysis (...) producing information instead of numbers" advocated in that paper.

Before turning to this problem, let us discuss the question of the free boundary. I believe (but could not prove) that for positive, not too large values of J, the situation is as in Fig. 4. The difficulty lies in establishing the *smoothness* of the free boundary S_0. For under this assumption, $n \times h = 0$ on S_0, and so b (parallel to h in the saturated region) is normal to S_0. Therefore, the flux of b through S_0 is equal to its area times b_0, and S_0 cuts the surface S_b of the circuit at right angles (since $n \cdot b = 0$ on S_b). So for a certain range of values of F (those such that F/b_0 is intermediate between the smaller and the larger cross-section area of the circuit), we can predict the situation of Fig. 4. Note that S_0 must cut (disconnect) the domain because of Ampère's theorem. (In the language of algebraic topology, S_0 is in the same homology class (relative to S_b) as the Σ of Fig. 3.)

Remark. One should not forget, in discussing this point, that the mathematical model has been obtained by going to the limit in two different ways: first by selecting the shape of γ, then by assuming that no flux goes through S_b. In real magnetic circuits, flux lines tend to avoid saturated regions and so may take a shortcut through the air, in contradiction with the previous assumption. The present model is valid if the dimensionless ratio, or *Stefan number* of the problem, $Lb_0/\mu_0 J$ (where L is the length of the path σ of Fig. 3), is large enough (because when it tends to infinity, the limit boundary condition is indeed $n \cdot b = 0$ on S_b), but not *too* large, because "squaring" the b–h curve as we did in Fig. 2 would then be unjustifiable. ◇

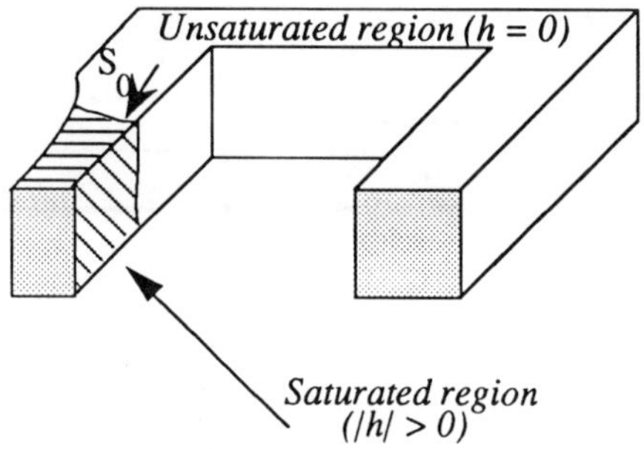

Figure 4. *Conjecture about the free boundary: it cuts the circuit, and intersects its surface at right angles.*

2. A symmetric presentation of convex analysis

The problem of finding the characteristic will now be put into the framework of convex analysis. We depart from standard presentations of this subject [3, 11, 17], by emphasizing the symmetry of its structures (in the spirit of Rockafellar [18], as pointed out in [2]). We shall note dom(A) and cod(A) the domain of a linear operator and its range respectively.

Let us consider the following abstract situation, in which all the elements of the previous one can easily be recognized. On a Hilbert space X, define a pair of Fenchel conjugate l.s.c. convex functions U and V. (For simplicity, we assume that U and V are everywhere defined and with bounded level sets, but this is not essential.) Let R and D be two linear, closed operators on X, with dense domains and closed images, and let $X_0 = \ker(R) \cap \ker(D)$. Assume that X_0 is of finite dimension d. Call X_R and X_D the ortho-complements $\ker(R) \ominus X_0$ and $\ker(D) \ominus X_0$. Then (Fig. 5), we have the orthogonal decompositions $X = X_R \oplus X_0 \oplus X_D \equiv \ker(R) \oplus X_D \equiv X_R \oplus \ker(D)$. Let $(\ ,\ )$ and $\langle\ ,\rangle$ denote the scalar products in $I\!R^d$ and in X, respectively.

Lemma 1. *There exist two closed linear operators $\mathcal{J}$ and $\mathcal{F}$, with respective domains* $\ker(R)$ *and* $\ker(D)$, *and onto $I\!R^d$, such that* $(x, y) = \langle \mathcal{J}(x), \mathcal{F}(y)\rangle\ \forall\, x \in \ker(R), y \in \ker(D)$.

Proof. By taking the orthogonal decompositions: $x = x_R + x_0, y = y_D + y_0$, one has $(x, y) = (x, y_0 + y_D) \equiv (x, y_0)$, then $(x, y) = (x_0, y_0) = \langle \mathcal{J}(x), \mathcal{F}(y)\rangle$ once a basis has been chosen in X_0. For closure, take a sequence $\{x_n \in \ker(R)\}$ such that $x_n \to x$ and $\mathcal{J}(x_n) \to J \in I\!R^d$; then $(x_n, y) = \langle \mathcal{J}(x_n), \mathcal{F}(y)\rangle$, wh ich results in $(x, y) = \langle J, \mathcal{F}(y)\rangle\ \forall\, y \in \ker(D)$ by passing to the limit, therefore $J = \mathcal{J}(x)$. Of course $\mathcal{J}$ and $\mathcal{F}$ depend on the chosen basis. ◇

In the case at hand, as recalled in Fig. 5, $X \equiv I\!L^2(D)$, and R is the restriction of rot (understood in the sense of distributions) to the linear subspace $\mathrm{dom}(R) \equiv \{h \in {I\!L^2}_{\mathrm{rot}}(D) : n \times h = 0 \text{ on } S_h\}$. A similar definition (with div, etc.) applies to D. Operators $\mathcal{J}$ and $\mathcal{F}$ are $\mathcal{J}(h) = \int_\sigma \tau \cdot h$ and $\mathcal{F}(b) = \int_\Sigma n \cdot b$. (Lemma 2 proves that these integrals are well defined, a fact which does not stem from frace theorems.)

Let us define the following functions on $I\!R^d$:

$$u(J) = \inf\{U(x') : x' \in \ker(R), \mathcal{J}(x') = J\}, v(F) = \inf\{V(y') : y' \in \ker(D), \mathcal{F}(y') = F\}.$$

Note that these minima are reached, since they are taken over closed convex sets.

Proposition 1. *Functions u and v are convex, l.s.c., and in duality.*

Proof. Clearly, $u(J) + v(F) \geq \langle J, F\rangle$. Now, given J, let x achieve the minimum $u(J)$. Since $U(x') \geq U(x)$ for all x' in the affine space $\{x' \in \ker(R) : \mathcal{J}(x') = J\}$, there exists (by

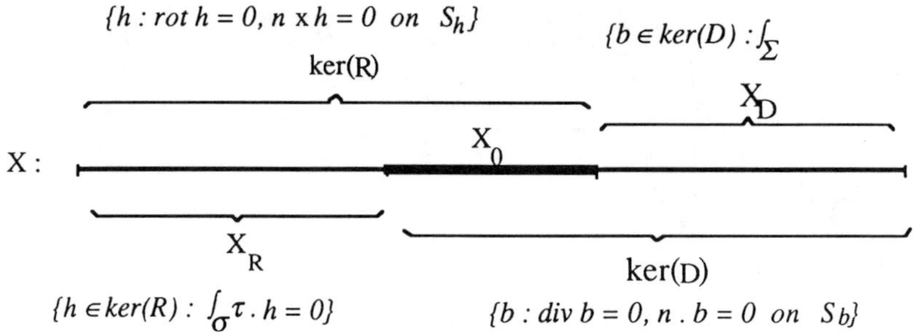

Figure 5. *Orthogonal decomposition of X (here $\mathbb{L}^2(D)$). In italics, an analytical description (via the properties of individual vector fields) of the three subspaces in the case under study. This is a special case of the classical "Hodge decomposition" [15, 12].*

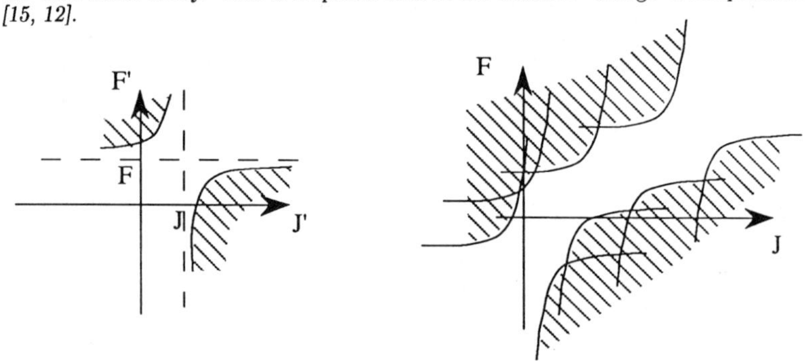

Figure 6 *($d = 1$). For any given J and F, the characteristic set lies between the two branches of the hyperbola $F' = F + a/(J' - J)$, where $a = u(J) + v(F) - JF$ (or, a fortiori, any larger value). On the right: making use of this property to locate the characteristic set inside a definite region of the J–F plane.*

Hahn-Banach's Theorem) some y orthogonal to this space (which implies $Dy = 0$) and such that

(11) $$U(x') - U(x) \geq (x' - x, y) \; \forall \, x' \in X.$$

Eq. (11) means that $y \in \partial U(x)$. Therefore $U(x) + V(y) = (x, y)$. Let $F = \mathcal{F}(y)$. Then $v(F) \leq V(y) \equiv (x, y) - U(x) = \langle J, F\rangle - u(J)$. So $u(J) = \sup\{\langle J, F\rangle - v(F) : F \in \mathbb{R}^d\}$, proving that u is the Fenchel transform of v. The converse is true by a symmetrical reasoning, hence the result. $\diamondsuit$

Definition. *The* characteristic set *of U and V with respect to X_0* (and to its basis) *is*

$$\Gamma = \{\{J, F\} \in \mathbb{R}^d \times \mathbb{R}^d : u(J) + v(F) = \langle J, F\rangle\}.$$

In our magnetostatics problem, the characteristic set, according to the definitions of u and v, consists of all pairs $\{J, F\}$ such that

$$0 = \inf\{U(h) + V(b) - \int_D h \cdot b : h \in \mathbb{L}^2_{\text{rot}}(D),\ b \in \mathbb{L}^2_{\text{div}}(D),\ (6), (7), (9) \text{ and } (10) \text{ hold}\},$$

since (8) holds when this positive quantity is equal to 0, and this is precisely the "characteristic curve" we purported to find.

Lemma 2. *Given F and G, the following inclusion holds* (cf. Fig. 6 for the case when $d = 1$):

$$\Gamma \subset \{\{J', F'\} \in \mathbb{R}^d \times \mathbb{R}^d : \langle J' - J, F - F'\rangle \leq u(J) + v(F) - \langle J, F\rangle\}$$

Proof. By duality,

$$u(J) + v(F) = \sup\{\langle J, F'\rangle - v(F') : F' \in \mathbb{R}^d\} + \sup\{\langle J', F\rangle - u(J') : J' \in \mathbb{R}^d\}$$

$$\geq \langle J, F'\rangle - v(F') + \langle J', F\rangle - u(J') \equiv \langle J, F'\rangle + \langle J', F\rangle - \langle J', F'\rangle \ \forall \{J', F'\} \in \Gamma,$$

thus $u(J)+v(F)-\langle J, F\rangle \geq \langle J, F'\rangle+\langle J', F\rangle-\langle J', F'\rangle-\langle J, F\rangle \equiv \langle J'-J, F-F'\rangle \ \forall \{J', F'\} \in \Gamma$, which is the claim. ◇

This has an important practical implication: suppose one has performed an approximate solution of the optimization problem :

$$\text{(12)} \qquad \operatorname{arginf}\{U(x) + V(y) - (x, y) : Rx = 0, Dy = 0, \mathcal{J}(x) = J\},$$

[resp.

$$\text{(13)} \qquad \operatorname{arginf}\{U(x) + V(y) - (x, y) : Rx = 0, Dy = 0, \mathcal{F}(y) = F\}],$$

thus obtaining numerical estimates x^*, y^* for x, y. Let $F = \mathcal{F}(y^*)$ [resp. $J = \mathcal{J}(x^*)$]. If the approximation has been "from inside" (Galerkin style), then $U(x^*) = u^*(J)$ and $V(y^*) = v^*(F)$ are upper bounds for $u(J)$ and $v(F)$. Let $a = u^*(J) + v^*(F) - \langle J, F\rangle$ (note that a is ≥ 0). Then, by Lemma 2, Γ lies in the set $\{\{J', F'\} : \langle J' - J, F - F'\rangle \leq a\}$. By repeating such computations for an array of values of J and F, *one thus obtains a set which surely contains the characteristic set Γ, and can be made to fit it as closely as computing resources permit* .

Before returning to the model problem, and to practical ways to solve (12) or (13), remark that they *split* into two separate optimization problems, due to Lemma 1. For instance, (12) is equivalent to finding

$$\inf\{U(x) : Rx = 0, \ \mathcal{J}(x) = J\}, \quad \inf\{V(y) - \langle J, \mathcal{F}(y)\rangle : Dy = 0\}.$$

3. Mixed elements

We now introduce the family of "Whitney elements" on a tetrahedral mesh. They were introduced in mathematics long ago for purposes foreign to numerical analysis [19].

Consider a tetrahedral tesselation of D, with the standard requirement for finite-element meshes: the intersection of two distinct tetrahedra is either a face, or an edge, or a vertex (node), or is empty. Call $\mathcal{N}, \mathcal{E}, \mathcal{F}$ and $\mathcal{V}$ the sets of nodes, edges, faces and tetrahedra ("volumes") of the mesh. We note w_n the continuous, piecewise linear function over D which is equal to 1 at node n, and to 0 at all other nodes (the standard "hat function" of finite element theory). We shall call W^0 the finite-dimensional vector space generated by the w_ns (usually referred to as "P^1").

An edge $e \in \mathcal{E}$ will be specified by its extremal nodes: $e = \{m, n\}$ (in this order, so an orientation of e is implied). To each edge $e = \{m, n\}$ we assign a vector field w_e (Whitney's "edge-element"):

$$w_e = w_m \nabla w_n - w_n \nabla w_m,$$

where ∇ stands for grad. This field is not continuous, but, as is readily checked, its *tangential part* is: calling n one of the two normal unitary vector fields associated with a given face,

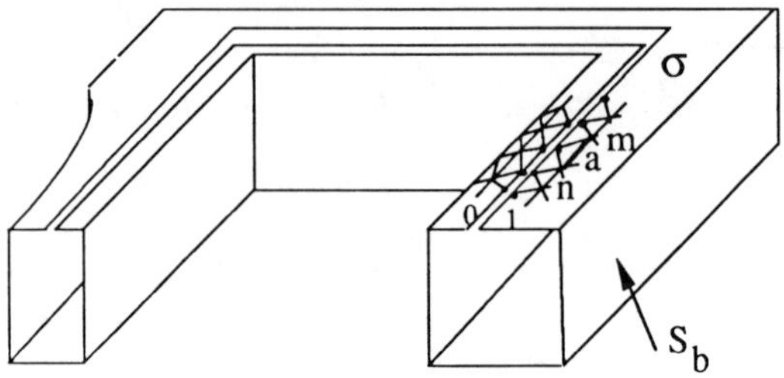

Figure 7. *Construction of a^1, using a "cut" of S_b along σ.*

the jump of $n \times w_e$ across this face is 0. Note that, in contrast, the *normal part* $n \cdot w_e$ is not continuous across the faces of tetrahedra which contain edge e. An easy computation will show that the circulation of w_e along edge e is equal to 1, and to 0 along other edges.

A face $f \in \mathcal{F}$ will be specified by its nodes: $f = \{l, m, n\}$ (again, in this order). To each such face, we assign a vector field w_f (Whitney's "face-element"):

$$w_f = 2(w_l \nabla w_m \times \nabla w_n + w_m \nabla w_n \times \nabla w_l + w_n \nabla w_l \times \nabla w_m).$$

Now, the normal part of w_f is continuous across faces and its flux through face f is equal to 1 (to 0 through other faces). The w_fs span W^2. Finally, a Whitney "volume-element" is a function w_v, constant and equal to $1/volume(v)$ on volume v, and 0 elsewhere, so the sum of w_v over v is equal to 1 (and to 0 over other tetrahedra). The w_vs span W^3, a space which is usually denoted by "P^0" in finite element texts.

The main interest of the "vectorial" Whitney elements of W^1 and W^2, as opposed to conventional node-based elements, is their ability to exactly model the kind of continuity which is expected from vector fields appearing in electromagnetism. Assume the magnetic field h and the induction field b are discretized as

$$h = \sum_{e \in \mathcal{E}} \underline{h}_e w_e, b = \sum_{f \in \mathcal{F}} \underline{b}_f w_f,$$

where the $\underline{h}_e$s and $\underline{b}_f$s are real coefficients. Then h (resp. b) enjoys continuity of its tangential (resp. normal) part across mesh faces, precisely what Physics requires. Moreover, the degrees of freedom (DoF) $\underline{h}_e$ and $\underline{b}_f$ have interesting interpretations as the circulations of h along the edges of the mesh and the fluxes of b through the faces.

The *functional relationships* between the different Whitney spaces of various degrees are also worthy of notice. One easily shows that the image of W^0 by the operator grad is in W^1, and other similar inclusions, as follows:

$$\text{grad}(W^0) \subset W^1, \quad \text{rot}(W^1) \subset W^2, \quad \text{div}(W^2) \subset W^3. \tag{14}$$

Let us now call W_h^p [resp. W_b^p], $p = 0$ to 3, the subspace of W^p obtained by equating to 0 all DoF relative to simplices which belong to the closure of S_h [resp. of S_b]. (Remark that $W_h^3 = W_b^3 = W^3$.) By doing this, we have $n \times h = 0$ on S_h if $h \in W_h^1$, and $n \cdot b = 0$ on S_b if $h \in W_b^2$, a neat way to satisfy boundary conditions in (6) and (7). Let us call $H = W_h^1$ and $B = W_b^2$.

We shall also have spaces named Φ and A :

(15) $$\Phi = \{\varphi \in W^0 : \varphi = J\varphi^1 + W_h^0\}, \quad A = \{a \in W^1 : a = Fa^1 + W_b^1\},$$

where φ^1 and a^1 are special elements, built as follows. To all nodes n in Σ (cf. Fig. 3), assign the DoF $\underline{\phi}_n = 0$. To all those in the remaining part of S_h, give the value $\underline{\phi}_n = 1$, and to all remaining nodes, just any value. Now set $\varphi^1 = \sum_{n\in\mathcal{N}} \underline{\phi}_n w_n$. The point of this construction is that $h^1 = \text{grad}\,\varphi^1$ is in W_h^1, and that $\mathcal{F}(h^1) = 1$. Moreover, as easily proved,

$$\{h \in H : \text{rot}\, h = 0\} = \text{grad}\, \Phi,$$

and $\mathcal{J}(h)$ is by construction the J of (15). As for a^1, the procedure is more involved (Fig. 7). First consider all the nodes in S^j, and double those which lie on σ. To all nodes on the left side of σ, assign the value $\underline{\phi}_n = 0$, to those on the right the value 1, any value to all others. Now, to surface edges like $a = \{m, n\}$, assign the edge-value $\underline{\text{a}}_e = \underline{\phi}_n - \underline{\phi}_m$. To all other edges in $\mathcal{E}$, give some arbitrary value as DoF. Finally, construct $a^1 = \sum_{e\in\mathcal{E}} \underline{\text{a}}_e w_e$. The point is to have the flux of $b^1 = \text{rot}\, a^1$ (an element of W_b^2) through Σ equal to 1. Now,

$$\{b \in B : \text{div}\, b = 0\} = \text{rot}\, A,$$

and $\mathcal{F}(b)$ is by construction the F of (15).

After this preparation, the construction of discrete analogues to the optimization problems (12) and (13) is staightforward. For instance, (12) will consist, in discrete form, in

$$\inf\{U(h) + V(b) - \int_D h \cdot b : h \in H, \text{rot}\, h = 0, b \in B, \text{div}\, b = 0, \mathcal{J}(h) = J\},$$

which splits into the two problems of finding

(16) $$\inf\{U(\text{grad}\,\varphi) : \varphi \in \Phi, \mathcal{J}(\text{grad}\,\varphi) = J\},$$

(17) $$\inf\{V(\text{rot}\, a) - J\mathcal{F}(\text{rot}\, a) : a \in A\},$$

two non-linear *unconstrained* optimization problems (the constraint $\mathcal{J}(\text{grad}\,\varphi) = J$ being disposed of as suggested by freezing the DoF J in (15) at the required value). The unknowns are, for the first one, the $\underline{\phi}_n$s for all nodes not in S_h, and for the second one, the $\underline{\text{a}}_e$s for all edges not in S_b, *plus* the extra degree of freedom F of (15). The discretization of problem (13) is similar.

To sum up: For an array of values of J, one solves (16) and (17). This gives not only an estimate of each corresponding flux $F = \mathcal{F}(\text{rot}\, a)$, and the space distribution of fields h and b at each of these regimes, but, as explained in Fig. 6, a set of the J–F plane which contains the characteristic.

Conclusion

We have thus achieved the objective of the introduction. We need not stress any further the obvious adequation of Whitney elements to the task, but one may wonder whether conventional, node-based, finite elements could not be used for a. After all, what is required of space A is to be made of vector fields which have a curl, and satisfy $n \cdot \text{rot}\, a = 0$ on S_b. For instance, one could look for a in $\mathbb{P}^1 = \{a = \sum_{n\in\mathcal{N}} \mathbf{a}_n w_n\}$, where $\mathbf{a}_n$ is a vector DoF, not a scalar. Objections to this proposal, to be developed elsewhere, are: 1) The boundary condition becomes very awkward. 2) One can prove that $\text{rot}\, \mathbb{P}^1 \subset \text{rot}\, W^1$, with strict inclusion. Therefore, the precision is better with edge-elements. 3) The connectivity of finite element matrices is better with edge-elements, giving more sparsity [4, 6]. 4) The stiffness matrix of the a-problem (in the linear case) is ill-conditioned if $I\!P^1$ elements are used. (In the non-linear case, this applies to each step of, say, a Newton-Raphson scheme.) This is linked with the problem of "spurious modes" in the computation of resonant cavities [7].

References

[1] P. Alexandrov, "Elementary concepts of topology", Dover (New York), 1961. (First published in 1932, Springer.)

[2] G. Allen, *Variational Inequalities, Complementary Problems and Duality Theory,* JMAA, 58 (1979), pp. 1–10.

[3] V. Barbu, Th. Precupeanu, "Convexity and Optimization in Banach Spaces", D. Reidel (Dordrecht), 1986.

[4] M. L. Barton, Z. J. Cendes, *New vector finite elements for three dimensional magnetic fields computations,* J. Appl. Phys., 61, 8 (1987), pp. 3919–21.

[5] A. Bossavit, *On the Condition 'h Normal to the Wall' in Magnetic Field Problems,* Internat. J. Numer. Methods Engrg., 24 (1987), pp. 1541–50.

[6] A. Bossavit, *Simplicial finite elements for scattering problems in electromagnetism,* Comput. Methods Appl. Mech. Engrg., 76 (1989), pp. 299–316.

[7] A. Bossavit, *Solving Maxwell's Equations in a Closed Cavity, and the Question of Spurious Modes,* IEEE Trans., MAG–26, 2 (1990), pp. 702–705.

[8] A. Bossavit, *Eddy-currents and forces in deformable conductors,* in "Mechanical Modellings of New Electromagnetic Materials" (Proc. IUTAM Symposium, Stockholm, 2–6 April 90, R. T. Hsieh, ed.), Elsevier North-Holland, to be published.

[9] A. Bossavit, *A Numerical Approach to Transient 3D Non-linear Eddy-current Problems,* Applied Electromagnetics in Materials, 1, 1 (1990), pp. 65-75.

[10] J. Dodziuk, *Finite-Difference Approach to the Hodge Theory of Harmonic Forms,* Amer. J. Math., 98, 1 (1976), pp. 79–104.

[11] I. Ekeland, R. Temam, "Analyse convexe et problèmes variationnels", Dunod Gauthier-Villars (Paris), 1973.

[12] K. O. Friedrichs, *Differential Forms on Riemannian Manifolds,* Comm. Pure Appl. Math., 3 (1953), pp. 551–90.

[13] P. Linz, *A critique of numerical analysis,* Bull. Amer. Math. Soc., 19, 2 (1988), pp. 407–16.

[14] J. J. Moreau, *Applications of convex analysis to the treatment of elastoplastic systems,* in "Applications of methods of Functional Analysis to problems in Mechanics", Symp. IUTAM-IMU, Lecture Notes in Math. 503 (P. Germain, B. Nayroles, eds.), Springer (Berlin), 1976.

[15] C. B. Morrey, "Multiple integrals in the calculus of variations", Springer-Verlag (New York), 1966.

[16] J. T. Oden, J. N. Reddy, *On Dual Complementary Variational Principles in Mathematical Physics,* Internat. J. Engrg. Sci., 12 (1974), pp. 1–29.

[17] P. D. Panagiotopoulos, "Inequality Problems in Mechanics and Applications", Birkhäuser (Boston), 1985.

[18] R. T. Rockafellar, "Convex Analysis", Princeton U.P. (Princeton), 1970.

[19] H. Whitney, "Geometric Integration Theory", Princeton U.P. (Princeton), 1957.

International Series of Numerical Mathematics, Vol. 99, © 1991 Birkhäuser Verlag Basel

Numerical solutions of two phase continuous casting problem

Zhiming Chen[1]

Institute of Mathematics
Academia Sinica, Beijing, China

Abstract. We propose here a numerical scheme to solve the continuous casting problem. The scheme is based on the nonequilibrium phase relaxation to smooth the enthalpy and the characteristic finite element method to treat the convection term. After deducing some stability estimates, we prove the convergence of the scheme. Two numerical examples are reported.

Keywords. Continuous casting, nonequilibrium phase relaxation, characteristic finite element method.

1980 Mathematics subject classifications: 65N05

1. Introduction

Let us consider the parabolic problem of the form

$$\frac{\partial u}{\partial t} + b(t)\frac{\partial u}{\partial x_3} - \Delta\theta = f \tag{1.1}$$

$$u \in H(\theta), \tag{1.2}$$

where $H(\theta)$ is a maximal monotone graph. If $b(t) = 0$, (1.1)-(1.2) is the weak formulation of a Stefan problem. In general, if $b(t) \geq 0$, (1.1)-(1.2) can be regard as the weak formulation of a continuous casting problem (see section 2). Here θ is the temperature, $H(\theta)$ is the enthalpy, and $b(t)$ is the velocity of the ingot.

The weak formulation of the classical Stefan problem has been discussed by many authors. For the existence and uniqueness of the weak solution, we refer to [5],[6]. As

[1]Present Address: Institute of Mathematics, University of Augsburg, Universitätsstr. 8, D-8900 Augsburg, West Germany.

soon as the numerical solutions are considered, one natural idea is to smooth the enthalpy $H(\theta)$, then (1.1)-(1.2) can be solved numerically by the standard methods for solving nonlinear parabolic equations, for example, the finite element method (see [7]). Another possible method first makes use of the fact that $H^{-1}(\theta)$ is a continuous function, therefore, (1.1)-(1.2) can be reformulated as follows (when $b(t) \equiv 0$)

$$\frac{\partial e}{\partial t} - \Delta U(e) = f, \tag{1.3}$$

where $U : R \longrightarrow R$ is a Lipschitz continuous increasing function, then (1.3) is solved by the finite element method (see [3]). One relatively new method whose idea is used in this paper is proposed by C.Verdi & A.Visintin. After decomposing the enthalpy $H(\theta)$, the method reformulates (1.1)-(1.2) into the following equivalent form (here $b(t) \equiv 0$)

$$\frac{\partial(a\theta + w)}{\partial t} - \Delta\theta = f, \tag{1.4}$$

$$w \in \Lambda(\theta), \tag{1.5}$$

where a is a positive constant, and $\Lambda(\theta)$ is a maximal graph. For any $\epsilon > 0$, (1.5) is approximated by the relaxed equation

$$\epsilon\frac{\partial w}{\partial t} + \Lambda^{-1}(w) \ni \theta. \tag{1.6}$$

Problem (1.4),(1.6) is then discretized in time by the semi-explicit scheme and in space by finite element method (see also [9]). At last we remark that error estimates have been given in the papers [3],[7],[9].

In general, F.Yi obtained in [10] the existence and uniqueness of the weak solution of problem (1.1)-(1.2) with non-homogenous boundary condition by a method similar to that in [5]. In order to get a numerical approximation scheme, we will also use the idea of characteristic finite element method which is proposed in [2] by J.Douglas,Jr. & T.F.Russell with the goal to solve a one-dimensional convection-dominated linear diffusion equation.

Set $\psi(t) = [1+b(t)^2]^{1/2}$ and $\tau(t)$ the characteristic direction of the operator $\frac{\partial}{\partial t}+b(t)\frac{\partial}{\partial x_3}$, then

$$\frac{\partial}{\partial\tau(t)} = \frac{1}{\psi(t)}\frac{\partial}{\partial t} + \frac{b(t)}{\psi(t)}\frac{\partial}{\partial x_3}$$

Therefore (1.1) is equivalent to

$$\psi(t)\frac{\partial u}{\partial\tau(t)} - \Delta\theta = f.$$

We denote that the time step $\tau > 0$ and $t^n = n\tau$, and set $\bar{x} = x - b(t)\tau e_3$, $\bar{u} = u(\bar{x}, t)$. Here $e_3 = (0,0,1)^T$ is the unit vector in x_3 dirction. If we further extend u oddly with respect to the plane $x_3 = 0$, we can suppose

$$\psi(t^n)\frac{\partial u^n}{\partial\tau(t^n)} \approx \psi(t^n)\frac{u(x,t^n) - \bar{u}(x,t^{n-1})}{[(x-\bar{x}^{n-1})^2+\tau^2]^{1/2}} = \frac{u^n - \bar{u}^{n-1}}{\tau}$$

where $u^n = u(\bullet, t^n)$,$\bar{x}^{n-1} = \bar{x}(t^{n-1})$ and $\bar{u}^{n-1} = \bar{u}(x, t^{n-1}) = u(\bar{x}^{n-1}, t^{n-1})$. Using the same decomposition for the enthalpy as in [9], we can approximate (1.1)-(1.2) by

$$a\frac{\theta^n - \bar{\theta}^{n-1}}{\tau} + \frac{w^n - \bar{w}^{n-1}}{\tau} - \Delta\theta^n = f^n \tag{1.7}$$

$$\epsilon\frac{w^n - w^{n-1}}{\tau} + \Lambda^{-1}(w^n) \ni \theta^n, \tag{1.8}$$

then we further approximate (1.7)-(1.8) by the finite element method and obtain a method which can be implemented directly on the computer.

This paper is organized as following: In section 2 we give the physical model of the continuous casting problem and its weak formulation; In section 3 we deduce the discrete scheme and discuss the existence, uniqueness and the numerical method of the discrete solution; In section 4 we prove a stabily result which leads to the convergence result in section 5; At last we report two numerical examples.

2. Continuous problem

Suppose Ω is a bounded domain in R^N and of the form $\Omega = \Gamma \times (0, l)$, where Γ is a bounded domain in R^{N-1} (Γ is simply a point when $N = 1$). Ω is the domain which is occupied by the mixture of solid-steel and liquid- steel. We put $Q = \Omega \times (0, T)(T > 0)$ and denote the enthalpy per unit volume by e, the relative temperature by θ, the liquid-steel concentration by χ (thus $\chi = 1$ in the liquid phase, $\chi = 0$ in the solid phase, $0 < \chi < 1$ in the mushy-region); We also denote the heat flux by q, the specific heat per unit by $C_p(\theta)$, the latent heat by L, the heat conductivity by $k(\theta)$, and $b(t)$ the velocity of the ingot in the x_N-direction.

The energy conservation law leads to

$$\frac{\partial e}{\partial t} + b(t)\frac{\partial e}{\partial x_N} = \nabla \bullet q \quad in\, D'(Q), \tag{2.1}$$

then from the Fourier's conduction law

$$q = -k(\theta)\nabla\theta \quad in\, Q, \tag{2.2}$$

and the constitutive relation

$$de = C_p(\theta)d\theta - Ld\chi \quad in\, Q, \tag{2.3}$$

we know

$$C_p(\theta)\left(\frac{\partial\theta}{\partial t} + b(t)\frac{\partial\theta}{\partial x_N}\right) + L\left(\frac{\partial\chi}{\partial t} + b(t)\frac{\partial\chi}{\partial x_N}\right) - \nabla(k(\theta)\nabla\theta) = 0 \tag{2,4}$$

holds in $D'(Q)$. Introduce the Kirchhoff's transformation

$$K : \theta \longrightarrow \hat{\theta} = \int_0^\theta k(\eta) d\eta, \quad \forall \theta \in R \tag{2.5}$$

then from $k(\theta) > 0$ we know K is invertiable, and thus we can define

$$\beta(\eta) = \int_0^\eta [C_p(K^{-1}(\xi))/k(K^{-1}(\xi))] d\xi, \quad \forall \eta \in R \tag{2.6}$$

therefore (2.4) can be written as

$$\left(\frac{\partial}{\partial t} + b(t)\frac{\partial}{\partial x_N}\right)[\beta(\hat{\theta}) + L\chi] - \Delta\hat{\theta} = 0 \tag{2.7}$$

in $D'(Q)$. Suppose H is the Heaviside graph, namely

$$H(\xi) = \begin{cases} 0, & \text{if } \xi < 0; \\ 0 \le \xi \le 1 & \text{if } \xi = 0; \\ 1, & \text{if } \xi > 0. \end{cases}$$

Introduce the equilibrium condition

$$\chi \in H(\theta), \quad in\, Q \tag{2.8}$$

and from $k(\theta) > 0$, we know that (2.8) is equivalent to

$$\chi \in H(\hat{\theta}) \quad in\, Q. \tag{2.9}$$

Therefore if we define a maximal monotone graph

$$\alpha(\eta) = \beta(\eta) + LH(\eta), \quad \forall \eta \in R \tag{2.10}$$

it is easy to see that (2.7),(2.9) are

$$\frac{\partial u}{\partial t} + b(t)\frac{\partial u}{\partial x_N} - \Delta\hat{\theta} = 0 \quad in\, D'(Q) \tag{2.11}$$

$$u \in \alpha(\hat{\theta}) \quad in\, Q. \tag{2.12}$$

For simplicity, we impose the following initial-boundary condition in order to make (2.11)-(2.12) being well-posed

$$\hat{\theta} = g(x,t) \quad on\, \partial\Omega \times (0,T) \tag{2.13}$$

$$u(x,0) = u_0(x) \quad on\, \Omega. \tag{2.14}$$

To give the weak formulation of (2.11)-(2.14), we denote $V = H^1(\Omega)$, V' = the dual space of V, and

$$_{V'}\langle Au, v\rangle_V = \int_\Omega \nabla u \bullet \nabla v dx \quad \forall u, v \in V.$$

In the sequel we also add a distributed heat source term f in (2.11) and assume that (here $\alpha_1, \alpha_2 > 0$)

$$\beta(\eta) = \begin{cases} \alpha_1\eta, & \text{if } \eta \geq 0; \\ \alpha_2\eta, & \text{if } \eta < 0. \end{cases}$$

If we suppose $u_0 \in V'$,$f \in L^2(0,T;V')$ and $G \in H^1(Q)$ satisfying $G\,|_{\partial\Omega\times(0,T)}= g$, then we can define the following weak problem:

Problem (P): Find $\theta \in L^2(0,T;V)$,$u \in H^1(0,T;V')$ such that

$$\frac{\partial u}{\partial t} + b(t)\frac{\partial u}{\partial x_N} + A\theta = f \quad in\, V',\ a.e.\, in\, (0,T) \tag{2.15}$$

$$_{V'}\langle u - \alpha(v), \theta - v\rangle_V \geq 0 \quad \forall v \in V,\ a.e.in\, (0,T) \tag{2.16}$$

$$\theta - G \in H_0^1(\Omega) \quad a.e.\, in\, (0,T) \tag{2.17}$$

$$u(x,0) = u_0(x) \quad in\, V'. \tag{2.18}$$

We remark that the above definition of the weak solution is equivalent to the definition in [10] and we will also prove the existence of the weak solution of (2.15)-(2.18) in section 5. Finally we remark that (2.12) and (2.16) is equivalent, because α is a maximal monotone graph.

3. Discrete Problem

In this section we will give the discrete scheme of the Problem (P). As we have already indicated in section 1, our method uses the ideas in [2],[9].

For positive constant a such that $a < min(\alpha_1, \alpha_2)$ (for example, $a = \frac{1}{2}min(\alpha_1, \alpha_2)$), as in [9], we define

$$w = u - a\theta \quad in\, Q \tag{3.1}$$

$$\Lambda(\eta) = \alpha(\eta) - a\eta, \quad \forall \eta \in R \tag{3.2}$$

thus Λ is also a maximal monotone graph and Λ^{-1} is a continuous function in R.

It is easy to see that function $\Phi : R \longrightarrow R$

$$\Phi(\eta) = \frac{1}{2(\alpha_2 - a)}\eta_-^2 + \frac{1}{2(\alpha_1 - a)}(\eta - L)_+^2 \tag{3.3}$$

is a weak lower semi-continuous and convex function having the subdifferential $\partial\Phi = \Lambda^{-1}$. Here $\eta_- = \min(\eta, 0)$ and $\eta_+ = \max(\eta, 0)$. From (3.1)-(3.2) we know (2.16) can be rewritten as

$$\begin{aligned} &u = a\theta + w \quad in\, Q \\ &w \in \Lambda(\theta). \end{aligned} \tag{3.4}$$

For any $\epsilon > 0$, as in [9], we will approximate the second equation of (3.4) by

$$\epsilon \frac{\partial w}{\partial t} + \Lambda^{-1}(w) = 0 \quad in\, Q. \tag{3.5}$$

We will make use of implicit difference scheme to discretize Problem (P) in time. Let us fix some positive integer M and let $\tau = T/M$ be the time step. For any $n = 1, 2, \ldots, M$,set $t^n = n\tau$,$I^n = [t^{n-1}, t^n]$ and $\partial Z^n = [Z^n - Z^{n-1}]/\tau$ for any given family $\{Z^n\}_{n=0}^M$. Moreover we set $Z^n = Z(x, t^n)$ for any function $Z(x,t)$ defined in Q. In order to deal with the term $b(t)\frac{\partial u}{\partial x_N}$ by characteristic finite element method, we first extend function u oddly with respect to the superplane $x_N = 0$ and write $\bar{x}^n = x - b^n\tau e_N$, where $e_N = (0, \ldots, 0, 1)^T \in R^N$ is a unit vector. Moreover we approximate $\frac{\partial u}{\partial t} + b(t)\frac{\partial u}{\partial x_N}$ by

$$\bar{\partial} u^n := \frac{u^n - \bar{u}^{n-1}}{\tau} = \frac{u(x, t^n) - u(\bar{x}^{n-1}, t^{n-1})}{\tau}.$$

In space we will use linear finite element discretization. Let $T_h = \{S_k\}_{k=1}^K$ be the triangulation of domain Ω, and for simplicity, let $\Omega = \cup\{S_k \mid k = 1, \ldots, K\}$. Further we let V_h be the linear finite element space and $\overset{\circ}{V}_h = V_h \cap H_0^1(\Omega)$. We denote by $\Pi_h\varphi$ the linear interpolate of any function $\varphi \in C^0(\bar{\Omega})$ and introduce the following quadrature formula

$$(\varphi, \psi)_h = \int_\Omega \Pi_h(\varphi\psi)dx \quad \forall \varphi, \psi \in C(\bar{\Omega})$$

as the approximation of the integral $(\varphi, \psi) = \int_\Omega \varphi\psi dx$. We also set $\|\varphi\|_h = (\varphi, \varphi)_h^{1/2}$. For any $\varphi, \psi \in V_h$, it is easy to prove the following facts (see [1])

$$\|\varphi\|_{L^2(\Omega)} \le \|\varphi\|_h \le C\|\varphi\|_{L^2(\Omega)} \tag{3.6}$$

$$|(\varphi, \psi)_h| \le C\|\varphi\|_{L^2(\Omega)}\|\psi\|_{L^2(\Omega)} \tag{3.7}$$

$$|(\varphi, \psi) - (\varphi, \psi)_h| \le Ch\|\varphi\|_{L^2(\Omega)}\|\nabla\psi\|_{L^2(\Omega)} \tag{3.8}$$

and with the triangle inequality

$$|(\varphi, \psi)_h| \le C\|\varphi\|_{V'}\|\psi\|_{H^1(\Omega)} + Ch\|\varphi\|_{L^2(\Omega)}\|\psi\|_{H^1(\Omega)}. \tag{3.9}$$

Now, let $\{P_j\}_{j=1}^{N'}$ be the interior nodes of the triangulation on Ω, $\{P_{N'+j}\}_{j=1}^{N^\partial}$ be the boundary nodes, and $\{\varphi_j\}_{j=1}^{\bar{N}}$ be the canonical bases of V_h, here $N' + N^\partial = \bar{N}$. We also set

$$\theta^0 = \alpha^{-1}(u^0), \ w^0 = u_0 - a\theta_0 \tag{3.10}$$

and impose following assumptions concerning the data:

(H1) The triangulation on Ω is quasi-uniform;

(H2) $u^0 \in L^2(\Omega)$ thus $\theta^0, w^0 \in L^2(\Omega)$;

(H3) $f \in H^1(0,T;L^2(\Omega))$;

(H4) $g \in C^{0,1}(\partial\Omega \times [0,T])$;

(H5) $b(t) \geq 0, b(t) \in C^1(R_+)$ and $\|b\|_{C^1(R_+)} \leq B$.

Since $g^n = g(x,t^n) \in C(\partial\Omega)$, we can set

$$\hat{g}^n = \sum_{j=1}^{N^\partial} g(P_{N'+j}, t^n)\varphi_{N'+j} \in V_h. \tag{3.11}$$

If we denote by E_h the L^2-projection operator from $L^2(\Omega)$ to V_h, we can introduce the following discrete problem.

Problem $(P_{\epsilon,h,\tau})$**:** For $n = 1,\ldots,M$,find $\Theta^n, W^n \in V_h$ such that

$$\Theta^0 = E_h\theta^0, \ W^0 = E_h w^0 \tag{3.12}$$

and for $n \geq 1$,

$$(a\bar{\partial}\Theta^n,\varphi)_h + (\bar{\partial}W^n,\varphi)_h + (\nabla\Theta^n,\nabla\varphi) = (f^n,\varphi)_h, \quad \forall\varphi \in \overset{\circ}{V}_h \tag{3.13}$$

$$\epsilon\,\bar{\partial}W^n + \Pi_h\Lambda^{-1}(W^n) = \Theta^n \quad on\,\Omega \tag{3.14}$$

$$\Theta^n - \hat{g}^n \in \overset{\circ}{V}_h \quad on\Omega. \tag{3.15}$$

In pratical computations, if θ^0, w^0 are smooth functions on Ω, we can set $\Theta^0 = \Pi_h\theta^0, W^0 = \Pi_h w^0$, and all the analysis in the sequel are still effective.

The unique solvability of nonlinear algebraic equations (3.12)-(3.15) is proved in following theorem.

Theorem 1. The solutions $\{\Theta^n\}_{n=1}^M, \{W^n\}_{n=1}^M$ of the Problem $(P_{\epsilon,h,\tau})$ are existent and unique.

Proof. First we note that Λ^{-1} is a increasing function and from (3.14) we get

$$W_j^n = \left(1 + \frac{\tau}{\epsilon}\Lambda^{-1}\right)^{-1} \left(\frac{\tau}{\epsilon}\Theta_j^n + W_j^{n-1}\right), \quad \forall j = 1, \ldots, \bar{N} \tag{3.16}$$

here $W_j^n = W^n(P_j)$, $\Theta_j^n = \Theta^n(P_j)$. Thus W_j^n is a increasing function of Θ_j^n. Therefore after substituting (3.16) into (3.13) and writing it as a nonlinear algebraic equations of $\{\Theta_j^n\}_{j=1}^{N'}$, we can prove that the obtained equations preserve unique solution $\{\Theta_j^n\}_{j=1}^{N'}$ by the method in [3] for the Stefan problem. ////

In pratical computation, we use alternative iteration methods to solve equations (3.13)-(3.15), that is, for some fixed $n \geq 1$,first set $\Theta^{n,0} = \Theta^{n-1}$ and substitute it into the right-hand of (3.14) and get $W^{n,0}$, then substitute$W^{n,0}$ into (3.13) to obtain $\Theta^{n,1}$; secondly set $\Theta^{n,0} = \Theta^{n,1}$ as a starting point and repeat above procedures. When the solutions $\Theta^{n,k}, \Theta^{n,k+1}$ of two iterations satisfy some stopping rule, for example,

$$\|\Theta^{n,k} - \Theta^{n,k+1}\|_{C(\bar{\Omega})} \leq \epsilon,$$

we finish the iteration and go to next time-step.

When W^n in (3.13) is known, (3.13) and (3.15) are standard finite element solution equations for a heat equation; When the right-hand Θ^n of (3.14) is $\Theta^{n,k}$ known, in order to get $\Theta^{n,k+1}$, (3.14) is eqivalent to

$$\frac{\epsilon}{\tau}W_j^n + \Lambda^{-1}(W_j^n) = \frac{\epsilon}{\tau}W_j^{n-1} + \Theta_j^{n,k}, \quad \forall j = 1, \ldots, \bar{N}$$

which is a one-dimensional nonlinear equations which can easily be solved on computer.

4. A Priori Estimates

In this section we will prove *a priori* estimates of the solution of Problem $(P_{\epsilon,h,\tau})$ which is the basis of the convergence theorem in next section. At first we require following lemma which is the generalization of a one-dimensional result in [2].

Lemma 1. For any $\eta \in L^2(\Omega)$, set

$$\bar{\eta}(x) = \begin{cases} \eta(x', x_N - b\tau), & \text{if } x \in \Gamma \times [b\tau, l); \\ \eta(x', b\tau - x_N), & \text{if } x \in \Gamma \times (0, b\tau). \end{cases} \tag{4.1}$$

where $x' = (x_1, \ldots, x_{N-1}) \in \Gamma$, then we have

$$\|\eta - \bar{\eta}\|_{H^{-1}(\Omega)} \leq C\tau\|\eta\|_{L^2(\Omega)}, \tag{4.2}$$

where C is a constant, only depending on $\max|b| = B$.

Proof. For any $\varphi \in C_0^\infty(\Omega)$, we have

$$\begin{aligned}\int_\Omega (\eta - \bar\eta)\varphi\, dx &= \int_\Gamma\int_0^l \eta\varphi\, dx - \int_\Gamma\int_0^{b\tau} \bar\eta\varphi\, dx - \int_\Gamma\int_{b\tau}^l \bar\eta\varphi\, dx \\ &= \int_\Gamma\int_0^{l-b\tau} \eta[\varphi(x',x_N) - \varphi(x',x_N+b\tau)]\, dx_N\, dx' \\ &\quad + \int_\Gamma\int_{l-b\tau}^l \eta\varphi\, dx - \int_\Gamma\int_0^{b\tau} \eta\varphi(x',b\tau - x_N)\, dx_N\, dx'\end{aligned} \tag{4.3}$$

here we have used (4.1) and the formula of variable substitution. In the following we estimate the right side of (4.3) term by term. At first

$$\begin{aligned}&\int_\Gamma\int_0^{l-b\tau} |\varphi(x',x_N) - \varphi(x',x_N+b\tau)|^2\, dx_N\, dx' \\ =&\int_\Gamma\int_0^{l-b\tau} \left|\int_0^{b\tau} \frac{\partial\varphi}{\partial x_N}(x',x_N+\xi)\, d\xi\right|^2 dx_N\, dx' \\ \le& B\tau\int_\Gamma\int_0^{l-b\tau}\int_0^{b\tau} \left|\frac{\partial\varphi}{\partial x_N}(x',x_N+\xi)\right|^2 d\xi dx_N dx' \\ =&B\tau\int_0^{b\tau}\int_\Gamma\int_\xi^{l-b\tau+\xi} \left|\frac{\partial\varphi}{\partial x_N}\right|^2 dx_N dx' d\xi \\ \le&(B\tau)^2\|\varphi\|^2_{H^1(\Omega)}.\end{aligned} \tag{4.4}$$

Because $\varphi \in C_0^\infty(\Omega)$,

$$\begin{aligned}\int_\Gamma\int_{l-b\tau}^l |\varphi|^2\, dx_N\, dx' &= \int_\Gamma\int_{l-b\tau}^l |\varphi - \varphi(x',l)|^2\, dx_N\, dx' \\ &= \int_\Gamma\int_{l-b\tau}^l \left|\int_{x_N}^l \frac{\partial\varphi}{\partial x_N}(x',\xi)\, d\xi\right|^2 dx_N\, dx' \\ &\le (B\tau)\int_\Gamma\int_{l-b\tau}^l\int_{x_N}^l \left|\frac{\partial\varphi}{\partial x_N}(x',\xi)\right|^2 d\xi dx_N dx' \\ &\le (B\tau)^2\|\varphi\|^2_{H^1(\Omega)}.\end{aligned} \tag{4.5}$$

With the same reason, we get

$$\int_\Gamma\int_0^{b\tau} |\varphi(x',b\tau - x_N)|^2\, dx_N\, dx' \le (B\tau)^2\|\varphi\|^2_{H^1(\Omega)}. \tag{4.6}$$

Then because of the fact that $C_0^\infty(\Omega)$ is dense in $H_0^1(\Omega)$ and (4.3)-(4.6), one can easily get (4.2). ////

Lemma 2. Suppose $\eta \in H_0^1(\Omega)$, the defintion of $\bar{\eta}$ is the same as in Lemma 1, then we have

$$\|\eta - \bar{\eta}\|_{L^2(\Omega)} \leq C\tau \|\eta\|_{H^1(\Omega)}, \tag{4.7}$$

where C is the constant depending only on B.

Proof. Using the formula of the variable substitution, it is easy to prove that

$$\|\bar{\eta}\|_{H^1(\Omega)} \leq C\|\eta\|_{H^1(\Omega)}, \quad \forall \eta \in H_0^1(\Omega) \tag{4.8}$$

then

$$\begin{aligned}\|\eta - \bar{\eta}\|^2_{L^2(\Omega)} =& 2\int_\Omega \eta(\eta - \bar{\eta})\,dx + \int_\Omega (\bar{\eta} - \eta)(\bar{\eta} + \eta)\,dx \\ \leq& 2\|\eta - \bar{\eta}\|_{H^{-1}(\Omega)}\|\eta\|_{H^1(\Omega)} + \|\eta - \bar{\eta}\|_{H^{-1}(\Omega)}\|\eta + \bar{\eta}\|_{H^1(\Omega)} \\ \leq& C\tau\|\eta\|_{L^2(\Omega)}\|\eta\|_{H^1(\Omega)},\end{aligned}$$

which is (4.7). ////

Remark 1. From the proof of Lemma 1 and Lemma 2, we see that if we set

$$V_1 = \{\eta \in H^1(\Omega) | \quad \eta|_{x_N=0} = \eta|_{x_N=l} = 0\},$$

then in fact we have shown

$$\|\eta - \bar{\eta}\|_{V_1'} \leq C\tau\|\eta\|_{L^2(\Omega)} \quad \forall \eta \in L^2(\Omega)$$

$$\|\eta - \bar{\eta}\|_{L^2(\Omega)} \leq C\tau\|\eta\|_{H^1(\Omega)} \quad \forall \eta \in V_1.$$

Lemma 3. (3.14) is equivalent to

$$\epsilon(\partial W^n, v)_h + (\Lambda^{-1}(W^n), v)_h = (\Theta^n, v)_h, \quad \forall v \in V_h \tag{4.9}$$

Proof. If we set $\gamma(W^n) = (\epsilon/\tau)W^n + \Lambda^{-1}(W^n)$ and $C^n = \Theta^n + (\epsilon/\tau)(W^{n-1}) \in V_h$, then we can reformulate (4.9) as

$$(\gamma(W^n), v)_h = (C^n, v)_h. \quad \forall v \in V_h \tag{4.10}$$

Since $(\varphi_i, \varphi_j)_h = (\int_\Omega \varphi_i)\delta_{ij}$, it is not difficult to show

$$(C^n, \varphi_i)_h = C^n(P_i)\int_\Omega \varphi_i. \quad \forall i = 1, \ldots, \bar{N}$$

Furthermore, we have

$$\begin{aligned}(\gamma(W^n), \varphi_i)_h =& \int_\Omega \sum_{j=1}^{\bar{N}} [\gamma(W^n(P_j))\varphi_i(P_j)]\,\varphi_j(x) \\ =& \gamma(W^n(P_i))\int_\Omega \varphi_i(x), \quad \forall i = 1, \ldots, \bar{N}\end{aligned}$$

Now from these two equalities and (4.10), we know

$$\frac{\epsilon}{\tau}W^n(P_j) + \Lambda^{-1}(W^n(P_j)) = \Theta^n(P_j) + \frac{\epsilon}{\tau}W^{n-1}(P_j), \quad \forall j = 1, \ldots, \bar{N} \tag{4.11}$$

which is eqivalent to (3.14). ////

Lemma 4. For any $v \in V_h$, we have

$$\int_\Omega \Pi_h \Phi(v)\, dx \geq \int_\Omega \Phi(v)\, dx. \tag{4.12}$$

Proof. Since Φ is a convex function and $\sum_{i=1}^{\bar{N}} \varphi_i(x) = 1$, we know

$$\begin{aligned}\int_\Omega \Phi(v)\, dx &= \int_\Omega \Phi\left(\sum_{i=1}^{\bar{N}} v(P_i)\varphi_i(x)\right) dx \\ &\leq \int_\Omega \sum_{i=1}^{\bar{N}} \varphi_i(x)\Phi(v(P_i))\, dx \\ &= \int_\Omega \Pi_h \Phi(v)\, dx, \quad \forall v \in V_h\end{aligned}$$

This proves (4.12). ////

Theorem 2. If (H1)-(H5) are satisfied, then the solutions $\{\Theta^n\}_{n=1}^M, \{W^n\}_{n=1}^M$ of the Problem $(P_{\epsilon,h,\tau})$ have the estimates

$$\begin{aligned}\max_{1\leq n\leq M} \|\Theta^n\|^2_{L^2(\Omega)} + \max_{1\leq n\leq M} \|W^n\|^2_{L^2(\Omega)} + \sum_{n=1}^M \|\Theta^n - \Theta^{n-1}\|^2_{L^2(\Omega)} \\ + \sum_{n=1}^M \tau\|\Theta^n\|^2_{H^1(\Omega)} + \epsilon \sum_{n=1}^M \tau\|\partial W^n\|^2_{L^2(\Omega)} \leq C,\end{aligned} \tag{4.13}$$

where C indepentent of ϵ, h, τ.

Proof. If we set $\hat{g}^n$ as in (3.11), then $\hat{\Theta}^n = \Theta^n - \hat{g}^n \in \overset{\circ}{V}_h$, and (3.13) can be rewritten as

$$(a\bar{\partial}\hat{\Theta}^n, \varphi)_h + (\bar{\partial}W^n, \varphi)_h + (\nabla\hat{\Theta}^n, \nabla\varphi) = (f^n, \varphi)_h - (a\bar{\partial}\hat{g}^n, \varphi)_h - (\nabla\hat{g}^n, \nabla\varphi). \tag{4.14}$$

We take $\varphi = \tau\hat{\Theta}^n$ in (4.14) and set $v = \tau\partial W^n \in V_h$ in (4.9), than we sum for $n = 1, \ldots, m$, for any positive integer $m \leq M$, we have

$$
\begin{aligned}
&\sum_{n=1}^{m} a\tau(\bar{\partial}\hat{\Theta}^n, \hat{\Theta}^n)_h + \sum_{n=1}^{m} \tau(\bar{\partial}W^n, \hat{\Theta}^n)_h + \sum_{n=1}^{m} \tau\|\nabla\hat{\Theta}^n\|^2_{L^2(\Omega)} \\
&\quad + \epsilon \sum_{n=1}^{m} \tau\|\partial W^n\|^2_h + \sum_{n=1}^{m} \tau(\Lambda^{-1}(W^n), \partial W^n)_h \\
&= \sum_{n=1}^{m} \tau(f^n, \hat{\Theta}^n)_h + \sum_{n=1}^{m} \tau(\Theta^n, \partial W^n)_h - \sum_{n=1}^{m} a\tau(\bar{\partial}\hat{g}^n, \hat{\Theta}^n)_h \\
&\quad - \sum_{n=1}^{m} \tau(\nabla\hat{g}^n, \nabla\hat{\Theta}^n)
\end{aligned}
\tag{4.15}
$$

which we write as (I) + ... + (V) = (VI) + ... + (IX). Now we estimate the terms (I)-(IX).

$$
\begin{aligned}
(\mathrm{I}) &= \sum_{n=1}^{m} a(\hat{\Theta}^n - \hat{\Theta}^{n-1}, \hat{\Theta}^n)_h - \sum_{n=1}^{m} (\overline{\hat{\Theta}^{n-1}} - \hat{\Theta}^{n-1}, \hat{\Theta}^n)_h \\
&= (\mathrm{I})_1 + (\mathrm{I})_2.
\end{aligned}
$$

It is easy to show

$$
(\mathrm{I})_1 \geq \frac{a}{2}\|\hat{\Theta}^m\|^2_{L^2(\Omega)} + \frac{a}{2}\sum_{n=1}^{m} \|\hat{\Theta}^n - \hat{\Theta}^{n-1}\|^2_{L^2(\Omega)} - \frac{a}{2}\|\hat{\Theta}^o\|^2_h \tag{4.16}
$$

By (3.9),Lemma 1,Lemma 2 and the inverse estimates of finite elements we have

$$
\begin{aligned}
(\mathrm{I})_2 &\leq C\sum_{n=1}^{m} \left(h\|\overline{\hat{\Theta}^{n-1}} - \hat{\Theta}^{n-1}\|_{L^2(\Omega)} + \|\overline{\hat{\Theta}^{n-1}} - \hat{\Theta}^{n-1}\|_{H^{-1}(\Omega)}\right) \|\hat{\Theta}^n\|_{H^1(\Omega)} \\
&\leq C\sum_{n=1}^{m} \tau \left(\|\hat{\Theta}^{n-1}\|_{L^2(\Omega)} + h\|\hat{\Theta}^{n-1}\|_{H^1(\Omega)}\right) \|\hat{\Theta}^n\|_{H^1(\Omega)} \\
&\leq C\sum_{n=1}^{m} \tau\|\hat{\Theta}^{n-1}\|_{L^2(\Omega)}\|\Theta^n\|_{H^1(\Omega)}.
\end{aligned}
\tag{4.17}
$$

Combine (4.16) with (4.17), it follows

$$
(\mathrm{I}) \geq \frac{a}{2}\|\hat{\Theta}^m\|^2_{L^2(\Omega)} + \frac{a}{2}\sum_{n=1}^{m} \|\hat{\Theta}^n - \hat{\Theta}^{n-1}\|^2_{L^2(\Omega)} - C\sum_{n=1}^{m} \tau\|\hat{\Theta}^{n-1}\|_{L^2(\Omega)}\|\hat{\Theta}^n\|_{H^1(\Omega)} - C. \tag{4.18}
$$

It is easy to see from (3.3) that for any $\psi \in L^2(\Omega)$, there exist constants C_1, C_2 such that

$$
\int_\Omega \Phi(\psi)\, dx \geq C_1\|\psi\|^2_{L^2(\Omega)} - C_2, \tag{4.19}
$$

then, since Λ^{-1} is the subdifferential of Φ , we obtain

$$\begin{aligned}(\mathrm{V}) &= \sum_{n=1}^{m}(\Lambda^{-1}(W^n), W^n - W^{n-1})_h \\ &\geq \sum_{n=1}^{m}\int_\Omega \Pi_h\left[\Phi(W^n) - \Phi(W^{n-1})\right]\, dx \\ &\geq C_1\|W^m\|^2_{L^2(\Omega)} - C_2,\end{aligned} \tag{4.20}$$

here we have used Lemma 4. From (3.7) and (H3), we know

$$|(\mathrm{VI})| \leq \delta\sum_{n=1}^{m}\tau\|\hat{\Theta}^n\|^2_{L^2(\Omega)} + C/\delta. \tag{4.21}$$

From (H4), similar to the argument in (4.17), we have

$$|(\mathrm{VIII})| \leq \delta\sum_{n=1}^{m}\tau\|\hat{\Theta}^n\|^2_{H^1(\Omega)} + C/\delta, \tag{4.22}$$

and

$$|(\mathrm{IX})| \leq \delta\sum_{n=1}^{m}\tau\|\hat{\Theta}^n\|^2_{H^1(\Omega)} + C/\delta. \tag{4.23}$$

At least, we have

$$\begin{aligned}(\mathrm{X}) &= (\mathrm{VII}) - (\mathrm{II}) \\ &= \sum_{n=1}^{m}\tau(\hat{g}^n, \partial W^n)_h + \sum_{n=1}^{m}(\bar{W}^{n-1} - W^{n-1}, \hat{\Theta}^n)_h \\ &= (\mathrm{X})_1 + (\mathrm{X})_2.\end{aligned} \tag{4.24}$$

From (H4) and the formula of the discrete integration by parts, we know

$$\begin{aligned}|(\mathrm{X})_1| &= |(\hat{g}^m, W^m)_h - (\hat{g}^1, W^0)_h - \sum_{n=2}^{m}(W^{n-1}, \hat{g}^n - \hat{g}^{n-1})_h| \\ &\leq \delta\|W^m\|^2_{L^2(\Omega)} + \frac{1}{2}\sum_{n=1}^{m}\tau\|W^{n-1}\|^2_{L^2(\Omega)} + C/\delta.\end{aligned} \tag{4.25}$$

Again with the argument similar to that in (4.17), we get

$$|(\mathrm{X})_2| \leq \delta\sum_{n=1}^{m}\tau\|\hat{\Theta}^n\|^2_{H^1(\Omega)} + (C/\delta)\sum_{n=1}^{m}\tau\|W^{n-1}\|^2_{L^2(\Omega)}. \tag{4.26}$$

Taking δ properly small and combining (4.15),(4.18),(4.20)-(4.26), we finally get

$$\begin{aligned}&\|\hat{\Theta}^m\|^2_{L^2(\Omega)} + \|W^m\|^2_{L^2(\Omega)} + \sum_{n=1}^{m} \|\hat{\Theta}^n - \hat{\Theta}^{n-1}\|^2_{L^2(\Omega)} \\ &+ \sum_{n=1}^{m} \tau \|\hat{\Theta}^n\|^2_{H^1(\Omega)} + \epsilon \sum_{n=1}^{m} \tau \|\partial W^n\|^2_{L^2(\Omega)} \\ \leq & C + C\sum_{n=1}^{m} \tau \|\hat{\Theta}^{n-1}\|^2_{L^2(\Omega)} + C\sum_{n=1}^{m} \tau \|W^{n-1}\|^2_{L^2(\Omega)}.\end{aligned}$$

By using the discrete Gronwall's inequality, we know (4.13) holds for $\hat{\Theta}^n$, then from (H4), it follows that (4.13) holds also for Θ^n. ////

5. Convergence Theorem

In this section we will prove that the solution of the Problem $(P_{\epsilon,h,\tau})$ converges to the solution of Problem (P) as $\epsilon, h, \tau \longrightarrow 0$. At first we prove

Lemma 5. Under the conditions of Theorem 2, and if we suppose that $h^2/\tau \leq C, h^2/\epsilon \leq C$, we have

$$\sum_{n=1}^{M} \tau \|\partial E^n\|^2_{H^{-1}(\Omega)} \leq C, \tag{5.1}$$

where C independent of ϵ, h, τ and $E^n = a\Theta^n + W^n$.

Proof. It is not difficult to prove this lemma from (3.13) by using Theorem 2 and standard estimate methods. We omit the details here. ////

In the sequel we denote by $\theta_{\epsilon,h,\tau}$ the function obtained by linear interpolation in time of $\{\Theta^n\}_{n=1}^M$ and set $\hat{\theta}_{\epsilon,h,\tau}(x,t) = \Theta^n(x)$ in each time interval I^n; We define $w_{\epsilon,h,\tau}, \hat{w}_{\epsilon,h,\tau}, \hat{f}_\tau$ in the same way. We also set $u_{\epsilon,h,\tau} = a\theta_{\epsilon,h,\tau} + w_{\epsilon,h,\tau}$ and $\hat{u}_{\epsilon,h,\tau} = \alpha\hat{\theta}_{\epsilon,h,\tau} + \hat{w}_{\epsilon,h,\tau}$, then from Theorem 2 and Lemma 5, it follows that

$$\theta_{\epsilon,h,\tau}, \hat{\theta}_{\epsilon,h,\tau} \quad \text{bounded in} \quad L^\infty(0,T;L^2(\Omega)) \cap L^2(0,T;H^1(\Omega)), \tag{5.2}$$

$$w_{\epsilon,h,\tau}, \hat{w}_{\epsilon,h,\tau} \quad \text{bounded in} \quad L^\infty(0,T;L^2(\Omega)), \tag{5.3}$$

$$u_{\epsilon,h,\tau} \quad \text{bounded in} \quad H^1(0,T;H^{-1}(\Omega)). \tag{5.4}$$

Now we are in the position to show the convergence of $\{\theta_{\epsilon,h,\tau}, w_{\epsilon,h,\tau}\}$ as $\epsilon, h, \tau \longrightarrow 0$. We will conside only the cases where $\epsilon, h, \tau \longrightarrow 0$ such that the relations

$$h^2/\tau \leq C, \quad h^2/\epsilon \leq C, \quad \tau^2/\epsilon \longrightarrow 0 \tag{5.5}$$

hold at the same time. The restriction (5.5) can be easily satisfied in pratical situations. All the limits in the rest of this paper are taken in the sense of (5.5),we will not mention that all the time. The first two restrictions in (5.5) come from Lemma 5, while the third restriction in (5.5) is the requirement of the next lemma.

Lemma 6. If

$$\theta_{\epsilon,h,\tau}, w_{\epsilon,h,\tau}, u_{\epsilon,h,\tau} \rightharpoonup \theta, w, u \quad in\, L^2(Q)$$

and

$$\hat{\theta}_{\epsilon,h,\tau}, \hat{w}_{\epsilon,h,\tau}, \hat{u}_{\epsilon,h,\tau} \rightharpoonup \hat{\theta}, \hat{w}, \hat{u} \quad in\, L^2(Q)$$

hold at the same time, then we have

$$\hat{\theta} = \theta, \quad \hat{w} = w, \quad \hat{u} = u. \tag{5.6}$$

Proof. By direct calculations, we have

$$\|\hat{w}_{\epsilon,h,\tau} - w_{\epsilon,h,\tau}\|^2_{L^2(Q)} = \frac{\tau^2}{3} \sum_{n=1}^{M} \tau \|\partial W^n\|^2_{L^2(\Omega)} \leq \frac{\tau^2}{3}(C/\epsilon) = C\frac{\tau^2}{\epsilon},$$

which implies $\hat{w} = w$. With the same argument, we can show $\hat{\theta} = \theta$ and $\hat{u} = u$. ////

Theorem 3. Under the conditions (H1)-(H5), there exist θ, w such that after extracting subsequences, as $\epsilon, h, \tau \longrightarrow 0$ in the sense of (5.5)

$$\theta_{\epsilon,h,\tau}, \hat{\theta}_{\epsilon,h,\tau} \rightharpoonup \theta, \quad in\, L^2(0,T;H^1(\Omega)), \tag{5.7}$$

$$w_{\epsilon,h,\tau}, \hat{w}_{\epsilon,h,\tau} \rightharpoonup w, \quad in\, L^2(0,T;L^2(\Omega)), \tag{5.8}$$

$$u_{\epsilon,h,\tau} \longrightarrow u, \quad in L^2(0,Y;H^{-1}(\Omega)), \tag{5.9}$$

then $\{\theta, w\}$ is the solution of Problem (P). Moreover if the solution of Problem (P) is unique, then the solution of Problem $(P_{\epsilon,h,\tau})$ is convergent to the unique solution of Problem (P).

Proof. By (5.2)-(5.4) and Aubin's Lemma (see [6],P.197) which says that a bounded set both in $L^2(0,T;L^2(\Omega))$ and $H^1(0,T;H^{-1}(\Omega))$ is relatively compact in $L^2(0,T;H^{-1}(\Omega))$, we know that (5.7)-(5.9) hold. Now we show that θ, w is the solution of Problem (P).

For any function $h(x,t)$ defined in Q, we denote by γ_τ the shift operator: $\gamma_\tau h = h(x, t-\tau)$ and set $Q_\tau = \Omega \times (\tau, T)$, then (3.13)-(3.14)(see also Lemma 3) can be written as

$$\begin{aligned}\left(\frac{\partial u_{\epsilon,h,\tau}}{\partial t}, \varphi\right)_h + \frac{1}{\tau}\left(\gamma_\tau \hat{u}_{\epsilon,h,\tau} - \overline{\gamma_\tau \hat{u}_{\epsilon,h,\tau}}, \varphi\right)_h + \left(\nabla \hat{\theta}_{\epsilon,h,\tau}, \nabla\varphi\right) \\ = \left(\hat{f}_\tau, \varphi\right)_h \quad \forall \varphi \in \overset{\circ}{V}_h \quad \text{a.e. in}\,(0,T)\end{aligned} \tag{5.10}$$

and

$$\epsilon(\frac{\partial w_{\epsilon,h,\tau}}{\partial t}, v)_h + (\Lambda^{-1}(\hat{w}_{\epsilon,h,\tau}), v)_h = (\hat{\theta}_{\epsilon,h,\tau}, v)_h \quad \forall v \in V_h \quad \text{a.e. in}\,(0,T). \tag{5.11}$$

Now we set $\eta_{\epsilon,h,\tau} = \gamma_\tau \hat{u}_{\epsilon,h,\tau}$, then for any interval $(t_1, t_2) \subset (0, T)$ and any $\varphi \in C_0^\infty(\Omega)$,

$$\begin{aligned}
&\int_{t_1}^{t_2} \frac{1}{\tau} \left(\eta_{\epsilon,h,\tau} - \overline{\eta_{\epsilon,h,\tau}}, \varphi\right) dt \\
=&\int_{t_1}^{t_2} \left\{ \frac{1}{\tau} \left[\int_\Gamma \int_0^{l-\gamma_\tau \hat{b}_\tau \tau} \eta_{\epsilon,h,\tau} \left(\varphi(x', x_N) - \varphi(x', x_N + \gamma_\tau \hat{b}_\tau \tau) \right) \right] dx_N dx' \right. \\
&\left. + \int_\Gamma \int_{l-\gamma_\tau \hat{b}_\tau \tau}^{l} \eta_{\epsilon,h,\tau} \varphi \, dx - \int_\Gamma \int_o^{\gamma_\tau \hat{b}_\tau \tau} \eta_{\epsilon,h,\tau} \varphi(x', \gamma_\tau \hat{b}_\tau \tau - x_N) \, dx_N dx' \right\} dt \\
=&(\mathrm{XI})_1 + (\mathrm{XI})_2 + (\mathrm{XI})_3.
\end{aligned} \tag{5.12}$$

At first, from the continuity of integration we have

$$\begin{aligned}
|(\mathrm{XI})_2| \le C \int_{t_1}^{t_2} \left[\int_\Gamma \int_{l-\gamma_\tau \hat{b}_\tau \tau}^{l} |\eta_{\epsilon,h,\tau}|^2 \right]^{1/2} \left[\int_\Gamma \int_{l-\gamma_\tau \hat{b}_\tau \tau}^{l} |\varphi|^2 \, dx \right]^{1/2} dt \\
\longrightarrow 0 \quad \text{as } \epsilon, \mathrm{h}, \tau \longrightarrow 0.
\end{aligned} \tag{5.13}$$

Similiarly

$$|(\mathrm{XI})_3| \longrightarrow 0, \quad \text{as } \epsilon, \mathrm{h}, \tau \longrightarrow 0. \tag{5.14}$$

But

$$\begin{aligned}
(\mathrm{XI})_1 =& - \int_{t_1}^{t_2} \int_\Gamma \int_0^{l-\gamma_\tau \hat{b}_\tau \tau} \eta_{\epsilon,h,\tau} \left(\frac{1}{\tau} \int_0^{\gamma_\tau \hat{b}_\tau \tau} \frac{\partial \varphi}{\partial x_N}(x', x_N + \zeta) \, d\zeta \right) dx \, dt \\
&\to - \int_{t_1}^{t_2} b(t) \left(u, \frac{\partial \varphi}{\partial x_N} \right) dt.
\end{aligned} \tag{5.15}$$

We deduce from (5.12)-(5.15)

$$\int_{t_1}^{t_2} \frac{1}{\tau} \left(\gamma_\tau \hat{u}_{\epsilon,h,\tau} - \overline{\gamma_\tau \hat{u}_{\epsilon,h,\tau}}, \varphi \right) dt \longrightarrow \int_{t_1}^{t_2} b(t) \left(u, \frac{\partial \varphi}{\partial x_N} \right) dt, \tag{5.16}$$

for any $\varphi \in C_0^\infty(\Omega)$ and any $(t_1, t_2) \subset (0, T)$. If we note the approximate property of the functions in $\overset{\circ}{V}_h$ with respect to the functions in $C_0^\infty(\Omega)$, when we let $\epsilon, h, \tau \longrightarrow 0$ in (5.10), sine the other terms are commen convergent results, we have

$$\begin{aligned}
&\int_{t_1}^{t_2} \left[\left(\frac{\partial u}{\partial t}, \varphi \right) - b(t) \left(u, \frac{\partial \varphi}{\partial x_N} \right) + (\nabla \theta, \nabla \varphi) \right] dt \\
=& \int_{t_1}^{t_2} (f, \varphi) \, dt, \quad \forall \varphi \in C_0^\infty(\Omega), \, \forall (t_1, t_2) \subset (0, T),
\end{aligned}$$

which leads to (2.15). In order to prove (2.16), from $\Lambda^{-1} = \partial\Phi$ we know that (5.11) is equivalent to

$$\int_{Q_\tau} \Pi_h \left[\epsilon \frac{\partial w_{\epsilon,h,\tau}}{\partial t}(\hat{w}_{\epsilon,h,\tau} - v_{h,\tau}) + (\Phi(\hat{w}_{\epsilon,h,\tau}) - \Phi(v_{h,\tau})) - \hat{\theta}_{\epsilon,h,\tau}(\hat{w}_{\epsilon,h,\tau} - v_{h,\tau})\right] \leq 0, \quad (5.17)$$

for any $v \in C^0(0,T;L^2(\Omega))$, here $v_{h,\tau} = E_h v^n$ in each time interval I^n.

Since by (4.13)

$$\epsilon^{1/2}\|\frac{\partial w_{\epsilon,h,\tau}}{\partial t}\|_{L^2(Q)} \leq C$$

we have

$$\liminf_{\epsilon,h,\tau\to 0} \quad \epsilon \int_{Q_\tau} \Pi_h \left[\frac{\partial w_{\epsilon,h,\tau}}{\partial t}(\hat{w}_{\epsilon,h,\tau} - v_{h,\tau})\right] dx\,dt = 0. \quad (5.18)$$

It is obvious from the weak lower semi-continuity and Lemma 4

$$\liminf_{\epsilon,h,\tau\to 0} \int_{Q_\tau} \Pi_h[\Phi(\hat{w}_{\epsilon,h,\tau}) - \Phi(v_{h,\tau})]\,dx\,dt \geq \int_Q [\Phi(w) - \Phi(v)]\,dx\,dt. \quad (5.19)$$

Since (5.7)-(5.9), we know

$$\begin{aligned} -\liminf_{\epsilon,h,\tau\to 0} \int_{Q_\tau} \hat{\theta}_{\epsilon,h,\tau}\hat{w}_{\epsilon,h,\tau} &= \liminf_{\epsilon,h,\tau\to 0} \quad [-\int_{Q_\tau} \hat{\theta}_{\epsilon,h,\tau}\hat{u}_{\epsilon,h,\tau} + a\int_{Q_\tau} \hat{\theta}^2_{\epsilon,h,\tau}] \\ &\geq -\int_Q \theta u + a\int_Q \theta^2 = -\int_Q \theta w. \end{aligned} \quad (5.20)$$

From (5.17)-(5.20), we know

$$\int_Q [\Phi(w) - \Phi(v)] - \int_Q \theta[w - v] \leq 0, \quad \forall v \in C^0(0,T;L^2(\Omega))$$

which is equivalent to (2.16). ////

Finally we remark that above discussions hold for general nonlinear enthalpy if (4.19) holds.

6. Numerical Examples

In following examples we always set $L = 1, b(t) = 0.5, \alpha_1 = \alpha_2 = 1$, and the triangulation is uniform. The first one-dimensional example shows that our convergence rate is greater that 0.5 which is the same as that in [9]; and for the second two-dimensional example we present the details of the computed results. In our computations we utilized the software system "Finite Element Programm Automatic Generator" which was created by G.-P. Liang. Our computations were performed on AST/286.

If $E_\theta^h = \left[\sum_{n=1}^{M} \tau \|\Theta^n - \theta^n\|^2_{L^2(\Omega)}\right]^{1/2}$ is the discrete solution computed with the parameter h, then from the relation $E_\theta^h = Ch^p$ it follows that $p = \log[E_\theta^{h_2}/E_\theta^{h_1}]/\log[h_1/h_2]$.

Example 1. Let $\Omega = (0,2), T = 0.2$. The exact solution is

$$\theta = \begin{cases} e^{\Phi(x,t)} - 1, & \text{if } \Phi(x,t) \le 0; \\ 2[e^{\Phi(x,t)} - 1], & \text{if } \Phi(x,t) > 0, \end{cases}$$

where $\Phi(x,t) = -x + 1.5t + 1 = 0$ is the free boundary. The following table shows the result computed by taking $\epsilon = h, \tau = h^{3/2}$.

NX	L^2-error	p
6	0.23285	
12	0.15851	0.555
24	0.09675	0.712
48	0.06061	0.675
96	0.03791	0.677
192	0.02435	0.639

Example 2. let $\Omega = (0,1) \times (0,0.5), T = 0.5$. The exact solution is

$$\theta = \begin{cases} e^{\Phi(x,y,t)} - 1, & \text{if } \Phi(x,y,t) \le 0; \\ 2[e^{\Phi(x,y,t)} - 1], & \text{if } \Phi(x,y,t) > 0, \end{cases}$$

where $\Phi(x,y,t) = -x - y + 0.5t + 0.6$. The increment in x and y direction is 0.05 and the time step is 0.05. NN is the alternative iteration number such that the L^∞-norm of the difference between two nonlinear iterations is less than 0.001. A-error is the absolute error $\sum_{j=1}^{\bar N} |\Theta_j^n - \theta_j^n|^2$. R-error is the relative error $\sum_{j=1}^{\bar N} |\Theta_j^n - \theta_j^n|^2 / \sum_{j=1}^{\bar N} |\Theta_j^n|^2$. L-error is the L^2-norm $\|\Theta^n - \theta^n\|^2_{L^2(\Omega)}$. At least T-error is the total error $\left[\sum_{n=1}^{M} \tau \|\Theta^n - \theta^n\|^2_{L^2(\Omega)}\right]^{1/2}$.

Time	NN	A-error	R-error	L-error
0.05	3	0.28140	0.00290	0.00259
0.10	4	0.49978	0.00444	0.00469
0.15	4	0.54777	0.00381	0.00514
0.20	4	0.49416	0.00251	0.00453
0.25	4	0.44205	0.00156	0.00401
0.30	4	0.49827	0.00120	0.00452
0.35	5	0.67756	0.00111	0.00621
0.40	5	0.98696	0.00111	0.00915
0.45	5	1.35799	0.00105	0.01280
0.50	5	1.84396	0.00100	0.01756
T-error = 0.05966				

7. Acknowledgment

This paper is a part of the author's thesis for his Master Degree of the Institute of Mathematics, Academia Sinica, Beijing, China. The author would like to express his sincere gratitude to his supervisor Prof. Liang Guo-Ping for his constant encouragement and his ardent help. The author is also indebted to Prof. C.Verdi for his helpful discussions during the conference in Finland.

References

[1] P.G. Ciarlet, "*The Finite Element Method for Elliptic Problems,*"North-Holland, 1978.

[2] J. Douglas,Jr., and T.F. Russell,*Numerical methods for convection-dominated diffusion problems based on combining the method of characteristics with finite element or finite difference procedures,* SIAM.J. Numer. Anal. 19 (1982), 871-885.

[3] C.M. Elliott, *Error analysis of the enthalpy method for the Stefan problem,* IAM. J. Numer. Anal. 7 (1987), 61-71.

[4] C.M. Elliott, and J.R. Ockendon, "*Weak and Variational methods for Moving Boundary Problem,*" Pitman, London, 1982.

[5] A. Friedman, *The Stefan problem in several space variables*, Trans. Amer. Math. Soc. 133 (1968), 51-87.

[6] J.W. Jerome, "*Approximation of Nonlinear Evolution Systems,*" Academic Press, 1983.

[7] J.W. Jerome, and M.E. Rose, *Error estimates for the multidimensional two-phase Stefan problem,* Math. Comput. 39 (1982), 377-414.

[8] A. Visitin, *Stefan problem with phase relaxation,* IMA. J. Appl. Math. 34 (1985), 225-245.

[9] C. Verdi, and A.Visintin, *Error estimates for a semi-explicit numerical scheme for Stefan-type problems,* Numer. Math. 52 (1988), 165-185.

[10] Yi Fahuai, *An evolutionary continuous casting problem of two phase and its periodic behaviour,* to appear in Journal P.D.E..

Numerical analysis of capillary free boundaries governed by the Navier-Stokes equations

C. Cuvelier, R.M.S.M. Schulkes

Commission of the European Communities
Joint Research Centre
Ispra, Italy

Delft University of Technology
Faculty of Technical Mathematics and Informatics
Delft, The Netherlands

Abstract

In many cases, problems in mechanics and physics can be described by partial differential equations for the unknown functions. In hydrodynamics these unknowns are, for instance, the velocity vector and the pressure distribution in the fluid. When there are additional geometrical unknowns we speak of free boundary (FB) problems. Two types of FB problems can be distinguished according to whether the FB depends on time or not. Generally, stationary FB problems are defined to be boundary value problems involving (partial) differential equations on whose domains parts of the boundary, the FBs, are unknown and must be determined as part of the solution. A moving FB problem is defined to be an initial-value problem for (partial) differential equations involving FBs.

Hydrodynamical FBs can be present as liquid-gas or liquid-solid interfaces or as the interface of two immiscible liquids. Capillary FBs are defined as FBs on which we must take into account capillary forces, i.e. forces due to intermolecular attractions having a nonvanishing resultant at the boundary of the liquid.

There are many technological and engineering-science applications in which capillary FBs play a dominant part. For instance, in lubrication, electrochemical plating, corrosion, coating, polymer technology, separation processes, metal- and glass-forming processes, crystal growth and aerospace technology, there are abundant technologically important fluid flows with capillary FBs.

A particular example of an FB problem is the motion of a viscous liquid, partly filling a vessel. This problem is of great engineering importance as exemplified by fuel sloshing of a liquid-propellant space vehicle, attitude control of spacecrafts or satellites, oil oscillations in a large storage tank, water oscillations in a reservoir due to an earthquake, and so on.

A situation of special interest, both from the technological and the purely mathematical point of view, is the study of the behaviour of liquids in an open container in a low-g environment, where capillary FBs must be taken into account. These problems can be formulated by the complete nonlinear (unsteady) equations of fluid motion in domains containing moving boundaries. It is evident that the analytical or numerical study of these problems is extremely difficult.

In some cases this type of problem can be simplified by assuming that the liquid is incompressible and inviscid and that the liquid motion is irrotational. These assumptions lead to a formulation in terms of the velocity potential that must satisfy the Laplace equation in a fixed or variable domain with appropriate boundary conditions. However, these assumptions lead to severe restrictions on the types of flow that can be considered. In the first place, the viscosity must be set equal to zero, which does not allow the liquid to verify the no-slip condition on the container wall. In the second place, only conservative external body forces can be taken into account. A model based on potential theory with rotation can also be considered.

A model for which these restrictions need not be made and which can be expected to give reliable results is the model of an incompressible, viscous fluid, the motion of which is governed by the Navier-Stokes equations.

Although many theoretical and numerical results are known for the case of an inviscid incompressible (perfect) fluid, results for stationary and moving FB problems governed by the Navier-Stokes equations are quite recent. Pukhnachev considered capillary FB problems for which the FB does not intersect the container wall; theorems concerning the unique solvability of the corresponding boundary value problem were established. Solonnikov obtained existence and uniqueness results for stationary FBs which intersect the container. Solonnikov's work is based on the earlier results of Pukhnachev and forms a basis for a computational (finite-element) approach as studied by Cuvelier; analyticity of capillary FB problems is proved by Bemelmans. An FB problem with vanishing surface tension is considered by Bemelmans. Moving FBs governed by the Navier-Stokes equations have been studied by Solonnikov using a Lagrangian formulation; the unique solvability of a solution in a small interval of time is proved under the condition that surface (or capillary) forces are negligible. Beale showed that, if the initial state is sufficiently close to equilibrium, a unique solution exists for all time in a space defined by Sobolev norms. Using a Lagrangian formulation, Allain proved the existence of a small-time solution even if the initial variations are not small with respect to the equilibrium state. Existence and uniqueness of a solution of a linearized moving FB problem and its numerical approximation have been studied by Cuvelier. Finally we refer to the encyclopedic work of Myshkis et al. on static capillary FBs, linear oscillations, liquid bridges, and thermocapillary convection, mainly by analytic methods.

In Cuvelier & Schulkes [1990] (see reference) we consider some particular static (i.e. in which the liquid moves like a rigid body), stationary (i.e. in which the liquid motion does not depend on time), and moving FB problems and solve them numerically by different methods. For static and stationary problems these methods are: the *trial method*, *Newtons's method*, and the *total linearization method*. A moving FB problem will be studied in the context of a perturbation approach.

The essential property of an FB problem is the existence of one boundary condition too many on the FB. By this we mean that if we neglect one of the boundary conditions on the FB, the (partial) differential equation can be solved on a fixed domain. The extra boundary condition is necessary to determine the (a priori) unknown position of the FB. This observation immediately leads to the principle of the trial method for FB problems.

The *trial method* assigns a shape to the FB and the (partial) differential equation is solved within that shape after one of the boundary conditions on the FB is disregarded. Next, a new FB-shape is computed that satisfies as closely as possible the boundary condition that was relaxed. This procedure is repeated until convergence is attained.

Newton's method also involves a deforming domain but eliminates the successive iteration between the surface position and the field variables by introducing, in the discrete case, the position of the nodes on the FB directly as degrees of freedom. This can then be coupled with a quasi-Newton iterative procedure, which results in the simultaneous calculation of the position of the FB and the field variables at the new nodal positions once convergence is attained.

The third method, called the *total linearization method* (TLM), linearizes the problem with respect to the FB and also to possible nonlinearities in the differential equation itself. The TLM reduces the influence of the geometrical unknowns to boundary integrals in the weak formulation of the problem.

For the moving FB problem we assume that the deviation from the static equilibrium is small and we use the following procdure. The (partial) differential equation, which at time t is defined in the region $\Omega(t)$, is solved by mapping it onto the region Ω_o determined by the static solution. The mapped problem is then expanded in a power series in the parameter characterizing the domain deformation. The perturbation problems which arise in the expansion are then solved successively in the standard region, and the resulting series is mapped back into the original domain.

The plan of Cuvelier & Schulkes [1990] is as follows:

In §1 we apply the trial method, Newton's method, and the total linearization method to a simple one-dimensional FB problem for which the solution is known. Our attention will be focused on the main characteristics of these methods, like convergence speed and computer implementation facilities.

In §2 the static capillary FB problem will be discussed. The two-dimensional Cartesian case of cylindrical containers is the subject of §2.1. In §2.2 we make some remarks on problems with rotational symmetry and on rigid rotation of liquid bridges. These problems are formulated by ordinary nonlinear differential equations on a fixed domain. This means that, although the solution of the differential equation describes the shape of a liquid-gas interface, the problem is not an FB problem in the mathematical sense, since the domain on which the differential equation is defined is known a priori. Two-dimensional noncylindrical containers are discussed in §2.3; three-dimensional noncylindrical containers with rotational symmetry, in §2.4. Problems in noncylindrical containers lead to an ordinary nonlinear differential equation in one dimension with FB points.

In §2.5 we study the static FB of a liquid in an open three-dimensional cylindrical container rotating rigidly about an arbitrary axis.

In §3 we formulate two stationary FB problems governed by the Navier-Stokes equations. The trial method will be applied to the motion of a liquid in an open vessel in §3.1, and some remarks will be made concerning the application of Newton's method.

In §3.2 the die-swell problem will be formulated and solved by the total linearization method.

In §4 we focus our attention on the analysis of a thermocapillary FB problem. This problem is formulated as a capillary FB problem governed by the Navier-Stokes equations coupled by the heat equation. Moreover, the coefficient of surface tension depends on temperature.

In §5 we consider a nonstationary capillary FB problem governed by the Navier-Stokes equations. The problem will be linearized with respect to the static situation. A stable and convergent numerical scheme in space and time is defined, and applied to compute (linearized) FBs, eigenfrequencies, damping factors, and vibration modes.

The paper is concluded by making some remarks on future research and applications in the area of capillary FBs governed by the Navier-Stokes equations.

The thermocapillary FB problems discussed in §4 are related to convection flow problems in crystal growth techniques. In this area we foresee two important developments.

The first is the crystal growth control problem. The determination of the melt-crystal interface is reminicent to the Stefan problem, because heat transfer in the crystal and in the melt is coupled by requirements of temperature continuity and energy conservation. In the heat-flux balance on this interface, the latent heat must be taken into account since it determines the growth rate of the crystal into the melt. In order to control the shape of the crystal in time we must study the combined effects of fluid (melt) motion and heat transfer in a variable domain bounded by capillary (melt-gas) and Stefan-type (melt-crystal) interfaces. Open research problems are of a purely mathematical (existence, uniqueness of solutions) as well as a practical numerical nature.

A second development could be the study of the transition from stationary to instationary (oscillatory) convection at low Prandtl numbers for increasing Grashof and Marangoni numbers while all data are independent of time. Benchmark computations for a simple situation are presented in a workshop report by Roux. For ground-based crystal growth experiments the melt-gas FB can be assumed to be planar. However, in a low-g situation a deforming interface could play a specific role in the onset of the oscillatory regimes, particularly for crystal growth experiments based on the floating zone technique. Study of this Hopf bifurcation problem is of great interest from both a practical and a theoretical point of view.

Concerning the problem of frequency analysis of a liquid in an open container (§5), we remark that an interesting research domain is formed by the frequency analysis of fluid-structure systems with applications in, for instance, the aerospace sciences (e.g. stabilization and attitude control of satellites). Particularly in a low-g environment, capillary effects play a dominant role.

The physics of fluid-structure interaction can be subdivided into two areas. The first covers small liquid and structure motions around an equilibrium position. This approach is related to the subject of §5; we also refer to the Ph.D. thesis of Schulkes. Particular questions related to this perturbation approach are: efficient computation of equilibrium states, the mathematical well-posedness of the linearized equations (coupling of the three dimensional parabolic Navier-Stokes equations and the hyperbolic equations of three-dimensional elasticity for structures), construction of stable and convergent numerical schemes, and the study of algorithms for computing eigenvalues of large linear systems. In the second area large motions are investigated. Large liquid and structure motions are important for liquid handling and for the determination of the liquid impact on the container walls. Related questions are: the parabolic-hyperbolic coupling of the equations in a variable domain, and the study of efficient numerical algorithms.

Key words
capillary free boundaries (static, stationary, moving), Laplace-Young equation, Navier-Stokes equations, die-swell, Grashof and Marangoni convection, vibration modes, eigenfrequencies, numerical analysis, trial method, Newton's method, total linearization method, finite element method

AMS(MOS) subject classification
35R35 (PDE, free boundaries), 65L10 (numerical analysis, ODE, BVP), 65N30 (PDE, FEM), 76D05 (hydrodynamics, Navier-Stokes equations)

Reference

C. Cuvelier and R.M.S.M. Schulkes [1990], Some numerical methods for the computation of capillary free boundaries governed by the Navier-Stokes equations, SIAM Review, Vol. 32, Issue 03.

International Series of Numerical Mathematics, Vol. 99, © 1991 Birkhäuser Verlag Basel

Optimal design for transonic flows

VLADIMÍR DANĚK[1] AND RAINO MÄKINEN[2]

[1]Institute of Thermomechanics
Czechoslovak Academy of Sciences, Prague, Czechoslovakia
[2]Department of Mathematics
University of Jyväskylä, Finland

Abstract. The feasibility of finite element and mathematical programming methods for finding an optimal shape for an symmetric airfoil in case of transonic flow is studied. The state problem is solved using multigrid-technique. Numerical examples are given.

Keywords: Optimal shape design, multigrid method, transonic flow, finite elements, mathematical programming

1980 Mathematics subject classifications: 65K10, 65N30, 76H05

INTRODUCTION

The design of airfoils with good aerodynamical properties is an important problem for the designers of turbomachines and aircrafts. Although the real problem is three dimensional and the gas is viscous, numerical simulations are usually done using two dimensional inviscid potential approximation.

The full potential equation generally is of mixed elliptic-hyperbolic type (elliptic in the subsonic regions and hyperbolic in the supersonic regions). If the flow is known to be purely subsonic, simplifications of the full potential equation are often used. Numerical approximations of the flow can be calculated using finite element or boundary element methods.

In this work we present the numerical realization for an optimal shape design problem associated with the design of a symmetric airfoil in the transonic case. The optimal shape design problem is discretized with finite elements and solved using multigrid and mathematical programming methods. Similar problem in the subsonic case was studied in [1], for example. For further study on shape optimization we refer to the monograph [**9**].

1. THE STATE PROBLEM

We consider 2-dimensional fluid flow around a symmetric profile S given in Figure 1.1.

Let the profile $S = S(\alpha)$ be defined by a continuously differentiable function α

$$S(\alpha) = \{(x, y) \in \mathbb{R}^2 \mid 0 \le x \le L,\ -\alpha(x) \le y \le \alpha(x)\}. \tag{1.1}$$

Due to symmetry only a half of the airfoil is considered. In practise there are many constraints on α. At least $\alpha > 0\ \forall x \in (0, L)$.

---

[2]Research supported by the Academy of Finland

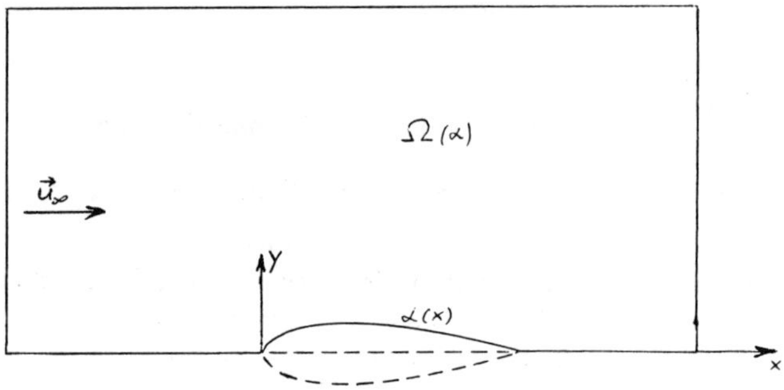

Figure 1.1

The fluid flow is considered steady, inviscid and irrotational in the region $\Omega = \Omega(\alpha)$. The state equation is then reduced to the full potential equation with Neumann boundary conditions

(1.2) $$\nabla \cdot (\rho \nabla \Phi) = 0 \quad \text{in } \Omega$$

(1.3) $$\rho \frac{\partial \Phi}{\partial n} = q \quad \text{on } \partial\Omega,$$

where Φ is the normalized velocity potential, $\frac{\partial \Phi}{\partial x_i} = \lambda_i = u_i/c^*$, c^* is the critical speed. The density ρ is connected with velocity by the isentropic relation

(1.4) $$\rho = \rho(|\nabla\Phi|^2) = \left(1 - \frac{\varkappa - 1}{\varkappa + 1}|\nabla\Phi|^2\right)^{\frac{1}{\varkappa - 1}},$$

where $\varkappa$ is the isentropic exponent (ratio of specific heats).

The equation (1.2) is a strongly nonlinear equation of the mixed type, elliptic in the subsonic region ($M < 1$) and hyperbolic in the supersonic region ($M > 1$). The relation between Mach number $M = |u|/c$ and normalized velocity $|\lambda|$ reads

(1.5) $$M^2 = \frac{2|\lambda|^2}{\varkappa + 1 - (\varkappa - 1)|\lambda|^2}.$$

Numerical solution of the state problem is obtained by FE method with artificial viscosity, SLOR iterative process and multigrid technique described in [**5**], [**7**]. A weak solution $\Phi \in W_2^1(\Omega)$ is defined by

(1.6) $$\int_\Omega \rho \nabla\Phi \cdot \nabla w \, d\Omega - \int_{\partial\Omega} qw \, ds = 0 \quad \forall w \in W_2^1(\Omega),$$

where w is a test function.

The artificial viscosity is included in the artificial density $\tilde{\rho}$

$$\tilde{\rho} = \rho - \mu \frac{\partial \rho}{\partial \overleftarrow{s}} \Delta s \tag{1.7}$$

which is used in (1.6) in place of ρ. Here $\frac{\partial}{\partial \overleftarrow{s}}$ is the upwind derivative and Δs is the mesh spacing.

The artificial viscosity coefficient μ is chosen such that the method is as robust as possible. It is necessary because in some step of the optimization process a "nonsmooth" profile might be created. The cost paid for this is smoothed shock wave. A stability analysis of transonic potential flow in dependance on μ was done in the work [**6**].

For a given α we suppose the existence of the solution $\Phi = \Phi(\alpha)$ of the problem (1.2)–(1.4) in the region $\Omega = \Omega(\alpha)$. The existence has not been proved for transonic flow, partial success was achieved in works [**2**] and [**8**].

2. The optimal design problem

Having the solution $\Phi = \Phi(\alpha)$ on the region $\Omega = \Omega(\alpha)$ with the profile $S = S(\alpha)$, we may set up an optimal control problem

$$\text{(P)} \qquad \begin{cases} \text{Find } \alpha^* \in U_{ad} \text{ such that} \\ J(\alpha^*) \leq J(\alpha) \quad \forall \alpha \in U_{ad}, \end{cases}$$

where $J(\alpha) = j(\Phi(\alpha))$ is a cost function and U_{ad} denotes the set of admissible controls α. We consider three types of cost funtions, namely

$$J^1(\alpha) = \int_0^L (M(x,\alpha(x)) - M_g(x,\alpha(x)))^2 \, dx \tag{2.1}$$

$$J^2(\alpha) = \int_0^L \left(\frac{\partial M(x,\alpha(x))}{\partial x} \right)^2 dx \tag{2.2}$$

$$J^3(\alpha) = \int_0^L \left(\max(0, -\frac{\partial M(x,\alpha(x))}{\partial x}) \right)^2 dx. \tag{2.3}$$

It is clear from eq. (1.5) that $M = M(|\nabla \Phi|)$.

The functional J^1 corresponds to the inverse problem: find a profile $S(\alpha)$ such that the Mach number distribution on the profile is the given function $M_g(x)$, $x \in (0, L)$. (The distance between M and M_g is measured in $L^2(0, L)$ norm.)

With the functional J^2 we try to minimize the velocity gradient along the profile, it is to obtain a solution as smooth as possible. The functional J^3 is used to minimize the negative part of the gradient (the shock wave).

The meaning of cost functionals J^2 and J^3 is doubtful in the transonic case, if considered with a solution of the continuous problem (1.2) with sharp discontinuity (shock wave). However, their meaning is clear when we consider a solution with a "smoothed" shock. This happens to be the case either by numerical viscosity (by discretization) or by adding an artificial viscosity member to the continuous problem (1.2).

3. Discretization

In order to be able to solve the problem using mathematical programming methods we have to perform the discretization of the state problem and the control parameter.

3.1 Discretization of the state problem. The state problem (1.6) is discretized in usual way by FEM. The space $W_2^1(\Omega(\alpha))$ in the weak form (1.6) is approximated by a finite-dimensional space $W_h(\Omega(\alpha))$, we use bilinear isoparametric elements. The eq. (1.6) is converted into the nonlinear algebraic system of equations

$$\mathbf{K}(\mathbf{q})\mathbf{q} = \mathbf{f}. \tag{3.1}$$

3.2 Parametrization of the profile. The unknown distributed parameter $\alpha(x)$ is approximated by a linear combination

$$\alpha_n(x) = \sum_{i=1}^{n} a_i B_i(x) \tag{3.2}$$

of n real parameters a_i and n linearly independent basis functions $B_i \in C([x_0, x_1])$, where $0 \leq x_0 < x_1 \leq L$.

Some possibilities for the sets of B_i are:

A) Parametrization using polynomials

$$\alpha_n(x) = a_1 x^{\frac{1}{2}} + \sum_{i=2}^{n} a_i x^{i-1}. \tag{3.3}$$

Many wellknown test profiles are expressed in this form, e.g. NACA 0012.

B) Parametrization using B-splines

$$\alpha_n(x) = \begin{cases} \text{B-spline function with keypoints} \\ \qquad (x_0, a_1), ..., (x_1, a_n), \text{if } x \in [x_0, x_1] \\ \alpha_g(x), \quad \text{otherwise,} \end{cases} \tag{3.4}$$

where α_g is a given profile. This form is useful if only a part of the profile is to be changed.

3.3 The discrete design problem. Our discretized design problem now reads

$$(\mathcal{P}_{n,h}) \qquad \begin{cases} \text{Find } \mathbf{a}^* \in U_n \text{ such that} \\ J_h(\mathbf{a}^*) \leq J_h(\mathbf{a}) \quad \forall \mathbf{a} \in U_n, \end{cases}$$

where $J_h(\mathbf{a}) = j_h(\mathbf{q}(\mathbf{a}))$ denotes the discretization of J and $\mathbf{q}(\mathbf{a})$ is the solution of (3.1) corresponding to $\mathbf{a} = (a_1, ..., a_n)$. The definition of U_n (constraints on $\mathbf{a}$) is provided later in each individual case.

4. Some properties of boundary parametrizations

We mention here some important properties of boundary parametrizations, in relation to imposed constraints.

The polynomial parametrization (3.3) is a natural choice as the singularity in the blunt leading edge automatically is taken into account by the term $x^{\frac{1}{2}}$. In this case the inclusion of pointwise constraints is difficult. For example, the constraint

$$\alpha_n(x) \geq 0 \ \forall x \in [0, L]$$

must be included in the problem (P_n) as a nonlinear constraint

$$\int_0^L (\alpha_n^-)^2 \, dx = 0, \tag{4.1}$$

where α_n^- denotes the negative part of α_n. On the other hand, it is easy to impose constraints on the area of the profile of the form

$$\text{vol } S \geq V_{\text{given}}. \tag{4.2}$$

Concerning the B-spline parametrization let

$$0 = t_1 = \ldots = t_{1+k} < t_{2+k} < \ldots < t_n = t_{n+1} = \ldots = t_{n+k} = L$$

be a fixed knot sequence. Then the B-spline function of order k is given by

$$\alpha_n(x) = \sum_{i=1,n} a_i B_{i,k,t}(x),$$

where $\{B_{i,k,t}\}_{i=1}^n$ are the B-spline basis functions of order k associated with the knot sequence $\{t_j\}$. The basis functions are piecewise polynomials of order $\leq k-1$ and have small supports.

B-spline functions have many attractive properties. For example the coefficients a_i model the function α_n:

Lemma. *For $t_i \leq x \leq t_{i+1}$, the value of the spline function $\alpha_n(x)$ is convex combination of the numbers $a_{i+1-k}, \ldots, a_i$.*

Proof: See **[3]**–page 154.

From the previous Lemma it follows that constraints of the type $\alpha_{\min} \leq \alpha_n(x) \leq \alpha_{\max}$ and $|\alpha_n'(x)| \leq C_1 \ \forall x \in [0, L]$ can be transformed into linear constraints on the B-spline coefficients.

The case of linear spline ($k = 2$) is trivial as the spline function is nothing else but the piecewise linear interpolate of the data $(t_1, a_1), \ldots, (t_n, a_n)$. Higher order B-splines in shape optimization of elastic structures have been utilized by Fleury and Braibant in [4].

Note that it is also possible to take the y-coordinates of the set of "keypoints"

$$(t_1, a_1), \ldots, (t_n, a_n) \in [0, L]$$

as design variables. The boundary curve α_n is then the spline interpolant of these points. In this case, however, it is difficult to pose geometric constraints on α_n outside the keypoints. For example $a_i \geq 0$, $i = 1, \ldots, n$ does not imply that $\alpha_n(x) \geq 0 \ \forall x \in [0, L]$.

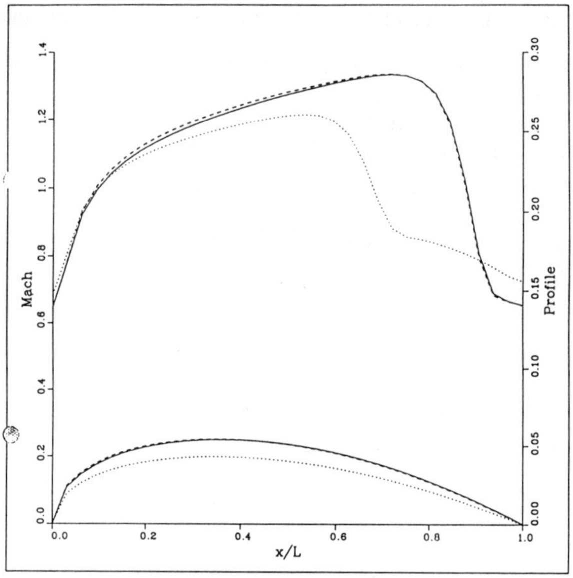

Figure 5.1

5. Numerical results

We present some numerical results using above mentioned cost functionals. In all examples polynomial parametrization (3.3) is used. In optimization, we use Sequential Quadratic Programming (SQP) algorithm E04UCF from the NAG-library. Gradients of the cost functionals are computed by the finite difference formula

$$\frac{\partial J^k(\mathbf{a})}{\partial a_i} = \frac{1}{\delta}\left(J^k(\mathbf{a}+\delta \mathbf{e}^{(i)}) - J^k(\mathbf{a})\right) + \mathcal{O}(\delta), \quad i = 1, ..., n; \quad \delta > 0. \tag{5.1}$$

The state problem was solved usually on the grid of 64×24 elements (1625 grid points) by SLOR-multigrid method (with 4 levels) until prescriped residual ($R = 10^{-6}$) was reached. Typically, 10 multigrid cycles in the beginning to one cycle in the end were required. All computations were done in double precision using HP 9000/345 workstation. Typical computing times were about 2 hours.

Example 5.1. In this example we calculate a Mach distribution on a profile. Then we use this Mach distribution as M_g and with a different starting profile try to get the original profile using cost function (2.1). The freestream Mach number is 0·85. In Figure 5.1 desired (solid), initial (dotted) and final (dashed) profiles and Mach distributions are shown. The resulting profile is very close to the original one, although the resulting parameters are different.

Example 5.2. In this example M_g is a given "flat" Mach distribution. We use 7 parameters and flat plate as the initial guess. The freestream Mach number is 0·80. In Figure 5.2 the final profile and Mach distribution (solid) together with M_g (dotted) are shown.

EXAMPLE 5.3. In this example we try to modify NACA0012 profile to get a "shock free" profile using cost function (2.3). We require the volume of the profile to be greater or equal to that of NACA0012. In this example a slightly finer mesh with 2025 gridpoints was used. The freestream Mach number is 0·80. In Figure 5.3 the initial (dotted) and final (solid) profiles with Mach distributions are shown. A new profile with thick rear part and weaker shock wave resulted.

6. CONCLUSIONS

The numerical tests in the previous Section show that improved designs according to the chosen cost function could be obtained. The multigrid solver used has been proved to be very efficient and reliable. The effectiveness of the NAG-library procedure depends on the proper choice of its tuning parameters and parameter δ in the finite difference formula (5.1).

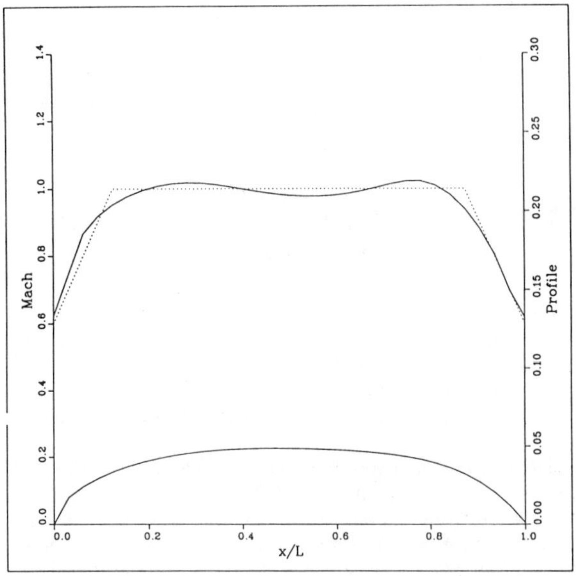

Figure 5.2

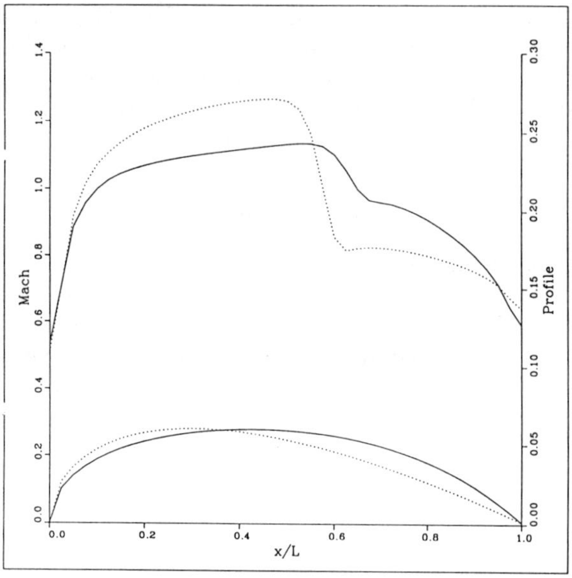

Figure 5.3

References

1. F. Angrand, *Optimum design for potential flows*, Int. J. Num. Meth. Fluids **3** (1983), 265–282.
2. H. Berger, G. Warnecke and W. Wendland, *A convergent finite element formulation for transonic flow*, Numerical Methods for Partial Differential Equations **6** (1990), 17–42.
3. C. de Boor, "A Practical Guide to Splines," Springer-Verlag, New York, 1978.
4. V. Braibant and C. Fleury, *Shape Optimal Design Using B-splines*, Comp. Meth. Appl. Mech. Eng. **44** (1984), 247–267.
5. V. Daněk, *Numerical Solution of Transonic Potential Flows with Finite Element Method Using Multigrid Technique*, Acta Technica ČSAV **3** (1986).
6. V. Daněk and F. Maršík, *Stability of numerical solution of transonic potential flow*, ZAMM, in print.
7. H. Deconinck and Ch. Hirsch, *A multigrid method for the transonic full potential equation discretized with FE on an arbitrary body fitted mesh*, Journal of Computational Physics **48** **N. 3** (1982), 344-365.
8. M. Feistauer and J. Nečas, *On the solvability of transonic potential flow problems*, Z. Anal. Anw. **4** (1985), 305–329.
9. J. Haslinger and P. Neittaanmäki, "Finite Element Approximation for Optimal Shape Design," John Wiley & Sons, Chichester, 1988.

[1] Institute of Thermomechanics, Czechoslovak Academy of Sciences, Dolejškova 5, 182 00 Prague 8, Czechoslovakia
[2] Department of Mathematics, University of Jyväskylä, Seminaarinkatu 15, SF–40100 Jyväskylä, Finland

International Series of Numerical Mathematics, Vol. 99, © 1991 Birkhäuser Verlag Basel

Penalties and Mixed Finite Element Analysis for Variational Inequalities

Christian Grossmann
Department of Mathematics
Dresden University of Technology

Abstract. Variational inequalities as a rule require discretization to approximate the wanted solution by means of the solution of an appropriate finite dimensional problem. On the other hand these auxiliary problems need a further numerical method for its solution. Penalty methods form a useful tool but the arising parameters have to be adjusted in a proper way. In the present paper we discuss as well discretization by finite elements as parameter selection rules. Furthermore the iteration process for solving the discrete problems is investigated.

Keywords. Variational inequalities, finite element approximation, penalty method, parameter selection, singular embedding.

1980 Mathematics subject classifications: 49A29, 65N30, 49D30

1. Weakly Nonlinear Variational Inequalities and a-priori Estimations

First we consider some abstract variational inequality problem in a real Hilbert space U. Let $G \subset U$ denote some given closed convex subset of U. We assume $G \neq \emptyset$. We denote by U^* the dual space to U, i.e. the space of all linear continuous functionals on U equipped with the usual norm $\|l\|_* := \sup\limits_{u \in U} \frac{|<l,u>|}{\|u\|}$ where $< \cdot, \cdot >$ denotes the dual pairing. Furthermore let be given some mapping $F : G \subset U \longrightarrow U^*$. We consider the following variational inequality problem:

- Find some $u \in G$ such that

  (1.1) $$< Fu, v - u > \geq 0 \qquad \text{for any } v \in G$$

  holds.

We suppose the mapping F to satisfy the following assumptions:

- There exists some constant $\gamma > 0$ such that

  (1.2) $$< Fu - Fv, u - v > \geq \gamma \|u - v\|^2 \qquad \text{for any } u, v \in G$$

- There exists some nondecreasing function $\nu : R_+ \longrightarrow R_+$ such that

  (1.3) $$\|Fu - Fv\|_* \leq \nu(\rho) \|u - v\| \qquad \text{for any } u, v \in G_\rho.$$

  Here G_ρ denotes the set defined by

  $$G_\rho := \{v \in G : \|v\| \leq \rho\}.$$

We remark that property (1.3) implies some nondecreasing function $\mu : R_+ \longrightarrow R_+$ to exist satisfying

$$(1.4) \qquad | < Fu, v > | \leq \mu(\|u\|)\|v\| \qquad \text{for any } u, v \in G.$$

Indeed, (1.3) leads to

$$\|Fu\|_* \leq \nu(\max\{\|u\|, \|v\|\})\|u - v\| + \|Fv\|_*$$

for any $u \in G$ and some arbitrary $v \in G$. Thus the function μ defined by

$$\mu(s) := \nu(\max\{s, \|v\|\})(s + \|v\|) + \|Fv\|_*$$

satisfies condition (1.4). Iterations techniques for variational inequality problems which are only semi-coercive instead of (1.2) are considered in [9] e.g..

THEOREM 1 *Let F satisfy the assumptions (1.2),(1.3). Then the variational inequality (1.1) has a unique solution $u \in G$. Furthermore the following estimation holds*

$$(1.5) \qquad \|u\| \leq \frac{1}{\gamma}\mu(\|v\|) + \|v\| \qquad \text{for any } v \in G.$$

Here μ denotes some function due to (1.4).

Proof: The theorem can be shown similarly to [4, theorem 3.1] and is given in [6]. Here we sketch only the main steps of the proof. First we show that for any $\rho > 0$ with $G_\rho \neq \emptyset$ the related restricted variational inequality

$$(1.6) \qquad < Fu_\rho, v - u_\rho > \geq 0 \qquad \text{for any } v \in G_\rho$$

possesses some solution $u_\rho \in G_\rho$. For fixed ρ this can be proven by using an appropriate mapping $T_\sigma : G_\rho \longrightarrow G_\rho$ defined by $T_\sigma u := w$ where $w \in G_\rho$ denotes the unique solution of the projection problem

$$(1.7) \qquad (w - u, v - w) + \sigma < Fu, v - w > \geq 0 \qquad \text{for any } v \in G_\rho.$$

The mapping T_σ is contractive for sufficiently small parameters $\sigma > 0$. Thus, a unique fixed point u_ρ of T_σ exists. With the variational inequality (1.7) defining T_σ we obtain that u_ρ satisfies (1.6).

Let $\tilde{u} \in G_\rho$ denote some arbitrary element. Then (1.6) results in

$$< F\tilde{u}, \tilde{u} - u_\rho > \geq < F\tilde{u} - Fu_\rho, \tilde{u} - u_\rho > .$$

Now, (1.2) and (1.4) lead to the estimation

$$\|u_\rho\| \leq \frac{1}{\gamma}\mu(\|\tilde{u}\|) + \|\tilde{u}\|.$$

This results in the following conclusion. If $\rho > 0$ is selected such that some $\tilde{u} \in G_\rho$ exists satisfying

$$\rho > \frac{1}{\gamma}\mu(\|\tilde{u}\|) + \|\tilde{u}\|$$

then u_ρ also solves the original problem (1.1). Furthermore estimation (1.5) has been shown. The uniqueness of the solution of (1.1) results from the supposed coercivity property (1.2).

Discretizing the original problem (1.1) by means of conform finite elements we approximate the space U by some finite dimensional space $U_h \subset U$. Furthermore the set G is replaced by some closed convex set $G_h \subset U_h$. For the sake of simplicity the mapping F should not be modified during discretization and we assume F to be defined on the whole space U. We remark that the discrete set G_h is not contained in G as a rule. Thus, we suppose F to satisfy the related properties (1.2), (1.3) in the discrete case also. Additionally we assume

$$< Fv - Fv_h, v - v_h >\geq \gamma \|v - v_h\|^2 \qquad \text{for any } v \in G,\ v_v \in G_h$$

and

$$\|Fu - Fv\|_* \leq \nu(\rho)\|u - v\| \qquad \text{for any } u, v \in U \text{ with } \|u\|, \|v\| \leq \rho.$$

We report from [6] the following

THEOREM 2 *Let be $G_h \neq \emptyset$. Under the assumptions made above the discrete problem*

$$(1.8) \qquad < Fu_h, v_h - u_h >\geq 0 \qquad \textit{for any } v_h \in G_h$$

has a unique solution $u_h \in G_h$. There the following estimations hold:

$$(1.9) \qquad \|u_h\| \leq \frac{1}{\gamma}\mu(\|v_h\|) + \|v_h\| \qquad \textit{for any } v_h \in G_h,$$

$$(1.10) \qquad \frac{\gamma}{2}\|u - u_h\|^2 \leq \inf_{v \in G} < Fu, v - u_h > + \inf_{v_v \in G_h} \{\|Fu\|_* \|v_h - u\| + \frac{\delta^2}{2\gamma}\|v_h - u\|^2\}$$

with $\delta := \nu(\max\{\|u\|, \|u_h\|\})$ and the solution u of problem (1.1).

Inequality (1.9) forms the discrete version of (1.5) and results from theorem 1. The estimation (1.10) has been shown by CIARLET [3] for the special case of obstacle problems.

Combining theorem 2 with the following convergence assumptions w.r.t. the approximation of the set G by the set G_h as made by GLOWINSKI\LIONS\TREMOLIERES [5]

- For any $v \in G$ there exists some $v_h \in G_h$ with $v_h \to v$ for $h \to +0$.
- $v_h \in G_h$, $v_h \rightharpoonup v$ for $h \to +0$ imply $v \in G$

we obtain the convergence of the discrete solutions u_h to the solution u of the original problem (1.1) for $h \to +0$.

In the construction of the set G_h we distinguish two principles. The most widespread technique consists in using a pointwise inequality instead of continuous inequality constraints. In the case of an obstacle condition

$$G = \{v \in U\ :\ v \geq g \text{ a.e. in } \Omega\}$$

on some domain Ω (compare section 2) we have in the discrete case

$$G_h = \{v_h \in U_h\ :\ v_h(x_i) \geq g(x_i),\ i = 1(1)N\}$$

where $\{x_i\}_{i=1}^N$ denotes the underlaying grid of the related finite element discretization.

Another type of discretization consists in applying an appropriate mixed finite element approach. Let V denote some further Hilbert space and V^* denotes the related dual space. Let $B : U \longrightarrow V^*$ be some given linear continuous mapping. We suppose the original constraint set G to be defined by

$$G := \{u \in U\ :< Bu, w >\geq< g, w > \text{ for any } w \in \mathcal{K}\}$$

where $\mathcal{K} \subset V$ denotes some closed convex cone and $g \in V^*$ is some given continuous linear functional. Then the solution u of the variational inequality problem (1.1) can be characterized in the following way.

THEOREM 3 *Let* $(u,w) \in U \times \mathcal{K}$ *satisfy the mixed variational inequalities*

$$\begin{array}{lclcl} < Fu, v > & - < Bv, w > & = & 0 & \text{for any } v \in U \\ < Bu, z - w > & & \geq & < g, z - w > & \text{for any } z \in \mathcal{K}. \end{array}$$

Then u *forms a solution of the variational inequality (1.1). If* B *additionally satisfies the condition*

$$\sup_{v \in U \setminus \{0\}} \frac{< Bv, w >}{\|v\|} \geq k\|w\| \text{ for any } \in \mathcal{K}$$

with some constant $k > 0$ *then we can estimate*

$$\begin{aligned} \|u\| &\leq \tfrac{1}{\gamma}\mu(\|\tilde{u}\|) + \|\tilde{u}\| \qquad \text{for any } \tilde{u} \in G, \\ \|w\| &\leq \tfrac{1}{k}\mu(\|u\|). \end{aligned}$$

Proof: We follow the arguments of proving the sufficiency condition for saddle points of the Lagrangean in optimization. Because $\mathcal{K}$ is a convex cone and $w \in \mathcal{K}$, we have $z := \tilde{z} + w \in \mathcal{K}$ for all $\tilde{z} \in \mathcal{K}$. Thus the second part of the characterization results in $< Bu, \tilde{z} > \geq < g, \tilde{z} >$ for any $\tilde{z} \in \mathcal{K}$ and therefore $u \in G$ holds. Choosing $\tilde{z} := 0$ and $\tilde{z} := 2w$ we obtain $< Bu - g, w > \leq 0$ and $< Bu - g, w > \geq 0$, respectively. This leads to the complementarity condition $< Bu - g, w > = 0$. With the first part of the characterization this leads to

$$< Fu, v - u > - < Bv - g, w > = 0 \quad \text{for any } v \in U.$$

Taking into account $w \in \mathcal{K}$ and the special structure of the constraint set G we obtain that u solves the variation inequality (1.1). The first estimation has been stated in theorem 1. So the second estimations remains to be shown. From the first part of the characterization and with property (1.4) we obtain

$$\frac{< Bv, w >}{\|v\|} = \frac{< Fu, v >}{\|v\|} \leq \mu(\|u\|) \text{ for any } v \in U,\ v \neq 0.$$

With the supposed condition this results in the second estimation.

We remark that theorem 3 partially generalizes saddle point results of BREZZI [2] to nonlinear problems. Turning back to the discretization in the mixed formulation both spaces U, V have to be approximated by some finite dimensional spaces $U_h \in U$, $V_h \in V$ and some closed convex cone $\mathcal{K}_h \in V_h$. Now, let the set G_h be defined by

$$G_h := \{u_h \in U_h : < Bu_h, w_h > \geq < g, w_h > \text{ for any } w_h \in \mathcal{K}_h\}.$$

Then theorem 3 can be formulated for the discrete case in a similar way.

2. Obstacle problems

In this chapter we specify our general problem (1.1) in the following way. We choose $U := H_0^1(\Omega)$ where $\Omega \subset R^2$ denotes some given polyhedron with the boundary Γ. Let the bilinear form $a(\cdot,\cdot)$ and the linear functional $< f, \cdot >$ be defined by

$$a(u,v) := \int_\Omega \nabla u^T \nabla v \, d\Omega \quad \text{and} \quad < f, v > := \int_\Omega f v \, d\Omega \quad \text{for any } u,\ v \in U,$$

respectively. We suppose that the data of the problem under consideration satisfy the following conditions

$$i)\ f \in C(\bar{\Omega}) \qquad ii)\ g \in W^2_\infty(\hat{\Omega}) \text{ with some domain } \hat{\Omega} \supset \bar{\Omega} \qquad iii)\ g|_\Gamma \le 0 \text{ on } \Gamma.$$

In the sequel we deal with the variational problem (compare [3], [10])

$$J(u) := \frac{1}{2}a(u,u) - < f, u > \to \text{ min ! } \quad \text{s.t. } u \in G \tag{2.1}$$

with $G := \{u \in H_0^1(\Omega) : u(x) \ge g(x) \text{ for any } x \in \Omega\}$. It is well known that this problem is equivalent to the variational inequality

$$a(u, v-u) \ge < f, v-u > \qquad \text{for any } v \in G. \tag{2.2}$$

In the discretization of (2.1) or (2.2) we restrict us to piecewise linear elements on an triangular grid on $\bar{\Omega}$. There the set $\bar{\Omega}$ should be covered by a feasible triangulation where the largest angle is bounded by $\alpha_{max} \le \frac{\pi}{2}$. Furthermore the triangulation is assumed to be quasiuniform such that a circle of the radius $\underline{\rho}h$ can be inscribed into each triangle and each triangle can be inscribed into some circle with the radius $\bar{\rho}h$. Here $\bar{\rho} > \underline{\rho} > 0$ denote some fixed constants and $h > 0$ denotes the meshsize parameter of the used grid. The inner grid points of the triangulation are denoted by $\Omega_h := \{x_i\}_{i=1}^N$. Then the space U_h is given by

$$U_h := lin\{\phi_i\}_{i=1}^N = \{u \in U \,:\, u(x) = \sum_{i=1}^N u_i\phi_i(x)\}$$

where $\{\phi_i\}_{i=1}^N$ are piecewise affine continuous functions satisfying $\phi_i(x_k) = \delta_{ik}$. As mentioned in section 1 we discretize the set G by

$$G_h = \{v \in U_h \,:\, v(x) \ge g(x) \text{ for each } x \in \Omega_h\}. \tag{2.3}$$

Under the condition made above the discrete variational problem

$$J(u) \longrightarrow \text{ min ! } \qquad \text{s.t. } u \in G_h \tag{2.4}$$

has a unique solution u_h and the estimation

$$\|u - u_h\| = O(h) \tag{2.5}$$

holds (compare [3]).

Problem (2.4) forms a large scale quadratic programming problem with lower bounds as constraints. Adapted numerical methods have to be applied to (2.4) instead of some standard quadratic programming code. In this paper we deal with special penalty methods and discuss optimal parameter selection rules as well as the influence of truncated iterations on nested grids. For fixed parameters $\alpha > 0$, $r > 0$ we define two types of penalty functions by

$$\Psi_1(t) := \alpha(t + \sqrt{t^2 + r}), \qquad \Psi_2(t) := \alpha\{t(t + \sqrt{t^2 + r}) + \frac{r}{2}\}. \tag{2.6}$$

These penalty functions have the following properties:

- The functions $\Psi_1(\cdot)$ and $\Psi_2(\cdot)$ uniformly approximate the well known loss functions $2\alpha \max\{0,t\}$ and $2\alpha \max^2\{0,t\}$, respectively, for $r \to +0$,

- $\Psi_1'(t) = \alpha(1 + \frac{t}{\sqrt{t^2+r}})$, $\quad \Psi_2'(t) = \frac{\Psi_1^2(t)}{\alpha\sqrt{t^2+r}}$,
- $\Psi_1''(t) = \frac{\alpha r}{(t^2+r)^{3/2}}$, $\quad \Psi_2''(t) = 2\alpha\frac{\sqrt{t^2+r}+t}{\sqrt{t^2+r}} + \alpha\frac{rt}{(t^2+r)^{3/2}}$,
- $\Psi(t) \geq 0$ for any $t \in R$, $\quad s \leq t$ implies $\Psi(s) \leq \Psi(t)$,
- $|\Psi_1'''(t)| \leq 3\alpha r^{-1}$, $\quad |\Psi_2'''(t)| \leq 3\alpha r^{-1/2}$.

Here and in the sequel we simply use the notation Ψ instead of Ψ_1 or Ψ_2 if there is no need to distinguish between both types of penalties. Using the functions introduced above we relate to the discrete problems (2.4) the finite dimensional unconstrained problems

$$J(u) + \Phi(u; r, \alpha) \longrightarrow \min ! \qquad \text{s.t. } u \in U_h \tag{2.7}$$

with $\Phi(u; r, \alpha) = \sum_{i=1}^{N} \Psi(g(x_i) - u(x_i))$. For any fixed parameters $r > 0, \alpha > 0$ problem (2.7) possesses a unique solution $u_h^{r,\alpha} \in U_h \subset U$. An optimal selection of the parameters $r > 0, \alpha > 0$ could be characterized by finding some rules $r = r(h)$, $\alpha = \alpha(h)$ satisfying two principles. First, the order of approximation of u_h by $u_h^{r,\alpha}$ is at least as good as the order of approximation of u by u_h, i.e. $\|u_h - u_h^{r,\alpha}\| = O(h)$ and, secondly, the conditioning of problem (2.7) is not worse than the conditioning of the related elliptic problem $J(u) \to \min !$ s.t. $u \in U_h$. In [7] we derived an optimal parameter selection rule for the penalty function Ψ_1. The principle used there can be applied to Ψ_2 in a similar way. From the numerical point of view the penalty function Ψ_2 is to prefer because Ψ_2' is convex which results in better convergence behaviour of Newton's method applied to (2.7) e.g..

The convergence analysis of the penalty techniques considered here rests on

THEOREM 4 *Under the made assumptions there exists some constant $c > 0$ such that*

$$\Psi'(0) > ch^2 \qquad \textit{implies} \qquad u_h^{r,\alpha} \in G_h \tag{2.8}$$

and we have the estimation

$$\|u_h - u_h^{r,\alpha}\| \leq [\frac{N}{\gamma}\Psi(0)]^{1/2}. \tag{2.9}$$

Proof: Similar to [7] we investigate the auxiliary problems

$$J(u) + \Phi(u; r, \alpha) \longrightarrow \min ! \qquad \text{s.t. } u \in G_h. \tag{2.10}$$

This problem has a unique solution $v_h^{r,\alpha}$. Indirectly we show $v_h^{r,\alpha} \in \operatorname{int} G_h$. If $\Psi'(0)$ exceeds $\frac{\partial}{\partial u_i}(J + \Phi)v_h^{r,\alpha}$ then $v_h^{r,\alpha} \in \partial G_h$ can't solve problem (2.10). Because the triangulation satisfies the angle condition $\alpha_{max} \leq \frac{\pi}{2}$ we have $a(\phi_j, \phi_i) \leq 0$ for each $j \neq i$. With

$$\frac{\partial}{\partial u_i}(J + \Phi)v_h^{r,\alpha} = \sum_{j=1}^{N} a(\phi_j, \phi_i)v_j - < f, \phi_i >$$

and $v_h^{r,\alpha} \in G_h$ we obtain

$$\frac{\partial}{\partial u_i}(J + \Phi)v_h^{r,\alpha} \leq a(g_h, \phi_i) - < f, \phi_i > .$$

Here v_j denote the coefficients of the representation of $v_h^{r,\alpha}$ over the base $\{\phi_j\}$ and $g_h \in U_h$ denotes the piecewise linear interpolation of the obstacle function g. Thus we obtain

$$\frac{\partial}{\partial u_i}(J + \Phi)v_h^{r,\alpha} \leq ch^2$$

with some constant $c > 0$ which depends on the functions f, g only, but, being independent of the stepsize $h > 0$ of the discretization. This proves statement (2.8). With $u_h \in G_h$ the estimation (2.9) is a direct consequence of the monotonicity and convexity of Ψ and of the coercivity (1.2).

Additionally estimating the eigenvalues of the matrices $\frac{\partial^2}{\partial u_i \partial u_j}(J + \Phi)u_h$ we can show (compare [7] for the case of Ψ_1) the following optimal parameter selection rules:

(2.11) $$\alpha(h) = dh^2 \quad , r(h) = h^4 \qquad \text{in the case } \Psi = \Psi_1,$$

(2.12) $$\alpha(h) = d \quad , r(h) = h^4 \qquad \text{in the case } \Psi = \Psi_2$$

with some constant $d > c$ and $c > 0$ according to (2.8). Combining this with (2.5) and theorem 4 we obtain

THEOREM 5 *Let the parameters $\alpha = \alpha(h)$, $r = r(h)$ be selected according to (2.11) and (2.12), respectively, then the estimation*

$$\|u - u_h^{r,\alpha}\| = O(h)$$

holds. Here $u \in G$ denotes the solution of the obstacle problem (2.1).

3. Iterative solution of the finite dimensional auxiliary problems

In this part we deal with the iterative treatment of the discrete auxiliary problems (2.7). Because of the convexity of the objective functional an element $u_h^{r,\alpha} \in U_h$ solves (2.7) if and only if it satisfies the variational equation

(3.1) $$< (J + \Phi)' u_h^{r,\alpha}, v_h >= 0 \text{ for any } v_h \in U_h.$$

Let us define a mapping $S_h(\cdot,\cdot) : U_h \times U_h \to R$ by

$$S_h(u_h, v_h) := -\sum_{i=1}^{N(h)} \Psi'(g_i - u_i)v_i \text{ for any } u_h, v_h \in U_h.$$

Here denotes $g_i := g(x_i)$, $u_i := u_h(x_i)$, $v_i := v_h(x_i)$ and $N = N(h)$ is the actual number of inner grid points. Now, (3.1) is equivalent to

(3.2) $$a(u_h^{r,\alpha}, v_h) - < f, v_h > + S_h(u_h^{r,\alpha}, v_h) = 0 \text{ for any } v_h \in U_h.$$

We linearize the operator S_h by means of the related mapping

$$D_h(u_h, w_h, v_h) := \sum_{i=1}^{N} \Psi''(g_i - u_i)w_i v_i \text{ for any } u_h, v_h, w_h \in U_h.$$

Because of $\Psi'' \geq 0$ we have

(3.3) $$D_h(u_h, v_h, v_h) \geq 0 \text{ for any } u_h, v_h \in U_h.$$

Applying Newton's method to (3.2) we obtain the recursion

(3.4) $$a(u_h^{l+1}, v_h) - < f, v_h > + S_h(u_h^l, v_h) + D_h(u_h^l, u_h^{l+1} - u_h^l, v_h) = 0 \text{ for any } v_h \in U_h,$$

$l = 1, 2, ...$ for determing a sequence $\{u_h^l\} \subset U_h$ to approximate the wanted solution $u_h^{r,\alpha} \in U_h$ of problem (3.1). In dependence of the initial guess u_h^1 the sequence $\{u_h^l\}$ is uniquely defined by (3.4).

We remark that the sparsity structure of the stiffness matrix related to the linear problems (3.4) is the same of the original elliptic problem without the unilateral bounds.

The convergence behaviour of Newton's method heavily depends on the choice of the starting element u_h^1. The embedding w.r.t. the parameter $h \to +0$ requires some adapted selection of the grids. The step size procedure for regular continuation processes as considered in [8] e.g. can't be applied directly because we deal with a singular embedding here. In the situation under consideration two types of singularities occur. First, we know the condition number of the discrete elliptic problems to be proportional to h^{-2} which tends to infinity for $h \to +0$. The second type of singular behaviour is induced by the penalty function as widely known. It should be remarked that Newton's method applied to discretized boundary value problems show some mesh independence principle (see [1]).

Next we estimate the contraction behaviour of the iteration (3.4). Combining (3.2) and (3.4) we obtain

$$a(u_h^{l+1} - u_h^{r,\alpha}, v_h) + D_h(u_h^l, u_h^{l+1} - u_h^{r,\alpha}, v_h) + D_h(u_h^l, u_h^{r,\alpha} - u_h^l, v_h) + S_h(u_h^l, v_h) - S_h(u_h^{r,\alpha}, v_h) = 0$$

for any $v_h \in U_h$. With (1.2), (3.3) and taking $v_h := u_h^{l+1} - u_h^{r,\alpha}$ this leads to

$$\gamma \| u_h^{l+1} - u_h^{r,\alpha} \|^2 \le S_h(u_h^{r,\alpha}, v_h) - S_h(u_h^l, v_h) - D_h(u_h^l, u_h^{r,\alpha} - u_h^l, v_h).$$

The right hand side of this inequality can by estimatated by the mean value theorem. With the definition of the mappings S_h, D_h we obtain

$$|S_h(u_h^{r,\alpha}, v_h) - S_h(u_h^l, v_h) - D_h(u_h^l, u_h^{r,\alpha} - u_h^l, v_h)| \le \frac{q_{r,\alpha}}{2} \sum_{i=1}^{N} |u_i^{r,\alpha} - u_i^l|^2 |u_i^{r,\alpha} - u_i^{l+1}|.$$

Here $q_{r,\alpha}$ denotes some global bound of $|\Psi'''|$ on R. As already mentioned we could choose $q_{r,\alpha} = 3\alpha r^{-1}$ and $q_{r,\alpha} = 3\alpha r^{-1/2}$ in the case $\Psi = \Psi_1$ and $\Psi = \Psi_2$, respectively. With the continuous embedding $H_0^1(\Omega) \hookrightarrow C(\bar{\Omega})$ we can estimate

$$\gamma \| u_h^{l+1} - u_h^{r,\alpha} \| \le c_1 \| u_h^l - u_h^{r,\alpha} \|^2 N q_{r,\alpha} \tag{3.5}$$

with some constant $c_1 > 0$. If the parameters $\alpha = \alpha(h)$, $r = r(h)$ are selected according to (2.11) and (2.12), respectively, we obtain $q_{r,\alpha} = O(h^{-2})$ in both cases of the penalty functions. On the basis of (3.5) this leads to a local area of contraction of Newton's method with a radius of the order $O(h^4)$. This could be improved by using alternative strategies for the parameter selection. But, we obtain a reduction of the order of convergence in this case.

It should be remarked that (3.5) forms a rough upper estimation because of applying (3.3) only to handle $D_h(u_h^l, u_h^{l+1} - u_h^{r,\alpha}, u_h^{l+1} - u_h^{r,\alpha})$. In practical realizations of the proposed iteration technique we obtained a better range of convergence of the used Newton method. Especially, truncated iterations could be applied on nested grids.

Finally, we investigate the principle behaviour of the used penalty technique in connection with Newton's method at a simple example which illustrates the effects we meet. Let us consider the one dimensional optimization problem

$$z(t) := -t \longrightarrow \min! \text{ s.t. } t \le 0. \tag{3.6}$$

Applying the penalty function Ψ_1 we obtain the related auxiliary problems

$$-t + \alpha(t + \sqrt{t^2 + r}) \longrightarrow \min! \text{ s.t. } t \in R. \tag{3.7}$$

Because the optimal Lagrange multiplier of (3.6) is given by $\lambda_* = 1$ we select the parameter $\alpha > 1$ fixed and investigate the dependency of (3.7) from $r > 0$ only. The point $t(r) \in R$ solves (3.7) if and only if it satisfies the nonlinear equation

$$P(t(r);r) := -1 + \alpha(1 + \frac{t(r)}{\sqrt{t^2(r)+r}}) = 0. \tag{3.8}$$

This results in $t(r) = a\sqrt{r}$, $r > 0$ with $a := \frac{1-\alpha}{\sqrt{2\alpha-1}}$. If Newton's method is applied to (3.8) we obtain

$$|t_{l+1} - t(r)| = \frac{|P''(\tau_l;r)|}{|P'(t_l;r)|}|t_l - t(r)|^2$$

with some intermediate value τ_l between t_l and $t(r)$. Ignoring higher order terms this leads to

$$|t_{l+1} - t(r)| \approx 3\frac{|a|}{1+a^2}r^{-1/2}|t_l - t(r)|^2. \tag{3.9}$$

Now, we consider the influence of the reduction of the parameter r to the iteration. Let the new value r be selected according to $r = \mu r_o$ with some $\mu \in (0,1)$. Here r_o denotes the r-value on the previous level. In the case of a sufficiently large number of Newton iterations on the old r-level we have $t_l \approx t(r_o)$ which leads to $|t_l - t(r)| \approx |a|\frac{1-\sqrt{\mu}}{\sqrt{\mu}}r^{1/2}$. With (3.9) this results in

$$|t_{l+1} - t(r)| \approx 3\frac{a^2}{1+a^2}\frac{1-\sqrt{\mu}}{\sqrt{\mu}}|t_l - t(t)|.$$

Thus, contraction is obtained for $\sqrt{\mu} > \frac{3a^2}{1+4a^2}$. Truncated Newton iterations can be investigated in a similar way.

References

[1] E.Algower and K.Böhmer, *A mesh independence principle for operator equations and their discretization,* report No.129, GMD, St.Augustin, 1985.

[2] F.Brezzi, *On the existence, uniqueness and approximation of saddle-point problems arising from Lagrange multipliers,* RAIRO **8** (1974)R2, 129-151.

[3] P.Ciarlet, "The finite element method for elliptic problems," North Holland, Amsterdam, 1978.

[4] I.Ekeland and R.Temam, "Convex analysis and variational problems," North Holland, Amsterdam, 1976.

[5] R.Glowinski, J.L.Lions and R.Tremolieres, "Numerical analysis of variational inequalities," Noth Holland, Amsterdam, 1981.

[6] C.Grossmann, *Mixed finite element methods and penalties for weakly nonlinear partial differential equations,* (C.Grossmann, H.Schönheinz and T.Riedrich, eds.) Mathematical Research Vol.21, Akademie-Verlag, Berlin (1984) 162-181.

[7] C.Grossmann and A.A.Kaplan, *On the solution of discretized obstacle problems by an adapted penalty method,* Computing **35** (1985), 295-306.

[8] J.Hackel, H.J.Wacker and W.Zulehner, *An efficient step size control for continuation methods* BIT **20** (1980), 475-485.

[9] A.A.Kaplan and R.Tichatschke, *Variational inequalities and semi-infinite convex programming problems,* (russ.), report No.27, Inst.Math., Novosibirsk, 1989.

[10] M.Krizek and P.Neittaanmäki, "Finite element approximation of variational problems and applications," Pitmans, London, 1990.

Christian Grossmann
Department of Mathematics
Dresden University of Technology
Mommsenstr.13
DDR-8027 Dresden
Germany

The nonuniqueness in a model for phase transitions in binary alloys

I. G. GÖTZ

Lavrentyev Institute of Hydrodynamics
Siberian Branch, Academy of Sciences of the USSR
Novosibirsk, 630090, USSR

Abstract. The nonuniqueness theorem for a self-similar solution in a model for phase transitions in binary mixtures has been proved. The existence of the generalized solution and the stability criterion are studied.

Keywords. Binary alloy, phase transition, degenerative system of equations

1980 Mathematics subject classifications: 35K65, 80A20, 34K15

1. Introduction

We consider the correctness of a problem in modelling phase transitions in binary alloys proposed by Götz and Meirmanov [**1**]. A similar model was earlier investigated by other methods by Donnelly [**2**], and by Luckhaus and Visintin [**3**]. In the former the initial-boundary value problem for the system of partial differential equations

$$\begin{aligned} C_t &= \operatorname{div}(\Lambda_{11}\nabla\frac{\mu}{\Theta} + \Lambda_{12}\nabla\frac{1}{\Theta}) \\ U_t &= \operatorname{div}(\Lambda_{21}\nabla\frac{\mu}{\Theta} + \Lambda_{22}\nabla\frac{1}{\Theta}) \end{aligned} \tag{1.1}$$

is investigated, with initial data for C and U, and homogeneous Dirichlet data for $\frac{\mu}{\Theta}$, $\frac{1}{\Theta}$. Here C is the concentration of impurity, U is the enthalpy of the alloy, μ is the difference of the chemical potentials of the alloy components and Θ is the temperature. The basic result obtained by Donnelly is an existence and uniqueness theorem in the case when $\Lambda_{ij} \equiv$ const. Here we show that this condition is essential. More precisely, if Λ_{ij} jump at the melting temperature, non-uniqueness of solutions occurs.

2. Formulation of the problem

The model proposed by Götz and Meirmanov [**1**] is based on a system of partial differential equations, which involves the heat conduction equation and the equation for diffusion of the impurity. In the case of one space variable we have

$$\begin{aligned} U_t &= (æ\Theta_y)_y \\ C_t &= (\lambda\vartheta_y)_y, \end{aligned} \tag{2.1}$$

where $\vartheta = \varphi^{-1}(\frac{\mu}{\Theta})$ (see [**1**]). This function also defines the non-constant melting temperature of the mixture, i.e. for $\Theta > \vartheta$ the medium is in the liquid phase, for $\Theta < \vartheta$ - in the solid phase, for $\Theta = \vartheta$ - in the so-called mushy region. Such a function was first suggested by Crowley and Ockendon [**4**], and by Fix [**5**].

As we see, the system (2.1) is presented in simplified form, without taking into account the Dufour and Soret effects ($\Lambda_{21}, \Lambda_{12} \equiv 0$). There are obvious correlations between the coefficients of system (2.1) and (1.1), namely

$$\Lambda_{11} = (\varphi^{-1})'(\frac{\mu}{\Theta})\lambda$$
$$\Lambda_{22} = -\Theta^2 æ.$$

Therefore the coefficients æ and λ are not constant for $\Lambda_{11}, \Lambda_{22} \equiv$ const. However, because the functions Θ and μ are continuous at the phase transition line, the coefficients æ and λ have the same property, if the suggestion by Donnelly is valid.

Here we take the coefficients æ and λ to be constant but different in liquid and solid phases,

$$\begin{aligned} æ &= æ^+ + (æ^- - æ^+)\Phi \\ \lambda &= \lambda^+ + (\lambda^- - \lambda^+)\Phi \end{aligned} \tag{2.2}$$

where Φ is the solid fraction,

$$\Phi = \begin{cases} 0 & \text{for } \Theta > \vartheta, \\ \in [0,1] & \text{for } \Theta = \vartheta, \\ 1 & \text{for } \Theta < \vartheta. \end{cases} \tag{2.3}$$

We also take simple equations of state for enthalpy and concentration of the impurity

$$\begin{aligned} U &= a^+\Theta + ((a^- - a^+)\Theta + k)\Phi \\ C &= C_L(\vartheta) + (C_S(\vartheta) - C_L(\vartheta))\Phi. \end{aligned} \tag{2.4}$$

Also, the solidus and liquidus curves C_S, C_L are taken to be linear corresponding to the case of low concentration of impurity

$$\begin{aligned} C_L(\vartheta) &= C^+(\vartheta - \vartheta_0) \\ C_S(\vartheta) &= C^-(\vartheta - \vartheta_0) \end{aligned} \tag{2.5}$$

where ϑ_0 is the melting temperature of the pure material.

Let us define:

$$\begin{aligned} &\text{the heat capacity - } U_\Theta(\Phi) = a^+ + (a^- - a^+)\Phi, \\ &\text{the latent heat } \quad \text{- } U_\Phi(\Theta) = (a^- - a^+)\Theta + k, \\ &C_\vartheta(\Phi) = C^+ + (C^- - C^+)\Phi, \\ &C_\Phi(\vartheta) = (C^- - C^+)(\vartheta - \vartheta_0). \end{aligned} \tag{2.6}$$

On physical grounds, we have

$$U_\Theta > 0, \quad U_\Phi < 0, \quad C_\vartheta > 0, \quad C_\Phi \geq 0. \tag{2.7}$$

We now consider solutions depending only on the self-similar variable $x = \frac{y}{\sqrt{t}}$. The system (2.1) transforms into

$$\begin{aligned} \frac{x}{2}U_x + (æ\Theta_x)_x &= 0 \\ \frac{x}{2}C_x + (\lambda\vartheta_x)_x &= 0. \end{aligned} \tag{2.8}$$

The points $x = 0; \infty$ correspond to $t > 0$, $y = 0$ and $t = 0$, $y > 0$ respectively. Therefore, the boundary value problem

$$\begin{aligned} U(+\infty) = U^\infty, \quad U(0) = U^0, \\ C(+\infty) = C^\infty, \quad C(0) = C^0 \end{aligned} \tag{2.9}$$

for the system (2.8) corresponds to the initial-boundary value problem

$$\begin{aligned} U = U^\infty, \quad C = C^\infty, \quad \text{for } t = 0, \quad y > 0, \\ U = U^0, \quad C = C^0, \quad \text{for } t > 0, \quad y = 0 \end{aligned} \tag{2.10}$$

for the system (2.1).

The system of ordinary differential equations (2.8) differs in type in the mushy region and in the solid and liquid phases. More precisely, in the solid or liquid phases $\Phi = 1$ or $\Phi = 0$, Θ and ϑ are unknown and

$$\begin{aligned} \frac{x}{2}\Theta_x + \frac{æ^\pm}{a^\pm}\Theta_{xx} &= 0 \\ \frac{x}{2}\vartheta_x + \frac{\lambda^\pm}{c^\pm}\vartheta_{xx} &= 0 \end{aligned} \tag{2.11}$$

in the mushy region $\Theta \equiv \vartheta$, ϑ and Φ are unknown and

$$\begin{aligned} &\frac{x}{2}(U_\Theta - (\frac{x}{2}U_\Phi + (æ^- - æ^+)\vartheta_x)\frac{(æC_\vartheta - \lambda U_\Theta)}{Z})\vartheta_x + æ\vartheta_{xx} = 0, \\ &\Phi_x = -\frac{x}{2}\vartheta_x\frac{(æC_\vartheta - \lambda U_\Theta)}{Z}, \end{aligned} \tag{2.12}$$

with $Z = (æC_\Phi - \lambda U_\Phi)\frac{x}{2} - (æ^-\lambda^+ - \lambda^-æ^+)\vartheta_x$.

DEFINITION. *We call the bounded functions Θ, ϑ, Φ a weak solution of the problem (2.8), (2.9) if the following conditions are satisfied:*

1. *Θ, ϑ, Φ satisfy the state equations (2.3),*
2. *$\Theta_x, \vartheta_x \in L_{2,\mathrm{loc}}((0,+\infty))$, and Θ, ϑ, Φ satisfy the identities*

$$\int_0^\infty \left[\frac{1}{2}U\varphi + (\frac{x}{2}U + æ\Theta_x)\varphi_x\right] dx = 0$$

$$\int_0^\infty \left[\frac{1}{2}C\varphi + (\frac{x}{2}C + \lambda\vartheta_x)\varphi_x\right] dx = 0$$

   for every finite test function $\varphi \in W_2^1((0,\infty))$.

3. *The boundary conditions (2.9) are satisfied in the ordinary sense, as limit values of the functions U and C for $x \to 0; +\infty$.*

3. Nonuniqueness

THEOREM 1. *Suppose that* $æ^+ \neq æ^-$ *or* $\lambda^+ \neq \lambda^-$ *or both. Then there exist* $x_1, x_2 \in (0, +\infty)$, U^1, U^2, C^1, C^2, *such that on the interval* (x_1, x_2) *the system of differential equations (2.8) with boundary conditions*

$$U(x_1) = U^1, \quad U(x_2) = U^2$$
$$C(x_1) = C^1, \quad C(x_2) = C^2 \tag{3.1}$$

has more than one solution.

PROOF: In order to prove this statement, we construct solutions for the system (2.8) with the structure

$$\begin{aligned} &\Theta < \vartheta \quad \text{for } x \in (x_1, a) \quad \text{(solid phase)} \\ &\Theta \equiv \vartheta \quad \text{for } x \in (a, b) \quad \text{(mushy region)} \\ &\Theta > \vartheta \quad \text{for } x \in (b, x_2) \quad \text{(liquid phase)} \end{aligned} \tag{3.2}$$

where $a < b$, $a, b \in (x_1, x_2)$.

The properties of the functions U_Φ, C_Φ and requirements of the theorem give that the combination $C_\Phi(æ^- - æ^+) - U_\Phi(\lambda^- - \lambda^+)$ is not identically equal to zero. Let us take $\vartheta^* > \vartheta_0$, so that for example

$$C_\Phi(\vartheta^*)(æ^- - æ^+) - U_\Phi(\vartheta^*)(\lambda^- - \lambda^+) > 0. \tag{3.3}$$

(If the reversed inequality is valid we must exchange liquid and solid phases in (3.2)).

In the interval (a, b) we must find the solution of (2.12). For this purpose it is necessary to prescribe initial data, for example at the point $x = a$:

$$\Phi(a + 0) = \Phi^*, \quad \vartheta(a) = \vartheta^*, \quad \vartheta_x(a + 0) = \vartheta_x^*. \tag{3.4}$$

It is not difficult to observe that the only condition for the existence of a smooth solution of differential equations (2.12) is strict positivity or negativity of the function Z:

$$Z = (æC_\Phi - \lambda U_\Phi)\frac{x}{2} - (\lambda^+ æ^- - \lambda^- æ^+)\vartheta_x > 0 \quad (\text{or } < 0) \tag{3.5}$$

for $x \in [a, b]$. The solution Φ and ϑ will be infinitely differentiable in this case, and they will have infinitely differentiable dependence on the initial data (3.4).

In order that this solution can be continued to the intervals (x_1, a), (b, x_2), we use the jump conditions at $x = a, b$:

$$\begin{aligned} &\Theta(a - 0) = \vartheta(a - 0) = \vartheta^* \\ &\frac{a}{2}C_\Phi(\vartheta^*)(1 - \Phi^*) + \lambda^- \vartheta_x(a - 0) - \lambda(\Phi^*)\vartheta_x^* = 0 \\ &\frac{a}{2}U_\Phi(\vartheta^*)(1 - \Phi^*) + æ^- \Theta_x(a - 0) - æ(\Phi^*)\vartheta_x^* = 0 \end{aligned} \tag{3.6}$$

$$\begin{aligned} &\Theta(b + 0) = \vartheta(b + 0) = \vartheta(b - 0) \\ &-\frac{b}{2}C_\Phi(\vartheta)\Phi|_{b-0} + \lambda^+ \vartheta_x(b + 0) - \lambda(\Phi)\vartheta_x|_{b-0} = 0 \\ &-\frac{b}{2}U_\Phi(\vartheta)\Phi|_{b-0} + æ^+ \Theta_x(b + 0) - æ(\Phi)\vartheta_x|_{b-0} = 0. \end{aligned} \tag{3.7}$$

The inequalities $\Theta_x(a-0) > \vartheta_x(a-0)$, $\Theta_x(b+0) > \vartheta_x(b+0)$ follow from (3.2). Hence,

$$\frac{a}{2} > \frac{\lambda^+æ^- - \lambda^-æ^+}{æ^- C_\Phi(\vartheta^*) - \lambda^- U_\Phi(\vartheta^*)} \vartheta_x^* = A_1 \tag{3.8}$$

$$\frac{b}{2} < \frac{\lambda^+æ^- - \lambda^-æ^+}{æ^+ C_\Phi(\vartheta(b)) - \lambda^+ U_\Phi(\vartheta(b))} \vartheta_x(b-0) = A_2. \tag{3.9}$$

Thus, three determining inequalities (3.5), (3.8), (3.9) have appeared, and our ability to construct the solution depends on them.

First let $b = a$. Choose ϑ_x^* so that $\text{sign}(\lambda^+æ^- - \lambda^-æ^+) = \text{sign}\, \vartheta_x^*$. Then the conditions (3.8), (3.9) reduce to

$$\frac{a}{2} \in (A_1, A_3) \tag{3.10}$$

$$\text{with} \quad A_3 = \vartheta_x^* \frac{\lambda^+æ^- - \lambda^-æ^+}{æ^+ C_\Phi(\vartheta^*) - \lambda^+ U_\Phi(\vartheta^*)}.$$

The inequality (3.3) shows that the interval (A_1, A_3) is not empty. Therefore, one can choose a value of a satisfying (3.10).

Now let $b > a$. Taking into account the smoothness of the solution obtained, the value A_2 tends to A_3 if b tends to a. Therefore, there exists b such that $A_1 < \frac{a}{2} < \frac{b}{2} < A_2$, i.e. (3.8), (3.9) are valid.

Let us consider again the inequality (3.5). The conditions (3.8), (3.9) yield that if Φ^* is nearly to 0 then $z|_{x=a} > 0$ and if Φ^* is nearly to 1 then $z|_{x=a} < 0$. Choosing Φ^* as above and decreasing the interval (a, b), we obtain one of the inequalities (3.5).

For the solution to be continued, for example, to the solid phase, we use the jump conditions (3.6). They allow the values $\Theta(a-0)$, $\vartheta(a-0)$, $\Theta_x(a-0)$, $\vartheta_x(a-0)$ to be determined. Using them as initial data, we find the solution of (2.11) for $x < a$:

$$\begin{aligned} \Theta(x) &= \vartheta(a) + \Theta_x(a-0) \times \int_a^x \exp\Big(\frac{(\tau^2 - a^2)a^-}{4æ^-}\Big) d\tau \\ \vartheta(x) &= \vartheta(a) + \vartheta_x(a-0) \times \int_a^x \exp\Big(\frac{(\tau^2 - a^2)c^-}{4\lambda^-}\Big) d\tau \end{aligned} \tag{3.11}$$

These formulae provide the necessary smoothness of the solution for $x < a$ and smooth dependence on the initial data. Since $\Theta_x(a-0) > \vartheta_x(a-0)$, there exists $x_1 < a$ such that $\Theta(x) < \vartheta(x)$ for $x \in [x_1, a)$ which corresponds to the solid phase. Doing the same for $x > b$, we choose $x_2 > b$ so that $\Theta(x) > \vartheta(x)$ for $x \in (b, x_2]$ which corresponds to the liquid phase. It is obvious that small variations in a and b do not affect the values x_1, x_2.

Thus, we have obtained infinitely differentiable functions $F : A \subset \mathbb{R}^5 \to \mathbb{R}^4$ using the rule $F(a, b, \vartheta^*, \Phi^*, \vartheta_x^*) = (U^1, U^2, C^1, C^2)$, $U^1 = U(x_1)$, $U^2 = U(x_2)$, $C^1 = C(x^1)$, $C^2 = C(x^2)$ where U, C are the solutions constructed above and A is the open set satisfying the conditions (3.5), (3.8), (3,9).

¿From Sard's theorem, the measure of the critical set of the function F equals zero. That means, for almost all $z_0 \in A$ the set $M = F^{-1}(F(z_0))$ is a smooth manifold with dimension $r = 5 -$ range $F(z_0)$. Because range $F(z_0) \leq 4$ therefore $r \geq 1$ and thus the set M does not consist of only one point. Different values of $z \in M$ correspond to the different solutions of the system (2.8) with identical boundary conditions

$$(U|_{x=x_1}, U|_{x=x_2}, C|_{x=x_1}, C|_{x=x_2}) = (U^1, U^2, C^1, C^2) = F(z_0).$$

This completes the proof.

Thus we have proved nonuniqueness of the solution of the boundary value problem (2.8), (3.1) in some small interval (x_1, x_2). Attempts at generalizing this result for the problem on the interval $(0, +\infty)$ encounter two obstacles. Firstly, it is necessary to find the inequality $\vartheta(x) \geq \vartheta_0$, which corresponds to $C(x) \geq 0$ and does not now follow from the properties of the system (2.8). Secondly, we must retain the structure (3.2).

For this obstacles to be surmounted we must impose additional requirements upon the coefficients of the system (2.8), for example

$$\lambda^+ æ^- - \lambda^- æ^+ > 0, \quad \lambda^+ U_\Theta(0) - æ^+ C_\vartheta(0) < 0. \tag{3.12}$$

4. Existence

The proof of a general existence theorem is complicated, because there are many technical details. We restrict ourselves to the special cases, when the different phases (liquid and solid) are given for $x = 0, +\infty$, and the coefficients satisfy the inequality

$$\frac{æ(\Phi)}{U_\Theta(\Phi)} \geq \frac{\lambda(\Phi)}{C_\vartheta(\Phi)} \quad \text{for every } \Phi \in [0,1]. \tag{4.1}$$

This condition is physically reasonable because the thermal conductivity $\frac{æ}{U_\Theta}$ is greater than the material diffusivity $\frac{\lambda}{C_\vartheta}$ for most alloys.

Theorem 2. *Suppose that the coefficients satisfy (4.1) and*

$$(\Theta^0 - \vartheta^0)(\Theta^\infty - \vartheta^\infty) < 0 \tag{4.2}$$

with $\Theta^{0,\infty}$, $\vartheta^{0,\infty}$ corresponding to the values $U^{0,\infty}$, $C^{0,\infty}$ as in the state equations (2.3), (2.4), (2.5).

Then there exists a weak solution of the problem (2.8), (2.9), and

1. *Θ_x, ϑ_x have bounded variation on $(0, +\infty)$,*
2. *Φ is monotone,*
3. *Either Θ or ϑ is monotone, and the other has no more than two monotonicity intervals.*

The main idea of the proof of this theorem is to make use of ε-regularization method. The system of differential equations (2.8) is degenerate in mushy regions, where it may be represented as a differential equation of second order for ϑ and a first-order differential equation for Φ. Let us take a positive number ε such that $\varepsilon < \frac{1}{2}\min\{|\Theta^0 - \vartheta^0|, |\Theta^\infty - \vartheta^\infty|\}$.

We regularize the state equation (2.3) as follows: $\Phi = \Phi_\varepsilon(\vartheta - \Theta)$, with Φ_ε a smooth, nondecreasing function:

$$\begin{aligned}\Phi'_\varepsilon(s) > 0 \quad &\text{for } s \in (-\varepsilon, \varepsilon),\\ \Phi_\varepsilon(s) = 1 \quad &\text{for } s \geq \varepsilon,\\ \Phi_\varepsilon(s) = 0 \quad &\text{for } s \leq -\varepsilon.\end{aligned}$$

The auxiliary problem for the functions Θ^ε, ϑ^ε is

$$\begin{aligned}&\frac{x}{2}U^\varepsilon_x + (æ(\Phi_\varepsilon)\Theta^\varepsilon_x)_x = 0,\\ &\frac{x}{2}C^\varepsilon_x + (\lambda(\Phi_\varepsilon)\vartheta^\varepsilon_x)_x = 0, \quad \text{in } (0, \frac{1}{\varepsilon})\end{aligned} \tag{4.3}$$

$$\begin{aligned}\Theta^\varepsilon(0) = \Theta^0, \qquad &\Theta^\varepsilon(\frac{1}{\varepsilon}) = \Theta^\infty\\ \vartheta^\varepsilon(0) = \vartheta^0, \qquad &\vartheta^\varepsilon(\frac{1}{\varepsilon}) = \vartheta^\infty\end{aligned} \tag{4.4}$$

Studying this nondegenerating problem on the bounded interval $(0, \frac{1}{\varepsilon})$ with the help of the maximum principle and tending ε to zero, we obtain the statements of the theorem.

5. Stability

As we observed above, the principal reason for nonuniqueness of the solution was the degenerateness of the differential equations in the mushy region. For the system of differential equations (2.1) this degenerateness changes from strictly parabolic (in liquid and solid) system to hyperbolic-parabolic (in mushy region). As known from the theory of nonlinear hyperbolic differential equations, there is so-called 'stability criterion', which has some physical meaning and almost always allows the choice of the unique solution. In the simpler case of a first-order differential equation with convex nonlinearity, this criterion is formulated as follows: the solution is stable if its characteristics do not leave the line of discontinuity. We now analyse our problem from this point of view.

Now, in the mushy region we have a strictly parabolic partial differential equation for ϑ and a first-order partial differential equation for the solid fraction Φ,

$$(U_\Phi\lambda - C_\Phi æ)\Phi_t + (\lambda^- æ^+ - \lambda^+ æ^-)\vartheta_y\Phi_y = -(C_\vartheta æ + U_\Phi\lambda)\vartheta_t. \tag{5.1}$$

Thus the equation of the characteristic is

$$\dot{Y}(t) = \frac{\lambda^+ æ^- - \lambda^- æ^+}{C_\Phi æ - U_\Phi\lambda}\vartheta_y. \tag{5.2}$$

In order that the characteristic $y = Y(t)$ should not leave the line $y = R(t)$ where the function Φ is discontinuous, on the right-hand side (or the left-hand side), the inequality

$$\dot{Y}(t) \leq \dot{R}(t) \qquad (\text{ or } \dot{Y}(t) \geq \dot{R}(t)) \tag{5.3}$$

must be satisfied. Since for a self-similar variable the line of discontinuity $y = R(t)$ transforms into $x = x_0$, then $R(t) = x_0\sqrt{t}$. Substituting $\vartheta_y = \frac{1}{\sqrt{t}}\vartheta_x$ into (5.2), we obtain from (5.3) the basic inequalities

$$\frac{x_0}{2} \geq \frac{\lambda^+æ^- - \lambda^-æ^+}{C_\Phi æ - U_\Phi \lambda}\vartheta_x \,|_{x_0+0} \tag{5.4}$$

$$\frac{x_0}{2} \leq \frac{\lambda^+æ^- - \lambda^-æ^+}{C_\Phi æ - U_\Phi \lambda}\vartheta_x \,|_{x_0-0}\,. \tag{5.5}$$

Stability criterion. We say that the solution of the problem (2.8), (2.9) is stable if the following properties are satisfied.

(1) Θ, ϑ are continuous; at any point $x \in (0, +\infty)$ there exist right and left limit values for the functions $\Phi, \Theta_x, \vartheta_x$;

(2) for every $x_0 \in (0, +\infty)$ the condition
$\Phi(x_0 + 0) \neq \Phi(x_0 - 0)$
$\Phi(x_0 + 0) \in (0, 1)$ (or $\Phi(x_0 - 0) \in (0, 1)$)
means that (5.4) (or (5.5)) is satisfied.

The second property means that there exists a mushy region to the right of x_0 (or to the left of x_0).

THEOREM 3. *The solution of the problem (2.8), (2.9), obtained by the ε-regularization method in Theorem 2, satisfies the stability criterion.*

This theorem gives one of the productive way, if we want to obtain the stable solution. The paper [7] includes the completed proofs of the Theorem 2 and 3.

References

1. Götz, I.G. and Meirmanov, A. M., *Modelling binary alloy solidification processes*, (Russian), Zh. Pricl. Mekh. Tech. Phis. **4** (1989), 39–45.
2. Donnelly, J. D. P., *A model for non-equilibrum thermodynamic processes involving phase changes*, J. Inst. Maths. Applics. **24** (1979), 425–438.
3. Luckhaus, S. and Visintin, A., *Phase transition in multicomponent systems*, Manuscripta Math. **43** (1983), 261–288.
4. Crowley, A. B. and Ockendon, J.R., *On the numerical solution of an alloy solidification problem*, Int. J. Heat Mass Transfer **22** (1979), 941–947.
5. Fix, G.J., *Numerical method for alloy solidification problems*, Moving boundary problems, Wilson, D. , Solomon, A.D., Boggs, P.S, Ed. Academic Press (1978), 109–128.
6. Götz, I.G., *Self-similar solution of the problem on solidification of binary alloy*, (Russian), Novosibirsk : Dinamika Sploshnoi Sredy **76** (1986), 74–89.
7. Götz, I.G., *On the correctness of a model for phase transitions in binary alloys*, European J. Appl. Math., in press (1990).

On the behaviour of mushy region in a Stefan problem

I.G.Götz
B.B.Zaltzman

Götz, Ivan Gotlibovich
Laurent'ev Institute of Hydrodynamics
Siberian Branch, Academy of Sciences of the USSR
Novosibirsk, 630090, USSR

Zaltzman, Boris Borisovich
Institute of Water and Ecological Problems
Siberian Branch, Academy of Sciences of the USSR
Novosibirsk, 630090, USSR

Abstract. The disappearance of the mushy region in the multidimensional Stefan problem is discussed here. One-phase problem is investigated completely from that point of view. Some criteria of disappearance of the mushy region in the two-phase Stefan problem are suggested. The behaviour of the mushy region in a corner point of domain is studied.

Keywords: Stefan problem, mushy region.

1980 Mathematics subject classifications: 25K05

1. Introduction

In this paper we study the qualitative properties of the weak solution of the Stefan problem. The distinction of this problem is degeneration of a nonllinear parabolic equation of a heat transfer in the whole interval of values of an unknown function U (the enthalpy). The study of the set of degeneration, so-called 'mushy region', was began by Meirmanov [**1**] for one-dimensional Stefan problem. He obtained very interesting and important result about the disappearance of the mushy region after finite time, if some energical criterion is fulfilled. If it is not, the mushy region exists for each instant. In this sense he completed the study of the behaviour of the mushy region for the one-dimensional Stefan problem. In paper [**2**] Meirmanov obtained the similar result for the spherical-symmetric solution of the Stefan problem.

Rogers, Berger [**3**] made the first attempt to investigate the behaviour of the mushy region in the multidimensional two-phase Stefan problem. They proved the nonincrease of the mushy region in the homogenous Stefan problem with constant Dirichlet data and almost uniformly continuous initial data.

Götz, Zaltzman [**4**] generalized the results of [**3**]: for an arbitrary bounded solution of the Stefan problem the mushy region is nonincreasing in time in a sense of the theory of sets.

This result takes place for the nonhomogeneous Stefan problem under some conditions on the behaviour of a heat source in the mushy region.

The measure of the mushy region in one-phase Stefan problem was estimated by Gustafsson and Mossino [5]. Their results take place till the first penetration of the liquid phase through the mushy region. They suggested also the constant temperature on the boundary of the domain: positive – on first, and zero – on second. In this paper (second part) we prove the completed result for the multidimensional one-phase Stefan problem. With the help of our criterion we can establish for an arbitrary bounded solution the disappearance of the mushy region after finite time or the existence of it for each instant.

The criteria of the disappearance of the mushy region after finite time for the two-phase Stefan problem are discussed in the third part. In the forth part we study the behavior of the mushy region in the corner points of the domain for the various angles.

2. The one-phase Stefan problem

We deal with the Stefan problem in the bounded domain $\Omega \subset \mathbb{R}^N$ with a smooth boundary $\Gamma \in C^1$.

$$\frac{\partial U}{\partial t} = \Delta\Theta \quad \text{in } Q_\infty = \Omega \times (0,\infty) \tag{2.1}$$

$$\Theta|_\Gamma = \Theta^1$$

$$U|_{t=0} = U_0 \tag{2.2}$$

Here $\Theta^1 \in L_\infty(\Gamma \times (0,\infty))$, $U_0 \in L_\infty(\Omega)$; $\Theta = \chi(U)$ is the nondecreasing Lipschitz-continuous function, $\Phi = \chi^{-1}$. The function χ is strongly monotone everywhere except the interval $U \in (-L,0)$, where $\chi = 0$, L is the latent heat of melting. The liquid phase of the material corresponds to the set $U \geq 0$, the solid phase – to the set $U \leq -L$, and the mushy zone – to the set $U \in (-L,0)$. By the mushy zone in physical variables we shall understand the set

$$M = \{(x,t) \mid x \in \Omega,\ 0 \leq t < +\infty,\ U(x,t) \in (-L,0)\},\ M(t_0) = M \cap \{t = t_0\}.$$

We name the Stefan problem one-phase, if $U > -L$ or $U < 0$ everywhere in Q_T. Without loss of generality we consider only the first case. Let us define the auxiliary functions $f_\varepsilon^1(x,x_0)$ as the solutions of the problems

$$\Delta_x f_\varepsilon^1(x,x_0) = \delta^\varepsilon(x - x_0)$$
$$f_\varepsilon^1(x,x_0)|_\Gamma = 0$$

where

$$\delta^\varepsilon(y) = 0 \text{ for } \|y\| > \varepsilon,\ \delta^\varepsilon(y) = 1/(\sigma_N \cdot \varepsilon^N) \text{ for } \|y\| \leq \varepsilon,$$

σ_N is the measure of a N-dimensional unit ball.

The functions δ^ε converge to the delta-function δ in the norm of the space of bounded measures as the parameter ε tends to zero. Therefore, taking the limit as $\varepsilon \to 0$, we observe that the function $f^1(x, x_0) = \lim_{\varepsilon \to 0} f^1_\varepsilon(x, x_0)$ is Green's function of the Dirichlet problem.

We see that $f^1_\varepsilon(x, x_0) < 0$, $f^1(x, x_0) < 0$ for every $x, x_0 \in \Omega$. With the help of local estimates of solutions of the elliptic problems we obtain the convergence of the normal derivatives $\frac{\partial}{\partial n} f^1_\varepsilon(x, x_0)|_\Gamma$ to the function $\frac{\partial}{\partial n} f^1(x, x_0)|_\Gamma$ in the norm of the space $L_2(\Gamma)$ for every $x_0 \notin \Gamma$.

Let us suppose that Green's function is known. It characterizes the geometry of the domain Ω and the place of the point x_0 in it.

We shall use the denotations:

$$G_1(t, x_0) = \int_\Omega U_0(x) \cdot f^1(x, x_0)\, dx - \int_0^t \int_\Gamma \frac{\partial}{\partial n} f^1(x, x_0) \cdot \Theta^1(x, \tau)\, dx\, d\tau$$

$$\beta(t) = \int_\Omega f^1(x, x_0)\, dx \cdot \max\{\sup U_0(x), \sup_{\substack{x \in \Gamma \\ 0 \le \tau \le t}} \Phi(\Theta^1(x, \tau))\}$$

$$A(x_0) = \{t \mid 0 \le t < \infty,\ G_1(t, x_0) < \beta(t)\}$$

Now we formulate the main statement of this part.

THEOREM 2.1. *The statements (i1)–(i3) are valid for the solution of the one-phase Stefan problem (2.1), (2.2) with* $U_0(x) > -L, \Theta^1(x, t) \ge 0$:

(*i1*) *For a.e.* $x_0 \in M(0)$:
If $G_1(\infty, x_0) < 0$ *then there exist a finite time* $-t_*(x_0)$ *of the disppearance of the mushy region at the point* x_0.

(*i2*) *For a. e.* $x_0 \in M(0)$*: If* $A(x)$ *is not empty, then we can estimate a time of the disappearance of the mushy region at the point* x_0*:*
$t_*(x_0) \le \bar{t}(x_0)$ *where* $\bar{t}(x_0) = \inf A(x_0)$.

(*i3*) *If* $\sup_{x \in M(0)} G_1(\infty, x) \ge 0$ *and* $U_0 \not\equiv 0$, *or* $\Theta^1 \not\equiv 0$, *or both, then* $|M(t)| > 0$ *for every* $t > 0$.

PROOF: Let us take $x_0 \in M(t)$. Using the function $f^1_\varepsilon(x, x_0)$ as the test function in the domain Q_t and, taking the limit as $\varepsilon \to 0$, we obtain the equality

$$\int_\Omega U(x, t) \cdot f^1(x, x_0)\, dx\, d\tau - \int_0^t \bar{\Theta}(x_0, \tau)\, d\tau = G_1(t, x_0) \tag{2.3}$$

where $\bar{\Theta}(x_0, \tau)$ is the average value of the function Θ with respect to space variables at the point (x_0, τ)

With the help of results [4] we conclude that the mushy region $M(t)$ is nondecreasing function in a sense of the theory of sets, i.e. $|M(\tau_1) \setminus M(\tau_2)| = 0$ for every $\tau_1 > \tau_2$. Therefore $M(\tau)$ includes the point x_0 for a.e. $x_0 \in M(t)$ if $\tau < t$. Using the Lebesque theorem we obtain that for a.e. $x_0 \in M(t)$ the average value of the function Θ at the point (x_0, τ) is equal to zero for every $\tau \in [0, t]$. This is the reason for the equality

$$\int_\Omega U(x,t) \cdot f^1(x, x_0)\, dx = G_1(t, x_0) \tag{2.4}$$

is valid for such (x_0, t), as a corollary of the statement (2.3).

Let the requirement of the first statement of the theorem is fulfilled, i.e. $G_1(\infty, x_0) < 0$, but at the same time $x_0 \in M(t)$ for every $t \in [0, +\infty)$. Then the equality (2.4) is valid for every $t > 0$.

The further proof of ($i1$) is divided into two parts.

$$\int_0^\infty \int_\Gamma \Theta^1(x, \tau)\ dx\ d\tau < \text{ const} \tag{a}$$

LEMMA 1. *If* (a) *holds then there exist the sequence $t_n \to \infty$ such that $\chi(U(x, t_n))$ converges to zero strongly in $L_1(\Omega)$, and the weak limit $U_\infty(x) = \lim_{n\to\infty} U(x, t_n)$ satisfies the inequality $-L \le U_\infty(x) \le 0$.*

PROOF OF THE LEMMA 1: Using a boundness of the solution we choose the sequences $\tau_n,\ t_n \to \infty$ for $n \to \infty$ with the properties

$$\begin{aligned}
&t_n - \tau_n \ge 1,\\
&(U(x, t_n) - U(x, \tau_n)) \to 0, \quad v_n(x) \to v(x) \text{ *weakly in } L_\infty(\Omega)\\
&\text{for } n \to \infty, \text{ where } v_n(x) = 1/(t_n - \tau_n) \cdot \int_{\tau_n}^{t_n} \Theta(x, \tau)\ d\tau.
\end{aligned}$$

Further we use an arbitrary function $\phi \in \overset{0}{H}{}^1(\Omega) \cap H^2(\Omega)$ as a test function in the domain $\Omega \times (\tau_n, t_n)$:

$$\int_\Omega (U(x, t_n) - U(x, \tau_n))\ dx - (t_n - \tau_n) \int_\Omega v_n \cdot \Delta\phi\ dx +$$
$$\int_\Gamma \int_{\tau_n}^{t_n} \Theta^1(x, \tau) \cdot \frac{\partial}{\partial n} \phi(x)\ d\tau\ dx = 0$$

The first integral tends to zero for $n \to \infty$ according to the choise of the sequences τ_n, t_n. The third integral vanishes for $n \to \infty$ too, because the whole integral $\int_\Gamma \int_{\tau_n}^{t_n} \Theta^1(x, \tau)\ d\tau\ dx$ is bounded. As a result we obtain the equality

$$\int_\Omega v \cdot \Delta\phi\ dx = 0.$$

Thus, the function v is the solution of the homogeneous Dirichlet problem. Hence, $v \equiv 0$. Since $v_n \ge 0$, then $v_n \to 0$ strongly, for example, in $L_2(\Omega)$ for $n \to \infty$. Therefore, there exists the sequence $\sigma_n \in [\tau_n, t_n]$ such that $\Theta(x, \sigma_n) \to 0$ strongly in $L_2(\Omega)$, $U(x, \sigma_n) \to U_\infty(x)$ *weakly in $L_\infty(\Omega)$, $-L \leq U_\infty(x) \leq 0$, for $x \in \Omega$. The proof of lemma 1 is over.

With the help of lemma 1 we obtain the contradiction, taking the limit as $\sigma_n \to \infty$ in the equality (2.4):

$$0 \leq \int_\Omega U_\infty(x) \cdot f^1(x, x_0)\, dx = G_1(\infty, x_0) < 0.$$

(b)
$$\int_0^\infty \int_\Gamma \Theta^1(x, \tau)\, dx\, d\tau = \infty.$$

In this case we have $\int_0^\infty \int_\Gamma \Theta^1(x,\tau) \cdot \frac{\partial}{\partial n} f^1(x, x_0)\, dx\, d\tau = \infty$. Since the left side of the equality (2.4) id bounded the contradiction follow. Thus, we complete the proof of the first statement of the theorem.

The second statement is proved with the help of the estimates

$$U(x,t) \leq \max\{\sup U_0(x), \sup_{0 \leq \tau \leq t} \Phi(\Theta^1)\}$$

$$\beta(t) \leq \int_\Omega U(x,t) \cdot f^1(x, x_0)\, dx = G_1(t, x_0) \text{ for } t \leq t_*(x_0)$$

Now we prove the third part of the theorem. Let us assume that for some t_*, $|M(t)| = 0$, for $t > t_*$. Because $U_0 \not\equiv 0$ or $\Theta^1 \not\equiv 0$, then with the help of the strong maximum principle we obtain that $\Theta(x,t) > 0$ for every $x \in \Omega, t > t_*$. Using the conditions of the theorem we find the point x_0, such that $G(\infty, x_0) \geq 0$. In particular, the integral $\int_0^\infty \int_\Gamma \frac{\partial}{\partial n} f^1(x, x_0) \cdot \Theta^1(x,t)\, dx\, dt$ is bounded and hence, the integral $\int_0^\infty \int_\Gamma \Theta^1(x,t)\, dx\, dt$ is finite too. The existence of a weak limit $U_\infty(x)$ $(-L \leq U_\infty(x) \leq 0)$ of the sequence $U(x, t_n)$ as $t_n \to \infty$ follows from the boundness of the previous integrals. With the help of (2.3) we obtain

$$\int_\Omega U_\infty(x) \cdot f^1(x, x_0)\, dx = \int_0^\infty \bar{\Theta}(x_0, \tau)\, d\tau + G_1(\infty, x_0) > 0$$

and hence $U_\infty \not\equiv 0$. Since $-L \leq U_\infty \leq 0$, then $|M(\infty)| \neq 0$, what contradicts above mentioned assumption. Thus, we complete the proof of the theorem.

3. Two-phase Stefan problem

We use a new auxiliary function for the study of the full Stefan problem. Let denote $f^2(x, x_0, \alpha) = (\nabla_{x_0} f^1(x, x_0), \vec{\alpha})$. The function $f^2(x, x_0, \alpha)$ is the weak solution of the problem

$$\Delta_x f^2(x, x_0, \alpha) = (\nabla \delta(x - x_0), \alpha)$$
$$f^2|_\Gamma = 0$$

As known about the properties of the Green's function of the Laplace equation, the function f^2 is integrable with respect the first variable over the domain Ω and it is a smooth function everywhere except the point x_0. Let us denote too:

$$G_2(t,x_0,\alpha) = \int_\Omega U_0(x)\cdot f^2(x,x_0,\alpha)dx - \int_0^t \int_\Omega \frac{\partial}{\partial n} f^2(x,x_0,\alpha)\cdot \Theta^1(x,\tau)\,dx\,d\tau$$

$$\beta_1(t,x_0) = -\int_\Omega f^1(x,x_0)dx \cdot \max\{\sup|U_0(x)|, \sup_{\substack{0\le\tau\le t\\ x\in\Gamma}} |\Phi(\Theta^1(x,\tau))|\}$$

$$\beta_2(t,x_0,\alpha) = \int_\Omega |f^2(x,x_0,\alpha)|\,dx \cdot \max\{\sup|U_0(x)|, \sup_{\substack{0\le\tau\le t\\ x\in\Gamma}} |\Phi(\Theta^1(x,\tau))|\}$$

$$A_1(x_0) = \{\tau \mid 0<\tau<\infty, G_1(\tau,x_0)\notin[-\beta_1(\tau,x_0),\beta_1(\tau,x_0)]\}$$

$$A_2(x_0,\alpha) = \{\tau \mid 0<\tau<\infty, G_2(\tau,x_0,\alpha)\notin[-\beta_2(\tau,x_0,\alpha),\beta_2(\tau,x_0,\alpha)]\}$$

THEOREM 3.1. *Suppose that U is a bounded solution of the Stefan problem (2.1), (2.2). Then for a.e. $x_0\in M(0)$ the next statement is valid:*

If $A_1(x_0)\neq\emptyset$, or $A_2(x_0,\alpha)\neq\emptyset$ for some α, or both, then the time of disappearance of the mushy region at the point x_0 may be estimated:

$$t_*(x_0) \le \min\{\inf A_1(x_0), \inf_{\alpha\in\mathbf{R}^N} A_2(x_0,\alpha)\} \tag{3.1}$$

PROOF: Let $x_0\in M(t)$. As we did above (in theorem 2.1), we use the functions $f^1(x,x_0)$ and $f^2(x,x_0,\alpha)$ as the test functions for the problem (2.1), (2.2). So we obtain the main equalities

$$\begin{aligned}\int_\Omega U(x,t)\cdot f^1(x,x_0)\,dx &= G_1(t,x_0)\\ \int_\Omega U(x,t)\cdot f^2(x,x_0,\alpha)\,dx &= G_2(t,x_0,\alpha)\end{aligned} \tag{3.2}$$

for a.e. $x_0\in M(t)$. Estimating the left-hand sides of the equalities (3.2) with the help of maximum principle:

$$|U(x,t)| \le \max\{\sup|U_0(x)|, \sup_{\substack{0\le\tau\le t\\ x\in\Gamma}} |\Phi(\Theta_1(x,\tau))|\}$$

we complete the proof of the theorem.

More appropriate result may be formulated when there exists the limit of boundary data as $t\to\infty$

$$\int_0^\infty \int_\Gamma |\Theta^1(x,t)-\Theta^1_\infty(x)|\;dx\;dt < \infty \tag{3.3}$$

In this case our solution converges to the solution of the stationary problem

$$\begin{aligned} &\Delta\Theta_\infty = 0 \\ &\Theta_\infty|_\Gamma = \Theta^1_\infty(x) \end{aligned} \tag{3.4}$$

If $\Theta^1_\infty \not\equiv 0$, then the measure of the set $\{x \in \Omega \mid \Theta_\infty(x) = 0\}$ is equal to zero, because Θ_∞ is a solution of the Laplace equation. Hence we can find the function $U_\infty(x) = \Phi(\Theta_\infty(x))$ in a unique fashion. If $\Theta^1_\infty \equiv 0$, then it is not possible, and U_∞ may be obtained only in an evolutionary process. Therefore, the formulation of the next theorem divides into two parts.

THEOREM 3.2. *Let (3.3) be fulfilled. Then for a.e. $x_0 \in M(0)$ the mushy region disappears after finite time at the point $x_0 \in M(0)$ if*

1. $\Theta^1_\infty \not\equiv 0$

$$\begin{aligned} &\int_\Omega U_\infty(x)\cdot f^1(x,x_0)\,dx \neq G_1(\infty,x_0) \text{ or} \\ &\int_\Omega U_\infty(x)\cdot f^2(x,x_0,\alpha)\,dx \neq G_2(\infty,x_0,\alpha) \text{ for some } \alpha \end{aligned} \tag{3.5}$$

2. $\Theta^1_\infty \equiv 0$

$$\begin{aligned} &G_1(\infty,x_0) \notin [0,-L\cdot\int_\Omega f^1(x,x_0)\,dx] \text{ or} \\ &G_1(\infty,x_0,\alpha) \notin [-L\cdot\int_\Omega |f^2(x,x_0)|\,dx, L\cdot\int_\Omega |f^2(x,x_0)|\,dx] \end{aligned} \tag{3.6}$$

The theorem 3.2 is a corollary of the equalities (3.2).

REMARK 1. If $\Theta^1_\infty \not\equiv 0$ the condition (3.5) may be replaced by more restricting:

$$\Theta_\infty(x_0) \neq 0, \text{ or } |\nabla\Theta_\infty(x_0)| \neq 0. \tag{3.7}$$

It is necessary to prove the statement (3.7) $\Longrightarrow$ (3.5) which immediately follows from the representations

$$\Theta_\infty(x_0) = \int_\Gamma \frac{\partial f^1}{\partial n}(x,x_0)\cdot\Theta^1_\infty(x)\,dx$$

$$\frac{\partial}{\partial\alpha}\Theta_\infty(x_0) = -\int_\Gamma \frac{\partial f^2}{\partial n}(x,x_0,\alpha)\cdot\Theta^1_\infty(x)\,dx.$$

So we see that the main results for the two-phase Stefan problem (theorems 3.1, 3.2) are much poorer than for the one-phase problem (theorem 2.1). Really, the behaviour of the mushy region in the one-phase problem can be completely described by means of the function $G_1(t,x)$: if $G_1(\infty,x) < 0$, then the mushy region disappears after finite time, if $G_1(\infty,x) \geq 0$, then the mushy region exists for each instant. For the total Stefan problem we can obtain only the criteria (3.1), (3.5), (3.6) for the disappearance of the mushy region $M(t)$ after finite time. If that cirteria are not fulfilled we know nothing about the disappearance of $M(t)$.Nevertheless, we have the arguments on the correctness of the choise of our criteria. In the next paragraph we construct the example — the solution for which the conditions (3.7) don't fulfill and the mushy region exists for each instant.

4. The behaviour of the mushy region in the corner point of a domain

Let $N = 2$, $\vec{x} = (x_1, x_2)$. We consider the one-phase Stefan problem in the sector $\Omega_{\varphi_0} = \{(r,\varphi) \mid 0 \leq r \leq 1,\ 0 \leq \varphi \leq \varphi_0\}$ with $r = \sqrt{x_1^2 + x_2^2}$, $\varphi = \operatorname{arctang} g\frac{x_1}{x_2}$. Let us set the boundary condition

$$\begin{aligned} &\Theta|_{\varphi=0} = 0,\ \Theta|_{\varphi=\varphi_0} = 0 \\ &\Theta|_{r=1} = \Theta^1 \equiv const > 0 \end{aligned} \tag{4.1}$$

and the initial data

$$U|_{t=0} = U_0. \tag{4.2}$$

Now formulate the requirements of the initial data:

(i) $\Phi(\Theta^1) \geq U_0 > -L$ and there exists $r_0 \in (0,1)$, such that $U_0 \equiv l$ for $r < r_0$, $U_0 \geq 0$ for $r \geq r_0$, $l \in (-L, 0)$.

(ii) the function U_0 is nondecreasing with respect the variables x_1, x_2 in the domain $\Omega_{\frac{\varphi_0}{2}}$, $U_0|_{\varphi=\varphi_1} = U_0|_{\varphi=\varphi_0-\varphi_1}$ for $\varphi_1 \in [0, \varphi_0]$.

Theorem 4.1. *Let $0 < \varphi_0 \leq \frac{\pi}{2}$ and the function U_0 satisfies the condition (i). Then there exists a nonincreasing function $r_0(t)$: $r_0(t) > 0$ for every $t \geq 0$, such that $U \equiv l$ for $0 \leq r \leq r_0(t)$, i.e. $M(t) \supset \Omega_{\varphi_0} \cap \{r < r_0(t)\}$, where U is the solution of the Stefan problem with the boundary-initial data (4.1), (4.2).*

The main idea of the proof of this theorem is using of the function $f = (\frac{1}{r^\gamma} - r^\gamma)\sin\gamma\varphi$, $\gamma = \frac{\pi}{\varphi_0}$ as a test function for the problem (2.1), (4.1), (4.2).

In addition to the theorem 4.1 we formulate the following result:

Theorem 4.2. *Let $\varphi_0 \in (\frac{\pi}{2}, 2\pi)$ and U_0 satisfies (i). Then the mushy region of the solution of the Stefan problem (2.1), (4.1), (4.2) disappears after finite time.*

The proof of this theorem is obtained with the help of the majorant's estimates.

Now we construct the example, announced in the end of the third part. Let $\Phi'(\Theta) = \Phi'(-\Theta)$ for $\Theta > 0$. Then the temperature satisfies the same nonlinear differential equation in the solid and liquid phases.

$$\Phi'(\Theta) \cdot \Theta_t - \Delta\Theta = 0$$

Therefore, if Θ and U are the solution of the equation (2.1), the functions $-\Theta, -U-L$ are the solutions of it too. We shall use this property. Let fix the natural number $n = 2, 3\ldots$ We study the solution of the Stefan problem in the circle K of the unit radius with the initial-boundary data

$$\Theta|_{r=1} = \Theta^1(\varphi) \qquad (4.3)$$
$$U|_{t=0} = U_0(r,\varphi),$$

where

$$\Theta^1(\varphi) = \begin{cases} C^2 \text{ for } \varphi \in (2i\frac{\pi}{n}, (2i+1)\frac{\pi}{n}) \\ -C^2 \text{ for } \varphi \in ((2i-1)\frac{\pi}{n}, 2i\frac{\pi}{n}) \end{cases} \quad \text{for } i \in [0,n] \qquad (4.4)$$
$$U_0|_{r<r_0} = -\frac{L}{2}$$
$$U_0(r,\varphi) = -U_0(r,\varphi - \frac{\pi}{n}) - L$$

where U_0 satisfies the conditions (i), (ii) in the domain $\Omega_{\frac{\pi}{n}}$. The required symmetry of the initial boundary data and the uniqueness theorem of the solution of the Stefan problem allow to conclude that the solution in hand in each of the sectors $\varphi \in (2i\frac{\pi}{n}, (2i+1)\frac{\pi}{n}), \varphi \in ((2i-1)\frac{\pi}{n}, 2i\frac{\pi}{n})$ coincides with the solution of the one-phase Stefan problem, studied in the theorem 4.1. Therefore, the statement of the theorem (4.1) is fulfilled for the solution in hand, i.e. there exists the nonincreasing function $r_0(t) > 0$ for $t > 0$, such that $U|_{r<r_o(t)} = -\frac{L}{2}$. Hence, the mushy region does not degenerate. For every instant the measure of $M(t) \supset \{r < r_0(t)\}$ is not equal to zero. At the same time, it is obvious that the equality $\Theta_\infty(0) = |\nabla\Theta_\infty(0)| = 0$ is valid for the solution Θ_∞ of the problem (3.4) in the domain K with boundary data satisfied (4.4). Thus, the requirement (3.7) is not valid, and at the same time the mushy region exists for each instant.

REFERENCES

1. Meirmanov A. M., *The structure of a generalized solution of the Stefan problem. Periodic solutions.*, Dokl.Akad.Nauk SSSR **272,** No 4, (1983), 789–791; English transl. in Soviet Math. Docl. **28** no 2, (1983), 440-443.
2. Meirmanov A. M., *On the disappearance of the mushy region in the Stefan problem with spherical symmetry.*, Dinamika sploshnoi sredy, Lavrentyev Institute of Hydrodynamics **91** (1989), 86–99.
3. Rogers J.C.W., Berger A.E., *Some properties of the nonlinear semigroup for the problem* $u_t - \Delta f(u) = 0.$, Nonlinear Anal., Theory Methods & Applications V.8, no 8 (1984), 909-939.
4. Götz I.G, Zaltzman B.B., *Nonincrease of mushy region in a nonhomogenous Stefan problem,* To be published in Quarterly of Applied Mathematics.
5. Gustafsson B, Mossino J., *Quelques inequalites isoperimetriques pour le probleme de Stefan,* Math. Analysis. C.R.Acad. Sci.Paris **305** Ser.1, 669-672.

International Series of Numerical Mathematics, Vol. 99, © 1991 Birkhäuser Verlag Basel

Optimal control of hemivariational inequalities. Approximation results.

J. Haslinger[1]
P.D. Panagiotopoulos[2]

[1]Faculty of Mathematics and Physics
Charles University
KFK MFF UK Malostranske 2/25
11800 Praha 1, Czechoslovakia
and
Department of Mathematics
University of Jyväskylä
Seminaarinkatu 15
40100 Jyväskylä 10, Finland

[2]Chair of Steel Structures
School of Technology of Aristotele University
Thessaloniki, Greece

Abstract. Approximation of the optimal control problem, governed by the hemivariational inequality is studied. It is proved that discrete optimal control problems are related to the continuous ones. Optimality conditions are applied in the case of one dimensional model example.

Keywords. Approximation of the hemivariational inequality, optimal control of the hemivariational inequality, optimality conditions.

1980 Mathematics subject classifications: 49A22, 49A52, 65K10

Introduction

In practice we often meet problems, in which consitutive laws are given by nonmonotone, possible multivalued fuctions (see [**1**]). These problems can not be treated in the frame of classical convex analysis, nevertheless the principle of virtual works is still available. The so called hemivariational inequality represents possible extension of classical variational inequality, permitting mathematical modelling of nonmonotone laws.

Considering the mechanical system, behaviour of which is described by a hemivariational inequality, it is natural to study the problem of its control. This contribution deals with the approximation of the above mentioned optimal control problem, continuous form of which is studied in [**2**]. Let us repeat the formulation of the problem as well as some basic results.

Let $b \in L^\infty_{\text{loc}}(\mathbf{R}^1)$ be a locally bounded and measurable function in $\mathbf{R}^1$. For any $\delta > 0$ set

$$\underline{b}_\delta(\xi) = \operatorname*{ess\,inf}_{|\tau-\xi|\le\delta} b(\tau), \quad \overline{b}_\delta(\xi) = \operatorname*{ess\,sup}_{|\tau-\xi|\le\delta} b(\tau)$$

$$\underline{b}(\xi) = \lim_{\delta\to 0+} \underline{b}_\delta(\xi), \quad \overline{b}(\xi) = \lim_{\delta\to 0+} \overline{b}_\delta(\xi).$$

Let $\hat{b}\colon \mathbf{R}^1 \to 2^{\mathbf{R}^1}$ be a multifunction, given by

$$\hat{b}(\xi) = [\underline{b}(\xi), \overline{b}(\xi)] \quad \forall \xi \in \mathbf{R}^1.$$

Next, we shall assume

$$\exists \bar{\xi} > 0 : \operatorname*{ess\,sup}_{\xi\in(-\infty,-\bar{\xi})} b(\xi) \le 0 \le \operatorname*{ess\,inf}_{\xi\in(\bar{\xi},+\infty)} b(\xi). \tag{0.1}$$

Further, let $\Omega \subseteq \mathbf{R}^N$ be a bounded domain with Lipschitz boundary $\partial\Omega$, V a Hilbert space, $H^1_0(\Omega) \subseteq V \subseteq H^1(\Omega)$ and such that $V \cap C(\overline{\Omega})$ is dense in V. Let $\mathcal{U}$ be another Hilbert space (of controls), $\mathcal{U}_{\text{ad}} \subseteq \mathcal{U}$ its non-empty, closed, convex subset. With any $u \in \mathcal{U}_{\text{ad}}$, the bilinear form $a_u : V \times V \to \mathbf{R}^1$ will be associated. We assume

$$\exists M = \text{const.} > 0 : |a_u(y,z)| \le M\|y\|\|z\| \quad \forall y, z \in V,\ \forall u \in \mathcal{U}_{\text{ad}}; \tag{0.2}$$

$$\exists \alpha = \text{const.} > 0 : a_u(z,z) \ge \alpha\|z\|^2 \quad \forall z \in V,\ \forall u \in \mathcal{U}_{\text{ad}}; \tag{0.3}$$

$$u_n \rightharpoonup u \text{ (weakly) in } \mathcal{U},\ u_n, u \in \mathcal{U}_{\text{ad}} \implies A(u_n) \to A(u) \text{ in } \mathcal{L}(V, V'), \tag{0.4}$$

where

$$a_u(y,z) = \langle A(u)y, z\rangle,\ A(u) \in \mathcal{L}(V, V').$$

Finally, let $B \in \mathcal{L}(U, V')$. With any $u \in \mathcal{U}_{\text{ad}}$ we associate the hemivariational inequality

$$(\mathcal{P}(u)) \qquad \begin{cases} \text{Find } y = y(u) \in V \text{ and } \mathcal{X} \equiv \mathcal{X}(u) \in L^1(\Omega) \cap V' \text{ s.t.} \\ a_u(y(u), z) + \int_\Omega \mathcal{X} z\, dx = \langle f + Bu, z\rangle \quad \forall z \in V \\ \mathcal{X}(x) \in \hat{b}(y(x)) \text{ a.e. in } \Omega. \end{cases}$$

It holds:

THEOREM 0.1. *If (0.1)-(0.3) are satisfied, $(\mathcal{P}(u))$ has at least one solution for any $u \in \mathcal{U}_{\text{ad}}$.*

The set of all solutions of $(\mathcal{P}(u))$ for a given $u \in \mathcal{U}_{\text{ad}}$ will be denoted by $X(u)$.
Let $\mathcal{J} : V \times \mathcal{U} \to \mathbf{R}^1$ be a cost functional satisfying

$$y_n \rightharpoonup y \text{ in } V,\ u_n \rightharpoonup u \text{ in } \mathcal{U} \implies \liminf_{n\to\infty} \mathcal{J}(y_n, u_n) \ge \mathcal{J}(y, u); \tag{0.5}$$

$$\forall R > 0\ \exists r > 0\ \forall \|u\| \ge r, u \in \mathcal{U}_{\text{ad}}\ \forall y \in V : \mathcal{J}(y, u) \ge R. \tag{0.6}$$

For any $u \in \mathcal{U}_{\mathrm{ad}}$ we define the intermediate problem

$$(\mathsf{P}(u)) \qquad \begin{cases} \text{Find } \bar{y} \in X(u) \text{ s.t.} \\ \mathcal{J}(\bar{y},u) \le \mathcal{J}(y,u) \quad \forall y \in X(u). \end{cases}$$

Denote $E(u) = \mathcal{J}(\bar{y},u)$, where $\bar{y} \in X(u)$ solves $(\mathsf{P}(u))$. The optimal control for the hemivariational inequality is defined as follows

$$(\mathsf{P}) \qquad \begin{cases} \text{Find } u^* \in \mathcal{U}_{\mathrm{ad}} \text{ such that} \\ E(u^*) \le E(u) \quad \forall u \in \mathcal{U}_{\mathrm{ad}}. \end{cases}$$

One has:

THEOREM 0.2. *If (0.1)-(0.6) are satisfied,* (P) *has at least one solution* u^*.

Next section deals with the finite element approximation of (P). We shall show that the discrete optimal control problems are related to a "restricted" continuous optimal control problem. A simple model example will be presented and optimality conditions, derived in [**3**], will be applied.

1. APPROXIMATION OF (P)

Let $h > 0$ be a discretization parameter and $V_h \subset V \cap C(\overline{\Omega})$, $\mathcal{U}_h \subset \mathcal{U}$ finite dimensional subspaces of V and $\mathcal{U}$, respectively. Let $\mathcal{U}^h_{\mathrm{ad}}$ be a closed, convex subset of $\mathcal{U}_h$, not necessarily contained in $\mathcal{U}_{\mathrm{ad}}$. For any $u_h \in \mathcal{U}^h_{\mathrm{ad}}$ fixed, we assume the following problem:

$$(\mathcal{P}(u_h))_h \qquad \begin{cases} \text{Find } y_h \in V_h \text{ s.t. there exists } \mathcal{X}_h \in L^1(\Omega) \cap V_h' \text{ and} \\ a_{u_h}(y_h, z_h) + \int_\Omega \mathcal{X}_h z_h \, dx = \langle f + Bu_h, z_h \rangle \quad \forall z_h \in V_h \\ \mathcal{X}_h(x) \in \hat{b}(y_h(x)) \text{ a.e. in } \Omega. \end{cases}$$

$X_h(u_h)$ will denote the set of all solutions of $(\mathcal{P}(u_h))_h$.

Using the same approach as in [**2**], one can prove the following propositions:

PROPOSITION 1.1. *If (0.2) and (0.3) hold for any* $u \in \mathcal{U}_{\mathrm{ad}} \cup \mathcal{U}^h_{\mathrm{ad}}$, *then* $X_h(u_h) \neq \emptyset$.

PROPOSITION 1.2. *It holds:*

$$\|X_h(u_h)\| = \sup_{y_h \in X_h(u_h)} \|y_h\| \le \frac{1}{\alpha}(\|f\|_{V'} + \|B\|\|u_h\|_{\mathcal{U}}) + C.$$

PROPOSITION 1.3. $X_h(u_h)$ *is compact for any* $h > 0$ *and any* $u_h \in \mathcal{U}^h_{\mathrm{ad}}$.

PROPOSITION 1.4. *If (0.4) holds on* $\mathcal{U}_{\mathrm{ad}} \cup \mathcal{U}^h_{\mathrm{ad}}$, *then the mapping* $u_h \to X_h(u_h)$ *is closed.*

Now, for any $u_h \in \mathcal{U}^h_{\mathrm{ad}}$ we define the intermediate problem

$$(\mathsf{P}(u_h))_h \qquad \begin{cases} \text{Find } \bar{y}_h \in X_h(u_h) \text{ such that} \\ \mathcal{J}(\bar{y}_h, u_h) \le \mathcal{J}(y_h, u_h) \quad \forall y_h \in X_h(u_h). \end{cases}$$

PROPOSITION 1.5. *For any* $u_h \in \mathcal{U}^h_{\mathrm{ad}}$ *there exists at least one solution of* $(\mathsf{P}(u_h))_h$.

By the approximation of (P) we mean the problem

$$(\mathsf{P})_h \qquad \begin{cases} \text{Find } u_h^* \in \mathcal{U}^h_{\mathrm{ad}} \text{ such that} \\ E(u_h^*) \le E(u_h) \quad \forall u_h \in \mathcal{U}^h_{\mathrm{ad}}, \end{cases}$$

where $E(u_h) = \mathcal{J}(\bar{y}_h, u_h)$. If (0.6) holds for any $u \in \mathcal{U}_{\mathrm{ad}} \cup \mathcal{U}^h_{\mathrm{ad}}$ then we immediately have

PROPOSITION 1.6. *$(\mathsf{P})_h$ has at least one solution for any $h > 0$.*

Next we shall examine the relation between (P) and $(\mathsf{P})_h$ when $h \to 0+$. To this end let us assume that two families $\{V_h\}$, $\{\mathcal{U}_h\}$ of finite dimensional subspaces of V and $\mathcal{U}$, respectively are given, $V_h \subset V \cap C(\overline{\Omega})$, $\dim V_h \to \infty$, $\dim \mathcal{U}_h \to \infty$, if $h \to 0+$. Let $\{\mathcal{U}_{\mathrm{ad}}^h\}$ be a family of closed convex subsets of $\mathcal{U}_h$, not necessarily contained in $\mathcal{U}_{\mathrm{ad}}$.

Next, we shall suppose

$$(1.1) \qquad \begin{cases} V \cap C(\overline{\Omega}) \text{ is dense in } V, \\ \forall v \in V \cap C(\overline{\Omega}) \quad \exists v_h \in V_h : v_h \to v \text{ in } C(\overline{\Omega}) \text{ and } V\text{-norm;} \end{cases}$$

$$(1.2) \qquad \forall u \in \mathcal{U}_{\mathrm{ad}} \quad \exists u_h \in \mathcal{U}_{\mathrm{ad}}^h : u_h \rightharpoonup u \text{ in } \mathcal{U};$$

$$(1.3) \qquad u_h \in \mathcal{U}_{\mathrm{ad}}^h,\ u_h \rightharpoonup u \implies u \in \mathcal{U}_{\mathrm{ad}}.$$

Further let us suppose:

$$(1.4) \qquad \exists M = \text{const.} > 0 : |a_u(y,z)| \le M\|y\|\|z\| \ \forall y,z \in V \ \forall u \in \mathcal{U}_{\mathrm{ad}} \cup \bigcup_{h>0} \mathcal{U}_{\mathrm{ad}}^h;$$

$$(1.5) \qquad \exists \alpha = \text{const.} > 0 : a_u(z,z) \ge \alpha\|z\|^2 \ \forall z \in V \ \forall u \in \mathcal{U}_{\mathrm{ad}} \cup \bigcup_{h>0} \mathcal{U}_{\mathrm{ad}}^h;$$

$$(1.6) \qquad \forall R > 0 \ \exists r > 0 \ \forall \|u\| \ge r, u \in \mathcal{U}_{\mathrm{ad}} \cup \bigcup_{h>0} \mathcal{U}_{\mathrm{ad}}^h \ \forall y \in V : \mathcal{J}(y,u) \ge R$$

$$(1.6)' \qquad u_h \rightharpoonup u,\ u_h \in \mathcal{U}_{\mathrm{ad}}^h \implies A(u_h) \to A(u) \text{ in } \mathcal{L}(V,V').$$

REMARK 1.1. If $\mathcal{U}_{\mathrm{ad}}^h \subset \mathcal{U}_{\mathrm{ad}}$ $\forall h > 0$ then (1.3) is automatically satisfied. Also (1.4)-(1.6)' are fullfilled because of (0.2), (0.3),(0.4) and (0.6).

Finally we assume

$$(1.7) \qquad \left.\begin{array}{l} y_h \rightharpoonup y \text{ in } V,\ y_h \in V_h \\ u_h \rightharpoonup u \text{ in } \mathcal{U},\ u_h \in \mathcal{U}_{\mathrm{ad}}^h \end{array}\right\} \implies \lim_{h\to 0+} \mathcal{J}(y_h,u_h) = \mathcal{J}(y,u).$$

First of all we prove

PROPOSITION 1.7. *Let $u_h \in \mathcal{U}_{\mathrm{ad}}^h$ be such that*

$$(1.8) \qquad u_h \rightharpoonup u \ \text{in } \mathcal{U}$$

and $y_h \in X_h(u_h)$. Then there is a subsequence of $\{y_h\}$ (denoted by the same symbol) and $y \in X(u)$ such that

$$(1.9) \qquad y_h \rightharpoonup y \ \text{in } V.$$

PROOF: $\{y_h\}$ is bounded as follows from (1.8) and Proposition 1.2. Thus there is a subsequence of $\{y_h\}$ and $y \in V$, satisfying (1.9).

Let us show that $y \in X(u)$. If $\bar{z} \in V \cap C(\overline{\Omega})$ is an arbitrary element, there exists a sequence $\{\bar{z}_h\}$, $\bar{z}_h \in V_h$ such that

$$\bar{z}_h \to \bar{z} \text{ in } C(\overline{\Omega}) \text{ and } V\text{-norm.} \tag{1.10}$$

As $y_h \in X_h(u_h)$, there exists $\mathcal{X}_h \in L^1(\Omega) \cap V_h'$ such that

$$a_{u_h}(y_h, \bar{z}_h) + \int_\Omega \mathcal{X}_h \bar{z}_h \, dx = \langle f + Bu_h, \bar{z}_h \rangle$$

$$\mathcal{X}_h(x) \in \hat{b}(y_h(x)) \text{ a.e. in } \Omega.$$

Using (1.6)', (1.8) and (1.9), we can write

$$\begin{cases} a_{u_h}(y_h, \bar{z}_h) \to a_u(y, \bar{z}) \\ \langle f + Bu_h, \bar{z}_h \rangle \to \langle f + Bu, \bar{z} \rangle. \end{cases} \tag{1.11}$$

Arguing in the same manner as in [**2**], one can show that $\{\mathcal{X}_h\}$ is weakly $L^1(\Omega)$ compact, i.e. $\exists \mathcal{X} \in L^1(\Omega)$ such that

$$\int_\Omega \mathcal{X}_h \bar{z}_h \, dx \to \int_\Omega \mathcal{X} \bar{z} \, dx. \tag{1.12}$$

It is readily seen that $\mathcal{X} \in V'$. Thus (1.11) and (1.12) yield:

$$a_u(y, \bar{z}) + \int_\Omega \mathcal{X} \bar{z} \, dx = \langle f + Bu, \bar{z} \rangle \quad \forall \bar{z} \in V.$$

The fact that

$$\mathcal{X}(x) \in \hat{b}(y(x)) \text{ a.e. in } \Omega$$

can be also proved in the same way as in [**2**].

For any $u \in \mathcal{U}_{\text{ad}}$ let

$$\tilde{X}(u) = \{y \in V \mid \exists \{u_h\},\ u_h \in \mathcal{U}_{\text{ad}}^h : u_h \rightharpoonup u \text{ in } \mathcal{U} \text{ and } y_h(u_h) \rightharpoonup y \text{ in } V, \text{ where } y_h(u_h) \in X_h(u_h)\}.$$

PROPOSITION 1.8. *It holds*

$$\emptyset \neq \tilde{X}(u) \subseteq X(u) \quad \forall u \in \mathcal{U}_{\text{ad}}.$$

PROOF: The non-emptiness of $\tilde{X}(u)$ is a consequence of (1.2) and the previous proposition. The inclusion follows also from the Proposition 1.7.

PROPOSITION 1.9. *$\tilde{X}(u)$ is weakly compact.*

PROOF: It is sufficent to prove that $\tilde{X}(u)$ is weakly closed in $X(u)$. But this is clear from the definition.

For any $u \in \mathcal{U}_{\text{ad}}$ we define the problem

$$(\tilde{\mathsf{P}}(u)) \qquad \begin{cases} \text{Find } \tilde{y} = \tilde{y}(u) \in \tilde{X}(u) \text{ s.t.} \\ \mathcal{J}(\tilde{y}, u) \leq \mathcal{J}(y, u) \quad \forall y \in \tilde{X}(u). \end{cases}$$

Such $\tilde{y}$ exists as follows from the Proposition 1.9.

Let $\tilde{E}(u) = \mathcal{J}(\tilde{y}, u)\ \forall u \in \mathcal{U}_{\text{ad}}$ and define the problem:

$$(\tilde{\mathsf{P}}) \qquad \begin{cases} \text{Find } \tilde{u}^* \in \mathcal{U}_{\text{ad}} \text{ such that} \\ \tilde{E}(\tilde{u}^*) \leq \tilde{E}(u) \quad \forall u \in \mathcal{U}_{\text{ad}}. \end{cases}$$

Now, we able to establish the relation between $(\tilde{\mathsf{P}})$ and $(\mathsf{P})_h$, $h \to 0+$.

THEOREM 1.1. *Let u_h^* be solution of $(\mathsf{P})_h$, $y_h^* \in V_h$ the solution of $(\mathsf{P}(u_h^*))_h$. Then there exist subsequences of $\{u_h^*\}$, $\{y_h^*\}$ and elements $\tilde{u}^* \in \mathcal{U}_{\text{ad}}$, $\tilde{y}^* \in V$ such that*

$$(1.13) \qquad \begin{cases} u_h^* \rightharpoonup \tilde{u}^*, \ h \to 0+ \\ y_h^* \rightharpoonup \tilde{y}^*, \ h \to 0+. \end{cases}$$

Moreover $\tilde{u}^*$ solves $(\tilde{\mathsf{P}})$ and $\tilde{y}^*$ is a solution of $(\tilde{\mathsf{P}}(\tilde{u}^*))$.

PROOF: $\{u_h^*\}$ as well as $\{y_h^*\}$ are bounded. Hence there exist above mentioned subsequences and elements, satisfying (1.13). Moreover $\tilde{y}^* \in \tilde{X}(\tilde{u}^*)$ as follows from the definition of $\tilde{X}(u)$ and Proposition 1.7. By the definition of $(\mathsf{P})_h$, we have

$$(1.14) \qquad \mathcal{J}(y_h^*, u_h^*) \leq \mathcal{J}(y_h, u_h) \quad \forall u_h \in \mathcal{U}_{\text{ad}}^h, \forall y_h \in X_h(u_h).$$

Let $\bar{u} \in \mathcal{U}_{\text{ad}}$ and $\bar{y} \in \tilde{X}(\bar{u})$ be given. Accordingly to the definition of $\tilde{X}(\bar{u})$, there is a sequence of $\bar{u}_h \in \mathcal{U}_{\text{ad}}^h$ such that

$$\bar{u}_h \rightharpoonup \bar{u}, \quad h \to 0+$$

and

$$\bar{y}_h \rightharpoonup \bar{y}, \quad h \to 0+, \ \bar{y}_h \in X_h(\bar{u}_h).$$

Substituting $\bar{u}_h$, $\bar{y}_h$ into the right side of (1.14), passing to the limit with $h \to 0+$ and using the property (1.7) we arrive at

$$\mathcal{J}(\tilde{y}^*, \tilde{u}^*) \leq \mathcal{J}(\bar{y}, \bar{u}) \quad \forall \bar{u} \in \mathcal{U}_{\text{ad}}, \ \forall \bar{y} \in \tilde{X}(u),$$

i.e. $\tilde{u}^*$ solves $(\tilde{\mathsf{P}})$ and $\tilde{y}^*$ is a solution of $(\tilde{\mathsf{P}}(\tilde{u}^*))$.

REMARK 1.2 If $\tilde{X}(u) = X(u)\ \forall u \in \mathcal{U}_{\mathrm{ad}}$ then $(\tilde{\mathbf{P}}(u))$ and $(\mathbf{P}(u))$, as well as $(\tilde{\mathbf{P}})$ and $(\mathbf{P})$ are identical. In that case, $(\mathbf{P})_h$ is a real approximation of $(\mathbf{P})$, otherwise, $(\mathbf{P})_h$ is the approximation of a certain restricted problem.

EXAMPLE. Let

$$\begin{aligned} &V = \{y \in H^2((0,1)) \mid y(0) = y'(0) = 0\} \\ &a(y,z) = \int_0^1 y'' z''\,dx, \quad f \equiv 0 \\ &Bu = u\delta_{\frac{1}{2}}, \quad u \in \mathbf{R}^1, \end{aligned}$$

where $\delta_{\frac{1}{2}}$ denotes the Dirac function, concentrated at the point $x = \frac{1}{2}$. Finally, set

$$\hat{b}(x) = \begin{cases} 0 & \text{for } x \le 0 \text{ and } x > 1 \\ x & \text{for } x \in (0,1) \\ [0,1] & \text{for } x = 1. \end{cases}$$

Corresponding hemivariational inequality reads as follows:

$$(\mathcal{P}(u)) \qquad \begin{cases} \text{Find } y \in V \text{ and } \mathcal{X} \in R^1 \text{ such that} \\ a(y,z) + \mathcal{X} z(1) = u z(\frac{1}{2}) \quad \forall z \in V \\ \mathcal{X} \in \hat{b}(y(1)). \end{cases}$$

$(\mathcal{P}(u))$ describes the deflection of the beam, which is clamped at $x = 0$ and supported by a nonlinear string at $x = 1$, the characteristic of which is given by the multivalued function $\hat{b}$. Our aim will be to determine minimal force u for which $y(1)$ is equal to 1, i.e. we choose as a cost functional

$$\mathcal{J}(y,u) = \frac{u^2}{2} + \frac{r}{2}|y(1) - 1|^2, \quad r > 0$$

and define the problem

$$(\mathbf{P}) \qquad \begin{cases} \text{Find } u^* \in \mathbf{R}^1 \text{ such that} \\ E(u^*) \le E(u) \quad u \in \mathbf{R}^1, \end{cases}$$

where

$$E(u) = \min_{y \in X(u)} \mathcal{J}(y,u), \quad u \in \mathcal{U}_{\mathrm{ad}}.$$

It is easy to see that $(\mathbf{P})$ has at least one solution. Let $D_h : 0 = x_0 < x_1 < \ldots < x_{n(h)} = 1$ be a partition of $[0,1]$ and set

$$V_h = \{y_h \in C^1([0,1]) \mid y_h|_{x_{i-1}x_i} \in P_3,\ y_h(0) = y_h'(0) = 0\} \subset V,$$

i.e. V_h contains piecewise cubic polynomials.

The approximation of $(\mathcal{P}(u))$ is defined as follows:

$$(\mathcal{P}(u))_h \qquad \begin{cases} \text{Find } y_h \in V_h \text{ and } \mathcal{X}_h \in \mathbf{R}^1 \text{ such that} \\ a(y_h, z_h) + \mathcal{X}_h z_h(1) = u z_h(\tfrac{1}{2}) \quad \forall z_h \in V_h \\ \mathcal{X}_h \in \hat{b}(y_h(1)). \end{cases}$$

Writing $(\mathcal{P}(u))_h$ is a matrix form, we arrive at

$$\mathsf{A}y + \begin{pmatrix} 0 \\ 0 \\ \vdots \\ 0 \\ 0 \\ \mathcal{X}_h \end{pmatrix} = \begin{pmatrix} 0 \\ \vdots \\ u \\ 0 \\ \vdots \\ 0 \end{pmatrix},$$

where A is a rigidity matrix. Taking into account the special form of our problem, one can eliminate all unknowns with exception of the last one. Finally we arrive at very simple hemivariational inequality for one variable, denoted by y, namely:

$$(1.15) \qquad \begin{cases} \mathcal{A}y + \mathcal{X} = \mathcal{B} \\ \mathcal{X} \in \hat{b}(y), \end{cases}$$

with $\mathcal{A} > 0$, which can be solved explicitely.

Let us assume that $\mathcal{A} = 1$ and solve

$$(1.16) \qquad \begin{cases} y + \mathcal{X} = \mathcal{B} \\ \mathcal{X} \in \hat{b}(y). \end{cases}$$

Then it is easy to see that

$$\begin{aligned}
& y = \mathcal{B},\ \mathcal{X} = 0 \quad \text{if } \mathcal{B} \le 0 \\
& y = \frac{\mathcal{B}}{2},\ \mathcal{X} = \frac{\mathcal{B}}{2} \quad \text{if } \mathcal{B} \in (0,1) \\
& \left.\begin{aligned} & y = 1,\ \mathcal{X} = 0 \\ & y = \frac{1}{2},\ \mathcal{X} = \frac{1}{2} \end{aligned}\right\} \quad \text{if } \mathcal{B} = 1 \\
& \left.\begin{aligned} & y = 1,\ \mathcal{X} = \mathcal{B} - 1 \\ & y = \frac{\mathcal{B}}{2},\ \mathcal{X} = \frac{\mathcal{B}}{2} \\ & y = \mathcal{B},\ \mathcal{X} = 0 \end{aligned}\right\} \quad \text{if } \mathcal{B} \in (1,2) \\
& \left.\begin{aligned} & y = 1,\ \mathcal{X} = 1 \\ & y = 2,\ \mathcal{X} = 0 \end{aligned}\right\} \quad \text{if } \mathcal{B} = 2 \\
& y = \mathcal{B},\ \mathcal{X} = 0 \quad \text{if } \mathcal{B} > 2.
\end{aligned}$$

Let $\mathcal{J}(y,\mathcal{B}) = \frac{\mathcal{B}^2}{2} + \frac{r}{2}|y-1|^2$. Then the problem

$$(\mathsf{P}) \qquad \begin{cases} \text{Find } \mathcal{B}^* \in \mathbf{R}^1 \text{ such that} \\ E(\mathcal{B}^*) \leq E(\mathcal{B}) \quad \forall \mathcal{B} \in \mathbf{R}^1 \end{cases}$$

with $E(\mathcal{B}) = \min_{y \in X(\mathcal{B})} \mathcal{J}(y,\mathcal{B})$ has exactly one solution, namely $\mathcal{B}^* = 1$ if r is sufficiently large. In that case $E(\mathcal{B}^*) = \frac{1}{2}$ and the corresponding state $y(\mathcal{B}^*) = 1$. Now, we shall apply optimality conditions, derived in [**3**]. We shall use the form of optimality conditions suitable just for our example.

THEOREM 1.2. *Let $(\mathcal{B}^*, y(\mathcal{B}^*))$ be a local minimum of* (P) *and $\mathcal{X}^* = \mathcal{B}^* - y(\mathcal{B}^*)$. Assume that p^* is a solution of the adjoint equation*

$$p = \nabla_{\mathcal{B}} \mathcal{J}(y(\mathcal{B}^*), \mathcal{B}^*).$$

Then the vector

$$(p^* + \nabla_y \mathcal{J}(y(\mathcal{B}^*), \mathcal{B}^*), p^*) \in (D((y(\mathcal{B}^*), \mathcal{X}^*)))^0, \tag{1.17}$$

where the symbol on the right hand side of the inclusion denotes the positive polar cone to a cone $D((y(\mathcal{B}^*), \mathcal{X}^*))$. $D((y(\mathcal{B}^*), \mathcal{X}^*))$ is a contigent cone of gf $\hat{b}$ at $(y(\mathcal{B}^*), \mathcal{X}^*)$, i.e.

$$D((y(\mathcal{B}^*), \mathcal{X}^*)) = \{(h,\xi) \in \mathbf{R}^2 \mid \exists y_l \to y(\mathcal{B}^*),\ \mathcal{X}_l \to \mathcal{X}^*,\ \vartheta_l \searrow 0,\ l \to \infty$$
$$\text{such that } \mathcal{X}_l \in \hat{b}(y_l) \text{ and } h = \lim_{l \to 0+} \frac{y_l - y_0}{\vartheta_l},\ \xi = \lim_{l \to 0+} \frac{\mathcal{X}_l - \mathcal{X}^*}{\vartheta_l}\}.$$

Moreover also

$$-\nabla_{\mathcal{B}} \mathcal{J}(y(\mathcal{B}^*), \mathcal{B}^*) \in N_{\hat{b}(y(\mathcal{B}^*))}(\mathcal{X}^*), \tag{1.18}$$

where the symbol on the right hand side is the Clarke's normal cone to a set $\hat{b}(y(\mathcal{B}^*))$ at $\mathcal{X}^*$.

In our example $y(\mathcal{B}^*) = \mathcal{B}^* = 1$ so that $\mathcal{X}^* = 0$. A direct analysis shows that

$$D((y(\mathcal{B}^*), \mathcal{X}^*)) = D((1,0)) = \{(h,\xi) | h \geq 0,\ \xi = 0\} \tag{1.19}$$

and $p^* = 1$. The condition (1.17), now reads

$$(1,1) \in (D((y(\mathcal{B}^*), \mathcal{X}^*)))^0,$$

which is true. Also (1.18) is satisfied, as

$$-\nabla_{\mathcal{B}} \mathcal{J}(1,1) = -1 \in N_{\hat{b}(1)}(0) = \mathbf{R}^1_-.$$

REFERENCES

[1] P.D. Panagiotopoulos, "Inequality Problems in Mechanics and Applications. Convex and Nonconvex Energy Functions.," Birkhäuser, Boston-Basel-Stuttgart, 1985.

[2] J. Haslinger, P.D. Panagiotopoulos, *Optimal Control of Hemivariational Inequalities. Continuous Case*, Proceedings of International Conference on Control and Estimation of Distributed Parameters Systems, Vorau (Styria), Austria, July 8-14, 1990.

[3] J.V. Outrata, *On the Control of Systems Described by Hemivariational Inequalities*, DFG preprint No. 212, 1990.

International Series of Numerical Mathematics, Vol. 99, © 1991 Birkhäuser Verlag Basel

A thermodynamical model of ferromagnetism and its numerical simulation

K.-H. Hoffmann
Kunkun Liu

University of Augsburg
Institut of Mathematics
Universitätsstrasse 8
D 8900 Augsburg, Germany

Abstract. A mathematical model on the thermodynamics of phase transitions of ferromagnetism is established for quasi-stationary electromagnetic fields. Theorems for the local and global existence results are given. Numerical methods together with practical numerical experiments are presented.

Keywords. Thermodynamical model of ferromagnetism, existence, numerical methods.

1980 Mathematics subject classifications: 35Q20, 35A40.

1. Introduction

For many years the discontinuities in physical behaviour which occur when a system undergoes a phase transition have attracted the attention of both experimental and theoretical physicists as well as numerous mathematicians. Particular interest has been focused on phenomena associated with critical points such as ferromagnetism, which is a typical example of the phenomena. In spite of the great difficulty of mathematical pathology, ferromagnetism has been studied with growing efforts this recent century (cf. **[1]**, **[5]**, **[8]**, **[10]**, **[11]**, **[14]**, **[18]**, **[20]**, **[23]**, **[28]**-**[35]** etc.).

A metallic material which has quite striking magnetic properties is called a ferromagnet. To be more specific, the magnetic effect, or the net effect of magnetic moments of atoms in a ferromagnet is much greater than those in other materials. For ferromagnetic materials, the magnetic moments induced by applied magnetic fields have a great effect on the fields themselves. In fact, the induced moments are so strong that they often have the dominant effect in producing the observed magnetic fields.

The most important feature of a ferromagnetic material is that it admits the existence of a critical temperature, coinciding with the *Curie* point Θ_c such that the system is ferromagnetic for the temperature $\Theta < \Theta_c$ and becomes paramagnetic above it. The ferromagnetic state can be characterized by a non-zero uniform magnetization, the average

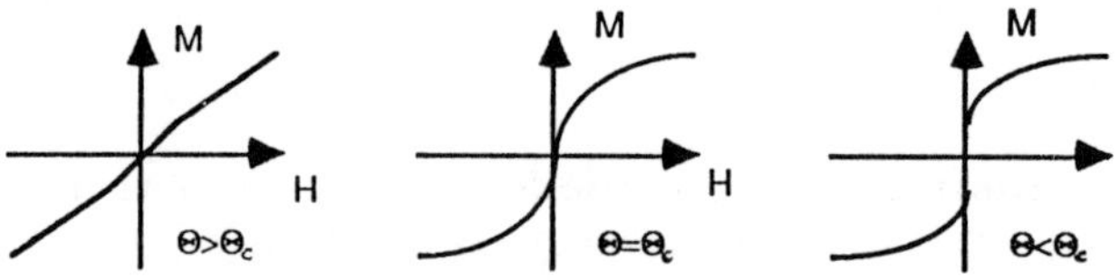

(M: magnetization H: magnetic field Θ: temperature)

density of magnetic moments – even without an applied magnetic field. This results in the phenomenon of the so-called spontaneous magnetization.

As demonstrated in the above figure, phase transitions occur when the spontaneous magnetization begins to appear. In fact, at the critical point, a paramagnetic-ferromagnetic transition of second order, induced by the temperature, is observed in the absence of an external magnetic field. In addition, below Θ_c the external field induces a phase transition of first order, which is accompanied by hysteresis. These are called ferromagnetic phase transitions.

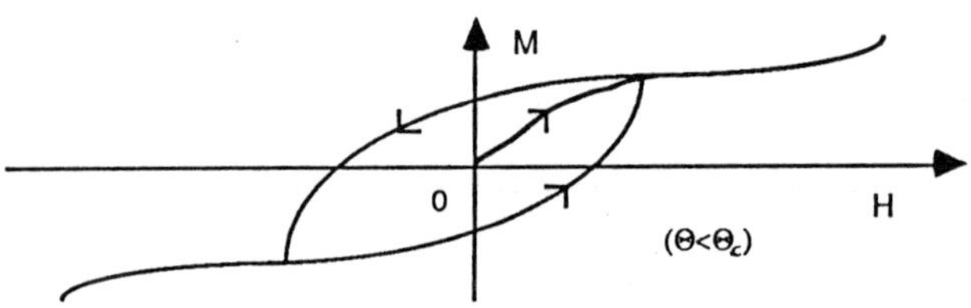

The above mentioned phenomena can be microscopically interpreted as follows: the induced magnetic moments of atoms are basically parallel in the low-temperature state (the ferromagnetic phase) and disordered in the high-temperature state (the paramagnetic phase) while they tend towards pointing to the direction of the applied external field as a whole.

In physics phase transitions were initially dealt with the phenomenological theory, which describes the phenomena on a macroscopic scale containing a large number of atoms and predicts the nature of the singularity of physical properties. This theory has proved itself fairly appropriate for describing ferromagnetic phase transitions.

In phenomenological theory a suitable order parameter is first defined in relation with the symmetry at the critical point to characterize the phase transitions. Moreover, a thermodynamical potential is constructed as a function of the temperature and the parameter such that another thermodynamic quantity, the so-called external field, can be determined. In the case of ferromagnetism the magnetization is suitable as the order parameter and the corresponding external field is the external magnetic field.

The discontinuities from phase transitions will be depicted by the phenomenological theory of second order phase transitions introduced by *Landau* [18]. Based on this theory a mathematical model is proposed for the quasi-stationary electromagnetic fields, which describes the evolution of coupled magnetic and thermic process of ferromagnetism in the vicinity of the critical point on a macroscopic scale. The model is constructed so as to admit the presence of time-dependent external actions such as distributed electromagnetic force, distributed heat supply and heat source at the boundary, which are suitable as control variables. By this model the thermal evolution of ferromagnetism is entirely characterized by the magnetic field and the temperature.

To obtain a good understanding of ferromagnetism, numerical simulation is performed with the respective boundary influence of the force, the heat and both combined. All the principal effects observed in the reality of ferromagnetism can be demonstrated in numerous simulation experiments.

At last it should be mentioned that many authors have developed general thermodynamic models of electromagnetic fields (for example, [4], [12], [22] and [26]). In addition, related works on the evolution of ferromagnetism can be found in [16], [24], [29]-[34].

2. Thermodynamical model

2.1. Basic hypotheses.

A thermodynamical process in a ferromagnetic body must be compatible with the *Maxwell* equations describing the evolution of the ferromagnetic field and should be subordinated to the fundamental laws of thermodynamics as well. Thus, the basic balance equations consist of the following:

- the balance equations of ferromagnetic forces; and
- the balance equation of energy

Let Ω be a homogenous ferromagnetic slab. In Ω the interactions among the magnetic moments of atoms as well as between these and the electric fields of crystal lattices, which possess the factor $1/c^2$ with c the velocity of light and are hence called the relativistic interactions, can be neglected because they are considerably weak compared with so-called exchange effects among atoms themselves. Therefore, Ω can be supposed to be isotropic for its magnetic properties. As a result of the isotropic hypothesis, the magnetization and the magnetic field always fall in the same direction. Furthermore, if the temperature is close to the *Curie* point, the magnetization is quite feeble. Thus, in the case the temperature is in the vicinity of the *Curie* point, the magnetostriction, i.e. the deformation due to the change of the magnetization can be ignored so that the mass density of Ω can be supposed to be a constant. For the sake of convenience we will normalize it to the unity throughout this article.

Denote by $\mathbf{H}$, $\mathbf{M}$, $\mathbf{E}$, $\mathbf{D}$, $\mathbf{I}$ and Θ the magnetic field, the magnetization, the electric field, the electric displacement, the conduction current and the absolute temperature, respectively. $\mathbf{I}$ is obviously parallel to the slab. In addition, since the magnetic field and the magnetization possess the same direction whereas $\mathbf{M}$ is perpendicular to the magnetic current, both of them are orthogonal to Ω. Therefore, if the xy-plane of the coordinate system in $\mathbf{R}^3$ is chosen to be parallel to the slab, $\mathbf{H}$, $\mathbf{M}$ and $\mathbf{I}$ have the following forms:

$$\mathbf{H} = (0,0,H)^T, \quad \mathbf{M} = (0,0,M)^T, \quad \mathbf{I} = (I_1, I_2, 0)^T.$$

Moreover, let us introduce the following thermodynamic quantities: the internal energy $U = U(M, \Theta)$, the *Helmholtz* free energy $F = F(M, \Theta)$, the entropy $S = S(M, \Theta)$, the heat flux $\mathbf{q}$ and the internal heat supply γ. Here the *Helmholtz* free energy F is defined by $F = U - \Theta S$. For a reversible infinitesimal process the internal energy U can be defined by

$$dU = \Theta dS + HdM. \tag{2.1.1}$$

Therefore, the free energy must satisfy

$$dF = -Sd\Theta + HdM.$$

2.2. Landau potential theory.

In 1937 *Landau* ([**18**]) established his famous theory of second order phase transitions, in which he assumed that the thermodynamical potential is analytic at the critical point and is invariant by the symmetric change of the order parameter. As a consequence, *Landau* could expand the thermodynamical potential in successive powers of the order parameter in the neighbourhood of the original, with the disappearing odd powers and require the coefficients to be smooth in the neighbourhood of the critical point. Moreover, through the hypotheses of the stability of the disordered state (in which the order parameter vanishes) and the instability of the ordered state (in which the order parameter does not vanish) the properties of the coefficients as functions of temperature can be determined.

According to *Landau*, the *Helmholtz* free energy F is analytic with respect to the magnetization M and the temperature Θ for ferromagnetism. According to the symmetric invariableness F can be expanded as a power series of even index of M:

$$F(M, \Theta) = \sum_{i=0,\infty} f_i(\Theta) M^{2i}$$

where f_i $(i = 0, 1, \dots)$ are some analytic functions of Θ. In order to get a second order phase transition at the *Curie* point Θ_c, $f_1(\Theta)$ must change its sign at Θ_c with positive value above Θ_c. In addition, it is also necessary that $f_2(\Theta_c) > 0$. Following *Landau*, f_2 can be assumed to be constant in the neighbourhood of Θ_c. Thus, if the high terms after M^4 are ignored, we can assume the free energy function in a modified *Landau* form

$$F(M, \Theta) = f_0(\Theta) + f_1(\Theta) M^2 + \frac{b}{4} M^4 \tag{2.2.1}$$

where b is a positive constant while f_i $(i = 0, 1)$ are some suitable smooth functions such that f_1 is negative below and positive above Θ_c. As a consequence, if the magnetic field H and the temperature Θ are given, then the magnetization M and the entropy S can be calculated in turn by

$$H = \partial F / \partial M, \ \ S = -\partial F / \partial \Theta. \tag{2.2.2}$$

It should be pointed out that for the simplest possibility $f_1(\Theta) = a(\Theta - \Theta_c)$ with $a > 0$ the *Landau* free energy can also be derived from a microscopic *Ising* model by using the mean-field approximation.

2.3. Magnetic equation.

As is well–known, the equations governing the electromagnetic phenomena are the group of *Maxwell* equations. Two essential equations read for a polarized system:

$$c \text{ rot } \mathbf{H} = \mathbf{I},$$
$$c \text{ rot } \mathbf{E} = -\frac{\partial(\mathbf{H}+\mathbf{M})}{\partial t}, \tag{2.3.1}$$

where c is the velocity of the light, if the field changes so slowly that the term $\frac{\partial D}{\partial t}$, called the displacement current, can be neglected in comparison with **I**.

(2.3.1) can be supplemented by a relation between the magnetic field, the current and the temperature. This is represented by the *Ohm* law

$$\mathbf{E} = \rho\mathbf{I} - \kappa\nabla\Theta + \mathbf{g}, \tag{2.3.2}$$

where $\rho > 0$ stands for the isothermal resistivity of the medium, $\kappa > 0$ is called the differential thermoelectric power ([**12**] and [**20**]). In (2.3.2) **g** has been added to represent a non–inductive applied electromagnetic force ([**31**]).

The homogeneity of Ω implies that both of κ and ρ are constants. Thus, combining (2.3.1) with (2.3.2) we obtain the following magnetic equation with $r = c^2\rho$:

$$\frac{\partial H}{\partial t} + \frac{\partial M}{\partial t} = r\Delta H + c\left(\frac{\partial g_2}{\partial x} - \frac{\partial g_1}{\partial y}\right). \tag{2.3.3}$$

2.4. Energy equation.

The balance equation for the internal energy reads (see [**12**])

$$\frac{dU}{dt} = -\operatorname{div}(\mathbf{q}) + \mathbf{E}I + H\frac{dM}{dt} + \gamma,$$

because the deformation of Ω is ignored. Thus, we have by (2.1.1)

$$\Theta\frac{dS}{dt} = -\operatorname{div}(\mathbf{q}) + \mathbf{E}I + \gamma,$$

If the *Maxwell* equations (2.3.1) and the modified *Ohm* law (2.3.2) are substituted into the above equation, then it can be rewritten as

$$\Theta\frac{dS}{dt} = -\operatorname{div}(\mathbf{q}) + c^2\rho|\operatorname{rot}\mathbf{H}|^2 + (\operatorname{rot}\mathbf{H})(c\kappa\nabla\Theta - c\mathbf{g}) + \gamma, \tag{2.4.1}$$

where the second term of the right side can be interpreted as the *Joule* heat, the dissipated energy due to the electromagnetic field doing its work.

Furthermore, the classical linear theory of heat conduction is based on the following *Fourier* law for the heat flux **q**:

$$\mathbf{q} = -k(\Theta)\nabla\Theta,$$

where $k(\Theta)$, a positive function, is called the thermal conductivity. However, according to this equation the speed of propagation of thermal disturbance is infinite. For remedying this shortcoming, [13] has developed a new general theory, associated with finite propagation speeds, for the behaviour of heat conduction of nonlinear materials with memory in which the linearized constitutive equation for the heat flux admits the following form

$$\mathbf{q} = -k(\Theta)\int_{[0,+\infty]} a(s)\nabla\Theta(t-s)\,ds. \tag{2.4.2}$$

Here $a : [0,+\infty) \to \mathbf{R}$ is a differentiable function with $a(+\infty) = 0$. In general, $a(.)$ can be postulated to satisfy

$$a(0) > 0, a'(0) < 0 \text{ and } \int_{[0,+\infty]} a(s)\,ds = 1$$

(cf. [9] and [27]). Going a step further, if the gradient of temperature varies slowly in the time, (2.4.2) can be approached by

$$\int_{[0,+\infty]} a(s)\nabla\Theta(t-s)\,ds \approx \nabla\Theta - \left(\int_{[0,+\infty]} s\,a(s)\,ds\right)\nabla\left(\frac{\partial\Theta}{\partial t}\right).$$

It is obviously reasonable to suppose that $-\infty < e = \int_{[0,+\infty]} s\,a(s)\,ds < 0$. This brings us to the following constitutive hypothesis, in place of the *Fourier* law, for the heat flux $\mathbf{q}$:

$$\mathbf{q} = -k(\Theta)\left(\nabla\Theta - e\nabla\left(\frac{\partial\Theta}{\partial t}\right)\right), \tag{2.4.3}$$

where $ek(\Theta)$ with a constant $e > 0$ represents the characteristic of heat conduction with regard to the thermal memory of the material. Consequently, we arrive at the following energy equation of the system by substituting (2.4.3) into (2.4.1):

$$\begin{aligned}\Theta\frac{\partial S}{\partial t} &= \operatorname{div}(k(\Theta)\nabla\Theta) + e\operatorname{div}\left(k(\Theta)\nabla(\frac{\partial\Theta}{\partial t})\right) + r|\nabla\mathbf{H}|^2\\ &+\left(\frac{\partial H}{\partial y}, -\frac{\partial H}{\partial x}\right)(q\nabla\Theta - c\mathbf{g}^*) + \gamma,\end{aligned} \tag{2.4.4}$$

where $q = c\kappa$ and $\mathbf{g}^* = (g_1, g_2)^T$.

2.5. One–dimensional reduction.

Now let us assume that the effect of galvanomagnetic type occurs in Ω, that is

$$I_1 = 0 \text{ and } \frac{\partial\Theta}{\partial y} = 0$$

([**12**]). In addition, in order to derive one–dimensional equations, the non–inductive electromagnetic force $\mathbf{g}$ is restricted to be uniform in the y–direction. In this case Θ is independent of y. Besides Θ, we are able to prove that $\mathbf{H}$, $\mathbf{M}$, $\mathbf{E}$ and $\mathbf{I}$ do not depend upon y either. In fact, $\frac{\partial H}{\partial y} = 0$ because by (2.3.1)

$$(0, I_2, 0)^T = c \operatorname{rot} \mathbf{H} = c \left(\frac{\partial H}{\partial y}, -\frac{\partial H}{\partial x}, 0 \right)^T .$$

In turn, the above equation yields $I_2 = -c\frac{\partial H}{\partial x}$. This shows the independence of $\mathbf{I}$ on y.

Moreover, $\mathbf{E} = (\kappa \frac{\partial \Theta}{\partial x}, \rho I_2, 0) - \mathbf{g}$ so that $\mathbf{E}$ does not depend on y as well. Lastly, since

$$\mathbf{M} = \mathbf{M}(t=0) - 2 \int_{[0,t]} \left(c \operatorname{rot}(\mathbf{E}) + \frac{\partial \mathbf{H}}{\partial t} \right) dt,$$

it follows that $\mathbf{M}$ depends only on x if its initial distribution $\mathbf{M}(t=0)$ is like that. As a result, from (2.3.3) and (2.4.4) we arrive at a one–dimensional system of differential equations:

$$\begin{aligned} &\frac{\partial H}{\partial t} + \frac{\partial M}{\partial t} = r \frac{\partial^2 H}{\partial x^2} + \frac{\partial \lambda}{\partial x}, \\ &\Theta \frac{\partial S}{\partial t} = \partial \left(k(\Theta) \left(\frac{\partial \Theta}{\partial x} + e \frac{\partial^2 \Theta}{\partial x \partial t} \right) \right) / \partial x + r \left(\frac{\partial H}{\partial x} \right)^2 + \lambda \frac{\partial H}{\partial x} + \gamma, \end{aligned} \tag{2.5.1}$$

where $\lambda = c g_2$, provided $M(t=0)$ is a function of x only.

3. Initial–boundary problem

3.1. Boundary conditions.

Since the electric field is tangentially continuous across an interface between different media while the magnetic field is discontinuous by the surface current, we assume on the boundary:

$$\mathbf{n} \times \mathbf{E} = 0, \mathbf{n} \times \mathbf{H} = \mathbf{J}.$$

Here $\mathbf{n}$ stands for the outward unit vector normal to the boundary of Ω and $\mathbf{J}$ is the surface current. In the case of a slab they reduce to the *Neumann* and the *Dirichlet* boundary condition, respectively:

$$\frac{\partial H}{\partial \mathbf{n}} = \phi, H^2 = |\mathbf{J}|^2.$$

For the temperature it is suitable to call for a boundary condition of mixed type in the form

$$\frac{\partial \Theta}{\partial \mathbf{n}} = \alpha(\Psi - \Theta) \text{ where } \alpha > 0 \text{ is a constant.}$$

3.2. Formulation of problem.

Let $\Omega = (0,1)$ and $\Gamma = \{0,1\}$ the boundary of Ω. Now we are in a position to formulate a mathematical problem on the one-dimensional thermodynamics of ferromagnetism:

PROBLEM (P). *For given functions* λ, γ, H_0, Θ_0 *and* Ψ *find a time value* $T > 0$ *and a pair functions* (H, Θ) *such that they satisfy the following*

1° *the process equations (2.5.1) in* $(0,T)\times\Omega$;
2° *the constitutive equations (2.2.2) with the free energy function (2.2.1);*
3° *the initial conditions at* $\{t=0\}\times\Omega:\ H=H_0,\ \Theta=\Theta_0$;
4° *the boundary conditions on* $[0,T]\times\Gamma$:

$$(1-q)H + q\frac{\partial H}{\partial \mathbf{n}} = 0,\quad \frac{\partial\Theta}{\partial \mathbf{n}} = \alpha(\Psi-\Theta) \tag{3.2.1}$$

where $q\in\{0,1\}$ *and* $\mathbf{n}$ *denotes the outward unit vector normal to the boundary.*

The boundary conditions (3.2.1) is of the *Diriclet* type if $q=0$ and of the *Neumann* type if $q=1$. Let $H_1^1(\Omega) = H^1(\Omega)$, then a variational form of (P) can be formulated as follows:

PROBLEM (VP). *Find a time value* $T > 0$ *and a pair functions* (H,Θ) *such that they satisfy:*

1° $H\in H^1(0,T;L^2(\Omega))\cap L^\infty(0,T;H_q^1(\Omega))$;
2° $\Theta\in H^1(0,T;H^1(\Omega))$ *and* $\Theta > 0$;
3° *the constitutive equations (2.2.2) with the free energy function (2.2.1);*
4° *the boundary trace* $\Theta_c|_\Gamma$ *is well-defined on* $[0,T]$;
5° *the variational equations (for any* $t\in[0,T]$);

$$\int_t\int_\Omega\left(\left(\frac{\partial H}{\partial t}+\frac{\partial M}{\partial t}-\frac{\partial\lambda}{\partial x}\right)\xi + r\frac{\partial H}{\partial x}\frac{\partial\xi}{\partial x}\right) = 0,\ \xi\in L^2(0,t;H_q^1(\Omega)),$$

$$\int_t\int_\Omega\left(\Theta\frac{\partial S}{\partial t}\varsigma + k(\Theta)\left(\frac{\partial\Theta}{\partial x}+e\frac{\partial^2\Theta}{\partial x\partial t}\right)\frac{\partial\varsigma}{\partial x} - \left(r\left(\frac{\partial H}{\partial x}\right)^2 + \lambda\frac{\partial H}{\partial x}+\gamma\right)\varsigma\right)$$
$$= \alpha\int_t\int_\Gamma k(\Theta)\left((\Psi-\Theta)+e\left(\frac{\partial\Psi}{\partial t}-\frac{\partial\Theta}{\partial t}\right)\right)\varsigma,\ \varsigma\in L^2(0,t;H^1(\Omega)).$$

3.3. Theoretical results.

We place restrictions on the free energy end the conduction coefficient as follows:

(a) $f_i\in C^3(\mathbf{R})$ $(i=0,1)$ such that f_1 is negative below and positive above Θ_c and

$$f_0''(\Theta)+f_1''(\Theta)M^2\le 0 \text{ for } (\Theta;M)\in[0,+\infty)\times[0,L] \text{ with } L>0.$$

(b) $|f_1(\Theta_c)|$ is small enough and f_i $(i=0,1)$ possess certain special properties afar from Θ_c.

(c) $k\in C^1(\mathbf{R})$ is bounded below: $k(\Theta)\ge k_0>0$; and $\Theta\mapsto\Theta k(\Theta)$ is monotone on $[0,+\infty)$, i.e.

$$(\Theta_1 k(\Theta_1)-\Theta_2 k(\Theta_2))(\Theta_1-\Theta_2)\ge 0 \text{ for any } \Theta_1,\Theta_2\in[0,+\infty).$$

In addition, the data are taken such that $H_0 \in H_q^1(\Omega)$, $0 < \Theta_0 \in H^1(\Omega)$, $\Psi \in H^1_{LOC}(0,+\infty)$, $\lambda \in L^\infty_{LOC}(0,+\infty; H^1(\Omega))$ and $\gamma \in L^2_{LOC}(0,+\infty; L^2(\Omega))$.

We are able to prove the following existences:

THEOREM 3.3.1. *(local existence) If the given data meet a trivial inequality, there exists a time value $T > 0$ such that the problem (VP) admits at least one solution (H, Θ) on the time interval $[0,T]$.*

THEOREM 3.3.2. *(global existence) Let $k(\theta) = c\Theta^2$ $(c > 0)$ and $\lambda = 0$. If $\Psi \in H^1(0,T)$, $\gamma \in L^1(0,T; L^1(\Omega)) \cap L^2(0,T; L^2(\Omega))$ for $T > 0$ such that $\gamma \geq 0$ and $\Psi \geq \delta \geq 0$ while certain inequalities on the data holds true, the problem (VP) admits at least one solution (H, Θ) on $[0,T]$ and $\Theta \geq \delta$.*

Furthermore, the uniqueness and the stability of the system can be established in a single-phase state, and a suitable control problem can therefore be dealt with.

4. NUMERICAL SIMULATION

4.1. Approximation by finite elements.

The system is going to be discretized by means of the finite element method in the space and the difference technique in time. To simplify the computation, we take into account a constant coefficient function $k(\Theta) \equiv k > 0$ and the following specific phenomenological structures:

$$f_0(\Theta) = -c\Theta \; log(\Theta), f_1(\Theta) = \frac{a}{2}(\Theta - \Theta_c) \text{ with } a \text{ and } c > 0,$$

which represent the original form of the free energy assumed by *Landau* himself as well as that from the mean field theory.

Let Ω_n be the uniform partition of n-order of Ω and denote by $\{f_{ni}(x)\}$ the corresponding group of the linear piece-continuous functions on Ω_n. The finite element subspace is then

$$V_n = \{v = \sum \zeta_i f_{ni}(x) : \zeta_i \in \mathbf{R} \; (i = 0, 1, ..., n)\}.$$

Thus, the finite element discretization of (VP) for $q = 1$ can be described as follows:

PROBLEM $(\mathrm{VP})_n$: Find a time value $T > 0$ and a pair functions (H, Θ) in the forms

$$H(t,x) = \sum_{i=0}^{n} h_i(t) f_{ni}(x), \;\; \Theta(t,x) = \sum_{i=0}^{n} \theta_i(t) f_{ni}(x)$$

such that the following are satisfied:

1° $h_i, \theta_i \in C^1[0,T]$ $(i = 0, 1, .., n)$ and $\Theta > 0$;

2° the initial conditions $h_i(0) = H_0(\frac{i}{n}), \theta_i(0) = \Theta_0(\frac{i}{n})\,(i = 0, 1, \ldots, n)$;

3° the variational equations (for any $t \in [0,T]$)

$$(4.1.1)\quad \begin{aligned} &\int_\Omega \Big(\frac{\partial H}{\partial t}+\frac{\partial M}{\partial t}\Big)\xi + r\int_\Omega \frac{\partial H}{\partial x}\frac{\partial \xi}{\partial x} = \int_\Omega \frac{\partial \lambda}{\partial x}\xi + r\int_\Gamma \phi\xi,\ \xi\in V_n,\\ &\int_\Omega \Big(c\frac{\partial \Theta}{\partial t} - a\Theta_c M\frac{\partial M}{\partial t}\Big)\zeta + k\int_\Omega \Big(\frac{\partial \Theta}{\partial x}+e\frac{\partial^2\Theta}{\partial x\partial t}\Big)\frac{\partial \zeta}{\partial x} =\\ &\alpha k\int_\Gamma \Big((\Psi-\Theta)+e\Big(\frac{\partial \Psi}{\partial t}-\frac{\partial \Theta}{\partial t}\Big)\Big)\zeta + \int_\Omega \Big(r\Big(\frac{\partial H}{\partial x}\Big)^2+\lambda\frac{\partial H}{\partial x}+\gamma\Big)\zeta,\zeta\in V_n \end{aligned}$$

where M is determined by the constitutive equation

$$H = a(\Theta-\Theta_c)M + bM^3$$

in the way:

(i) choose M_0 such that $H(0) = a(\Theta(0)-\Theta_c)M_0 + bM_0^3$;
(ii) $a(\Theta-\Theta_c)+3bM^2 \geq 0$; and
(iii) If $\Theta < \Theta_c$, M jumps from negative to positive at t when $H = H_\Theta = \frac{2a(\Theta_c-\Theta)^{\frac{3}{2}}}{3\sqrt{3b}}$ or conversely from positive to negative at t when $H = -H_\Theta$.

Since the fluctuation of the temperature can be limited in the neighborhood of the *Curie* point, the coefficient Θ of MM_t in the thermic equation has been demanded to take Θ_c as its value. At the same time, to observe the effect caused by the boundary action of the applied magnetic field, a non-homogeneous boundary condition has been brought in the first equation of (4.1.1).

THEOREM 4.1.1. *If $\lambda\in C(0,T_0;H^1(\Omega))$, $\gamma\in C(0,T_0;L^2(\Omega))$ and $\Psi\in C^1[0,T_0]$ for given $T_0>0$, there exists a time value $T>0$ such that $(VP)_n$ admits a unique solution (H,Θ) on $[0,T]$.*

PROOF: Denote $M = g(H,\Theta,M_0)$. Since $a(\Theta-\Theta_c)M+bM^3 = 0$ if and only if $H=M=0$ and $\Theta=\Theta_c$, we can write M_t in the form $M_t = Q(H_t - aM\Theta_t)$ where $Q = Q(M,\Theta)$ is defined as follows:

$$Q = 0 \text{ if } M=0 \text{ and } \Theta=\Theta_c;$$
$$\text{or } \big(a(\Theta-\Theta_c)+3bM^2\big)^{-1} \text{ otherwise.}$$

Substituting $\xi = \Theta_c f_{ni}$ and $\zeta = f_{ni}\,(i=0,1,...,n)$ into (4.1.1), we obtain a system of ordinary differential equations:

$$\mathbf{A}(\mathbf{U})\mathbf{U}_t = \mathbf{B}(\mathbf{U},t)$$

where the coefficent matrix $\mathbf{A}$, the vectors $\mathbf{B}$ and $\mathbf{U}$ are given in the following block forms

$$A = \begin{bmatrix} \mathbf{A}_1 & \mathbf{A}_2\\ \mathbf{A}_3 & \mathbf{A}_4\end{bmatrix}, \mathbf{U} = (\mathbf{u}_1,\mathbf{u}_2)^T \text{ and } \mathbf{B} = (\mathbf{b}_1,\mathbf{b}_2)^T$$

whereas the submatrices $\mathbf{A}_i$, the subvectors $\mathbf{b}_i$ and $\mathbf{u}_i$ are defined as follows:

$$
\begin{aligned}
(\mathbf{A}_1)_{ij} &= \Theta_c \int (1+Q) f_{ni} f_{nj}, \\
(\mathbf{A}_4)_{ij} &= \int (c + a^2 \Theta_c M^2 Q) f_{ni} f_{nj} + k\Big(\int \frac{\partial f_{ni}}{\partial x} \frac{\partial f_{nj}}{\partial x} + \alpha \int_\Gamma f_{ni} f_{nj} \Big), \\
(\mathbf{A}_2)_{ij} &= (\mathbf{A}_3)_{ij} = -a\Theta_c \int MQ f_{ni} f_{nj}; \\
(\mathbf{u}_1)_i &= h_i; \\
(\mathbf{u}_2)_i &= \theta_i; \\
(\mathbf{b}_1)_i &= \Theta_c\Big(-r \int \frac{\partial H}{\partial t} \frac{\partial f_{ni}}{\partial x} + \int \lambda f_{ni} \Big), \\
(\mathbf{b}_2)_i &= -k \int \frac{\partial \Theta}{\partial x} \frac{\partial f_{ni}}{\partial x} + \int \left(r \left(\frac{\partial H}{\partial x} \right)^2 + \lambda \frac{\partial H}{\partial x} + \gamma \right) f_{ni} \\
&\quad + \alpha k \int_\Gamma \Big((\Psi - \Theta) + e \frac{\partial \Psi}{\partial t} \Big) f_{ni}.
\end{aligned}
$$

Furthermore, for $\mathbf{X} = (\mathbf{x}, \mathbf{y})^T$ with $\mathbf{x}$ and $\mathbf{y} \in \mathbf{R}^{n+1}$, let $X = \sum x_i f_{ni}$, $Y = \sum y_i f_{ni}$. Then we have

$$
\begin{aligned}
\mathbf{x}^T \mathbf{A}_1 \mathbf{x} &= \Theta_c \int (1+Q) X^2, \\
\mathbf{y}^T \mathbf{A}_4 \mathbf{y} &= \int (c + a^2 \Theta_c M^2 Q) Y^2 + ek\Big(\int \left(\frac{\partial Y}{\partial x} \right)^2 + \alpha (y_0^2 + y_n^2) \Big) \quad \text{and} \\
\mathbf{x}^T \mathbf{A}_2 \mathbf{y} + \mathbf{y}^T \mathbf{A}_3 \mathbf{x} &= -2a\Theta_c \int MQXY \geq -\Theta_c \int QX^2 - a^2 \Theta_c \int M^2 Q Y^2.
\end{aligned}
$$

By summation one arrive at the following inequality:

$$
\begin{aligned}
\mathbf{X}^T \mathbf{A} \mathbf{X} &\geq \Theta_c \int X^2 + c \int Y^2 + ek\Big(\int \left(\frac{\partial Y}{\partial x} \right)^2 + \alpha (y_0^2 + y_n^2) \Big) \\
&\geq C|X|^2
\end{aligned}
$$

where $C > 0$ is an independent constant, which means that A is positive definite and its inverse is uniformly bounded. This immediately yields the conclusion.

4.2. Iterative procedure.

Let us discretize $(VP)_n$ by the difference on the time interval $[0, T]$ where $T = m\,\Delta t$ with a positive integer m and a time step $\Delta t > 0$. These results in a system of algebraic equations:

$$
\begin{aligned}
\mathbf{A}^j(\mathbf{M}^j, \Theta^j)\mathbf{H}^j &= u(\mathbf{M}^j, \Theta^j, \Theta^{j-1}), \\
\mathbf{B}\Theta^j &= v(\mathbf{H}^j, \mathbf{M}^j, \mathbf{M}^{j-1})
\end{aligned}
$$

$(j = 1, 2, ..., m)$ where $\mathbf{A}^j, \mathbf{B}, \mathbf{H}^j, \mathbf{M}^j$ and Θ^j are some matrices and vectors of $(n-1)$ -order. In the present situation, for $i = 0, 1, ..., n$ the j-component of $\mathbf{M}^j$, as a function of $(\mathbf{H}^j)_i$ and $(\Theta^j)_i$, can be determined according to the following:

(i) If $q = [\frac{H}{2b}]^2 + [\frac{a(\Theta-\Theta_c)}{3b}] \geq 0, M = [\frac{H}{2b} + \sqrt{q}]^{\frac{1}{3}} + [\frac{H}{2b} - \sqrt{q}]^{\frac{1}{3}}$;

(ii) If $q < 0, M \in \{M_1, M_2\}$ jumps from negative (positive) to positive (negative) at t for H_Θ $(-H_\Theta)$, where the components are calculated by

$$M_i = 2[\frac{a(\Theta_c - \Theta)}{3b}]^{\frac{1}{2}} \cos\{\frac{\tau + 2(i-1)\pi}{3}\} \, (i = 1, 2),$$
$$\tau = \arccos\{\frac{H}{2b(a\frac{\Theta_c - \Theta}{3b})^{\frac{3}{2}}}\}.$$

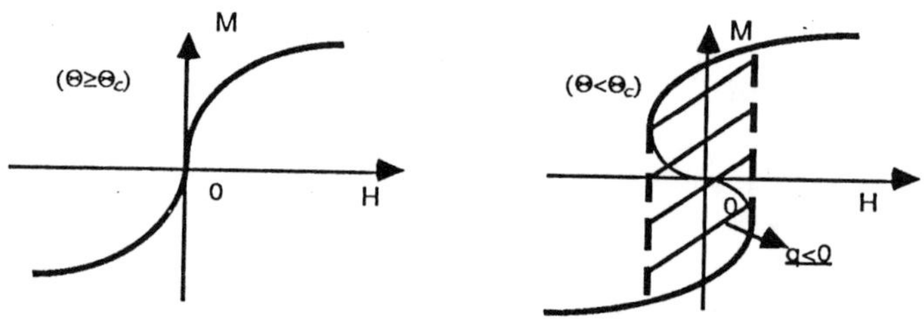

Using the notation $\mathbf{M}^j = g(\mathbf{H}^j, \Theta^j, M_0)$ we can construct an iterative process as follows:

(i) $j = 0 : (\mathbf{H}^0)_i = H_0(\frac{i}{n}), (\Theta^0)_i = \Theta_0(\frac{i}{n}), (M^0)_i = M_0(\frac{i}{n}) (i = 0, 1, ..., n)$;

(ii) $j = 1, 2, ..., m$: let $\mathbf{H}^{j,0} = \mathbf{H}^{j-1}, \mathbf{M}^{j,0} = \mathbf{M}^{j-1}, \Theta^{j,0} = \Theta^{j-1}$; compute $\mathbf{H}^j = H^{j,n(j)}$ and $\Theta^j = \Theta^{j,n(j)}$ by the following iterations:

$$\begin{aligned} \mathbf{A}^j(\mathbf{M}^{j,i-1}, \Theta^{j,i-1})\mathbf{H}^{j,i} &= u(\mathbf{M}^{j,i-1}, \Theta^{j,i-1}, \Theta^{j-1}), \\ (\mathbf{M}^{j,i})^* &= g(\mathbf{H}^{j,i}, \Theta^{j,i-1}, \mathbf{M}_0), \\ \mathbf{B}\Theta^{j,i} &= v(\mathbf{H}^{j,i}, (\mathbf{M}^{j,i})^*, \mathbf{M}^{j-1}), \\ \mathbf{M}^{j,i} &= g(\mathbf{H}^{j,i}, \Theta^{j,i}, \mathbf{M}_0) \end{aligned}$$

$(i = 1, 2, ..., n(j))$ such that $\|\mathbf{H}^{j,n(j)} - \mathbf{H}^{j,n(j)-1}\|_1 < \varepsilon$ ($\varepsilon > 0$ is the accuracy).

4.3. Numerical experiments.

We are going to concentrate on the effect of the system under external actions on the boundary. Therefore, the distributed electromagnetism force λ and heat supply γ will not be taken into account, i.e. they vanish in our experiments.

Some selected results of simulant experiments are reported in which $a = 0.05, b = r = k = l, e = 0, \Theta_c = 20$ and $\mathbf{H}_0 = 0$ whereras $n = 50, m = 1000$ and $\Delta t = 0.001$. The time evolution of the distributions of the magnetization and the magnetic field in the space are illustrated.

Experiment 1 (temperature-activated) : $\Theta_0 = 21, \alpha = 5, \phi = 0$ and Ψ is illustrated by

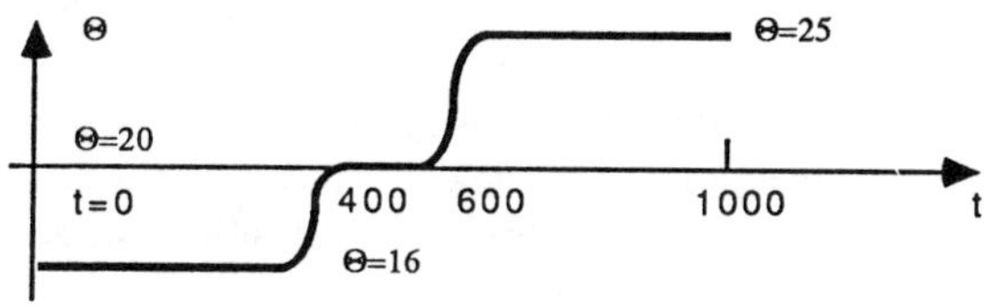

Experiment 2 (field-activated) : $\Theta_0 = 18$, $\alpha = 0$, and ϕ looks as follows :

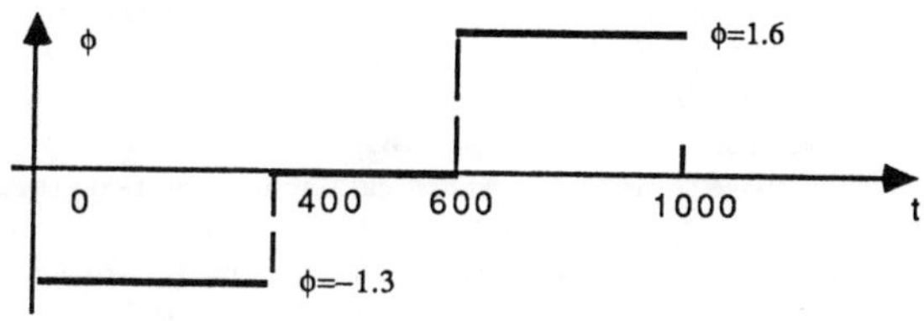

Experiment 3 (simultaneously temperature - and field-activated) : $\Theta_0 = 20, \alpha = 5$, whereas ϕ and Ψ are analogous to those in Experiment 1 and 2 :

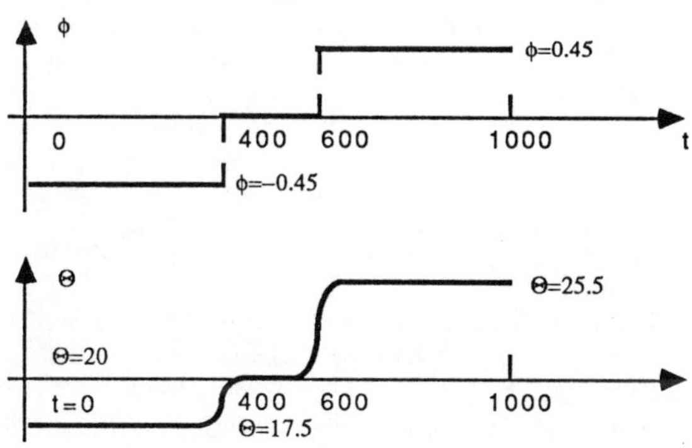

In the above-mentioned experiments all the main effects observed in the reality of

ferromagnetism can be shown. For example, the phase transitions of second order induced by the temperature at the critical point, and the first order transformations induced by the magnetic field under the lower temperature. In particular, in the state of lower temperature the system splits into some domains of different orientation, which trend towards stable of cooling.

It coincides with the result of the theoretical analysis that the temperature is always continuous while the magnetic field changes continuously in the direction of both the spatial variable x and the time t. In addition, the magnetization has a jump in the course the temperature crosses the critical point. On the other hand, as the temperature goes beyond the *Currie* point, both the magnetic field and the magnetization become smooth, and the higher the temperature is, the nearer to zero they are.

References

1. M. Ausloos & R. J. Elliott, *Magnetic phase transitions*, Springer Series in Solid-State Science **48** (1983), Springer-Verlag, Berlin.
2. P. R. Beesack, *Gronwall inequalities*, Carleton Mathematical Lecture Notes **11** (1975), Carleton.
3. E. Brézin, J. C. Le Guillou & J. Zinn-Justin, *Field theoretical approach to critical phenomena*, pages 125–247 in Vol. 6 of [**5**] (1976).
4. B. D. Coleman & E. H. Dill, *On the thermodynamics of electromagnetic fields in materials with memory*, Arch. Rat. Mech. Anal. **41** (1971), 132–162.
5. C. Domb & M. S. Green, Phase transitions and critical phenomena **1–6** (1972-1976), Academic Press, London.
6. G. Duvaut & J. L. Lions, "Inequalities in mechanics and physics," Springer-Verlag, Berlin, 1976.
7. F. Falk, *Landau theory and martensitic phase transitions*, J. de Physique C-4 No. 12 (1982), 3–15.
8. R. P. Feynman, R. B. Leighton & M. Sands, "The Feynman Lectures on Physics II," Addison-Wesley Publishing company, Reading, 1977.
9. J. M. Finn & L. T. Wheeler, *Wave propagational aspects of the generalized theory of heat conduction*, Z. Angew. Math. Phys (1972), 927–940.
10. J. Frochlich, *On the mathematics of phase transitions and critical phenomena*, in "Proc. of the Intern. Congress of Mathematicians" (1978), 896–904, Helsinki.
11. F. Gautier, *Introduction to the study of phase transitions*, in "Solid State Phase Transitions in Metals and Alloys", 223–336, Ecole d'été d'Aussois 1978, les éditions de physique, Orsay.
12. S. R. de Groot & P. Mazur, "Non-equilibrium thermodynamics," Dover Publications, New York, 1984.
13. M. E. Curtin & A. C. Pipkin, *A general Theory of Heat conduction with finite wave speeds*, Arch. Rat. Mech. Anal. **31** (1968), 113–126.
14. A. Hubert, "Theorie der Domänenwände in geordneten Medien," Springer-Verlag, Berlin, 1974.
15. J. D. Jackson, "Classical electrodynamics, Second Edition," John Wiley & Sons, New York, 1975.
16. W. I. Khan, *On the magnetic inhomogenity on Landau-Gintzburg Theory*, J. Phas. C: Solid State Phys. **19** (1986), 1969–2978.
17. A. Kufner, O. John & S. Fuck, "Function Spaces," Noordhoff International Publishing, Leyden, 1977.
18. L. D. Landau, Collected papers of L. D. Landau, ed. by D. ter Haar (1965), Pergamon Press, Oxford.
19. L. D. Landau & E. M. Lifshitz, Statistische Physik (1966), Akademie-Verlag, Berlin.
19. L. D. Landau & E. M. Lifshitz, Elektrodynamik der Kontinua (1967), Akademie-Verlag, Berlin.
21. M. Luban, *Generalized Landau Theories*, pages 37–50 in Vol. 5A of [**5**] (1976).
22. M. F. MacCarthy, *Thermodynamics of electromagnetic materials with memory*, Arch. Rat. mech. Anal. **41** (1971), 333-353.
23. D. C. Mattis, *The theory of magnetism I & II*, Springer Series in Solid-State Sceince **17** & **55** (1981 & 1985), Springer-Verlag, Berlin.

24. W. L. Miranker & B. E. Willner, *Global Analysis of magnetic domains*, Quart. Appl. Math **37** (1979), 219–238.
25. A. R. Mitchell & R. Wait, The finite element method in partial differential equations (1978), John Wiley & Sons, Chinceste.
26. I. Müller, "Thermodynamik," Uni.-Verlag, Düsseldorf, 1973.
27. J. W. Nunziato, *On heat conduction in materials with memory*, Quart. Appl Math. **29** (1971), 187–204.
28. H. E. Stanley, "Introduction to phase transitions and critical phenomena," Oxford Univ. Press, Oxford, 1985.
29. A. Visintin, *On some microscopic models of ferromagnetism*, Rend. Sem. Mat. Univ. Politec. Torino **43** (1985), 371–388.
30. A. Visintin, *On Landay Lifshitz' equations for ferromagnetism*, Japan J. Appl. Math. **2** (1985), 69–84.
31. A. Visintin, *On the evolution of ferromagnetic media*, Math. Modelling **5** (1984), 43–61.
32. A. Visintin, *Coupled thermic and electromagnetic evolution in a ferromagnetic body*, 436. Instituto di Analisi Numerica del C. N. R., Pavia (1984).
33. A. Visintin, *On the Preisach model for hysteresis*, Nonl. Anal. **8** (1984), 977-996.
34. A. Visintin, *On hysteresis in phase transitions*, Control and Cybernetics **14** (1985), 297–307.
35. H. P. J. Wijn, *Ferromagnetism*, Encyclopedia of Physics **18.2** (1966), Springer-Verlag, Berlin.
36. I. R. Yukhnovskii, "Phase transitions of the second order," World Scientific Publishing, Singapore, 1987.

Computational stability of an initially radial solution of a growth/dissolution problem in a nonradial implementation

S. JENSEN[1]*, E. LAITINEN[2], P. NEITTAANMÄKI[2] AND T.I. SEIDMAN[1]**

[1]Department of Mathematics and Statistics
University of Maryland, Baltimore Country
Baltimore, MD 21228, USA

[2]Department of Mathematics, University of Jyväskylä
Seminaarinkatu 15, 40100 Jyväskylä, Finland

Abstract. We consider a free boundary problem modelling the growth/dissolution of a crystal. The aim is to investigate the following question: Does the solution to the crystal growth problem posed in two dimensions with radially symmetric initial and boundary condition evolve as a radially symmetric solution?

Keywords. Free boundary problem, crystal growth, stability of the solution.

1980 Mathematics subject classifications: 49B25

1. INTRODUCTION

Consider the solution of some substance surrounding a 'crystal grain' of pure material. Letting $\Omega = \Omega(t)$ be the bounded spatial region in $\mathbf{R}^n$ occupied by the solution and $Q(t) = \{(t,x) \mid x \in \Omega(t), \quad 0 < t < T\}$, we assume that the concentration C satisfies the diffusion-reaction equation

$$C_t = \triangle C \quad \text{in } Q(t). \tag{1.1}$$

Let us first consider the problem in a context of radial symmetry: $0 \le r := |x| \le 1$ with the crystal grain occupying $0 \le r \le R(t)$ so

$$\Omega(t) = \{x \mid R(t) < r := |x| < 1\} \text{ and}$$

$$Q(t) = \{(x,t) \mid R(t) < r := |x| < 1, \quad 0 < t < T\}.$$

Note that by a suitable choice of units, we can take the diffusion coefficient and the outer radius each to be 1: we will also normalize u so the 'pure' concentration for the crystal, itself, is 1.

*The work of S. Jensen was partially supported under Office of Naval Research Contract No. N00014-87-K-0427 and N00014-90-J-1238

**The work of T.I. Seidman was partially supported under NSF grant ECS-8814788.

The motion of the crystal boundary is given by a function $R: [0,T] \mapsto [0,1]$ determined by

$$\left\{ \begin{array}{l} \dot{R}(t) = h \\ R(0) = R_0 \end{array} \right. \tag{1.2}$$

for an appropriate function $h = h(t)$: one has growth for $h > 0$, dissolution for $h < 0$.

We suppose that the solution of the diffusion-reaction equation satisfies the boundary conditions

$$C(x,t)\Big|_{|x|=1} = \alpha(t) \tag{1.3}$$

$$\frac{\partial}{\partial n} C(x,t)\Big|_{|x|=R(t)} = (1-C)h \tag{1.4}$$

and the initial conditions $R(0) = R_0$ with $0 < R_0 < 1$ and

$$C(x,0) = C_0(x), \quad R_0 < |x| < 1 \tag{1.5}$$

with $0 \leq C_0(x) < 1$. The Dirichlet boundary data $\alpha(t)$ $(0 \leq \alpha(t) \leq 1, \quad t \in [0,T])$ may be viewed as a control variable; with our normalized concentration, the flux boundary condition (1.4) corresponds to conservation of mass at the moving crystal boundary.

If h were given *a priori* in (1.2), then we could simply adjoin the 'conservation of mass' boundary condition (1.4) at $|x| = R(t)$ to have a **moving boundary problem**, specified by the pair $\{\alpha, h\}$ and the initial conditions. Actually, the crystal growth is determined by a constitutive relation of the form

$$h = H(\kappa, \omega) \tag{1.6}$$

where κ is the curvature and $\omega = C\Big|_{r=R(t)+}$. We suppose that H takes the form

$$H(\kappa,\omega) = K(\omega - c_* G(\kappa)) \tag{1.7}$$

with

$$G(\kappa) = 1 + \gamma\ \kappa + ...$$

for some positive constants K, c_*, γ. We assume that H is smooth and that $H(\cdot, 0) \leq 0$.

For our numerical computation we will take Ω to be 2-dimensional $(n = 2)$. In order to be able to compare our results with those of [**7**], we will again employ the Ostwald-Freundlich law: $G(R) = \gamma_0\ \mathrm{e}^{\kappa}$ (cf [**6,3**]) as in [**1,7**]; we take $K = 1$, $c_* = 0.01$. Then (1.7) can be written in terms of ω and κ as follows:

$$H(\kappa,\omega) = \omega - 0.01\ \mathrm{e}^{\kappa}. \tag{1.8}$$

It is convenient to reformulate the problem (1.1)–(1.5) on a fixed, one-dimensional spatial domain. Thus, we make a change of variables: $x \mapsto y$, setting

$$u(y,t) = C(x,t) \quad \text{with } y := \frac{1-|x|}{1-R(t)}. \tag{1.9}$$

Note that $y = \rho(1-r)$ where $\rho(\cdot) := 1/(1-R(\cdot)) > 1$ so $R = 1 - 1/\rho$ and $|x| = r = 1 - y/\rho$ with $\rho_0 = 1/(1-R_0) > 1$. The problem (1.1)–(1.5) now just becomes:

$$\begin{cases} \dot{\rho} = \rho^2 h & \text{on } (0,T) \\ u_t = \rho^2 u_{yy} - \rho \left[\dfrac{(d-1)\rho}{\rho - y} + yh \right] u_y & \text{on } (0,1) \times (0,T) \\ -\rho u_y = (1 - u(\cdot,1))h & \text{at } y = 1 \\ u = \alpha [= \text{ control}] & \text{at } y = 0 \\ \rho = \rho_0 \quad \text{and } u = u_0 & \text{at } t = 0\,. \end{cases} \tag{1.10}$$

Note that $y = 0, 1$ correspond to $r = 1, R(t)$. Of course we obtain $\rho_0 > 1$ and $u_0(\cdot)$ on (0,1) from (1.2)–(1.5). The free boundary problem just couples this with (1.6), no longer taking h as given; we assume H is now formulated as $H(\omega, \rho)$.

The existence and uniqueness of a weak solution for the coupled problem (1.10), (1.7) for each $\alpha \in H^1(0,T)$ with $0 \le \alpha \le 1$ has been demonstrated in [**4**] and for $\alpha \in L^2(0,T)$ in [**9,10**].

2. The control problem

Consider the control problem

$$\underset{\alpha \in U_{\text{ad}}}{\text{Minimize}} \{ J(\alpha) \equiv \frac{1}{2} \int_0^T (\rho - \rho_*)^2 \, dt \} \tag{2.1}$$

subject to (1.10), (1.7), where the set of admissible controls is $U_{\text{ad}} = \{ \alpha \mid \alpha_0 \le \alpha(t) \le \alpha_1 \}$ with given α_0 and α_1.

Consider the problem (2.1) subject to (ρ, u) satisfying the nonlinear parabolic system

$$\begin{cases} \rho_t(t) = \rho(t)^2 (u(1,t) - \gamma_0 \, e^{\delta \rho(t)/(\rho(t)-1)}), \quad t \in (0,1) \\ u_t(y,t) = \rho(t)^2 u_{yy}(y,t) - \rho \left[\dfrac{\rho(t)}{\rho(t) - y} + y(u(1,t) - \gamma_0 \, e^{1/(1-1/\rho(t))}) \right] u_y, \\ \qquad y \in (0,1), \quad t \in (0,1) \end{cases} \tag{2.2}$$

with boundary conditions

$$\begin{cases} u(0,t) = \alpha(t) \\ u_y(1,t) = -\dfrac{1}{\rho(t)} (1 - u(1,t) - \gamma_0 \, e^{1/(1-1/\rho(t))}), \quad t \in (0,1) \end{cases} \tag{2.3}$$

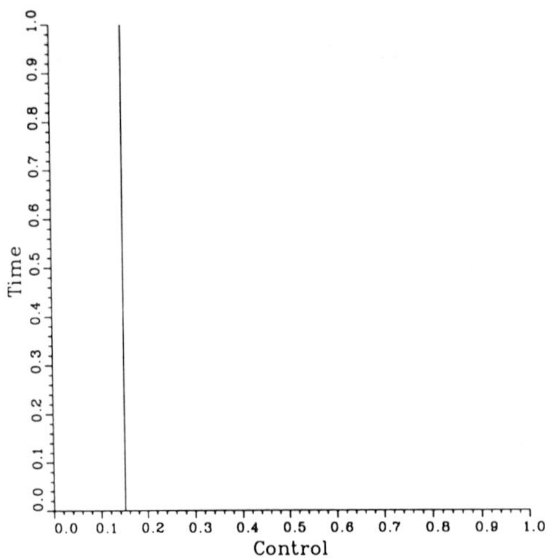

Figure 2.1.

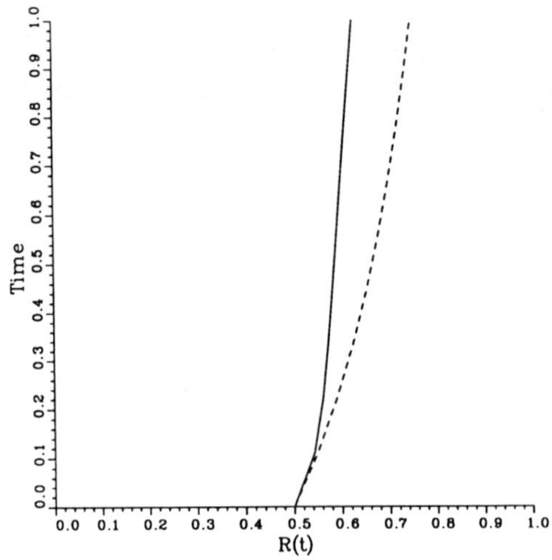

Figure 2.2.

and with initial conditions

$$\begin{cases} \rho(0) = \rho_0 \\ u(y,0) = u_0(y), \quad y \in (0,1). \end{cases} \tag{2.4}$$

One can derive the discrete analogue to (2.1)–(2.4) in the usual way. We have applied the trapezoidal rule for computing $J(\alpha)$, finite element method with linear elements in the space discretization of (2.2)–(2.3) and the implicit Euler method in time discretization. The resulting nonlinear state system can be solved by a combination of Newton and overrelaxation methods, for example. In order to apply efficient nonlinear programming algorithms for minimizing the discretized cost functional J one must compute $\nabla_\alpha J$. This can be done in a well known manner by applying the adjoint state technique for the discretized state system (see [7]).

In (2.1)–(2.4), let $\rho_*(t) = 2 + 2t$ (i.e. $R_*(t) = 1 - 1/(2+2t)$), $\gamma_0 = 0.01$, $\rho_0 = 2$ and $u_0(y) = -y(y-2)$, i.e.,

$$C(r,0) = C_0(r) = \begin{cases} 1, & 0 \le r \le 1/2 \\ -4r(r-1), & 1/2 < r \le 1\,. \end{cases}$$

In the following numerical results the discretization parameters were taken as $\Delta y = 1/20$ (in space discretization) and $\Delta t = 1/20$ (in time discretization), resulting in 21 unknowns for the minimization of J. The conjugate gradient algorithm with box constraints $\alpha_{\min} = 0.05$ and $\alpha_{\max} = 0.85$ was used for this minimization.

As an initial guess for α we took $\alpha(t) = 0.15$ (Figure 2.1) as in [7]. Figure 2.2 shows $R(t)$ (–line) and $R_*(t)$ (- - -line). In Figure 2.5 we see the corresponding concentration $C(t,y)$.

In Figure 2.3 we see the numerical approximation to the optimal control α after 3 iterations of the conjugate gradient algorithm. Figure 2.4 shows the corresponding values of $R(t)$ (—line) and $R_*(t)$ (- - -line) and in Figure 2.6 the corresponding values of the concentration can be seen.

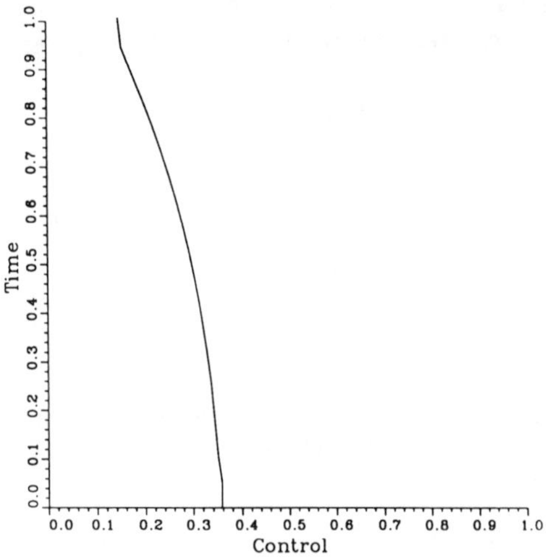

Figure 2.3.

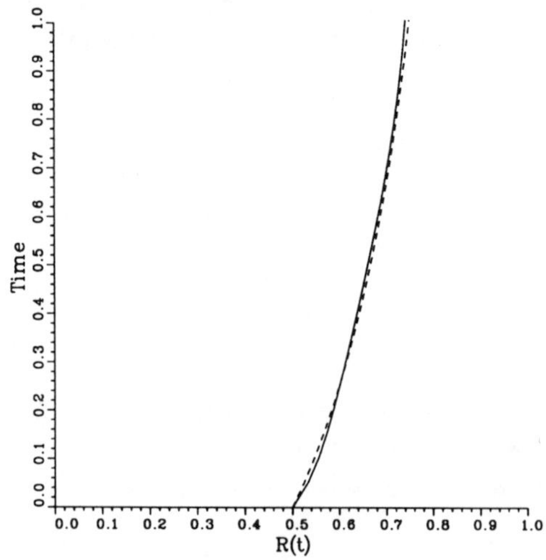

Figure 2.4.

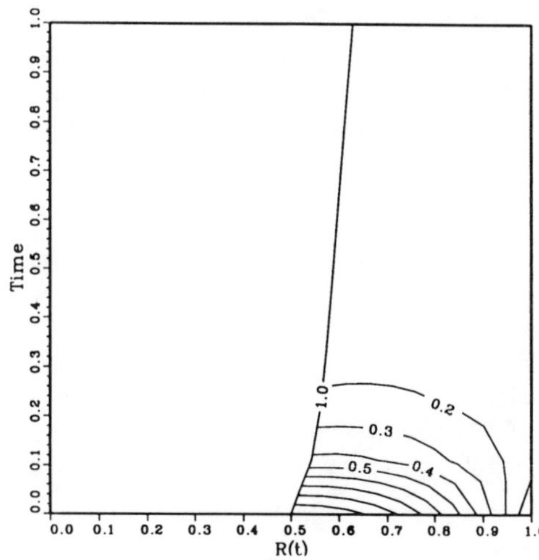

Figure 2.5.

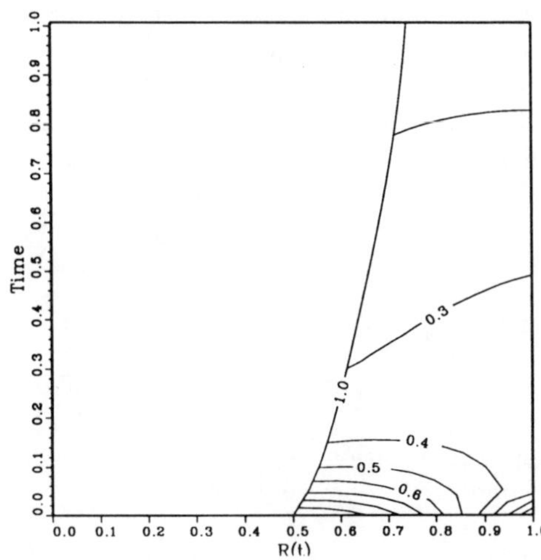

Figure 2.6.

3. Computational stability of the radial solution

In this chapter we describe some two-dimensional computations aimed at investigating the following question: Does the solution to the crystal growth problem posed in two dimensions with radially symmetric initial and boundary conditions evolve stably as a radially symmetric solution? This question is natural, since [**4,10**] showed the well-posedness of this solution only when radial symmetry is imposed *a priori*.

The two-dimensional numerical solution is computed via a finite difference method. We divide the discussion into two parts: the evolution of the grain boundary and the diffusion process exterior to the grain.

The key idea, as proposed in [**8**], is to introduce an auxiliary function

$$\varphi : (-1,1)^2 \times [0,T] \to \mathbf{R}. \tag{3.1}$$

We wish to emphasize that this function φ has no direct physical significance and that this class of methods is only superficially related to those of [**1**], [**5**]. The domain occupied by the grain is then $\mathcal{G} = \mathcal{G}(t) = \{x : \varphi(x,t) > 0\}$ with boundary

$$\Gamma = \Gamma(t) = \{x : \varphi(x,t) = 0\}$$

and one has diffusion of the concentration C in the complement $\Omega = \mathcal{G}^C$ as earlier. No longer assuming radiality, the equation of motion of the boundary Γ is expressed by taking the normal velocity of the boundary $\dot{\Gamma}$ to be a function of the curvature κ of the boundary at that point and the concentration at the boundary just outside the grain, $\omega = C|_\Gamma$ — i.e., $\dot{\Gamma} = H(\kappa,\omega)$ as in (1.6); see chapter 1). The experimentally determined function H is usually taken in the form of (1.7). In order to compare the results of chapter 2 we continue to suppose that H is defined by (1.8). Note, however, that the method we use in no way depends on this particular choice of G.

Using φ of (3.1), we can express

$$\begin{aligned} \vec{n} &= -\,\nabla\varphi/|\nabla\varphi|, \\ \dot{\Gamma} &= -\,\varphi_t/|\nabla\varphi|, \\ \kappa &= -\,\frac{\varphi_{yy}\varphi_x^2 - 2\varphi_{xy}\varphi_x\varphi_y + \varphi_{xx}\varphi_y^2}{|\nabla\varphi|^3} \end{aligned} \tag{3.2}$$

and the equation of motion of the boundary becomes $-\varphi_t/|\nabla\varphi| = H(\kappa,\omega)$, which is a Hamilton-Jacobi-like problem for φ:

$$\varphi_t + H(\kappa,\omega)|\nabla\varphi| = 0 \tag{3.3}$$

for which take the initial conditions to be

$$\varphi(x,0) = |x| - .5 \tag{3.4}$$

with the initial boundary a circle of radius .5. Since φ is to be globally defined, we also need to define ω globally. This we do by letting $\omega = C$ in $\Omega_{\text{num}} = \mathcal{G}^C_{\text{num}}$ (i.e., in the grid-complement of the grain region $\mathcal{G}$) and extending ω in a C^1-manner in towards the origin (using $C|_\Gamma$ and $\partial C/\partial n$) where we give ω the value of C at the outer boundary (=0.15 as in Example 2.1). Initially, $\kappa = 1/r$ which diverges at the origin. We redefine κ at those gridpoints where $H < 0$ to be such that $H = 0$. To discretize (3.3), we split H into

$$H(\kappa,\omega) = H_0 + H_1, \text{ where,} \tag{3.5}$$

$$H_0 = \omega - c_*, \text{ and } H_1 = c_*(G(\kappa) - 1). \tag{3.6}$$

Note that H_1 vanishes at zero curvature and is thrown to the right hand side and approximated by centered differences. The Hamilton-Jacobi problem with H_0 is approximated by an upwind first order Godunov scheme as described in [**8**]:

$$\begin{aligned} \varphi_{i,j}^{n+1} &= \varphi_{i,j} - \Delta t\, g_{\text{ HJGod.}}, \text{ where} \\ (g_{\text{ HJGod.}})^2 &= \sum_{\text{var}=x,y} (\min(D_-^{\text{ var}}\varphi_{i,j}, 0))^2 + (\max(D_+^{\text{ var}}\varphi_{i,j}, 0))^2 \end{aligned} \tag{3.7}$$

($D_\pm$ denotes the first order forward (backward) difference operator and we suppressed the superscript n on the right hand side). This is fully upwind and monotone; we monitored that the Courant-Friedrichs-Lewy number never exceeded 1.

Having described the numerical approximation procedure for the evolution of the boundary, we proceed to the diffusion process. The diffusion equation (1.1) is discretized using a 5-point Laplacian in $\Omega_{\text{ num}}$. The concentration C satisfies a conservation boundary condition at Γ: $\partial C/\partial n = \dot{\Gamma}(1 - C)$. For a center point with any of its four neighbours in Ω or on Γ, we redefine the value of C at any such 'grain' neighbour before performing the 5-point Laplacian by enforcing the Neumann boundary condition in a standard way, [**11**] — accurate of first order. We locate the boundary (from φ), and can then extend C linearly away from Γ to a point in $\Omega_{\text{ num}}$ lying on a grid-line where we in turn assume C is the linear interpolant between the end-point values.

By symmetry, we are merely computing the solution in the first quadrant. The computational domain is a square imbedded inside the disc on which the comparison (radial) problem is defined. Thus, at the outer boundary of the square, Dirichlet boundary conditions for C are inherited from the '1D' radial solution which is here computed simultaneously using finite differences also (by transforming the r variable to one in a fixed domain as above, setting the curvature to be the reciprocal of the grain radius, and taking the concentration to be a constant —0.15 — on the unit circle, i.e. $\alpha = 0.15$ in (1.10)). We note that this method for '1D' is slightly different from that used in [**7**] but reproduces those results accurately at constant boundary data. Finally, we take (first order) forward Euler as our time-discretization. Needless to say, this is not the most efficient procedure imaginable but has been adopted to permit rapid implementation. There is a small layer near Γ in which C is monotonically increasing away from Γ — this is what drives the growth of the grain. The layer width is not large, which puts an upper bound on any reasonable Δx (space discretization parameter equidistant step in x_1- and x_2-direction) and this in turn puts a severe restriction on k (the time discretization parameter), since stability requires that $\Delta t/(\Delta x)^2 \leq 1/2$.

Note that with a Cartesian grid, our numerical solution is *automatically perturbed* away from a radial one. The proof of well-posedness in [**4**,**10**] has not yet been carried over to this case, so theoretically it is not known at present whether the 2D continuous problem with perturbed initial data is well-posed. The question remains whether this perturbation grows exponentially and if so in what time scale.

In Fig. 3.1, we have displayed the grain boundary as it evolves from $t = 0$ to $t = 0.1$. From the '1D' radial computation, we know that the grain grows fastest during this interval; its radius increases by roughly 10%. We seem to see that the boundary stays radial for some time, but slowly becomes nonradial. Fig. 3.2 shows how far the 2D solution is from being radial at four times in (0,0.1]. At $t = .1$ the relative deviation is .11 % (for $\Delta x = 1.75 \cdot 10^{-2}$, $\Delta t = 2.5 \cdot 10^{-5}$). This should be compared to the relative error of boundary representation using piecewise linear interpolation of the initial φ on the cartesian grid which is 0.04 %.

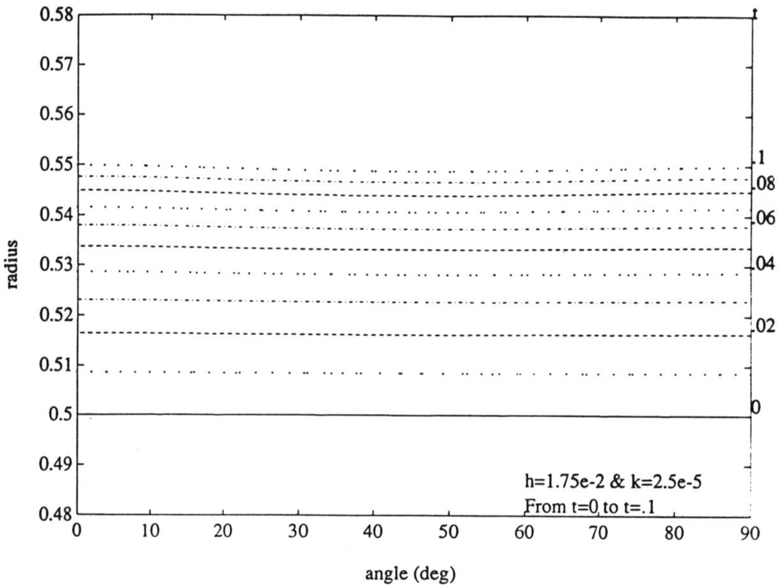

Figure 3.1. Crystal boundary evolving

Fig. 3.3 shows the evolution of the 2D computed mean radius compared to the radius obtained by the 1D computation. At $t = .1$ the relative deviation is .38 % (for $\Delta x = 1.75 \cdot 10^{-2}$, $\Delta t = 2.5 \cdot 10^{-5}$). Fig. 3.4 gives the relative difference between the mean concentration at $\Gamma_{2D,\text{num}}$ for 2D and the concentration at $\Gamma_{1D,\text{num}}$ $((\bar{c}_{2D} - c_{1D})/c_{1D})$. In Fig. 3.5 we display the difference in angle between the radius vector at the midpoint between two points on $\Gamma_{2D,\text{num}}$ and the normal vector there at time $t = 0.1$. Finally, returning to Fig. 3.3 we see the mean radius approximation history for three values of h.

Note the one-sided convergence. We believe this is due to the effect on the approximate computation of ω of the concavity of the exact C exterior to the grain near the boundary

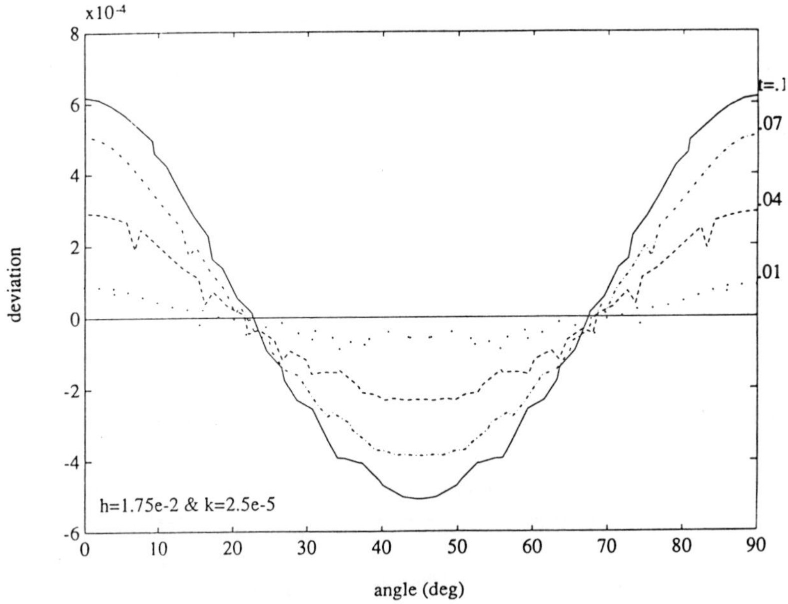

Figure 3.2. Evolving deviation from mean for grain radius

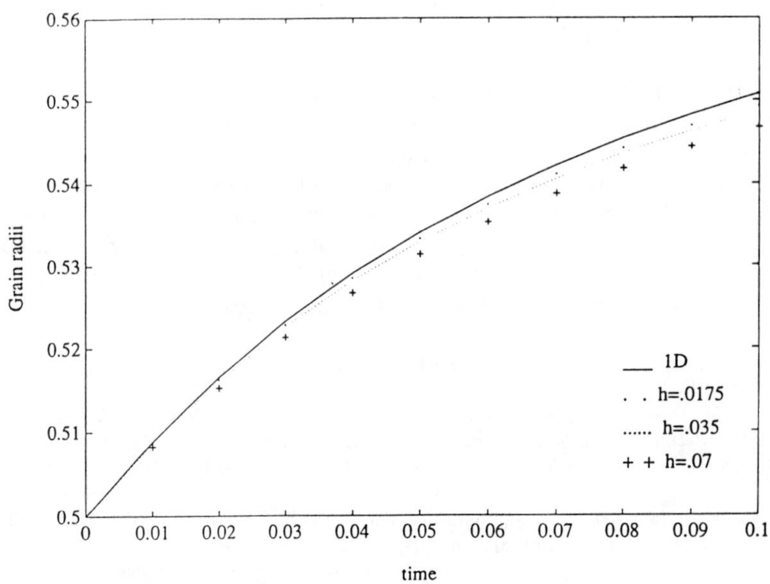

Figure 3.3. Evolving mean radius for 2D and 1D

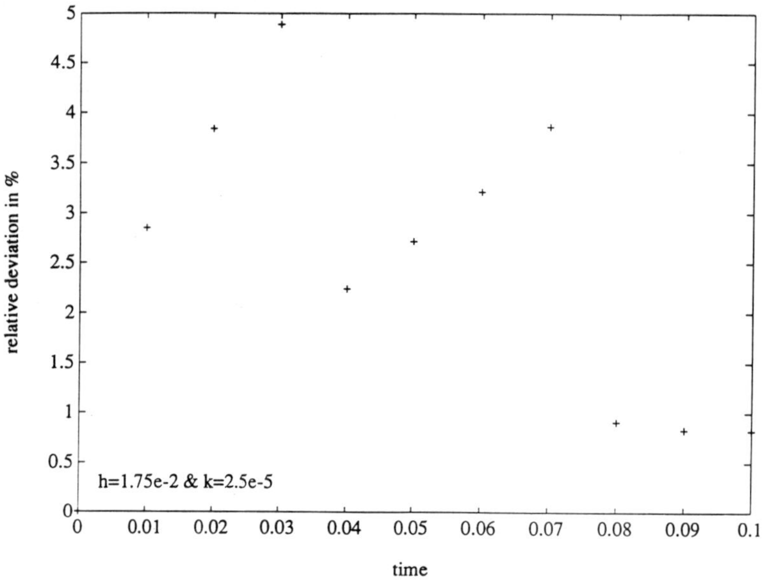

Figure 3.4. Relative difference in mean boundary concentration

compared to the piecewise linearity of the computed C. If one presumes fastest convergence at the grid nodes, the piecewise bilinear interpolant will then systematically underapproximate the exact C. Since the speed $\dot{\Gamma}$ is linearly increasing with ω, we therefore can expect to underapproximate the speed.

The fact that the crystal grows fastest along the axes can now be attributed to the grid alignment relative to the boundary. Along the two axes the boundary sees a grid length of Δx whereas along the line $y = x$, the boundary sees a grid length of $\sqrt{2}\Delta x$.

We note some possible future alternatives. One would consist of a shift from finite differences to a feedback finite element scheme. Another would be to discard the global φ, e.g., approximating the curvature by computing osculating circles as in [**2**] when tracking Γ. Finally, of course, there would be the methods as in [**1**], [**5**] which reformulate the problem so the grain boundary no longer appears explicitly at all.

References

1. G. Caginalp, *The Dynamics of a Conserved Phase Field System: Stefan-like, Hele-Shaw, and Cahn-Hilliard Models as Asymptotic Limits.*, IMA J. Appl. Math, **44**, 1990, 77–94.
2. A. J. Chorin, *Curvature and Solidification.*, J. Comp. Phys, **58**, 1985, 472–490.
3. F. Conrad and M. Cournil, *Free boundary problems in dissolution-growth processes*, In Proc. of Conference on "Boundary Control and Boundary Variations " (J.P. Zolesio, ed.), Lecture Notes in Control and Information Science, 100, Springer, New York, 1988, 116–136..
4. F. Conrad, D. Hilhorst, and T. I. Seidman, *Well-posedness of a moving boundary problem arising in a dissolution-growth process.*, Nonlinear Anal-TMA **15**, 1990, 445–465.
5. M. E. Gurtin, *On a nonequilibrium thermodynamics of capillarity and phase.*, Technical Report 88-6, Dept. of Math., Carnegie–Mellon University, 1988.

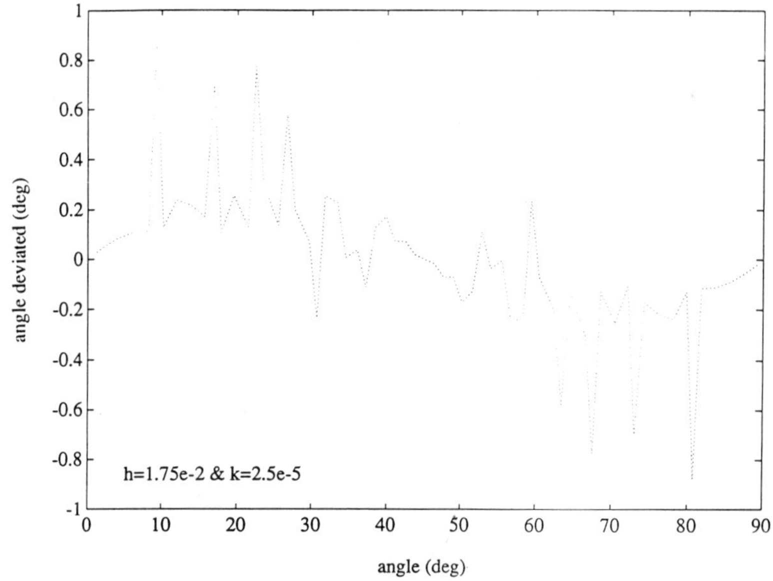

Figure 3.5. Angular deviation of normal vector from radius vector

6. F. Kaleydjian and M. Cournil, *Stability of steady states in some solid-liquid systems.*, Reactivity of Solids, **4**, 1986, 1–21.
7. P. Neittaanmäki and T. I. Seidman, *Optimal solutions for a free boundary problem for crystal growth.*, in "Proc. Control and Estimation of Distributed Parameter Systems (F. Kappel, K. Kunisch, W. Schappacher, eds.) ISNM91, 1989, 323–334."
8. S. Osher and J. A. Sethian, *Fronts propagating with curvature dependent speed: algorithms based on Hamilton-Jacobi formulations.*, J. Comp. Phys. **72**, 1988, 12–49.
9. T. I. Seidman, *Some control-theoretic questions for a free boundary problem*, in " Proc. of Control of Partial Differential Equations (Lecture Notes in Computer and Information Sciences, 114) " (A. Bermúdez, ed.), Springer, New York, 1989, pp. 265–276..
10. T. I. Seidman, *Optimal control and well-posedness for a free boundary problem*, in "Proc. 5th International Conf. on Free Boundary Problems (Montréal, 1990)."
11. G. A. Sod, *Numerical Methods in Fluid Dynamics*, Cambridge University Press, 1985.

International Series of Numerical Mathematics, Vol. 99, © 1991 Birkhäuser Verlag Basel

Shape Optimization for Multi-Phase Stefan Problems

Atsushi KADOYA and Nobuyuki KENMOCHI

Department of Mathematics
Graduate School of Science and Technology
Chiba University, Chiba-shi, 260 Japan

and

Department of Mathematics
Faculty of Education, Chiba University
Chiba-shi, 260 Japan

Abstract. We consider problems of shape optimization in which the driving actions are performed by geometry on the lateral boundary or geometry of the domain. We prove the existence of an optimal solution and discuss its approximation.

1. Introduction

In this paper we consider two optimization problems (a) and (b) mentioned below. In both of the problems the "states" are governed by a nonlinear degenerate parabolic equation of the form

$$u_t - \Delta\beta(u) = f \quad \text{in } Q := (0,T) \times \Omega. \tag{1.1}$$

Here Ω is a bounded domain in R^N with smooth boundary $\partial\Omega$, $0 < T < +\infty$, and β is a non-decreasing function on R such that

$$\begin{cases} \beta(0) = 0, & \\ |\beta(r)| \geq C_0|r| - C_0' & \text{for all } r \in R, \\ |\beta(r) - \beta(r')| \leq L_0|r - r'| & \text{for all } r, r' \in R, \end{cases} \tag{1.2}$$

where $C_0 > 0$, $C_0' \geq 0$ and $L_0 > 0$ are constants. Equation (1.1) is described as the enthalpy formulation of multi-phase Stefan problems; in this formulation u represents the enthalpy and $\beta(u)$ the temperature.

(a) Shape optimization on the lateral boundary

In our optimization problem the state is the weak solution u of the following initial-boundary value problem:

$$SP(\Gamma)\begin{cases} u_t - \Delta\beta(u) = f & \text{in } Q = (0,T) \times \Omega, \\ u(0,\cdot) = u_0 & \text{in } \Omega, \\ \beta(u) = g & \text{on } (0,T) \times \Gamma, \\ \dfrac{\partial\beta(u)}{\partial n} = h & \text{on } (0,T) \times \Gamma',\ \Gamma' = \partial\Omega - \Gamma, \end{cases}$$

where Γ is a compact subset of $\partial\Omega$ with positive surface measure $\sigma(\Gamma)$ and f, u_0, g and h are given functions. In the usual problem, driving variables are functions g and h, i.e. the driving space is a subset of $L^2((0,T)\times\Gamma)\times L^2((0,T)\times\Gamma')$ for a fixed $\Gamma\subset\partial\Omega$. However, in the problem which is proposed in this paper, fixing the data g, h, f and u_0, we take Γ as the driving variable and define the driving space Π by

$$\Pi=\{\Gamma\subset\partial\Omega;\Gamma \text{ is compact in } \partial\Omega,\ \sigma(\Gamma)>0\}. \tag{1.3}$$

Moreover, the cost functional $J(\Gamma)$ is defined by the formula:

$$J(\Gamma):=\frac{1}{2}\int_Q|\beta(u_\Gamma)-\beta_d|^2dx\,dt+\frac{1}{2}\int_{(0,T)\times(\partial\Omega-\Gamma)}|h|^2d\sigma dt, \tag{1.4}$$

where β_d is a given function in $L^2(Q)$ and u_Γ is the weak solution of $SP(\Gamma)$ for $\Gamma\in\Pi$. Given a subset Π_c of Π, our optimization problem $P(\Pi_c)$ is to find $\Gamma_*\in\Pi_c$ such that $J(\Gamma_*)$ is the minimum of J over Π_c, i.e.

$$P(\Pi_c)\quad \text{find } \Gamma_*\in\Pi_c \text{ such that } J(\Gamma_*)=\inf_{\Gamma\in\Pi_c}J(\Gamma).$$

(b) **Optimization of the domain**

The other optimization problem treated in this paper is concerned with optimal shape design of the domain Ω in which the state equation (1.1) is formulated. In this problem, Ω is the driving variable and the driving space O is given by

$$O:=\{\Omega\subset\hat{\Omega};\ \Omega \text{ is a non-empty bounded domain with smooth } \partial\Omega\subset\hat{\Omega}\},$$

where $\hat{\Omega}$ is a fixed bounded domain in R^N with smooth boundary $\partial\hat{\Omega}$, and for each $\Omega\in O$ the state is represented by the weak solution $u=u_\Omega$ of the following problem:

$$SP(\Omega)\begin{cases} u_t-\Delta\beta(u)=f & \text{in } Q=(0,T)\times\Omega,\\ u(0,\cdot)=u_0 & \text{in } \Omega,\\ \beta(u)=g & \text{on } (0,T)\times\partial\Omega,\end{cases}$$

where g is a given function defined on $(0,T)\times\hat{\Omega}$. When the cost functional $J(\Omega)$ is defined by the formula:

$$J(\Omega):=\frac{1}{2}\int_{(0,T)\times\Omega}|\beta(u_\Omega)-\beta_d|^2dx\,dt+\frac{1}{2}\int_{(0,T)\times(\hat{\Omega}-\Omega)}|g-\beta_d|^2dx\,dt$$

for a given function $\beta_d\in L^2((0,T)\times\hat{\Omega})$, our optimization problem $P(O_c)$, with a subset O_c of O, is to find a domain $\Omega_*\in O_c$ such that $J(\Omega_*)$ is the minimum of J over O_c, i.e.

$$P(O_c)\quad \text{find } \Omega_*\in O_c \text{ such that } J(\Omega_*)=\inf_{\Omega\in O_c}J(\Omega).$$

In proving the existence of solutions to $P(\Pi_c)$ and $P(O_c)$, the main step is to investigate the dependence of weak solutions u_Γ and u_Ω upon driving variables Γ and Ω, respectively. In fact, based on some results in [13], we introduce a notion of convergence in the driving space Π (resp.O) and show that the cost functional $J(\Gamma)$ (resp.$J(\Omega)$) is continuous with respect to it. The continuous dependence of $J(\Gamma)$ (resp.$J(\Omega)$) upon Γ(resp.Ω) immediately gives the existence of a solution to $P(\Pi_c)$(resp.$P(O_c)$) under some compactness assumption on Π_c (resp.O_c).

We quote some results [1,14,15,17 – 19] on optimal control problems associated with multi-phase Stefan problems established so far; in most of them the domain Ω and the part Γ of Dirichlet boundary condition are fixed, and functions f, g and h are taken as control variables.

In this paper, we give existence results for $P(\Pi_c)$ and $P(O_c)$ with sketch of the proofs and discuss their penalty mehtod-approximations from the numerical view-point. For their detailed proofs, see the authors' papers [7,8].

In general, for a (real) Banach space X we denote by $|v|_X$ the norm of $v \in X$ and by "$v_n \to v$ in X (as $n \to \infty$)" the strong convergence in X, unless otherwise stated. Also, we denote by $C_w([0,T];X)$ $(0 < T < +\infty)$ the space of all weakly continuous functions $v : [0,T] \to X$ and mean by "$v_n \to v$ in $C_w([0,T];X)$" that

$$\langle z, v_n(t)\rangle \to \langle z, v(t)\rangle \text{ uniformly in } t \in [0,T] \text{ as } n \to \infty$$

for each $z \in X^*$, where X^* is the dual space of X and $\langle \cdot, \cdot \rangle$ stands for the duality paring between X^* and X.

Let us now recall the convergence of a sequence $\{K_n\}$ of closed convex subsets K_n in a Banach space X. We say that K_n converges to a closed convex set K in X (as $n \to \infty$) in the sense of Mosco [13], if the following two conditions $(M1)$ and $(M2)$ are satisfied:

$(M1)$ If $\{n_k\}$ is a subsequence of $\{n\}$, $z_k \in K_{n_k}$ and $z_k \to z$ weakly in X as $k \to \infty$, then $z \in K$.

$(M2)$ For each $z \in K$, there exists a sequence $\{z_n\}$ such that $z_n \in K_n$ and $z_n \to z$ in X.

2. Problem $P(\Pi_c)$

2.1. Existence result

Let Ω be a fixed bounded domain in R^N with smooth boundary $\partial\Omega$, β be a non-decreasing function on R satisfying (1.2) and Π be the set defined by (1.3). We put

$$Q := (0,T) \times \Omega, \quad \Sigma := (0,T) \times \partial\Omega,$$
$$a(z,w) := \int_\Omega \nabla z \cdot \nabla w \, dx \quad \text{for } z, w \in H^1(\Omega)$$

and for each $\Gamma \in \Pi$

$$V(\Gamma) := \{z \in H^1(\Omega); z = 0 \text{ a.e. on } \Gamma\}.$$

Clearly $V(\Gamma)$ is a closed subspace of $H^1(\Omega)$.

Throughout this section, we suppose for the data f, g, h and u_0 of Stefan problem $SP(\Gamma)$ and the function β_d in formula (1.4) that

$$\begin{cases} f \in L^2(Q), \ g \in W^{2,2}(0,T;H^2(\Omega)), \\ h \in W^{2,2}(0,T;L^2(\partial\Omega)), u_0 \in L^2(\Omega), \beta_d \in L^2(Q). \end{cases} \tag{2.1}$$

For each $\Gamma \in \Pi$, the weak formulation of $SP(\Gamma)$ is stated in the following definition.

DEFINITION 2.1. A function $u : [0,T] \to L^2(\Omega)$ is called a weak solution of $SP(\Gamma)$, if the following conditions (w1) $\sim$ (w3) are satisfied:

(w1) $u \in C_w([0,T];L^2(\Omega))$ and $u(0) = u_0$;
(w2) $\beta(u) - g \in L^2(0,T;V(\Gamma))$;
(w3) $-\int_Q u\eta_t dxdt + \int_0^T a(\beta(u), \eta)dt = \int_Q f\eta dxdt + \int_\Sigma h\eta d\sigma dt$

for all $\eta \in L^2(0,T;V(\Gamma))$ with $\eta_t \in L^2(Q)$ and $\eta(0,\cdot) = \eta(T,\cdot) = 0$.

Problem $SP(\Gamma)$ admits a unique weak solution in the sense of Definition 2.1 (c.f. [2,4,9,12, 16]).

Now, we introduce a notion of convergence in the set Π.

DEFINITION 2.2. Let $\{\Gamma_n\}$ be a sequence in Π and $\Gamma \in \Pi$. Then we say that Γ_n converges to Γ in Π as $n \to \infty$, which is denoted by "$\Gamma_n \to \Gamma$ in Π as $n \to \infty$", if the following two conditions (i) and (ii) are satisfied:

(i) $\chi_{\Gamma_n} \to \chi_\Gamma$ in $L^1(\partial\Omega)$ as $n \to \infty$, where χ_{Γ_n} (resp.χ_Γ) is the characteristic function of Γ_n (resp.Γ) on $\partial\Omega$.

(ii) $V(\Gamma_n) \to V(\Gamma)$ in $H^1(\Omega)$ as $n \to \infty$ in the sense of Mosco.

The next theorem is concerned with the dependence of weak solution u_Γ to $SP(\Gamma)$ upon Γ.

THEOREM 2.1. *Let $\{\Gamma_n\} \subset \Pi$ and $\Gamma \in \Pi$ such that $\Gamma_n \to \Gamma$ in Π (as $n \to \infty$), and let u_n and u be the weak solutions of $SP(\Gamma_n)$ and $SP(\Gamma)$, respectively. Then we have:*

$$u_n \to u \quad in\ C_w([0,T]; L^2(\Omega))$$

and

$$\begin{cases} \beta(u_n) \to \beta(u) & in\ L^2(0,T;H^1(\Omega)) \cap C_{loc}((0,T]; L^2(\Omega)), \\ \beta(u_n(t)) \to \beta(u(t)) & weakly\ in\ H^1(\Omega)\ for\ each\ t \in (0,T]. \end{cases}$$

Proof. (see [7] for details). First we prove the following uniform estimates for u_n and $\beta_n := \beta(u_n)$:

$$\begin{cases} \sup_{t\in[0,T]} |u_n(t)|_{L^2(\Omega)} \le M_0, & \sup_{t\in(0,T]} |t^{1/2}\beta_n(t)|_{H^1(\Omega)} \le M_0, \\ |\beta_n|_{L^2(0,T;H^1(\Omega))} \le M_0, & |t^{1/2}\frac{\partial}{\partial t}\beta_n|_{L^2(Q)} \le M_0 \end{cases} \tag{2.2}$$

for all n, where M_0 is a positive constant independent of n. In fact, we obtain estimates (2.2) by an extensive use of the technique in [2,3], taking account of the fact that there is a constant $N_0 > 0$ such that

$$|z|_{L^2(\Omega)} \le N_0 |\nabla z|_{L^2(\Omega)} \text{ for all} z \in V(\Gamma_n),\ n = 1,2,\dots. \tag{2.3}$$

Inequality (2.3) is derived from the convergence $\chi_{\Gamma_n} \to \chi_\Gamma$ in $L^1(\partial\Omega)$, since it implies that $\sigma(\Gamma_n) \ge \sigma_0$ for all n and for a constant $\sigma_0 > 0$ independent of n. It should be noted that the bound M_0 in estimates (2.2) depends on the data f, g, h, u_0 and the constant N_0 of (2.3).

Next, let $\{u_k := u_{n_k}\}$ be any subsequence of $\{u_n\}$ such that

$$u_k \to \tilde{u} \text{ weakly* in } L^\infty(0,T;L^2(\Omega)) \text{ (as } k \to \infty) \tag{2.4}$$

and

$$\beta_k := \beta_{n_k} \to \tilde{\beta} \text{ weakly in } L^2(0,T;H^1(\Omega)) \tag{2.5}$$

for some $\tilde{u} \in L^\infty(0,T;L^2(\Omega))$ and $\tilde{\beta} \in L^2(0,T;H^1(\Omega))$. Then we moreover see that

$$u_k \to \tilde{u} \text{ in } C_w([0,T];L^2(\Omega)), \tag{2.6}$$

$$\beta_k \to \tilde{\beta} \text{ in } L^2(Q) \cap C_{loc}((0,T]; L^2(\Omega)), \tag{2.7}$$

and

$$\beta_k(t) \to \tilde{\beta}(t) \text{ in } H^1(\Omega) \text{ for each } 0 < t \le T. \tag{2.8}$$

In fact, it follows from (w3) of Definition 2.1 and uniform estimate (2.2) that $\{u'_k\}(u'_k = (d/dt)u_k)$ is bounded in $W^{1,2}(0,T; H^{-1}(\Omega))$ (note here that $V(\Gamma_k) \subset L^2(\Omega) \subset H^{-1}(\Omega)$ with densely defined and compact injections). Therefore $u_k \to \tilde{u}$ in $C([0,T]; H^{-1}(\Omega))$, which implies (2.6). Next, by the standard compactness argument, we derive (2.7) and (2.8) from (2.2) and (2.5). By the way we see that

$$\tilde{\beta} = \beta(\tilde{u}),$$

which is seen from (2.4), (2.7) and the maximal monotonicity of β as an operator in $L^2(Q)$.

Now, by the usual procedure of passage to the limit in k we see that $\tilde{u}$ is a weak solution of $SP(\Gamma)$; in this step we essentially use the convergence of $V(\Gamma_n) \to V(\Gamma)$ in $H^1(\Omega)$ in the sence of Mosco, and obtain at the same time

$$\beta_k \to \tilde{\beta} := \beta(\tilde{u}) \text{ in } L^2(0,T; H^1(\Omega)). \tag{2.9}$$

Since the weak solution of $SP(\Gamma)$ is unique, it follows that $\tilde{u} = u$ and the convergences (2.6) $\sim$ (2.8) and (2.9) hold without extracting any subsequence $\{u_k\}$ of $\{u_n\}$. $\diamond$

Concerning problem $P(\Pi_c)$ associated with cost functional $J(\Gamma)$ given by (1.4), we have the following existence theorem.

THEOREM 2.2. *Let Π_c be a non-empty subset of Π satisfying the following compactness condition (Γ):*

(Γ) *For any sequence $\{\Gamma_n\}$ in Π_c there are a subsequence $\{\Gamma_{n_k}\}$ and a set $\Gamma \in \Pi_c$ such that $\Gamma_{n_k} \to \Gamma$ in Π as $k \to \infty$.*

Then $P(\Pi_c)$ has at least one solution Γ_*.

Proof. Let $\{\Gamma_n\}$ be a sequence in Π_c such that $J(\Gamma_n) \to J_* := \inf\{J(\Gamma); \Gamma \in \Pi_c\}$. Then, by assumption (Γ) we may assume that $\Gamma_n \to \Gamma_*$ in Π for some $\Gamma_* \in \Pi_c$. Clearly, from Theorem 2.1 it follows that $J(\Gamma_n) \to J(\Gamma_*) = J_*$, so that Γ_* is a solution of $P(\Pi_c)$. $\diamond$

2.2. Approximation for $SP(\Gamma)$ and $P(\Pi_c)$

Our main idea is to approximate $SP(\Gamma)$ by smooth problems of non-degenerate parabolic type with smooth flux condition on the whole $\partial\Omega$.

Let $\{\beta^\varepsilon\} = \{\beta^\varepsilon; 0 < \varepsilon \le 1\}$ be a family of (smooth) functions $\beta^\varepsilon : R \to R$ such that

$(\beta 1)$ $\qquad |\beta^\varepsilon(r) - \beta(r)| \le \varepsilon(|r|+1) \quad$ for all $r \in R$;

$(\beta 2)$
$$\begin{cases} \beta^\varepsilon(0) = 0, \ |\beta^\varepsilon(r)| \ge \tilde{C}_0 |r| - \tilde{C}'_0 & \text{for all } r \in R, \\ |\beta^\varepsilon(r) - \beta^\varepsilon(r')| \le \tilde{L}_0 |r - r'| & \text{for all } r, r' \in R, \\ \dfrac{d}{dr}\beta^\varepsilon(r) \ge \varepsilon & \text{for a.e. } r \in R, \end{cases}$$

where $\tilde{C}_0 > 0$, $\tilde{C}_0' > 0$ and $\tilde{L}_0 > 0$ are constants independent of ε .

Also, let Π_c be a non-empty subset of Π having property (Γ), and let $\{\chi_\Gamma^\nu; 0 < \nu \le 1, \Gamma \in \Pi_c\}$ be a family of smooth functions on $\partial\Omega$. Suppose that the following conditions $(\chi 1) \sim (\chi 3)$ hold :

$(\chi 1)$ $\{ \chi_\Gamma^\nu \}$ is bounded in $L^\infty(\partial\Omega)$, $\chi_\Gamma^\nu \ge \chi_\Gamma$ on $\partial\Omega$ and supp $(\chi_\Gamma^\nu) \subset \{x \in \partial\Omega; dist(x,\Gamma) \le \nu\}$ for any $\nu \in (0,1]$ and $\Gamma \in \Pi_c$.

$(\chi 2)$ For each $\nu \in (0,1]$, $\{\chi_\Gamma^\nu; \Gamma \in \Pi_c\}$ is compact in $L^1(\partial\Omega)$.

$(\chi 3)$ Let $V(\nu,\Gamma) := \{z \in H^1(\Omega); \chi_\Gamma^\nu z = 0$ a.e.on $\partial\Omega\}$ for $\nu \in (0,1]$ and $\Gamma \in \Pi_c$. If $\nu_n \in (0,1]$, $\nu_n \to 0$ (as $n \to \infty$) and $\Gamma_n \in \Pi_c$, then there are a subsequence $\{n_k\}$ and $\Gamma \in \Pi_c$ such that $\chi_{\Gamma_{n_k}}^{\nu_{n_k}} \to \chi_\Gamma$ in $L^1(\partial\Omega)$ as $k \to \infty$, and $V(\nu_{n_k}, \Gamma_{n_k}) \to V(\Gamma)$ in $H^1(\Omega)$ as $k \to \infty$ in the sense of Mosco.

Now, we introduce the approximate problem $SP(\Gamma)^{\varepsilon\nu\mu}$, $\varepsilon, \nu, \mu \in (0,1]$, for $SP(\Gamma)$:

$$SP(\Gamma)^{\varepsilon\nu\mu} \begin{cases} u_t - \Delta\beta^\varepsilon(u) = f & \text{in } Q\ , \\ u(0,\cdot) = u_0 & \text{in } \Omega\ , \\ \dfrac{\partial\beta^\varepsilon(u)}{\partial n} = -\dfrac{\chi_\Gamma^\nu}{\mu}(\beta^\varepsilon(u) - g) + (1-\chi_\Gamma^\nu)h & \text{on } \Sigma\ . \end{cases}$$

Applying an abstract result [10; Chapter 2] (or [11]) to $SP(\Gamma)^{\varepsilon\nu\mu}$, we see that $SP(\Gamma)^{\varepsilon\nu\mu}$ has one and only one solution u such that $u \in C([0,T]; L^2(\Omega))$, $t^{1/2}\beta^\varepsilon(u) \in L^\infty(0,T;H^1(\Omega))$ and $t^{1/2}(d/dt)\beta^\varepsilon(u) \in L^2(Q)$.

Our approximate optimization problem $P(\Pi_c)^{\varepsilon\nu\mu}$, associated with $SP(\Gamma)^{\varepsilon\nu\mu}$, is formulated as follows:

$$P(\Pi_c)^{\varepsilon\nu\mu} \quad \text{find } \Gamma_*^{\varepsilon\nu\mu} \in \Pi_c \text{ such that } J^{\varepsilon\nu\mu}(\Gamma_*^{\varepsilon\nu\mu}) = \inf_{\Gamma\in\Pi_c} J^{\varepsilon\nu\mu}(\Gamma),$$

where

$$J^{\varepsilon\nu\mu}(\Gamma) = \frac{1}{2}\int_Q |\beta^\varepsilon(u_\Gamma^{\varepsilon\nu\mu}) - \beta_d|^2\, dxdt + \frac{1}{2}\int_\Sigma (1-\chi_\Gamma^\nu)\, |h|^2\, d\sigma dt,$$

$u_\Gamma^{\varepsilon\nu\mu}$ being the solution of $SP(\Gamma)^{\varepsilon\nu\mu}$.

Concerning problems $P(\Pi_c)^{\varepsilon\nu\mu}$ we have:

THEOREM 2.3. *(1) For each $\varepsilon,\nu,\mu \in (0,1]$, $P(\Pi_c)^{\varepsilon\nu\mu}$ has at least one solution $\Gamma_*^{\varepsilon\nu\mu}$.*

(2) Let $\{\varepsilon_n\}, \{\nu_n\}, \{\mu_n\}$ be null sequences and Γ_*^n be a solution of $P(\Pi_c)^{\varepsilon_n\nu_n\mu_n}$. If $V(\nu_n, \Gamma_*^n) \to V(\Gamma_*)$ in $H^1(\Omega)$ as $n \to \infty$ in the sense of Mosco, $\chi_{\Gamma_*^n}^{\nu_n} \to \chi_{\Gamma_*}$ in $L^1(\partial\Omega)$ as $n \to \infty$, and $\Gamma_* \in \Pi_c$, then Γ_* is a solution of $P(\Pi_c)$.

Proof. (see [7] for details). The results (1) and (2) of the theorem are based on the uniform boundedness of solutions $u = u_\Gamma^{\varepsilon\nu\mu}$ to $SP(\Gamma)^{\varepsilon\nu\mu}$ by a common constant $M_1 > 0$:

$$\begin{cases} |u_\Gamma^{\varepsilon\nu\mu}|_{C([0,T];L^2(\Omega))} \le M_1, \ |\beta^\varepsilon(u_\Gamma^{\varepsilon\nu\mu})|_{L^2(0,T;H^1(\Omega))} \le M_1, \\ \dfrac{1}{\mu}\displaystyle\int_\Sigma \chi_\Gamma^\nu |\beta^\varepsilon(u_\Gamma^{\varepsilon\nu\mu}) - g|^2 d\sigma dt \le M_1, \\ |t^{1/2}\beta^\varepsilon(u_\Gamma^{\varepsilon\nu\mu})|_{L^\infty(0,T;H^1(\Omega))} \le M_1, \ |t^{1/2}\dfrac{d}{dt}\beta^\varepsilon(u_\Gamma^{\varepsilon\nu\mu})|_{L^2(Q))} \le M_1, \\ \displaystyle\sup_{t\in(0,T]} \frac{t}{\mu}\int_{\partial\Omega} \chi_\Gamma^\nu |\beta^\varepsilon(u_\Gamma^{\varepsilon\nu\mu}(t)) - g(t)|^2 d\sigma \le M_1, \end{cases} \tag{2.10}$$

for all $\varepsilon, \nu, \mu \in (0,1]$ and all $\Gamma \in \Pi_c$. These estimates (2.10) are derived from the energy inequalities which are obtained by multiplying $u_t - \Delta\beta^\varepsilon(u) = f$ by $\beta^\varepsilon(u) - g$ or $t(\partial/\partial t)(\beta^\varepsilon(u) - g)$, where $u = u_\Gamma^{\varepsilon\nu\mu}$.

Now, fix $\varepsilon, \nu, \mu \in (0,1]$ and put $I_* = \inf\{J^{\varepsilon\nu\mu}(\Gamma); \Gamma \in \Pi_c\}$. Let $\{\Gamma_n\}$ be a sequence in Π_c such that $J^{\varepsilon\nu\mu}(\Gamma_n) \to I_*$ (as $n \to \infty$). By condition (χ2), we may assume that $\chi^\nu_{\Gamma_n} \to \chi^\nu_\Gamma$ in $L^1(\partial\Omega)$ for some $\Gamma \in \Pi_c$. Then, denoting by u_n and u the solutions of $SP(\Gamma_n)^{\varepsilon\nu\mu}$ and $SP(\Gamma)^{\varepsilon\nu\mu}$, we see that $u_n \to u$ in $C([0,T]; L^2(\Omega))$, and $J^{\varepsilon\nu\mu}(\Gamma_n) \to J^{\varepsilon\nu\mu}(\Gamma)$. Hence $I_* = J^{\varepsilon\nu\mu}(\Gamma)$ and Γ is a solution of $P(\Pi_c)^{\varepsilon\nu\mu}$, and thus we have (1).

Finally we show (2). With the same notations and under the same assumptions as in the statement (2) of the theorem, let u_{*n} and u_* be the solutions of $SP(\Gamma^n_*)^{\varepsilon_n\nu_n\mu_n}$ and $SP(\Gamma_*)$, respectively. Then, in a similar way to that in the proof of Theorem 2.1, we see from (2.10) that

$$\beta^{\varepsilon_n}(u_{*n}) \to \beta(u_*) \text{ in } L^2(Q) \text{ (as } n \to \infty),$$

so that

$$J^{\varepsilon_n\nu_n\mu_n}(\Gamma^n_*) \to J(\Gamma_*).$$

Next, let Γ_0 be any solution of $P(\Pi_c)^{\varepsilon_n\nu_n\mu_n}$ and u be the weak solution of $SP(\Gamma_0)$. Then, as above,

$$\beta^{\varepsilon_n}(u_n) \to \beta(u) \text{ in } L^2(Q).$$

Therefore $J(\Gamma_0) = \lim_{n\to\infty} J^{\varepsilon_n\nu_n\mu_n}(\Gamma_0) \geq \lim_{n\to\infty} J^{\varepsilon_n\nu_n\mu_n}(\Gamma^n_*) = J(\Gamma_*)$. This shows that $J(\Gamma_*) = \inf\{J(\Gamma); \Gamma \in \Pi_c\}$ and thus Γ_* is a solution of $P(\Pi_c)$. ◇

EXAMPLE 2.1. Let Θ be the class of all C^1-diffeomorphisms from $\overline{\Omega}$ onto itself, and Γ_0 be a $(N-1)$-dimensional smooth manifold in $\partial\Omega$ such that $\sigma(\Gamma_0) > 0$ and $\sigma(\partial\Gamma_0) = 0$, where $\partial\Gamma_0$ is the boundary of Γ_0 in $\partial\Omega$. Given a non-empty compact subset Θ_c of Θ, put

$$\Pi_c = \{\theta(\Gamma_0); \theta \in \Theta_c\}.$$

Then, condition (Γ) is satisfied as well as the class $\{\chi^\nu_\Gamma\}$, satisfying (χ1) -(χ3), is easily constructed.

3. Problem $P(O_c)$

3.1. Existence result

Let $\hat{\Omega}$ and O be as in the Introduction, and β be a non-decreasing function satisfying (1.2). For simplicity, we use the following notations:

$$a(u,v) := \int_{\hat{\Omega}} \nabla u \cdot \nabla v \, dx \quad \text{for } u, v \in H^1(\hat{\Omega}),$$
$$(u,v) := \int_{\hat{\Omega}} u \cdot v \, dx \quad \text{for } u, v \in L^2(\hat{\Omega})$$

and for each $\Omega \in O$,

$$a_\Omega(u,v) := \int_\Omega \nabla u \cdot \nabla v \, dx \quad \text{for } u, v \in H^1(\Omega),$$
$$(u,v)_\Omega := \int_\Omega u \cdot v \, dx \quad \text{for } u, v \in L^2(\Omega),$$
$$Q(\Omega) := (0,T) \times \Omega,$$
$$V(\Omega) := \{z \in H^1(\hat{\Omega}); z = 0 \text{ a.e on } \hat{\Omega} - \Omega\}.$$

Throughout this section we suppose that

$$\begin{cases} f \in L^2(Q_0) \; (Q_0 = (0,T) \times \hat{\Omega}), \; u_0 \in L^2(\hat{\Omega}), \\ g \in W^{2,2}(0,T; H^1(\hat{\Omega})) \cap L^\infty(0,T; H^2(\hat{\Omega})). \end{cases} \tag{3.1}$$

First, we give the weak formulation of $SP(\Omega)$ for $\Omega \in O$.

DEFINITION 3.1. A function $u : [0,T] \to L^2(\Omega)$ is called a weak solution of $SP(\Omega)$, if the following conditions (w1) $\sim$ (w3) are satisfied:

(w1) $u \in C_w([0,T]; L^2(\Omega))$ and $u(0) = u_0$;

(w2) $\beta(u) - g \in L^2(0,T; H_0^1(\Omega))$;

(w3) $-\int_{Q(\Omega)} u\eta_t dxdt + \int_0^T a_\Omega(\beta(u),\eta)dt = \int_{Q(\Omega)} f\eta dxdt$
for all $\eta \in L^2(0,T; H_0^1(\Omega))$ with $\eta_t \in L^2(Q(\Omega))$ and $\eta(0,\cdot) = \eta(T,\cdot) = 0$.

Based on the unique solvability of $SP(\Omega)$ for any $\Omega \in O$, we consider a domain optimization problem $P(O_c)$ as is formulated in the Introduction for a given non-empty subset O_c of O.

Just as in section 2, we introduce a notion of convergence in O.

DEFINITION 3.2. Let $\{\Omega_n\}$ be a sequence in O and $\Omega \in O$. Then we say that Ω_n converges to Ω in O as $n \to \infty$, which is denoted by "$\Omega_n \to \Omega$ in O as $n \to \infty$", if the following two conditions (i) and (ii) are satisfied:

(i) $\chi_{\Omega_n} \to \chi_\Omega$ in $L^1(\hat{\Omega})$ as $n \to \infty$, where χ_{Ω_n} (resp.χ_Ω) is the characteristic function of Ω_n (resp.Ω) on $\hat{\Omega}$.

(ii) $V(\Omega_n) \to V(\Omega)$ in $H^1(\hat{\Omega})$ as $n \to \infty$ in the sense of Mosco.

The continuous dependence of the weak solution u_Ω of $SP(\Omega)$ upon Ω is stated in the following theorem.

THEOREM 3.1. *Assume that $\Omega_n \to \Omega$ in O as $n \to \infty$. Let u_n and u be the weak solutions of $SP(\Omega_n)$ and $SP(\Omega)$, respectively. Then, as $n \to \infty$,*

$$(u_n(t), z)_{\Omega_n} \to (u(t), z)_\Omega \quad \text{uniformly in } t \in [0,T] \quad \text{for each } z \in L^2(\hat{\Omega}) \tag{3.2}$$

and

$$\beta^*(u_n) \to \beta^*(u) \quad \text{in } L^2(Q_0), \tag{3.3}$$

where

$$\beta^*(u_n)\ (resp.\beta^*(u)) := \begin{cases} \beta(u_n)\ (resp.\beta(u)) \text{ on } Q(\Omega_n)\ (resp.Q(\Omega)), \\ g \text{ otherwise.} \end{cases}$$

Proof. (see [8] for details). From the usual energy inequalities for solution u_n of $SP(\Omega_n)$ we obtain the following uniform estimates:

$$\begin{cases} |u_n|_{L^\infty(0,T;L^2(\Omega_n))} \le M_0, & |\beta(u_n)|_{L^2(0,T;H^1(\Omega_n))} \le M_0, \\ |t^{1/2}\beta(u_n)|_{L^\infty(0,T;H^1(\Omega_n))} \le M_0, & |t^{1/2}\dfrac{\partial}{\partial t}\beta(u_n)|_{L^2(Q(\Omega_n))} \le M_0, \end{cases} \tag{3.4}$$

for all n, where M_0 is a positive constant independent of n. Under the assumption that $\Omega_n \to \Omega$ in O, we can see convergences (3.2) and (3.3) from estimates (3.4). $\diamond$

THEOREM 3.2. *Let O_c be a non-empty subset of O satisfying the following compactness condition (O):*

(O) For any sequence $\{\Omega_n\}$ in O_c there are a subsequence $\{\Omega_{n_k}\}$ and a set $\Omega \in O_c$ such that $\Omega_{n_k} \to \Omega$ in O as $k \to \infty$.

Then $P(O_c)$ has at least one solution Ω_*.

This existence theorem is an immediate consequence of Theorem3.1.

3.2. Approximation for $SP(\Omega)$ and $P(O_c)$

We employ the same idea for approximations of $SP(\Omega)$ and $P(O_c)$ as in the case of $SP(\Gamma)$ and $P(\Pi_c)$. Let $\{\beta^\varepsilon\}$ be a family of (smooth) functions $\beta^\varepsilon : R \to R$ satisfying properties ($\beta 1$) and ($\beta 2$). Also, given a non-empty subset O_c of O, satisfying condition (O), let $\{\chi^\nu_\Omega; 0 < \nu \le 1, \Omega \in O_c\}$ be a family of smooth functions on $\hat{\Omega}$. Suppose the following conditions $(\chi 1)' \sim (\chi 3)'$ hold:

$(\chi 1)'$ $0 \le \chi_\Omega \le \chi^\nu_\Gamma \le 1$ on $\hat{\Omega}$ and supp $(\chi^\nu_\Omega) \subset \{x \in \hat{\Omega}; dist(x, \Omega) \le \nu\}$ for any $\nu \in (0,1]$ and $\Omega \in O_c$.

$(\chi 2)'$ For each $\nu \in (0,1]$, $\{\chi^\nu_\Omega; \Omega \in O_c\}$ is compact in $L^1(\hat{\Omega})$.

$(\chi 3)'$ If $\nu_n \in (0,1]$, $\nu_n \to 0$ (as $n \to \infty$) and $\Omega_n \in O_c$, then there are a subsequence $\{\Omega_{n_k}\}$ and $\Omega \in O_c$ such that $\chi^{\nu_{n_k}}_{\Omega_{n_k}} \to \chi_\Omega$ in $L^1(\hat{\Omega})$ as $k \to \infty$, and $V(\Omega_{n_k}) \to V(\Omega)$ in $H^1(\hat{\Omega})$ as $k \to \infty$ in the sense of Mosco.

We now consider approximate problems $SP(\Omega)^{\varepsilon\nu\mu}$ and the corresponding approximate optimization problem $P(O_c)^{\varepsilon\nu\mu}$, with parameters $\varepsilon, \nu, \mu, \in (0,1]$:

$$SP(\Omega)^{\varepsilon\nu\mu} \begin{cases} u_t - \Delta\beta^\varepsilon(u) + \dfrac{1-\chi^\nu_\Omega}{\mu}(\beta^\varepsilon(u) - g) = f & \text{in } Q_0 , \\ u(0,\cdot) = u_0 & \text{in } \hat{\Omega} , \\ \beta^\varepsilon(u) = g & \text{on } \Sigma_0 := (0,T) \times \partial\hat{\Omega}; \end{cases}$$

$$P(O_c)^{\varepsilon\nu\mu} \quad \text{find } \Omega^{\varepsilon\nu\mu}_* \in O_c \text{ such that } J^{\varepsilon\nu\mu}(\Omega^{\varepsilon\nu\mu}_*) = \inf_{\Omega \in O_c} J^{\varepsilon\nu\mu}(\Omega),$$

where

$$J^{\varepsilon\nu\mu}(\Omega) = \frac{1}{2}\int_{Q(\Omega)} | \beta^\varepsilon(u^{\varepsilon\nu\mu}_\Omega) - \beta_d |^2 \, dxdt + \frac{1}{2}\int_{Q_0 - Q(\Omega)} | g - \beta_d |^2 \, dxdt,$$

$u^{\varepsilon\nu\mu}_\Omega$ being the solution of $SP(\Omega)^{\varepsilon\nu\mu}$.

Concerning the existence of a solution to $P(O_c)^{\varepsilon\nu\mu}$ and its convergence as $\varepsilon, \nu, \mu \to 0$, we have:

THEOREM 3.3. *(1) For each $\varepsilon, \nu, \mu \in (0,1]$, $P(O_c)^{\varepsilon\nu\mu}$ has at least one solution $\Omega^{\varepsilon\nu\mu}_*$.*

(2) Let $\{\varepsilon_n\}, \{\nu_n\}, \{\mu_n\}$ be null sequences and Ω^n_* be a solution of $P(O_c)^{\varepsilon_n\nu_n\mu_n}$. Assume that $\Omega_* \in O_c$, $\chi^{\nu_n}_{\Omega^n_*} \to \chi_{\Omega_*}$ in $L^1(\hat{\Omega})$ as $n \to \infty$ and $V(\Omega^n_*) \to V(\Omega_*)$ in $H^1(\hat{\Omega})$ as $n \to \infty$ in the sense of Mosco. Then Ω_* is a solution of $P(O_c)$.

Proof. See [8] for details.

Finally we give a typical example of O_c in the application of our results.

EXAMPLE 3.1. Let Θ be the class of all C^1-diffeomorphisms from $\overline{\hat{\Omega}}$ onto itself, and Ω_0 be a non-empty domain with smooth boundary $\partial\Omega_0$ such that $\overline{\Omega_0} \subset \hat{\Omega}$. Given a non-empty compact subset Θ_c of Θ, put

$$O_c = \{\theta(\Omega_0); \theta \in \Theta_c\}. \tag{3.5}$$

For this class O_c, condition (O) clearly holds, and it is easy to construct a family $\{\chi^\nu_\Omega\}$ which satisfies $(\chi 1)' \sim (\chi 3)'$.

In general, a class O_c, having property (O), possibly contains many subdomains Ω of $\hat{\Omega}$

with different topology, namely, it is not able to represent O_c in the form (3.5) with a fixed domain Ω_0 and a class Θ_c of C^1-diffeomorphisms on $\overline{\hat{\Omega}}$.

EXAMPLE 3.2. Let $\hat{\Omega} := \{x; |x| < 2\} \subset R^3$, $\Omega_a := \{x; a < |x| < 1\}$ for any $0 < a \leq \frac{1}{2}$ and $\Omega = \{x; |x| < 1\}$. Put $O_c := \{\Omega_a; 0 < a \leq \frac{1}{2}\} \cup \{\Omega\}$. Then, $\Omega_a \to \Omega$ in O as $a \to 0$, since the 2-capacity of singleton is zero(c.f. [13; Lemma 1.8]). Hence, clearly O_c satisfies property (O). It is easy to see that this class O_c cannot be represented in the form (3.5), since there is no C^1-diffeomorphism between Ω_a and Ω.

As far as problems of domain optimization are concerned, there are many interesting studies, for instance [5,6] in which elliptic problems were treated; their approach might be possible to the case of Stefan problems.

References

[1] A.Bermudez and C.Saguez, Optimal control of variational inequalities, Control Cyb. 14(1985),9 - 30.

[2] A.Damlamian, Some results on the multi-phase Stefan problem, Comm. P.D.E. 2. (1977), 1017 - 1044.

[3] A.Damlamian and N.Kenmochi, Asymptotic behavior of solutions to a multi-phase Stefan problem.Japan J. Appl. Math., 3(1986),15 - 36.

[4] A.Friedman, The Stefan problem in several space variables,Trans. Amer. Math. Soc. 133(1968),51 - 87.

[5] J.Haslinger and P.Neittaanmäki, Finite Element Approximation for Optimal Shape Design: Theory and Applications, John Willy & Sons Ltd, Chichester-New York-Brisbane-Toronto-Singapore, 1988.

[6] J.Haslinger, P.Neittaanmäki and D.Tiba, On state constrained optimal shape design problems, Optimal Control of Partial Differential Equations II, ISNM 78, Birkhäuser, Basel-Boston-Stuttgart, 1987,109 -122.

[7] A.Kadoya and N.Kenmochi, Shape optimization on the lateral boundary for multi-phase Stefan problems, Tech. Report Math. Sci., Vol.6, No.7, Chiba Univ., 1990.

[8] A.Kadoya and N.Kenmochi, Optimal shape design in multi-phase Stefan problems, Tech. Report Math. Sci., Vol.6, No.8, Chiba Univ., 1990.

[9] S.L. Kamenomostskaja, On Stefan's problem,Mat. Sb. 53(1961),489 - 514.

[10] N.Kenmochi, Solvability of nonlinear evolution equations with time-dependent constraints and applications, Bull. Fac. Education,Chiba Univ. 30(1981),1 - 87.

[11] N.Kenmochi and I.Pawlow, A class of nonlinear elliptic-parabolic equations with time-dependent constraints,Nonlinear Anal. 10(1986),1181 - 1202.

[12] O.A. Ladyzenskaja, V.A. Solonnikov and N.N. Ural'ceva, Linear and Quasi-Linear Equations of Parabolic Type, Transl. Math. Monogr. 23, Amer. Math. Soc., Providence R.I.,1968.

[13] U.Mosco, Convergence of convex sets and of solutions of variational inequarities, Advances Math. 3(1969),510 - 585.

[14] P.Neittaanmäki and D.Tiba, On the approximation of the boundary control in two-phase Stefan-type problems,Control Cyb. 16(1987),33 -44.

[15] M.Niezgodka, Mathematical Modelling of Phase Transitions, Inst. Math. Augsburg Univ., 1985.

[16] O.A.Oleinik, On a method of solving the general Stefan problem,Soviet Math. Dokl. 1(1960),1350 - 1354.

[17] I.Pawlow, Analysis and control in free boundary problems,Bull. Fac. Education, Chiba Univ. 36(1988),9 - 67.

[18] C.Saguez, Contrôle Optimal de Systèmes à frontière libre, Thèse, Univ. Technologique, Compiegne, 1980.

[19] D.Tiba, Boundary control for a Stefan problem,Optimal Control of Partial Differential Equations,ISNM Vol.68,Birkhäuser Verlag,Basel-Boston-Stuttgart,1983,229 - 242.

Semi-analytical investigation of unsteady free-boundary flows

E.A. KARABUT

Lavrentyev Institute of Hydrodynamics
Siberian Division of the USSR Academy of Science
Novosibirsk, 630090, USSR

Abstract. The methods which are intermediate between purely analytical and purely computational ones belong to a semi-analytical group, according to the classification by M. Van Dyke. They are mainly the methods of processing the series and sequences. This group comprises the well-known algorithms based on the Padé approximants and continuous fractions as well as convergence acceleration algorithms, Domb-Sykes test, etc. The author uses this technique to investigate an unsteady inviscid incompressible free-boundary flow. The solution is obtained in the form of a power series in time, the coefficients for it being computed. The obtained series are summarized and the singularities are revealed. The main emphasis is made on the application of the two new methods. The first is based on the change of variables of special form, and the second is based on the study of zeros on the coefficient of power series.

Keywords. Padé approximant, analytic continuation, zeros of polynomials, incompressible inviscid fluids.

1980 Mathematics subject classifications: 30B10, 65B10, 76B10.

1. CHANGE OF VARIABLES IN POWER SERIES

As a result of the change of variables

$$t(u) = b_1 u + b_2 u^2 + \dots$$

in the power series

$$f(t) = a_0 + a_1 t + a_2 t^2 + \dots \tag{1.1}$$

a new power series is obtained

$$\hat{f}(u) = f(t(u)) = c_0 + c_1 u + c_2 u^2 + \dots \tag{1.2}$$

N coefficients of which are expressed through N coefficients of the initial series.

If the initial series at the point t_0 diverges, a new series may occur to be converging. Let R, $\hat{R}$ be the radii of convergence of (1.1), (1.2), respectively. If $|t_0| > R$, the value $f(t_0)$ is impossible to be calculated by direct summation of (1.1). The point t_0 is mapped in the general case onto several points of the u-plane (probably, onto an infinite number of points). Let u_0 be one of them such that $|u_0| < \hat{R}$, and besides, let in the case of an analytical continuation of $t(u)$ from the origin to u_0 in any way contained in the circle $|u| < \hat{R}$ the value of t_0 to be obtained. Then the series (1.2) converges to $\hat{f}(u_0) = f(t_0)$ at the point u_0. The velocity of convergence of (1.2) depends on the quantity, position and character of the singularities $\hat{f}(u)$. The numerical examples and some simple considerations show, however, that the ratio $\lambda_{t(u)} = \frac{\hat{R}}{|u_0|}$ is main parameter. As this value increases, the convergence of (1.2), as a rule, is accelerated.

Let $f(t)$ be analytical in the domain D. If the $t(u)$ conformly maps the circle onto D, $\hat{f}(u)$ is analytical in this circle. Consequently, the change of variables for the analytical continuation may be found as follows. Let us choose the domain D containing the origin and the point t_0 under consideration and not containing the singularities $f(t)$. The mapping of the circle $|u| < 1$ onto D with the normalization $t(0) = 0$ is used as a change of variables. The point t_0 transforms into u_0 lying inside the circle, therefore, series (1.2) converges at this point. As follow from the theorem, the domain D should be as large as possible.

THEOREM 1.1. *[4] Let the function $f(t)$ be analytical in the domains D_1, D_2, and there is at least one singularity $f(t)$ on the boundary of each of them. The functions $t_1(u)$, $t_2(u)$ are used as a change of variables, they conformly map the circle $|u| < 1$ onto D_1, D_2, respectively, and $t_1(0) = 0$, $t_2(0) = 0$. It is claimed that if $D_1 \subset D_2$, $\lambda_{t_2} > \lambda_{t_1}$.*

If we confine ourselves with considering a one-sheeted domain, that one having a maximum square represents an exterior of the cuts directed from the singularities to infinity. This paper considers the Mittag-Leffler (M-L) star with its cuts coinciding with the beams, which start from the origin.

Let $f(t)$ have singularities: $t_1 = r_1 e^{i\varphi_1 \pi}, \ldots, t_n = r_n e^{i\varphi_n \pi}$. It is not difficult to see that the function $t(u)$ which conformally maps a unit circle onto the M-L star of the function $f(t)$ is in the form [4]:

$$t = c\frac{u}{(u-a_1)^{\alpha_1} \ldots (u-a_n)^{\alpha_n}}, \qquad c = \text{const}.$$

Here $a_1 = e^{i\theta_1}, \ldots, a_n = e^{i\theta_n}$ – are the points of the u-plane corresponding to infinite vertices of the M-L star. The values $\alpha_1, \alpha_2, \ldots$ are angles between the beams of the M-L star: $\alpha_1 = \varphi_2 - \varphi_1$, $\alpha_2 = \varphi_3 - \varphi_2, \ldots$.

If $\lambda_{t(u)}$ is insufficient for the point of our interest such a change of variables may be repeated. To do so, the unit circle in the u_2-plane is mapped onto the M-L star of the function $\hat{f}(u)$. In this case
$\lambda_{t(u_2)} > \lambda_{t(u)}$.

2. Zeros of power series coefficients

Let us consider the functions of two variables represented in the form of power series in one variable

$$f(\zeta, t) = f^{(0)}(\zeta) + f^{(1)}(\zeta)t + f^{(2)}(\zeta)t^2 + \ldots .$$

For some functions the zeros of this series coefficients behave in a rather regular manner and asymptotically draw up along the limiting lines [5] as the number of the coefficient increases.

It is known that if there exists the limit

$$\lim_{n\to\infty} \frac{f^{(n-1)}(\zeta)}{f^{(n)}(\zeta)} = t_j(\zeta), \tag{2.1}$$

$t_j(\zeta)$ is one of singular points $f(\zeta, t)$. The inverse is incorrect, generally speaking, i.e. if $t_j(\zeta)$ is the singularity closest to the origin from here it does not follow that the limit of (2.1) exists. Below the function $f(\zeta, t)$ will be considered which possesses the following property.

PROPERTY 2.1. *For each point ζ belonging to one of the sets*

$$D_j = [\zeta : |t_j(\zeta)| < |t_i(\zeta)|, \ \forall i \neq j]$$

(D_j is, as a rule, one or several domains) there exists the limit (2.1), the convergence being uniform inside D_j.

By virtue of a uniform convergence for an arbitrary set

$$\Omega \subset D_1 \cup D_2 \cup D_3 \ \cdots$$

a number may be found beginning from which the sequence $\{\frac{f^{(n-1)}(\zeta)}{f^{(n)}(\zeta)}\}$ is bounded, i.e. it does not contain zeros $f^{(n)}(\zeta)$. Thus, if each point ζ belongs to one of the closed sets $\bar{D}_j$ all the zeros are groupped along the boundary

$$\partial D_1 \cup \partial D_2 \cup \partial D_3 \ \cdots .$$

Thus, it is expected that the zeros $f^{(n)}(\zeta)$ would arrange along the lines $|t_i(\zeta)| = |t_j(\zeta)|$ such that the j-th singularity is the closest one to the origin $t = 0$ on one side of this line and the i-th singularity is the closest on the other side of it. Knowing the form of these lines, it is possible to investigate asymptotical properties of $f^{(n)}$ when $n \to \infty$ and to define the relation between the behaviour of different singularities [**5**].

3. THE PROBLEM OF A BUBBLE

Let us consider a plane, potential unsteady flow of an ideal incompressible free-boundary liquid. A general problem which may be solved using power series in time consists in finding deformations in time of the domain occupied by a liquid if pressure of the boundary is constant (shear stress is absent). An initial configuration of the domain and an initial velocity field are assumed to be known.

Let $Z(\zeta, t)$ be a conformal mapping of the fixed domain D of the plane ζ onto the flow region and $U(\zeta, t)$ is a complex velocity. If D is assumed to be the interior (exterior) of the unit circle, in order to find the two functions analytical inside the circle (outside it) there exist two boundary conditions [**2**]:

$$\operatorname{Im} \zeta(Z_\zeta U_t - U_\zeta Z_t + U_\zeta \bar{U}) = 0, \quad |\zeta| = 1 \tag{3.1}$$

$$\text{Re}\,(\zeta Z_\zeta U - Z_t \frac{\bar{Z}_\zeta}{\zeta}) = 0, \quad |\zeta| = 1 \tag{3.2}$$

Substituting here the series

$$Z(\zeta,t) = Z^{(0)}(\zeta) + Z^{(1)}(\zeta)t + Z^{(2)}(\zeta)t^2 + \cdots \tag{3.3}$$

$$U(\zeta,t) = U^{(0)}(\zeta) + U^{(1)}(\zeta)t + U^{(2)}(\zeta)t^2 + \cdots \tag{3.4}$$

we obtain the recurrent boundary conditions for a successive finding of the coefficients belonging to these power series. The possibility of using computers is based on the following theorem:

THEOREM 3.1. *[**2**] Let D be an interior of the unit circle, and boundary conditions (3.1), (3.2) be valid on its boundaries. Then, if $Z_\zeta^{(0)}$, $U^{(0)}$ are rational functions of ζ and $Z_\zeta^{(0)} \neq 0, \infty$ when $|\zeta| \leq 1$, the functions $Z^{(k)}$, $U^{(k)}$, $k \geq 1$ analytical when $|\zeta| \leq 1$ are also rational functions.*

An analogous theorem is valid if D is an exterior of the unit circle.

We shall restrict ourselves with considering the simplest example of this class of problems with rational initial data. Let D be the exterior of the unit circle and

$$Z^{(0)} = i\zeta, \quad U^{(0)} = -\frac{i}{\zeta^2}.$$

This corresponds to the problem of inertia motion of a cylindrical cavity in an infinite liquid. Let for $t = 0$ there be a circular cylindrical cavity of unit radius in a liquid which moves with a unit velocity (liquid at infinity is at rest). It is necessary to find a necessive deformation of the cavity when $t > 0$ if zero pressure is maintained inside it and the cavity volume is constant. In numerical calculation it is more convenient to introduce a normalized time $\tau = 4t$, since in this case the orders of coefficients value are not too high.

The problem was first considered in [**6**], where the free surface form is defined on the basis of finite-difference methods. Similar problems on motion of initial spherical or cylidrical cavities were solved by some authors. Of particular interest is work [**1**] where the problem of rising a circular cylindrical cavity in a heavy liquid is considered. As far as the formulation of the problem and the methods of investigation are concerned, [**1**] is close to this present one. Analyticity in t when $t = 0$ in the problem of rising of an initially spherical bubble is proved in [**7**].

THEOREM 3.2. *[**2**] The problem of motion of a cavity has the solution*

$$Z^{(k)} = i\zeta \sum_{j=0}^{[\frac{k}{2}]} \frac{c_{2j}^k}{\zeta^{k-2j}}, \quad U^{(k)} = \frac{i}{\zeta^2} \sum_{j=0}^{[\frac{k}{2}]} \frac{d_{2j}^k}{\zeta^{k-2j}},$$

where c_j^k, d_j^k are the real numbers related by the formulae ($k \geq 1$, $2m \leq k$, $m \neq 0$):

$$\sum_{q=0}^{m} \sum_{j=2q}^{2q+k-2m} [j(2q-2m-1)-2(1-q)(k-j)] c_{2(m-q)}^{k-j} d_{2q}^{j} -$$
$$(k-2m+1) \sum_{l=0}^{m-1} \sum_{j=0}^{m-1-l} d_{2j}^{2j+l} d_{2(m-j-l-1)}^{k-2j-l-1} = 0,$$
$$\sum_{q=0}^{m} \sum_{j=2q}^{2q+k-2m-1} (2q+k-2m-j-2) c_{2(m-q)}^{k-j-1} d_{2q}^{j} +$$
$$\sum_{l=0}^{m} \sum_{j=0}^{m-l} [k(l-1)+(l+2j)(k-2m)] c_{2j}^{2j+l} c_{2(m-j-l)}^{k-l-2j} = 0.$$

These recurrent formulae provide the value listed in Table 1. The rows correspond to the powers t, and the columns correspond to the powers $1/\zeta$. The solution has the form

$$Z(\zeta,t) = i\zeta \left[1 + \frac{t}{\zeta} - \frac{t^2}{\zeta^2} + t^3\left(-\frac{2}{3\zeta} + \frac{2}{\zeta^3}\right) + \mathcal{O}(t^4)\right].$$
$$U(\zeta,t) = \frac{i}{\zeta^2} \left[-1 + \frac{2t}{\zeta} + t^2\left(1 - \frac{5}{\zeta^2}\right) + t^3\left(-\frac{16}{3\zeta} + \frac{14}{\zeta^3}\right) + \mathcal{O}(t^4)\right].$$

c_{i-j}^{i}						
i \ j	0	1	2	3	4	5
0	1					
1	0	1				
2	0	0	-1			
3	0	$-\frac{2}{3}$	0	2		
4	$\frac{1}{2}$	0	$\frac{7}{3}$	0	-5	
5	0	$-\frac{34}{15}$	0	$-\frac{41}{5}$	0	14

Table 1.

	d^i_{i-j}					
i \ j	0	1	2	3	4	5
0	-1					
1	0	2				
2	1	0	-5			
3	0	$-\frac{16}{3}$	0	14		
4	$\frac{5}{3}$	0	$\frac{68}{3}$	0	-42	
5	0	$-\frac{107}{15}$	0	$-\frac{452}{5}$	0	132

4. Semi-analytical investigation

The number of coefficients may be increased due to use of the computers. The only limitation is related to the storage of approximation errors resulting from arithmetical operations. About 100 coefficients were found. To find greater number of coefficients, it is necessary to increase the mantissa length (24 decimal digits were used).

Let us consider 256 points on the free surface $\zeta = e^{i\theta}$ ($\theta = \frac{j\pi}{128}$; $j = 0, 1, \ldots, 256$) and construct for each of them own power series (3.3). Then we summarize the series (using the first seventy coefficients) at $\tau = 0; 0.6; 1.2$. In each summation procedure, a complex number is obtained, which is denoted by a circle in Fig. 1a. As is seen when $\tau = 1.2$ the series diverge although a part of the free surface remains smooth. It is impossible to construct a free surface by summarizing the series when $\tau > 1.2$. A power series needs to be extended beyond the circle of its convergence. Presented in Fig. 1b are the results of the Padé summation. The free surface is destroyed at $\tau = 1.8$.

The data on singularities in the plane of complex time which restrict the convergence of series (3.3), (3.4) were mainly obtained, using the two methods. The first is related to the well-known theorem: if there exists

$$\lim_{n\to\infty} \frac{Z^{(n-1)}(\zeta)}{Z^{(n)}(\zeta)} = t_0(\zeta),$$

$t_0(\zeta)$ is the singularity $Z(\zeta, t)$ closest to the point $t = 0$. Using the convergence acceleration algorithms, it is possible to determine the limit of sequence $\frac{Z^{(n-1)}(\zeta)}{Z^{(n)}(\zeta)}$ with a high accuracy. The convergence acceleration algorithms such as ϵ-algorithm, u-algorithm, θ-algorithm and the Neville table were used. The ρ-algorithm occured to be the best.

The second method is based on the use of the Padé diagram. The zeros and poles of the Padé approximant were noticed to arrange along some lines, cuts, the tops of which show to a singularity. There are 5 singular points. With varying ζ, one cut moves, it corresponds to a movable singular point $t_0(\zeta)$. Its site is different for different points in

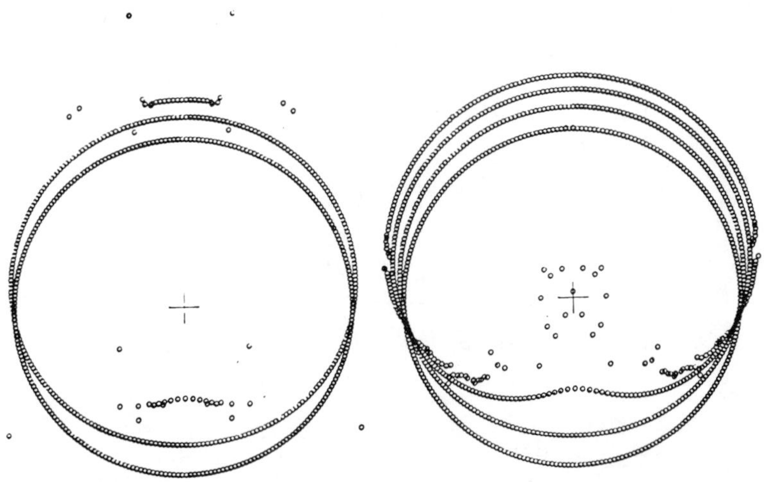

(a) Direct summation. (b) Padé summation.

Figure 1.
For 256 points of a free surface uniformly distributed over the plane ζ, 70 initial coefficients of the power series for conformal mapping have been found. Then they have been summed by different methods

a liquid. As $|\zeta|$ decreases, a movable singularity approaches to the origin. The remaining four cuts are unmovable, they correspond to the singularities

$$t_1, t_2, t_3, t_4 \simeq \pm\frac{3}{8}\exp\left(\pm\frac{i\pi}{12}\right).$$

The behaviour of the singularities was investigated for all points including $|\zeta| < 1$, i.e. the points having no physical sense. The results are demonstrated in Fig. 2, where the complex time plane is shown, and the unmovable singularities are denoted by small crosses. The lines correspond to the trajectories of movable singularity which describes them when the argument ζ ($|\zeta| = \text{const.}$) is varied. Shown in this figure are 15 lines for $|\zeta|$ ranging from 0.125 to 1.875.

With the Domb-Sykes test it has been established that the movable singularity is a singularity of square-root type.

Now let us consider again 256 points on a free surface. It is known now where the singularities are placed. It is appropriate to use the above-mentioned change of variables. For obtaining a new power series after such a change, the Padé approximants [31/31] have been found and their values for $\tau = 0$; 0.6; 1.2; 1.8; 2.4 have been determined (they are denoted by small circles in Fig. 3a). It is seen that when $\tau = 1.8$ the whole of the free surface remains smooth, in contrast to Fig. 1b. The free surface after an analogous double

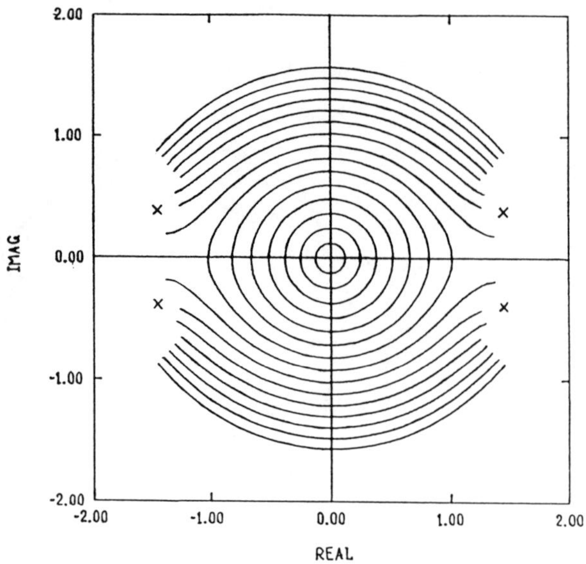

Figure 2. The site of singularities in the complex plane τ. The crosses denote unmovable singularities. The lines are the trajectories of a movable singularity which are described by it with varying the argument ζ ($|\zeta| = \text{const.}$). 15 lines are displayed for $|\zeta|$ ranging from 0.125 to 1.875.

changeis shown in Fig. 3b. Here when $\tau = 2.4$ it is allways smooth and even when $\tau = 3.0$ the most part of it is smooth, too.

Fig. 4 shows the roots of equation $Z^{(89)}(\zeta) = 0$. Their ordered behaviour may be explained now, since the sites of singularities in the complex-time plane are known. This implies that the zeroes of the coefficients must arrange asymptotically along the lines $|t_0(\zeta)| = \frac{3}{8}$ as the number of the coefficients under consideration increases. This confirms the data presented in Fig. 4 where seven lines are displayed: $|4t_0(\zeta)| = 0.9$; 1.1; 1.3; 1.5; ...; 2.1.

The information on asymptotical properties of the coefficients may be obtained, by investigating, along with zeroes, a movable singularity when $|\zeta| < 1$. The function $t_0(\zeta)$ is likely to be an analytical one when $\zeta = 0$. The following conditional theorem provides the example of obtaining a constructive result from a nonconstructive assumption.

THEOREM 4.1. *[5] If $t_0(\zeta)$ is analytical when $\zeta = 0$, then we have*

$$c_{2m}^n = (-1)^{n-1}\binom{2n-2}{n-1} n^{m-1}\left[\frac{(2\ln 2 - \frac{3}{2})^m}{m!} + \mathcal{O}\left(\frac{1}{n}\right)\right],$$

when m is fixed, $n \to \infty$.

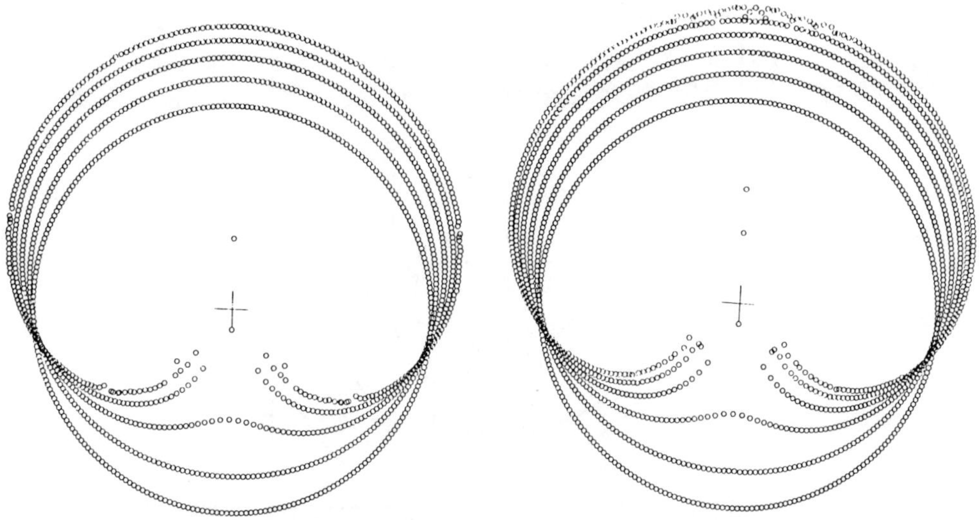

(a) Padé summation after a single change of variables.

(b) Padé summation after a repeated change of variables.

Figure 3.

The comparison of the above formula with the obtained values shows that an asymptotical behaviour has been predicted correctly.

The proposed model seems to be very promising. Although complicated in terms of application, it admits a deep research of the problem. It allows a free surface to be constructed for large times and the appearance of singularities on it to be recorded.

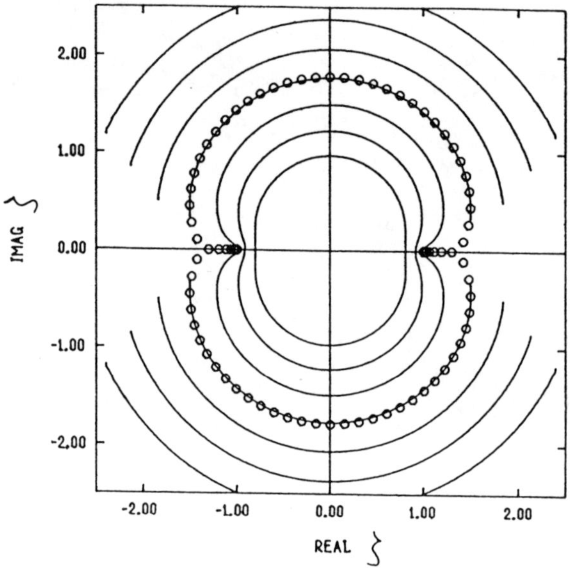

Figure 4. The roots of equations $Z^{(89)}(\zeta) = 0$. Seven lines of the movable singularity modulus constancy have been displayed. The roots are arranged along the line $|t_0(\zeta)| = 3/8$.

References

[1] Baumel R.T., Burley S.K., Freeman D.F., Gammel J.L., Nuttal J., *The rise of a cylindrical bubble in an inviscid liquid.*, Canadian Journal of Physics **60 (7)** (1982), 999–1007.

[2] Karabut E.A., *Application of power series in time in the problem of motion of a cylindrical cavity in a liquid. I. Finding the coefficients of power series.*, Dinamika sploshnoi sredy **78** (1986), 56–73.

[3] Karabut E.A., *Application of power series in time in the problem of motion of a cylindrical cavity in a liquid. II. Finding singular points.*, Dinamika sploshnoi sredy **80** (1987), 63–81.

[4] Karabut E.A., *Application of power series in time in the problem of motion of a cylindrical cavity in a liquid. III. Change of variables in a power series.*, Dinamika sploshnoi sredy **81** (1987), 51–77.

[5] Karabut E.A., *Application of power series in time in the problem of motion of a cylindrical cavity in a liquid. IV. Asymptotical properties of the power series coefficients.*, Dinamika sploshnoi sredy **88** (1988), 65–88.

[6] Woinow O.W., Woinow W.W., *Numerical method of account unsteady inviscid incompressible free-boundary flows.*, Dokl. akad. nayk. **221 (3)** (1975), 559–562.

[7] Belykh V.N., *The Existence and Uniqueness Theorem for solving the problem of a spherical bubble*, Dinamika sploshnoi sredy **12** (1972), 63–76.

On the convergence of solutions in problems of optimal control of variational inequality of the fourth-order

A.M. KHLUDNEV

Lavrentyev Institute of Hydrodynamics
Siberian Division of the USSR Academy of Science
Novosibirsk, 630090, USSR

Abstract. A variational inequality of the fourth-order for the operator

$$\omega \longrightarrow \varepsilon^3 \Delta^2 \omega - \Delta \omega$$

describing the problem of contact between an elastic plate and two rigid dies for every ε is considered. The plate is subjected to given normal tensile forces. Constraints on the function ω also depend on ε. A set of functions defining the die shape is used as a control region. The cost functional characterizes the deviation of the plate deflection from a given function. The problem of optimal control consists of finding out the most favourable forms of dies. Along with the above-mentioned problem, one more is considered which is concerned with the control of the variational inequality of the second order and describes the contact between the membrane and the two dies ($\varepsilon = 0$). The limit procedure $\varepsilon \to 0$ which means vanishing of the plate thickness is analysed.

Keywords. Variational inequality, optimal control, contact problem.

1980 Mathematics subject classifications: 73C60, 35K85

1. THE CONTROL OF THE VARIATIONAL INEQUALITY OF THE FOURTH-ORDER

Let $\Omega \subset \mathbf{R}^2$ be the bounded domain with a smooth boundary Γ; $H^S(\Omega)$ be Sobolev space of functions having the derivatives up to the order S, summed with the square; $H_0^S(\Omega)$ be the closure of infinitely differentiable functions in the norm $H^S(\Omega)$. Let further Ψ_1, Ψ_2 be the convex closed sets in $H^2(\Omega)$ such that for every $\psi_i \in \Psi_i$, the following inequalities are valid:

$$\begin{aligned} &\psi_1 \leq -\delta_0, \quad \psi_2 \geq \delta \quad \text{over } \Gamma, \\ &\psi_1(x) \leq \psi_2(x) - \delta, \quad x \in \Omega, \end{aligned}$$

where δ_0 =const> 0, δ =const> 0. Further it will be necessary to know the maxima of the two values δ_0, δ. Let, for convenience, assume that $\delta \geq \delta_0$. Let us define the convex and closed set in $H^2(\Omega) \cap H_0^1(\Omega)$ for fixed $\psi_1 \in \Psi_1, \psi_2 \in \Psi_2$:

$$K^2_{\psi,\varepsilon} = \{\omega \mid \psi_1(x) \leq \omega(x) \leq \psi_2(x) - \varepsilon, \ x \in \Omega\},$$

where $\varepsilon < \delta$, and the pair (ψ_1, ψ_2) is denoted by ψ. Let us consider the variational inequality

$$(1)\qquad \omega \in K^2_{\psi,\varepsilon}: \quad \varepsilon^3\langle \Delta\omega, \Delta\overline{\omega} - \Delta\omega\rangle + \langle \nabla\omega, \nabla\overline{\omega} - \nabla\omega\rangle \geq 0 \quad \forall \overline{\omega} \in K^2_{\psi,\varepsilon}.$$

Symbol $\langle\cdot,\cdot\rangle$ denotes the scalar product in $L^2(\Omega)$. For fixed $\varepsilon > 0$, inequality (1) has a unique solution $\omega = \omega(\psi)$. This inequality describes the equilibrium state of the plate being between two dies. The die shapes are prescribed by the equations $z = \psi_1(x), z = \psi_2(x)$; ω is the plate deflection, ε is the thickness. Regularity and other properties of the solutions of the fourth-order variational inequalities with constraints on the unknown function were considered in [**1–4**]. Let $\Psi = \Psi_1 \times \Psi_2$ and ω_0 be a given function. The problem of optimal control which will be analysed in this section deals with minimization of the functional, determined on the set Ψ. Let us define the functional

$$\mathcal{J}_\varepsilon(\psi) = \|\omega(\psi) - \omega_0\| + \|\psi\|_2,$$

where the norm in $H^S(\Omega)$ is denoted by $\|\cdot\|_S, \|\cdot\|_0 \equiv \|\cdot\|$. It is necessary to find the element $\psi \in \Psi$, such that

$$(2)\qquad \mathcal{J}_\varepsilon(\psi) \leq \mathcal{J}_\varepsilon(\overline{\psi}) \quad \forall \overline{\psi} \in \Psi.$$

It should be noted that ε in this problem is assumed to be fixed. As we shall consider a limit procedure when $\varepsilon \to 0$, the dependence of the functional on ε is stated. The first statement to be proved is that the solution of the problem of optimal control under consideration exists.

THEOREM 1. *The solution of the problem (2) exists.*

PROOF: Let $\psi^n \in \Psi$ be the minimizing sequence. This sequence is bounded in $H^2(\Omega) \times H^2(\Omega)$. It is appropriate to choose from this sequence a weakly converging subsequence without changing the notation. We assume that

$$(3)\qquad \begin{cases} \psi^n \to \psi & \text{weakly in } H^2(\Omega) \times H^2(\Omega) \text{ and} \\ & \text{uniformly in } \overline{\Omega}. \end{cases}$$

$(3)_2$ is a consequence of compactness of the embedding from $H^2(\Omega)$ into $C(\overline{\Omega})$ in a two-dimensional space. For every $\psi^n \in \Psi$ we are able to find the solution of the variational inequality

$$(4)\qquad \omega^n \in K^2_{\psi^n,\varepsilon}: \quad \varepsilon^3\langle \Delta\omega^n, \Delta\overline{\omega}^n - \Delta\omega^n\rangle + \langle \nabla\omega^n, \nabla\overline{\omega}^n - \nabla\omega^n\rangle \geq 0 \quad \forall \overline{\omega}^n \in K^2_{\psi^n,\varepsilon}.$$

A priori estimate of solutions ω^n will be obtained from (4), if the following supplementary statement will be proved. For every $\overline{\omega} \in K^2_{\psi,\varepsilon}$, we can constract the sequence $\overline{\omega}^n \in K^2_{\psi^n,\varepsilon}$ such that

$$\overline{\omega}^n \to \overline{\omega} \quad \text{strongly in } H^2(\Omega) \cap H^1_0(\Omega).$$

Here ψ is a limit of $\{\psi^n\}$. Let us prove this statement. First of all, it should be noted that by virtue of imbedding theorems, $\overline{\omega}$ is continuous function in $\overline{\Omega}$. Let us consider the closed set

$$M_1 = \{x \in \Omega \mid \psi_1(x) \le \overline{\omega}(x) \le \psi_1(x) + \frac{\delta_0}{8}\},$$

and let M_1^ν be its ν-neighbourhood. Analogously, let us introduce the set

$$M_2 = \{x \in \Omega \mid \psi_2(x) - \varepsilon - \frac{\delta_0}{8} \le \overline{\omega}(x) \le \psi_2(x) - \varepsilon\}$$

and its ν-neighbourhood M_2^ν. Now let us choose functions $\xi_1, \xi_2 \in H^2(\Omega)$ possessing the properties (see [**5**])

$$\xi_1(x) = \begin{cases} 1, & x \in M_1 \\ 0, & x \in M_1^\nu \end{cases}, \qquad 0 \le \xi_1(x) \le 1,$$

$$\xi_2(x) = \begin{cases} -1, & x \in M_2 \\ 0, & x \in M_2^\nu \end{cases}, \qquad -1 \le \xi_2(x) \le 0\ .$$

If ν is small enough, the following inequalities are valid on the sets M_1^ν, M_2^ν:

$$\psi_1(x) \le \overline{\omega}(x) \le \psi_1(x) + \frac{\delta_0}{4}, \quad \psi_2(x) - \varepsilon - \frac{\delta_0}{4} \le \overline{\omega}(x) \le \psi_2(x) - \varepsilon\ .$$

By virtue of a uniform convergence of the sequence ψ^n we may assume that

$$|\psi_i^n(x) - \psi_i(x)| < \frac{1}{n^2}, \quad x \in \Omega,\ i = 1,2.$$

Taking into account the above-mentioned considerations, one may verify that the sequence

$$\overline{\omega}^n = \overline{\omega} + \frac{\delta_0}{4n}\xi_1 + \frac{\delta_0}{4n}\xi_2$$

possesses the required properties. Namely, for sufficiently large n

$$\psi_1^n(x) \le \overline{\omega}^n(x) \le \psi_2^n(x) - \varepsilon, \quad x \in \Omega,$$

and $\overline{\omega}^n$ is strongly converging to the function $\overline{\omega}$ in $H^2(\Omega) \cap H_0^1(\Omega)$. Now let us turn to the variational inequality (4). Let $\psi = (\psi_1, \psi_2)$ be the limit in (3). We choose an arbitrary function $\overline{\omega} \in K_{\psi,\varepsilon}^2$ and construct the sequence of elements $\overline{\omega}^n \in K_{\psi^n,\varepsilon}^2$ strongly converging to $\overline{\omega}$. The existence of such a sequence has been just proved. Substituting $\overline{\omega}^n$ in (4) we arrive at the inequality

$$\varepsilon^3 \|\Delta\omega^n\|^2 + \|\nabla\omega^n\|^2 \le c \tag{5}$$

with the constant independent of n. As a consequence of (3) one can assume that

$$\omega^n \to \omega \quad \text{weakly in } H^2(\Omega) \cap H_0^1(\Omega).$$

Clearly $\omega \in K^2_{\psi,\varepsilon}$.

Passing to the limit with $n \to \infty$ in (4) we immediately get

$$\omega \in K^2_{\psi,\varepsilon} : \quad \varepsilon^3 \langle \Delta\omega, \Delta\overline{\omega} - \Delta\omega \rangle + \langle \nabla\omega, \nabla\overline{\omega} - \nabla\omega \rangle \geq 0 \quad \forall \overline{\omega} \in K^2_{\psi,\varepsilon}.$$

This means that $\omega = \omega(\psi)$. Consequently, using again the weak lower semicontinuity of the norm in $L^2(\Omega)$, we obtain

$$j_\varepsilon \equiv \inf_{\overline{\psi} \in \Psi} \mathcal{J}_\varepsilon(\overline{\psi}) = \underline{\lim}_{n \to \infty} \mathcal{J}_\varepsilon(\psi^n) \geq \mathcal{J}_\varepsilon(\psi) \geq j_\varepsilon.$$

Thus, the function ψ is a solution of problem (2). The theorem has been proved. □

2. Control of the second-order variational inequality

Let $\psi \in \Psi$ be the arbitrary element and define the set

$$K^1_\psi = \{ \omega \in H^1_0(\Omega) \mid \psi_1(x) \leq \omega(x) \leq \psi_2(x), \ x \in \Omega \} .$$

The solution of the following variational inequality exists and is unique:

$$\omega \in K^1_\psi : \quad \langle \nabla\omega, \nabla\overline{\omega} - \nabla\omega \rangle \geq 0 \quad \forall \overline{\omega} \in K^1_\psi . \tag{6}$$

Let us introduce the cost functional

$$\mathcal{J}_0(\psi) = \|\omega(\psi) - \omega_0\| + \|\psi\|_2,$$

where $\omega = \omega(\psi)$ is the solution of (6). The problem of optimal control which is considered in this section is to minimize the functional $\mathcal{J}_0$ on Ψ, i.e. to to find $\psi \in \Psi$ such that

$$\mathcal{J}_0(\psi) \leq \mathcal{J}_0(\overline{\omega}) \quad \forall \overline{\psi} \in \Psi. \tag{7}$$

Theorem 2. *The solution of the problem (7) exists.*

Proof: Let us choose a minimizing sequence $\psi^n \in \Psi$. By virtue of its boundedness in space $H^2(\Omega) \times H^2(\Omega)$, one may suppose that $\psi_i^n \to \psi_i$ strongly in $H^2(\Omega)$ and uniformly in $\overline{\Omega}, i = 1, 2$. Now let us denote a couple (ψ_1, ψ_2) by ψ and prove that ψ solves the problem under consideration. Analogously to the previous section one can prove that for every $\overline{\omega} \in K^1_\psi$ there exists the sequence $\overline{\omega}^n \in K^1_{\psi^n}$ having the property:

$$\overline{\omega}^n \to \overline{\omega} \quad \text{strongly in } H^1_0(\Omega).$$

Indeed, one may construct a sequence of smooth functions $\hat{\omega}^n$ strongly converging to $\overline{\omega}$. Assume that $\tilde{\omega}^n = \max\{\psi_1^n, \hat{\omega}^n\}$. Then $\tilde{\omega}^n \to \max\{\psi_1, \overline{\omega}\}, \tilde{\omega}^n \geq \psi_1^n$. Then assume that $\overline{\omega}^n = \min\{\psi_2^n, \tilde{\omega}^n\}$. Thereby $\overline{\omega}^n \to \min\{\psi_2, \overline{\omega}\}$, and, besides, $\psi_1^n \leq \overline{\omega}^n \leq \psi_2^n$. Thus, the required sequence exists. Now let us turn to the variational inequality

$$\omega^n \in K^1_{\psi^n} : \quad \langle \nabla\omega^n, \nabla\overline{\omega}^n - \nabla\omega^n \rangle \geq 0 \quad \forall \overline{\omega}^n \in K^1_{\psi^n}. \tag{8}$$

Let $\overline{\omega} \in K^1_\psi$ be given and let $\overline{\omega}^n \in K^1_{\psi^n}$ be strongly converging to $\overline{\omega}$. Substituting these elements into (8) we obtain an uniform estimate

$$\|\nabla \omega^n\|^2 \leq c.$$

Without loosing the generality, we assume that

$$\omega^n \to \omega \quad \text{weakly in } H^1_0(\Omega).$$

Clearly $\omega \in K^1_\psi$.

Limit procedure in (8) gives

$$\omega \in K^1_\psi : \quad \langle \nabla \omega, \nabla \overline{\omega} - \nabla \omega \rangle \geq 0 \quad \forall \overline{\omega} \in K^1_\psi,$$

so that $\omega = \omega(\psi)$. Now it is not difficult to prove that the function $\psi \in \Psi$ is the solution of problem (7). Indeed,

$$j_0 = \inf_{\psi \in \Psi} \mathcal{J}_0(\overline{\omega}) = \underline{\lim}\, \mathcal{J}_0(\psi^n) \geq \mathcal{J}_0(\psi) \geq j_0.$$

The theorem has been proved.

□

3. The limit procedure for $\varepsilon \to 0$

The statement characterizing the behaviour of the solutions of the problem (2) when $\varepsilon \to 0$ will be proved in this section. Namely, let ψ^ε be the solution of the problem (2), and $\omega^\varepsilon = \omega(\psi^\varepsilon)$ be the corresponding solution of variational inequality (1),

$$j_\varepsilon = \mathcal{J}_\varepsilon(\psi^\varepsilon), \quad j_0 = \inf_{\psi \in \Psi} \mathcal{J}_0(\psi).$$

THEOREM 3. *From the sequence of solutions $\psi^\varepsilon, \omega^\varepsilon$ we may choose subsequence such that for $\varepsilon \to 0$*

$$\begin{aligned} &\psi^\varepsilon \to \psi \quad \text{weakly in } H^2(\Omega) \times H^2(\Omega), \\ &\omega^\varepsilon \to \omega \quad \text{weakly in } H^1_0(\Omega), \\ &j_\varepsilon \to j_0. \end{aligned}$$

Here ψ is the solution of the problem of optimal control (7), and $\omega = \omega(\psi)$ is defined from variational inequality (6).

PROOF: Let us choose an arbitrary fixed element $\psi \in \Psi$. Then

$$\mathcal{J}_\varepsilon(\psi^\varepsilon) \leq \mathcal{J}_\varepsilon(\psi)\,. \tag{9}$$

We shall prove that the right-hand part of this inequality is bounded with respect to ε, $\varepsilon \leq \varepsilon_0$. To this end it is sufficient to establish that $\omega^\varepsilon(\psi)$ are bounded in space $L^2(\Omega)$. Let us consider the variational inequality

(10)

$$\omega^\varepsilon(\psi) \in K^2_{\psi,\varepsilon} : \quad \varepsilon^3 \langle \Delta\omega^\varepsilon(\psi), \Delta\overline{\omega}^\varepsilon - \Delta\omega^\varepsilon(\psi)\rangle + \langle \nabla\omega^\varepsilon(\psi), \nabla\overline{\omega}^\varepsilon - \nabla\omega^\varepsilon(\psi)\rangle \geq 0 \quad \forall \overline{\omega}^\varepsilon \in K^2_{\psi,\varepsilon}.$$

Accordingly by the definition of the set $K^2_{\psi,\varepsilon}$ the trial functions satisfy the inequalities

$$\psi_1(x) \le \overline{\omega}^\varepsilon(x) \le \psi_2(x) - \varepsilon, \quad x \in \Omega.$$

Let us construct the function $\overline{\omega}$ such that it belongs to $K^2_{\psi,\varepsilon}$ for every $\varepsilon \le \varepsilon_0$. Substituting this function into (10), we obtain the estimate

$$\varepsilon^3 \|\Delta\omega^\varepsilon(\psi)\|^2 + \|\nabla\omega^\varepsilon(\psi)\|^2 \le c,$$

which is uniform with respect to $\varepsilon \le \varepsilon_0$. This means that the right-hand side of the inequality (9) is bounded for $\varepsilon \le \varepsilon_0$. Therefore,

$$\|\psi^\varepsilon\|_2 \le c$$

with the constant independent of $\varepsilon, \varepsilon \le \varepsilon_0$. Choosing the subsequence if necessary, one may assume that

$$\psi^\varepsilon \to \tilde{\psi} \quad \text{weakly in } H^2(\Omega) \times H^2(\Omega) \text{ and uniformly in } \overline{\Omega}.$$

Then from the variational inequality

$$\omega^\varepsilon \in K^2_{\psi^\varepsilon,\varepsilon}: \quad \varepsilon^3\langle\Delta\omega^\varepsilon, \Delta\overline{\omega}^\varepsilon - \Delta\omega^\varepsilon\rangle + \langle\nabla\omega^\varepsilon, \nabla\overline{\omega}^\varepsilon - \nabla\omega^\varepsilon\rangle \ge 0 \quad \forall \overline{\omega}^\varepsilon \in K^2_{\psi^\varepsilon,\varepsilon} \tag{11}$$

we have the estimate uniform with respect to $\varepsilon \le \varepsilon_0$

$$\varepsilon^3\|\Delta\omega^\varepsilon\|^2 + \|\nabla\omega^\varepsilon\|^2 \le c\,. \tag{12}$$

Indeed, let us take an arbitrary fixed element $\overline{\omega} \in H^2(\Omega) \cap H^1_0(\Omega)$ satisfying $\tilde{\psi}_1(x) \le \overline{\omega}(x) \le \tilde{\psi}_2(x)$ such that

$$\psi_1^\varepsilon(x) \le \overline{\omega}^\varepsilon(x) \le \psi_2^\varepsilon(x) - \varepsilon,$$
$$\overline{\omega}^\varepsilon \to \overline{\omega} \quad \text{strongly in } H^2(\Omega) \cap H^1_0(\Omega).$$

Such construction may be realized analogously in Theorem 1. One assume

$$|\psi_i^\varepsilon(x) - \tilde{\psi}_i(x)| < \varepsilon, \quad x \in \Omega,\ i = 1, 2.$$

Let us introduce the closed sets

$$M_1 = \{x \in \Omega \mid \tilde{\psi}_1(x) \le \overline{\omega}(x) \le \tilde{\psi}_1(x) + \frac{\delta_0}{8}\},$$
$$M_2 = \{x \in \Omega \mid \tilde{\psi}_2(x) - \frac{\delta_0}{8} \le \overline{\omega}(x) \le \tilde{\psi}_2(x)\};$$

and let M_1^ν, M_2^ν be their ν-neighbourhoods where the following inequalities are fulfilled:

$$\tilde{\psi}_1 \le \varpi \le \tilde{\psi}_1 + \frac{\delta_0}{4}, \quad \tilde{\psi}_2 - \frac{\delta_0}{4} \le \varpi \le \tilde{\psi}_2.$$

Let us constract functions ξ_1, ξ_2 satisfying the conditions

$$\xi_1(x) = \begin{cases} 1, & x \in M_1 \\ 0, & x \in M_1^\nu \end{cases}, \qquad 0 \le \xi_1(x) \le 1,$$

$$\xi_2(x) = \begin{cases} -1, & x \in M_2 \\ 0, & x \in M_2^\nu \end{cases}, \qquad -1 \le \xi_2(x) \le 0 .$$

Then for small ε the function $\varpi^\varepsilon = \varpi + \frac{\delta_0\sqrt{\varepsilon}}{4}\xi_1 + \frac{\delta_0\sqrt{\varepsilon}}{4}\xi_2$ satisfies the inequalities

$$\psi_1^\varepsilon(x) \le \varpi^\varepsilon(x) \le \psi_2^\varepsilon(x) - \varepsilon, \quad x \in \Omega,$$

and strongly tends to ϖ in space $H^2(\Omega) \cap H_0^1(\Omega)$. Subsitution of the functions ϖ^ε into variational inequality (11) leads to a priori estimate (12). We assume that when $\varepsilon \to 0$

$$\begin{aligned} \omega^\varepsilon &\to \omega \quad \text{weakly in } H_0^1(\Omega), \\ \varepsilon^3\omega^\varepsilon &\to 0 \quad \text{weakly in } H^2(\Omega) \cap H_0^1(\Omega). \end{aligned}$$

Substituting the elements into (11) and taking the limit with $n \to \infty$, we get

(13) $$\omega \in K_{\tilde{\psi}}^1 : \quad \langle \nabla\omega, \nabla\varpi - \nabla\omega \rangle \ge 0 \quad \forall \varpi \in K_{\tilde{\psi}}^1 \cap H^2(\Omega).$$

Below it will be proved (see Lemma) that the functions from $K_{\tilde{\psi}}^1$ may be approximated by the functions from $K_{\tilde{\psi}}^1 \cap H^2(\Omega)$. This means that the inequality (13) is fulfilled for every $\varpi \in K_{\tilde{\psi}}^1$ so that $\omega = \omega(\tilde{\psi})$. Then taking into account a weak lower semicontinuity of the norm $\|\cdot\|$, we get

(14) $$\underline{\lim}\, j_\varepsilon = \underline{\lim}\, \mathcal{J}_\varepsilon(\psi^\varepsilon) \ge \mathcal{J}_0(\tilde{\psi}).$$

Further, we will need the following statement: for any $\psi \in \Psi$ fixed, from the sequence $\mathcal{J}_\varepsilon(\psi)$ a subsequence may be chosen such that

$$\mathcal{J}_\varepsilon(\psi) \to \mathcal{J}_0(\psi), \quad \varepsilon \to 0.$$

Indeed, from the variational inequality

(15)
$$\omega^\varepsilon(\psi) \in K_{\psi,\varepsilon}^2 : \quad \varepsilon^3\langle \Delta\omega^\varepsilon(\psi), \Delta\varpi^\varepsilon - \Delta\omega^\varepsilon(\psi)\rangle + \langle \nabla\omega^\varepsilon(\psi), \nabla\varpi^\varepsilon - \nabla\omega^\varepsilon(\psi)\rangle \ge 0 \quad \forall \varpi^\varepsilon \in K_{\psi,\varepsilon}^2$$

we get the estimate, uniform with respect to $\varepsilon \le \varepsilon_0$

$$\varepsilon^3\|\Delta\omega^\varepsilon(\psi)\|^2 + \|\nabla\omega^\varepsilon(\psi)\|^2 \le c.$$

Thus there exists a subsequence of $\{\psi^\varepsilon\}$ (denoted by the same symbol) such that

$$\begin{aligned} \omega^\varepsilon(\psi) \to \omega \quad & \text{weakly in } H_0^1(\Omega), \quad \text{strongly in } L^2(\Omega), \\ \varepsilon^3\omega^\varepsilon(\omega) \to 0 \quad & \text{weakly in } H^2(\Omega) \cap H_0^1(\Omega), \end{aligned}$$

thereby $\omega \in K_\psi^1$. Now we can pass to the limit for $\varepsilon \to 0$ by the same way as earlier. We get

$$\omega \in K_\psi^1 : \quad \langle \nabla\omega, \nabla\overline{\omega} - \nabla\omega \rangle \geq 0 \quad \forall \overline{\omega} \in K_\psi^1 \cap H^2(\Omega).$$

according to the Lemma, proved below, one may conclude that this inequality is valid for any element $\overline{\omega} \in K_\psi^1$, therefore $\omega = \omega(\psi)$. Taking into account a strong convergence $\omega^\varepsilon(\psi)$ to ω in $L^2(\Omega)$ we get

$$\mathcal{J}_\varepsilon(\psi) \equiv \|\omega^\varepsilon(\psi) - \omega_0\| + \|\psi\|_2 \to \mathcal{J}_0(\psi).$$

Now let us choose the solution ψ of the problem of optimal control (7). Then

$$j_\varepsilon = \mathcal{J}_\varepsilon(\psi^\varepsilon) \leq \mathcal{J}_\varepsilon(\psi),$$

and using the above consideration

$$\overline{\lim}\, j_\varepsilon \leq \mathcal{J}_0(\psi).$$

Taking into account (14) we come to the conclusion that $\tilde{\psi}$ is the solution of the problem (7) and $j_\varepsilon \to j_0$. The theorem has been proved.

□

In conclusion, let us establish the validity of the supplementary statement, used in the proof of Theorem 3.

LEMMA. *For any function $\overline{\omega} \in K_\psi^1$ one may construct the sequence $\overline{\omega}^n \in K_\psi^1 \cap H^2(\Omega)$ such that*

(16) $$\overline{\omega}^n \to \overline{\omega} \quad \textit{strongly in } H_0^1(\Omega).$$

PROOF: Let $H_0^{1,p}(\Omega)$ denote the space of functions having the first generalized derivatives, summarized with power $p > 2$, and being equal to zero on Γ. The elements of this space are continuous in $\overline{\Omega}$. First of all, it should be noted that one can construct the sequence of functions $\overline{\omega}^n \in K_\psi^1 \cap H_0^{1,p}(\Omega)$ satisfying condition (16). Indeed, if $\hat{\omega}^n \in C_0^\infty(\Omega)$ and $\overline{\omega}^n \to \overline{\omega}$ strongly in $H_0^1(\Omega)$, the sequence $\overline{\omega}^n = \min\{\psi_2, \quad \max\{\psi_1, \hat{\omega}^n\}\}$ converges to the function $\overline{\omega}$ in $H_0^1(\Omega)$ and satisfies the above mentioned inclusion. Thus, Lemma can be proved if for any function $\overline{\omega} \in K_\psi^1 \cap H_0^{1,p}(\Omega)$ there exists the sequence $\overline{\omega}^n \in K_\psi^1 \cap H^2(\Omega)$ satisfying condition (16). To justify this fact, let us construct the function ξ_1, $\xi_2 \in H^2(\Omega)$ in the same way as in Theorem 1, with the only difference that in this case $\varepsilon = 0$. Then the sequence $\overline{\omega}^n = \overline{\omega} + \frac{\sigma_0}{4n}\xi_1 + \frac{\sigma_0}{4n}\xi_2$ converges to $\overline{\omega}$ in $H_0^1(\Omega)$. It is significant that there is a non zero "gap" between $\hat{\omega}^n$ and functions ψ_1, ψ_2. Namely,

$$\psi_1(x) < \hat{\omega}^n(x) < \psi_2(x), \quad x \in \Omega.$$

Let us extend the functions $\hat{\omega}^n$ from Ω by zero and introduce averaging $(\hat{\omega}^n)_{\varepsilon_n}$ with a smooth kernel. The parameter ε_n is chosen so small that $\|(\hat{\omega}^n)_{\varepsilon_n} - \hat{\omega}^n\| < \frac{1}{n}$ and

$$\psi_1(x) < (\hat{\omega}^n)_{\varepsilon_n}(x) < \psi_2(x), \quad x \in \Omega. \tag{17}$$

Now let us consider the sequence of function $(\hat{\omega}^n)_{\varepsilon_n}$ in the outer neighbourhood Ω_1 of the boundary Γ. These functions may be extended into Ω so that in $\Omega\backslash\Omega_0$ the extensions denoted by v_n vanish. The domain Ω_0 is chosen as an inner neighbourhood of the boundary Γ, where the following inequalities are fulfilled

$$|\overline{\omega}| < \frac{\nu}{2}, \quad \psi_1 < -\nu, \quad \psi_2 > \nu \tag{18}$$

with some constant $\nu > 0$. By virtue of finiteness of functions ξ_1, ξ_2, one may also assume that the equalities $\hat{\omega}^n = \overline{\omega}$ are valid in Ω_0. In particular, it means that for large n the functions $(\hat{\omega}^n)_{\varepsilon_n}$ coincide with $(\overline{\omega})_{\varepsilon_n}$ in Ω_1. For the above-mentioned extensions v_n the inequalities are valid [**6**] in $\overline{\Omega}$

$$\|v_n\|_{1,\Omega} \le c\|(\overline{\omega})_{\varepsilon_n}\|_{1,\Omega_1}, \tag{19}$$

$$\max_{\Omega} |v_n| \le c \max_{\Omega_1} |(\overline{\omega})_{\varepsilon_n}| \tag{20}$$

with constant c independent of n. It follows from the construction that the right-hand sides of inequalities (19), (20) vanish when $n \to \infty$. Therefore, the required sequence may be determined as $\overline{\omega}^n = (\hat{\omega}^n)_{\varepsilon_n} - v_n$. Indeed, by virtue of (18)–(20) from inequalities (17) it follows that

$$\psi_1(x) \le \overline{\omega}^n(x) \le \psi_2(x).$$

Moreover, the sequence of functions $\overline{\omega}^n$ strongly converges to $\overline{\omega}$. The Lemma has been proved.

□

Optimal control problem for the operator $\omega \to \varepsilon\Delta^2\omega - \varphi(\|\nabla\omega\|^2)\Delta\omega$ with one-side obstacle was considered in [**7**].

References

[1] Caffarelli, L. A., Friedman, A. and Torelli, A., *The two-obstacle problem for the biharmonic operator*, No. 2, Pacific J. Math. **103** (1982), 325–335.

[2] Caffarelli, L.A. and Friedman A., *The obstacle problemfor the biharmonic operator*, Ann.Scuola Norm. Sup. Pisa, ser.IV, V.6,No.1 (1979), 151–184.

[3] Schild B., *A regularity result for polyharmonic variationalinequalities with thin obstacles*, Ann.Scuola Norm. Sup. Pisa, V.11,No.1 (1984), 87–122.

[4] Khludnev, A.M., *Variational approach to the problem ofcontact between a shallow shell and a rigid body*, in "Differentsial'nye uravneniia s chastnymi proizvodnymi," Trudy seminara Soboleva, Novosibirsk, No.2, 1981, pp. 109–114.

[5] Schwartz, L., "Analyse Mathematique," Vol.1, 1967.

[6] Mikhailov, V.P., "Partial differential equations," M., Nauka Publishers, 1976.

[7] Khludnev, A.M., *The limiting transitions in optimal control problem for the fourth-order operator*, in "Differential'nye uravneniia," V.25, No.8, 1989, pp. 1427–1435.

A fixed-grid finite element method for solidification [1]

Douglas A. Kurtze

Department of Physics
North Dakota State University

Abstract. I present a method for numerical integration of time-dependent diffusion problems with dynamically moving boundaries such as solidification fronts. The method is meant to be used for problems in which supercooling (and possibly superheating) occurs, and in which the effects of nonequilibrium interface kinetics and surface tension at the front are important. Thus it is necessary to track the front; this is done by using the Stefan boundary condition to move the front explicitly at the beginning of each time step. The diffusion field is then updated by a Galerkin finite element method. In order to generalize the Galerkin discretization to these problems in a systematic way, I base the finite element calculation on space-time finite elements: The spatial grid is fixed, but grid cells which are crossed by the front are divided into solid and liquid portions, with Galerkin integrals calculated separately over each portion. Results will be presented for the growth of a dendrite in a narrow channel.

Keywords. Free boundary problem, finite element, heat conduction, solidification

1980 *Mathematics subject classifications:* 65M60, 35R35, 80-08

Several moving-boundary problems have, in recent years, been of great interest to condensed matter physicists. [1] Most of these problems are concerned with the shape and rate of advance of phase transition fronts, such as solidification fronts. The greatest theoretical interest is in discovering what general principles (if any!) underlie the process by which the front selects its ultimate shape and velocity.

A typical problem of this sort is that of *directional solidification*, [1] in which an ampoule full of a molten mixture is pulled at a constant velocity V past a hot contact, at a temperature above the melting temperature of the mixture, and a cold contact, which is below the melting temperature. For velocities which are not too large, the solidification front is just a straight line perpendicular to the pulling direction, which is stationary (in the laboratory frame) at some location between the contacts. For V above some critical value, however, this state becomes unstable [2] against perturbations of the shape of the front. After the onset of this "morphological" or "Mullins-Sekerka" instability, the front

[1] This material is based upon work supported by the U.S. National Science Foundation under Grant No. DMR83-11053.

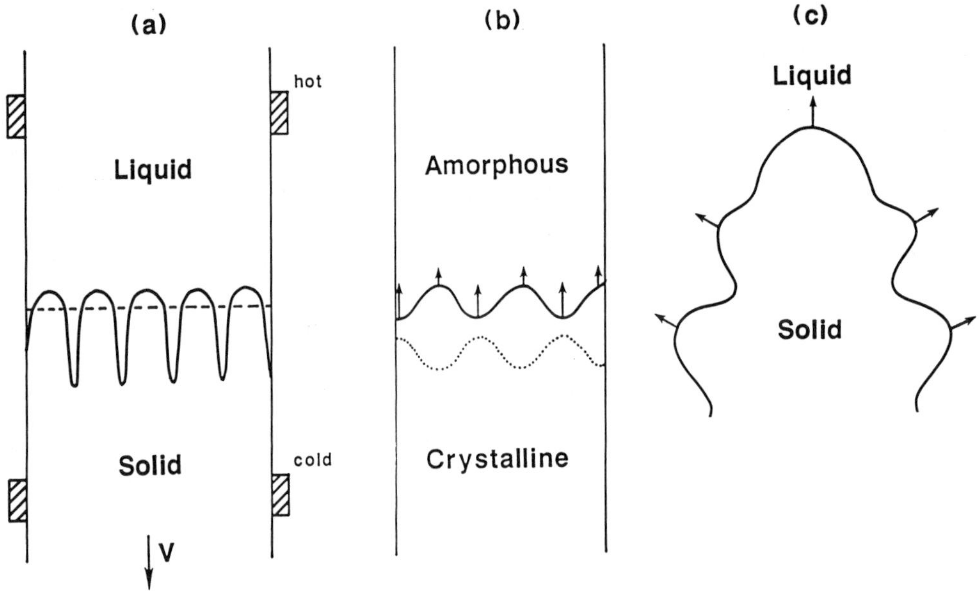

Figure 1. Geometry of three phase transition problems: (a) directional solidification of a binary mixture; (b) explosive crystallization; (c) dendritic solidification of a pure melt.

takes on a new shape which is periodic in space, as depicted in Fig. 1(a). A weakly nonlinear analysis of the model equations for this system, valid near the onset of the instability, shows [3] that there is a *continuum* of linearly stable periodic patterns, with wavelengths filling some finite range. The main theoretical problem is to understand how the ultimate pattern is selected. This includes answering such questions as:

- Which physical effects are crucial for determining the final state, and which can safely be neglected (i.e., make only quantitative changes)?
- Is there in fact a unique final wavelength, independent of the initial conditions?
- Is there a unique final wavelength when noise is present, and is noise necessary for the system to reach it?

Very similar questions are also asked about hydrodynamic instabilities, which share many of the features of the directional solidification problem.

A second problem of this type is *explosive crystallization*, [4] in which an amorphous material crystallizes, releasing a latent heat of crystallization. Since the crystallization of an amorphous material is thermally activated, this process is autocatalytic. As in the case of directional solidification, the model equations for explosive crystallization admit a simple exact solution in which the crystallization front is a straight line advancing at a constant speed across the sample, and under certain conditions this solution becomes linearly unstable against perturbations of the front position or shape. However, the form which the front takes on after the onset of this instability is not stationary, but rather oscillates in time: depending on the parameters, the front may remain a straight line but advance with an oscillating velocity, or it may take on a wavy shape and advance in an oscillatory "leapfrog" fashion, as shown in Fig. 1(b). In one form of this problem, in which the front is driven by a heat source which is scanned at a constant velocity across the sample, a multiple-scales analysis [5] shows that a *unique* wavelength is selected for a certain small region of parameter space. Outside this region, however, the weakly nonlinear analysis is similar to that for directional solidification, and so the same questions remain to be answered.

A somewhat different problem, but one which has attracted great interest, is that of *dendritic solidification* [6] of a pure, supercooled melt. This problem has no simple solution, except for the parabolic, constantly advancing "needle-crystal" solution obtained by Ivantsov when surface tension effects are neglected. Unfortunately, surface tension is a crucial physical effect in this problem, appearing as a singular perturbation to the problem solved by Ivantsov. The needle-crystal solution predicts the existence of a continuum of possible growth velocities for any given undercooling, while experimentally a unique, reproducible growth velocity is observed for each undercooling. Intense theoretical effort has recently shown that including surface tension breaks the continuum down to at most a discrete set of possible velocities, of which only one gives a linearly stable solution. Real dendrites, however, do not advance steadily keeping a constant parabolic shape, but rather they throw off sidebranches as they grow, as shown in Fig. 1(c). There is little theoretical understanding of the formation of sidebranches – of what controls their size and spacing, or even of whether they are the result of some subtle finite-amplitude instability which selects a preferred spacing or else reflect the random noise which generates them.

In order to study problems like these numerically, I have developed an algorithm to integrate two-dimensional, fully time-dependent diffusion problems which have moving fronts. The algorithm is sufficiently general to handle all three of the problems described above, although at present it does not allow changes in the topology of the front. The basic equations used to model these problems consist of a diffusion equation (for impurity concentration in directional solidification and for temperature in the other two problems) in a moving reference frame,

$$u_t = \nabla \cdot (D \nabla u) + V u_x$$

(where the diffusion coefficient D can differ in the two phases), with Dirichlet or Neumann conditions imposed on the boundary of the computational region and two boundary conditions specified on the moving front: a flux, or Stefan, condition relating the release of latent heat (or the rejection of impurity) at the front to the normal velocity of advance v_n of the front,

$$v_n = (\hat{n} \cdot \nabla u)_{solid} - (\hat{n} \cdot \nabla u)_{liquid};$$

on the front in terms of the curvature κ of the front and its normal velocity,

$$u = f(v_n, \kappa).$$

For the dendrite and directional solidification problems, f is usually taken to be independent of v_n, while for explosive crystallization it is probably sufficient to let it depend only on v_n.

Several of the features of a numerical method for solving these problems are dictated, or at least strongly suggested, by the nature of the problems. The choice of a *finite element* method over a finite difference method is not forced by the nature of the problems at hand. However, the geometrical flexibility of finite element methods, coming from their ability to incorporate irregular grids in a natural way, makes them very attractive. This flexibility is important both because we wish to solve different problems with quite different geometries, and because the diffusion fields in these problems show no interesting behavior away from the front, and so we would like to concentrate the computational effort near the front. Since some of the problems of interest involve supercooling and superheating, we are forced to use a *front-tracking* method. Single-domain or enthalpy methods will not work, because the enthalpy is not a single-valued function of temperature when supercooling is allowed. It then becomes necessary to track the front in order to know which branch of the enthalpy function is the relevant one. We base the calculation on the untransformed *primitive equations*, because boundary fixing methods, which rest on the assumption that the moving front is itself given by a single-valued function in some coordinate system, are unable to accomodate the complicated front shapes we expect to see in our problems. (In fact, we will eventually want to solve problems in which the topology of the front changes.) The complexity of the expected front shapes also makes it likely that a moving grid method, which keeps grid points on the moving front, would have trouble, and so I have chosen to use a *fixed grid* method instead.

The method I have devised is in essence a standard Galerkin method for two-dimensional, time-dependent diffusion problems, modified to incorporate the moving front. There are three problems to be solved in order to make this modification; we will consider them in turn below. First, we need a way of representing the moving front, and interpolation functions to represent the diffusion field in elements which are crossed by the front. Second, we need an algorithm for advancing the front in each time step. Third, we need a systematic way to find the discretized equations for the diffusion field which come from elements crossed by the front. As I will discuss, each of these problems leads to some difficulties with roundoff error, which the algorithm handles in ways which are effective (if sometimes rather inelegant).

I represent the moving front as a piecewise linear curve defined by its intersections with the fixed lines of the triangular finite element grid. In each element which is not crossed by the front, the diffusion field is approximated in the standard way by a linear function. An element which is crossed by the front is naturally divided into (in general) a triangular segment and a quadrilateral segment; in the former the diffusion field is approximated by a linear function and in the latter by an isoparametric. The front is not allowed to cross a single element twice. The value of the diffusion field at a point on the front is given in terms of the local mean curvature of the front by the Gibbs-Thomson boundary condition. In principle, we would calculate the curvature at such a point by fitting a circle through it and its two neighbors on the front. However, this procedure is subject to a catastrophic loss of significance when the neighbors are too close to the front point under consideration, as often happens when this front point gets close to a grid point. Thus instead of using the neighboring front points, the algorithm uses two points which are not too close: each front point lies on a line segment joining two grid points, and so the curvature is calculated using the nearest front points on either side which lie on line segments which do not share an endpoint with the segment which the point under consideration lies on.

The first stage in advancing the solution through a time step is to move the front. This is done explicitly, [7] using the flux boundary condition to determine the normal velocity of any front point from the gradients of the diffusion field on its solid and liquid sides. In principle, we would calculate the gradient on, say, the liquid side of a given front point by averaging the gradients in all elements on the liquid side which contain that front point. However, this procedure is again susceptible to catastrophic roundoff error when the front point is too close to a grid point. Thus instead, the algorithm averages the gradients in all elements on the liquid side which contain the *grid point* on the liquid side of the front point. In order to decrease further the influence of small liquid regions, in which the gradient cannot be calculated accurately, the average is weighted by the areas of the liquid portions of these elements. The same is then done for the grid point on the solid side. The front point is then moved the appropriate distance normal to the front (i.e., normal to the circle which was used to determine the curvature). After all of the front points have been moved in this way, they are connected by line segments, and the intersections of these line segments with the grid lines are taken to be the new front points.

It turns out that the second stage, the generation of discretized equations for the diffusion field, is quite difficult if the front enters or leaves an element during a time step. In order to avoid this, the algorithm automatically decreases the time step to be just small enough for the front to *reach* a grid point. This could mean that the algorithm might take a long series of very short time steps, as the front passes through several grid points at different but nearby times. In order to mitigate this, and also to help control some of the roundoff difficulties which occur at various places in the calculation, any front point which lies within a prescribed distance of a grid point at the end of a time step is moved onto the grid point. In practice, it seems to be sufficient to take this distance to be no larger than 10^{-4} of the grid spacing; in addition, only a rather small number of front points move at a significant speed during most runs.

In order to generate the discretized equations which will be solved for the new values of the diffusion field, we need a way of systematically generalizing the Galerkin procedure to a situation in which the front, at which the field value is given by the Gibbs-Thomson boundary condition, moves during the time step. This is done by using space-time finite elements [8]: the triangular spatial elements are extended in the time direction to form triangular prisms. The diffusion field within the element is still represented as a linear or isoparametric function, but the parameters of these functions, namely the values of the diffusion field at the vertices and the positions of the front points (if any), are allowed to vary linearly in time. The discretized equations are then generated by requiring the residual to be orthogonal to a set of basis functions; the basis function associated with each grid point takes the value 1 at that point and 0 at all other grid and front points at the *new* time, and 0 everywhere at the *old* time. Some care is required in evaluating the orthogonality integrals, since some significant roundoff errors arise again when a quadrilateral segment is almost degenerate. The resulting linear equations for the new values of the diffusion field can then be solved by standard methods. In fact, it is the solution of these equations which dominates the computational time.

To test the code, I started it with initial conditions which should lead to the well-known one-dimensional similarity solution of the Stefan problem, for which the position of the free boundary is given by

$$s(t) = 2(\sqrt{t+1} - 1).$$

With a grid spacing of 0.03125 and a nominal time step of 0.04, the computed solution differs from the exact solution by 4

As an example of the results of the code, I show a sketch in Fig. 2 of the growth of a dendrite in a channel. This was run on the same grid as the test case above, and in fact the initial conditions were the same except that a small perturbation was added to the front shape. The width of the channel is equal to unity, and the capillary length d_0, which enters in the Gibbs-Thomson condition

$$u = -d_0 \kappa,$$

has the value 10^{-5}. The figure shows the position of the front from $t = 15$ to $t = 80$ in equal intervals. Clearly, the initial perturbation grows into a single, broad finger growing up the channel, which later splits into two fingers which occupy somewhat less of the channel. After a time of 80 the system has not yet reached a steady state. This can be seen easily from the fact that in steady state, energy conservation requires [9] that the dendrite occupy a fraction of the width of the channel equal to the undercooling, while

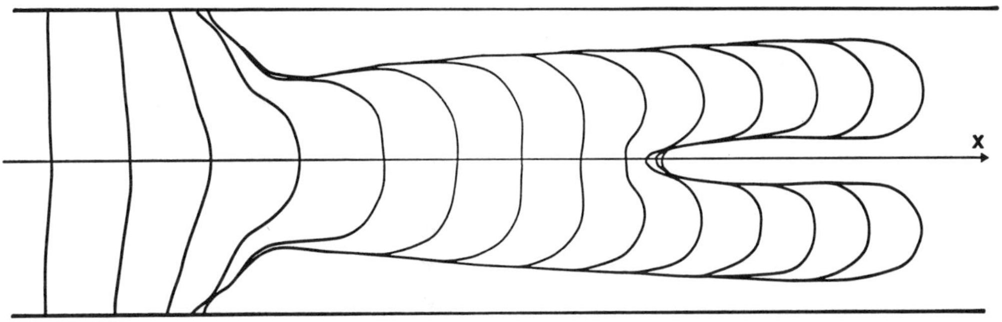

Figure 2. Computed growth of a dendrite in an insulated channel. The solid region advances in the positive x direction.

the undercooling in this run is much less than that fraction, namely 0.3. However, the numerical results suggest that the dendrite reaches its steady-state width by splitting, and then adjusting the width of the fingers when they have come to occupy approximately the correct fraction of the channel width.

REFERENCES

[1] For a review, see J.S. Langer, *Instabilities and pattern formation in crystal growth*, Revs. Mod. Phys. **52** (1980), 1-28.

[2] W.W. Mullins and R.F. Sekerka, *Stability of a planar interface during solidification of a dilute binary alloy*, J. Appl. Phys. **35** (1964), 444-451.

[3] D.J. Wollkind and L.A. Segel, *A nonlinear stability analysis of the freezing of a dilute binary alloy*, Phil. Trans. R. Soc. (Lond.) **268** (1970), 351-380.

[4] See, e.g., D.A. Kurtze, W. van Saarloos, and J.D. Weeks, *Front propagation in self-sustained and laser-driven explosive crystal growth: stability analysis and morphological aspects*, Phys. Rev. B **30** (1984), 1398-1415 and references therein.

[5] D.A. Kurtze, *Nonlinear development of morphological instabilities in explosive crystallization*, Phys. Rev. B **40** (1989), 11104-11119.

[6] For a recent review, see D.A. Kessler, J. Koplik, and H. Levine, *Pattern selection in fingered growth phenomena*, Adv. Phys. **37** (1988), 255-339.

[7] J. Yoo and B. Rubinsky, *Numerical computation using finite elements for the moving interface in heat transfer problems with phase transformation*, Numer. Heat Transfer **6** (1983), 209-222.

[8] R. Bonnerot and P. Jamet, *Numerical computation of the free boundary for the two-dimensional Stefan problem by space-time finite elements*, J. Computational Phys. **25** (1977), 163-181.

[9] D.A. Kessler, J. Koplik, and H. Levine, *Dendritic growth in a channel*, Phys. Rev. A **34** (1986), 4980-4987.

Domain decomposition method to realize implicit mesh schemes for some singular parabolic equations

A.V. Lapin

Department of Numerical Mathematics
Kazan University
Lenin street 18, Kazan 420008, USSR

Abstract. New algorithmes are proposed for the approximate realization of implicit mesh schemes (constructed via f.e.m. or f.d.m.) for a class of singular parabolic equations including, among others, one–phase and two–phase Stefan problems. These algorithmes are theoretically based on the estimates of movement rate for the mesh free boundary and on the estimates of the boundary perturbation impact on the solution of a mesh scheme. The approximate realization of a mesh scheme consists in its replacement by two problems in overlapping mesh subdomains, one of them being linear mesh problem and, the other, a nonlinear problem. To solve each of these problems, a method of decomposition of the domain into small domains can be then used.

Keywords. Variational inequality, phase transition, Stefan problem, mesh scheme, domain decomposition.

1980 Mathematics subject classifications:

Introduction

We consider singular parabolic equations which can be formally written in one of the following forms

$$\frac{\partial u}{\partial t} + Au + B(u) \ni f \text{ or } \frac{\partial u}{\partial t} + Au + B(\frac{\partial u}{\partial t}) \ni f \text{ or } \frac{\partial B(u)}{\partial t} + Au \ni f \tag{1}$$

with linear differential operator A and maximal monotone operator B. Linear parabolic equation with one–sided boundary conditions, one–phase Stefan problem (after Duvaut–transformation) and two–phase Stefan problem (in enthalpy formulation) are the examples of these singular parabolic equations. These problems and numerical methods of its solution are studied in a large number of publications (see [**1–4**], [**6**], [**8–12**] and the references therein). Many authors investigated, among other things, the convergence and accuracy of difference and finite element schemes. This paper treats the implicit mesh schemes for some problems of the form (1). Its solution at each time step requires to solve a nonlinear algebraic problem. We suggest a new approach to solve this problem, which is essentially as follows. The original mesh domain is decomposed into a set of overlapping subdomains. In the subdomains mesh problems are solved independently. The linear mesh schemes constitute the larger part of these problems, while nonlinear problems, the smaller part, as it corresponds to a mesh equations in neighbourhood of free boundary. Thus, effective algorithms to solve a linear equation being at our disposition, we can solve the whole problem much more effective than by any direct way.

In section 1 we study a simple implicit difference scheme for a one–sided boundary problem, we suggest an algorithm based on domain decomposition and we estimate its computational cost. Some remarks concerning the iterative procedure are presented and a problem with constaintes on $\partial u/\partial t$ is analysed.

In section 2 we formulate the two–phase Stefan problem, we construct a difference scheme and investigate the movement rate for the phase transition mesh boundary. Finally we carry out an approximate splitting of the nonlinear mesh problem for a fixed time step into linear and nonlinear problems, last one being located in the neighbourhood of the mesh boundary of the phase transition from the preceding time step.

The paper is based on results of articles [**6, 8**], where reader can find more details concerning algorithms for one– or two–phase Stefan problems.

One–sided boundary problem

Let $\Omega = (0,1)\times(0,1)$ be the unit square with the boundary $\Gamma = \Gamma_0 \cup \Gamma_1$, where $\Gamma_1 = \{x \mid x_1 = 0, \quad 0 < x_2 < 1\}$. We seek function $u(x,t)$ satisfying the following relations:

$$(2)\qquad \begin{cases} \dfrac{\partial u}{\partial t} - \Delta u = f(x,t) \text{ in } \Omega\times(0,T); \\ u = 0 \text{ in } \Gamma_0\times(0,T) \\ u \geq 0, \quad \dfrac{\partial u}{\partial n} \geq 0, \quad u\dfrac{\partial u}{\partial n} = 0 \text{ in } \Gamma_1\times(0,T); \\ u(\cdot,0) = u_0; \end{cases}$$

where n is the vector of the normal to Ω and $f(x,t)$ are given functions. For the variational formulation of the problem (2) as well as for existence and uniqueness of the weak solution see, for example, [**2–4**].

Let us approximate problem (2) by a difference scheme. Construct on $\bar\Omega = \Omega\cup\Gamma$ a uniform mesh ω with step $h > 0$ and define $\omega = \bar\omega\cap\Omega$, $\gamma_0 = \bar\omega\cap\Gamma_0$, $\gamma_1 = \bar\omega\cap\Gamma_1$. Let H_h be a space of mesh functions defined on $\bar\omega$ and $K_h = \{y \in H_h \mid y(x) = 0 \text{ in } \Gamma_0, \quad y(x) \geq 0 \text{ in } \gamma_1\}$. Assume also that

$$(y,v) = h^2\sum_{x\in\omega} y(x)v(x) + \frac{h^2}{2}\sum_{x\in\gamma_1} y(x)v(x);$$

$$Ay(x) = \begin{cases} -\partial_1\bar\partial_1 y - \partial_2\bar\partial_2 y, & x \in \omega \\ -\partial_2\bar\partial_2 y - \dfrac{2}{h}\partial y, & x\in\gamma_1 \end{cases},$$

where $\partial_1 y(x) = h^{-1}(y(x_1+h,x_2) - y(x_1,x_2))$, $\bar\partial_1 y(x) = h^{-1}(y(x_1,x_2) - y(x_1-h,x_2))$ and $\partial_2 y$, $\bar\partial_2 y$ are defined in a similar way. Finally, let as define the mesh $\omega_\tau = \{t = 0,\tau,...,N\tau = T\}$ with step $\tau > 0$ on the segment $[0,T]$. The mesh function $y(x,t) \equiv y(t)$ such that for all $t\in\omega_\tau$, $t > 0$, it satisfies the variational inequality

$$(3)\quad \tau^{-1}(y(t)-y(t-\tau), v-y(t)) + (Ay(t), v-y(t)) \geq (f, v-y(t)) \quad \forall v\in K_h, \quad y(t)\in K_h$$

and the initial condition

$$y(0) = u_0 \tag{4}$$

is said to be the solution to the difference scheme for the problem (2). Above we denote by f and u_0 mesh functions approximating the right-hand-side f and the initial function u_0 in (2).

Problem (3), (4) for each $t \in \omega_\tau$, $t > 0$, is a finite-dimensional variational inequality with the positive definite operator $E + \tau A$ (E is identity). Therefore it has a unique solution. For more details see [4], where convergence of difference scheme is also studied.

Let us rewrite the variational inequality (3) for fixed time level $t > 0$ in the form of equation:

$$(E + \tau A)y(t) + By(t) \ni F \tag{5}$$

where $F \equiv \tau f + y(t-\tau)$, $B = \tau \partial I_{K_h}$ is diagonal maximal monotone operator (∂I_{K_h} is subdifferential of the indicator function of set K_h). Our goal is to construct algorithm to solve equation (5) with given accuracy $\varepsilon > 0$. For this reason we'll formulate the following auxillary results.

Let x^* belong to $\bar{\omega}$, then $\eta(x^*) = \{x \in \bar{\omega} \mid x = x^* \underline{+} l_i h, \quad l_1 = (1,0), \quad l_2 = (0,1)\}$ is the mesh neighbourhood of x^*. The set $D \subseteq \bar{\omega}$ is connected if for any two points x', $x'' \in D$ there exist $x_i \in D$ such that

$$x' \in \eta(x_1),\ x_2 \in \eta(x_2), \ldots, x_n \in \eta(x'').$$

The set $\partial D = \{x \in \bar{\omega} \backslash D \mid \eta(x) \cap D \neq \emptyset\}$ is said to be the boundary of the set D.

LEMMA 1. *[5] Let G be a connected mesh subdomain of $\bar{\omega}$ and w be the solution of following linear difference scheme:*

$$(E + \tau A)w(x) = 0, \quad x \in G; \quad w(x) = \varphi(x), \quad x \in \partial G \tag{6}$$

If $\partial_1 G = \mathrm{supp}\varphi \subseteq \partial G$ then there exists $c_0 = const \neq c_0(\tau, h, \varphi)$ such that

$$\mid w(x) \mid \leq \exp(-d_1/c_0\sqrt{\tau}) \max_{x \in \partial_1 G} \mid \varphi(x) \mid \quad \text{for } x \in G\colon \rho(x, \partial_1 G) \geq d_1. \tag{7}$$

LEMMA 2. *Let $C : \mathbf{R}^n \to \mathbf{R}^n$ be a M-matrix and $B : \mathbf{R}^n \to 2^{\mathbf{R}^n}$ be a diagonal maximal monotone operator (i.e. $Bu = \mathrm{diag}(b_1(u_1), \ldots, b_n(u_n))$, $b_i(u_i)$-maximal monotone operator in $\mathbf{R}^1$). If u^1, u^2 are the solutions of equations:*

$$(E + \tau C)u^i + Bu^i \ni F^i, \quad i = 1, 2$$

then

$$-(E + \tau C)^{-1}(F^1 - F^2)^- \ll u^1 - u^2 \ll (E + \tau C)^{-1}(F^1 - F^2)^+. \tag{8}$$

Above $u \ll v$ means $u_i \leq v_i \quad \forall i$ and F^+ (F^-) means nonnegative (nonpositive) part of F.

As a consequence of inequality (8) we have

$$\mid u^1 - u^2 \mid \ll (E + \tau C)^{-1}(F^1 - F^2). \tag{9}$$

The matrix of mesh operator A in the problem (3), as well as the matrix of its restriction to any connected subdomain of $\bar{\omega}$, is M-matrix. Thus, the results of lemma 1,2 permit us to prove

THEOREM 1. *Let y^1, y^2 be solutions of problems:*

$$(E+\tau A)y^i(x) + By^i(x) \ni 0 \text{ for } x \in G$$
$$y^i(x) = \varphi^i(x) \text{ for } x \in \partial G,$$

where G is connected subdomain of $\bar{\omega}$. If $\partial_1 G = supp(\varphi^1 - \varphi^2)$, then

$$(10) \quad \begin{cases} \text{for } x \in G \text{ such that } \rho(x, \partial_1 G) \geq d_1 \text{ the following estimation holds:} \\ \mid y^1(x) - y^2(x) \mid \leq \exp(-d_1/c_0\sqrt{\tau}) \max\limits_{x \in \partial_1 G} \mid \varphi^1(x) - \varphi^2(x) \mid \end{cases}$$

The theorem 1 gives us the estimation of the boundary perturbation impact on the solution of the equation (5). Due to this result we are able to propose the following algorithm to solve (5) with given accuracy $\varepsilon > 0$.

Let $y(t)$, $y(t-\tau)$ be the values of solution of mesh scheme (3), (4) on time levels t and $t-\tau$. Define $\rho(\varepsilon)$ such that $\rho(\varepsilon) \cdot \max_{x\in\gamma_0} \mid y(t) - y(t-\tau) \mid \leq \varepsilon$ and assume $d_1(\varepsilon) = c_0\sqrt{\tau}\ln(1/\rho(\varepsilon))$.

ALGORITHM 1 (iteration-free method to solve equation (5))

Step1: Solve linear mesh scheme (in $\bar{\omega}$):

$$(11) \quad \begin{cases} (E+\tau A)w_0(x) = F(x) \text{ in } \omega; \\ w_0(x) = 0 \text{ in } \gamma_0; \\ w_0(x) = y(x, t-\tau) \text{ in } \gamma_1 \end{cases}$$

Step2: Solve nonlinear problem in subdomain $\bar{\omega}_1$:

$$(12) \quad \begin{cases} (E+\tau A)w_1(x) + Bw_1(x) \ni F(x) \text{ in } \omega_1 \cup \gamma_1; \\ w_1(x) = 0 \text{ in } \gamma_0 \cap \bar{\omega}_1; \\ w_1(x) = w_0(x) \text{ in } \tilde{\gamma}, \end{cases}$$

where $\bar{w}_1(x) = \{x \in \bar{\omega} \mid \rho(x, \gamma_1) \leq d_1\}$, $\quad \tilde{\gamma} = \partial\omega_1 \cap \omega$.

THEOREM 2. *Assume*

$$w(x) = \begin{cases} w_o(x) \text{ in } \omega_0 = \bar{\omega}/\bar{\omega}_1; \\ w_1(x) \text{ in } \bar{\omega}_1, \end{cases}$$

then

$$(13) \quad \max_{x\in\bar{\omega}} \mid w(x) - y(x,t) \mid \leq \varepsilon,$$

$y(x,t)$ being the solution of equation (5).

REMARK 1 The same algorithm is applicable and the result of theorem 2 is valid if we construct the finite element scheme for problem (2) with picewise linear elements on the regular accute-type triangulation and if we use quadrature rule for the mass matrix being diagonal.

Let us briefly discuss the computational cost of the Algorithm 1 in comparison with direct solution of equation (5). Let for simplicity $\tau = h = n^{-1}$, $\varepsilon = n^{-\sigma}$ with any constant $\sigma > 0$. In this case the condition number of matrix $E + \tau A$ is equal to $\mathcal{O}(n)$, card $\bar{\omega} = n^2$, card $\bar{\omega}_1 = \mathcal{O}(n^{3/2}\ln n)$. Here and in that follows we will not mark the dependence on σ. If we use the iterative splitting method [7] to solve the equation (5), then it requires $\mathcal{O}(n^{1/2}\ln n)$ iterations. Thus the total computational cost is $n^2 \times \mathcal{O}(n^{1/2}\ln n) = \mathcal{O}(n^{5/2}\ln n)$ arithmetic operations. On the other hand the same iterative process being applied to the subproblem (11) requires $\mathcal{O}(n^{1/2}\ln n \times n^{3/2}\ln n) = \mathcal{O}(n^2\ln^2 n)$ arithmetic operations. As we solve linear mesh scheme (11) by the domain decomposition method from [5], then it requires $\mathcal{O}(n^2 \ln\ln n)$ arithmetic operations. So the total computational cost of Algorithm 1 is $\mathcal{O}(n^2\ln^2 n)$ arithmetical operations.

REMARK 2 To know width $d_1(\varepsilon)$ of the strip ω_1 we have to estimate c_0. If no, it is possible to choose any $d_1 > 0$ and to compute $y(t)$ by iterative procedure repeating step 1 and step 2 of Algorithm 1. This algorithm is very fast convergent. Moreover, if we choose $d_1 = \mathcal{O}(n^{1/2}\ln n)$ (with the same propositions as above) then the total computational cost will become equal to $\mathcal{O}(n^2\ln^2 n)$.

REMARK 3 Let us consider the variational inequality with constraints to $\partial u/\partial t$, namely

$$(14)\qquad \begin{cases} \int_\Omega \{u'(t)(v - u'(t)) + \nabla u(t)\cdot\nabla(v - u'(t))\}\,d\Omega \geq \int_\Omega f(v - u(t))\,d\Omega; \\ \forall v \in K, \quad u'(t) \in K \text{ for almost all } t \in (0,T); \\ u(\cdot,0) = u_0, \end{cases}$$

where $K = \{u \in H^1(\Omega) \mid u(x) \geq 0 \text{ in } \Gamma_1, \quad u(x) = 0 \text{ in } \Gamma_0\}$, Ω being as in problem (2). Using the same notations as above we can write the difference scheme for (14) for fixed time level t in the following form:

$$(15)\qquad (E + \tau A)y(t) + B\left(\frac{y(t) - y(t-\tau)}{\tau}\right) \ni F.$$

As operator $Cy(t) := B\left(\frac{y(t)-y(t-\tau)}{\tau}\right)$ is again the diagonal maximal monotone operator, we can apply the previous results as well as Algorithm 1 to this problem.

2. TWO–PHASE STEFAN PROBLEM

For the sake of simplicity we will assume the domain Ω being unit square with the boundary $\partial\Omega = \Gamma_1 \cap \Gamma_2 \cap \Gamma_3$, where $\Gamma_1 = \{x_1 = 0\}$, $\Gamma_3 = \{x_1 = 1\}$ and $\Gamma_2 = \{x_2 = 0\} \cup \{x_2 = 1\}$. We'll study the two–phase Stefan problem in the enthalpy formulation which can be written as follows:

$$(16)\qquad \begin{cases} \dfrac{\partial v}{\partial t} - \Delta u = 0, \quad v \in \gamma(u) \text{ in } \Omega \times (0,T) \\ u = u_0(t) > 0 \text{ in } \Gamma_1 \times (0,T) \\ u = u_1(t) < 0 \text{ in } \Gamma_3 \times (0,T) \\ \dfrac{\partial u}{\partial n} = 0 \text{ in } \Gamma_2 \times (0,T) \\ v(\cdot,0) = v_0 \end{cases}$$

where $\gamma(t) = c_0 t + \tilde{\gamma}(t)$, $\tilde{\gamma}(t) = \{0, t \leq 0; \quad [0, c_1], \quad t = 0; c_1 + c_2 t, \quad t > 0\}$, all constants being positive. The existence and uniqueness of a weak solution to problem (16) are well–known. Also different mesh schemes for this problem are studied, see, among others, [**10–12**]. We construct implicit difference scheme on uniform mesh as in Section 1. Let A be the standard five–point approximation of Laplace operator and B be the diagonal maximal monotone operator of the form (we use the same notations for mesh sets and functions as in Section 1):

$$By(x) = \tilde{\gamma}(y(x)) \quad \forall x \in \omega.$$

Then the difference scheme for the problem (16) is as follows:

$$(17)\qquad \begin{cases} \tau^{-1}(w(t) - w(t-\tau)) + Ay(t) = 0,\ w(t) \in \gamma(y(t)),\ \forall t \in \omega_\tau : t > 0 \\ w(0) = v_0\,. \end{cases}$$

Corresponding equation for fixed time level $t > 0$ can be written in the form

$$(18)\qquad (c_0 E + \tau A)y(t) + By(t) \ni F := w(t-\tau).$$

We see that comparison result of Lemma 2 is valid for the equation (18). But for application of a variant of Algorithm 1 we need to know the location of mesh free boundary. This is the result of the following

THEOREM 3. *[8] Let $\Omega_0(t) = \{x \in \Omega \mid y(x,t) = 0\}$ and $\Omega_0(t-\tau)$ is defined in the similar way. There exists constant $C \neq C(\tau, h)$ such that*

$$(19)\qquad \rho(x, \Omega_0(t-\tau)) \leq d_0 := C\sqrt{\tau} + h \quad \forall x \in \Omega_0(t).$$

As we know the mesh function $y(t-\tau) \equiv y(x, t-\tau)$ and thus the set $\Omega_0(t-\tau)$ (a curve or "mushy region") we can use the estimate (19) to obtain a strip inside which the unknown "mesh free boundary" $\Omega_0(t)$ is located. This fact allows as to use some version of Algorithm 1 to solve the equation (18) with given accuracy $\varepsilon > 0$. One of them we propose below.

Let $\Omega_+(t) := \{x \in \Omega \mid y(x,t) > 0\}$; $\Omega_-(t)$, $\Omega_+(t-\tau)$, $\Omega_-(t-\tau)$ are defined in the similar manner. Let further

$$G_0^0 := \{x \in \Omega \mid \rho(x, \Omega_0(t-\tau)) \leq d_0\};$$

$$G_+ := \Omega_+(t-\tau)\backslash G_0^0 \subset \Omega_+(t); \quad G_- := \Omega_-(t-\tau)\backslash G_0^0 \subset \Omega_-(t).$$

We assume $\bar{d}_1(\varepsilon)$ be defined similar to $d_1(\varepsilon)$ in Section 1 and furthermore we define

$$G_0 = \{x \in \Omega \mid \rho(x, G_0^0) \leq \bar{d}_1(\varepsilon)\};$$

$$G_+^0 = \Omega_+(t-\tau)\backslash G_0 \quad G_-^0 = \Omega_-(t-\tau)\backslash G_0.$$

ALGORITHM 2

Step1: We solve in subdomains G_+ and G_- linear mesh schemes corresponding to (18) with Dirichlet boundary conditions on parts $\partial G_+ \cap \Omega$ and $\partial G_- \cap \Omega$ of boundaries, using known values of $y(x, t-\tau)$. Let their solutions be $z^+(x)$ and $z^-(x)$ respectively.

Step2: We solve nonlinear problem of the form (18) in G_0 using the known values of z^+ and z^- on the corresponding parts of ∂G_0. We denote its solution by $z^0(x)$. The following results holds.

THERОREM 4. *[**8**] Let* $z(x) = \{z^+(x)$ *in* $G_+^0, \quad z^0(x)$ *in* $G_0, \quad z^-(x)$ *in* $G_-^0\}$*, then*

$$\max_x \mid z(x) - y(x,t) \mid \leq \varepsilon. \tag{20}$$

REMARK 4 We can carry out some iteration steps in the case that "width" of G_0 is not enough to ensure the desirable accuracy (of Remark 2).

REMARK 5 We can decompose the domain G_0 (as well as G_+ and G_-) into set of overlapping subdomains to solve the corresponding nonlinear (or linear) mesh problem independently in each subdomain. For more details see [**6**] (for one–phase Stefan problem).

REFERENCES

[1] F. Brezzi and L.H. Cafarelli, *Convergence of the discrete free boundaries for finite element approximations*, Istit. di Anal. Numer. CRN, Pavia, Preprint No 323 (1982).

[2] G. Duvaut and J.L. Lions, "Les inéquations en Mécanique et en Physique," Dunod, Paris, 1972.

[3] A. Friedman, "Variational principles and free boundary problems," Wiley Interscience, New York, 1982.

[4] R. Glowinski, J.L. Lions and R. Trémoliéres, "Analyse Numerique des Inéquations Variationelles," Dunod, Paris, 1976.

[5] Yu.A. Kuznetsov, *New algorithms for approximate realization of implicit difference schemes*, Preprint No 142, Dept. Numer. Math. USSR Academy Sciences, Moscow (in Russian) (1987).

[6] Yu.A. Kuznetsov and A.V. Lapin, *Domain decomposition method to realize an implicit difference scheme for the one–phase Stefan problem*, Sov. J. Numer. Anal. Math. Modelling 3 (1988), 487–504.

[7] A.V. Lapin and D.O. Solovyev, *Solution of mesh obstacle problems*, Sov J. Numer. Anal. Math. Modelling 2 (1987), 449–481.

[8] A.V. Lapin, *Domain decomposition method for mesh approximation of two–phase Stefan problem*, Preprint No 856, Centre of Calculations, USSR Academy Sciences, Novosibirsk (in Russian) (1989).

[9] A.M. Meirmanov, "Stefan problem," (in Russian), Nauka, Novosibirsk, 1986.
[10] R.H. Nochetto, *Error estimates for multidimensional singular parabolic equations*, Japan J. Appl. Math. 4 (1987), 111–138.
[11] R.H. Nochetto and C. Verdi, *Approximation of degenerate parabolic problems using numerical integration*, Istit. di Anal. Numez., CRN, Pavia, Preprint No. 5051 (1986).
[12] C. Verdi, *Optimal error estimates for an approximation of degenerate parabolic problems*, Numer. Funct Anal. Optim. 9 (1987), 657–670.

A mathematical model of a two-phase region in thawing soil

A.M.MAXIMOV
G.G.TSYPKIN

Institute for problems in mechanics
The USSR Academy of sciences,
Prospect Vernadskogo 101, 117526 Moscow, USSR

Abstract. A mathematical model of phase transitions in frozen soil containing unfrozen water is proposed. It is assumed that the frozen soil is saturated with ice and unfrozen mineralized water. It is shown that introducing the phase transition front in order to describe the thawing of frozen soil leads to the overdetermination of the problem posed. In this case the temperature curve in the frozen soil does not coincide with the local phase transition temperature curve derived from the pressure and impurity concentration values but lies below (supercooling) or above (superheating) it. A noncontradictory theoretical description can be constructed if one assumes that the phase transition occupies an extended two-phase region containing ice-mineralized water mixture in the state of local thermodynamic equilibrium.

Keywords: Phase transitions, Stefan problem, ground freezing.

Classification: 76S05, 80A20.

INTRODUCTION

Phase transitions in freezing and thawing soils are accompanied by a redistribution of the moisture and dissolved impurities. The traditional approach to the description of such heat and mass transfer processes is based on the introduction of a phase transition front, at which an abrupt change in moisture content takes place. However, field observations and experiments [**1**] clearly show that the phase transition is not localized on a certain surface but occupies an extended zone characterized by a water content and temperature distributions. A semiempirical phase transition model, in which the existence of a phase transition zone - a mixture of ice and unfrozen water - was assumed, was proposed in [**2**]. The water content varies over the entire phase transition zone and is assumed to be a single-valued function of temperature determined experimentally.

The investigation of the process of crystallization of a binary melt has revealed the possibility of supercooling of the melt ahead of the crystallization front [**3**]. In [**4**] , in order to eliminate this contradiction, it was proposed that a two-phase zone, located between the solid and liquid phases, in which both phases coexist in a state of thermodynamic equilibrium, be introduced.

In [**5,6**] it was shown that the freezing of a water-saturated porous medium in the front regime may be accompanied by supercooling if the dependence of the phase transition point on the fluid pressure and the dissolved impurity concentration is taken into account.

A model of the two-phase region, using the condition of local thermodynamic equilibrium for a water-ice mixture was developed.

The study reported here investigated the problem of the interaction of frozen soil with a salt solution. This problem arises, for example, in drilling wells in frozen rock, when the circulating drilling solution is an aqueous salt solution [**7**]. A series of natural processes in frozen soils is based on the interaction between groundwaters having different, possible negative, temperatures and different degrees of mineralization [**8**] and on the thawing of the frozen bed of northern seas in contact with saline seawater [**9**].

1. Formulation of the Problem

By frozen soil we understand a porous medium saturated with ice and unfrozen mineralized water. It is assumed that there is no gas phase. Then in a porous medium with porosity m the liquid phase (water) occupies a volume νm , and the solid phase (ice) a volume $(1-\nu)m$. We assume that when the ice is formed all the dissolved impurity is expelled into the volume of unfrozen water. The ice and unfrozen water coexists in the frozen soil under conditions of thermodynamic equilibrium

$$T = T_f(P, c) \equiv T_w - \alpha c - \eta(P - P_a) \tag{1.1}$$

Here, T is temperature, $T_f(P, c)$ is the phase transition temperature, T_w is the phase transition temperature of the pure water at atmospheric pressure, c is the mass concentration of the salt in the solution, P is pressure, P_a is atmospheric pressure, and α and η are the phase transition coefficients.

We assume that the solid phase is stationary and that the motion of the liquid obeys Darcy's law

$$v_w = -\frac{k f_w(\nu)}{\mu_w} \text{grad } P \tag{1.2}$$

Here, v_w is the rate of filtration, f_w is the relative phase permeability of the liquid phase in the frozen soil, which depends on the water content ν, μ_w is the water viscosity. We also assume that the water, the skeleton and the ice are weakly compressible.

The basic equations describing the dynamics of the two-phase region (and hence the frozen soil) can be derived from the conservation laws on the basis of the mechanics of heterogeneous media [**10**] . Then, using the procedure for deriving the equation of filtration, we obtain the equation for the pressure

$$\frac{\partial P}{\partial t} + K_f(1 - \rho_i/\rho_w)\frac{\partial \nu}{\partial t} = \kappa_f \Delta P + \frac{k K_f}{m\mu_w}\frac{df_w}{d\nu}\text{grad } \nu \text{ grad } P, \tag{1.3}$$

where

$$\kappa_f(\nu) = \frac{k f_w(\nu) K_f(\nu)}{m\mu_w},$$
$$K_f(\nu) = [\nu(K_s{}^{-1} + K_w{}^{-1}) + (1-\nu)(K_s{}^{-1} + K_i{}^{-1})\rho_i/\rho_w]^{-1}.$$

Here, k is the permeability, ρ is the density, K is the compression modulus; the subscripts are as follows: w - water, i - ice, s - skeleton of porous medium, f - two-phase (frozen) region.

If the permeability of the soil is low enough, then, as estimates show, convective heat and impurity transfer can be neglected. Using the weak compressibility of the components and the fact that the kinetic energy of the flow is small, and assuming that the component temperatures and pressures are equal [**10**], we obtain the energy equation

$$(\rho C)_f \frac{\partial T}{\partial t} + mq\frac{\partial \nu}{\partial t} = \operatorname{div} \lambda_f \operatorname{grad} T, \tag{1.4}$$

where

$$\begin{aligned}(\rho C)_f &= (1-m)\rho_s C_s + m\nu\rho_w C_w + m(1-\nu)\rho_i C_i,\\ \lambda_f &= (1-m)\lambda_s + m\nu\lambda_w + m(1-\nu)\lambda_i,\\ q &= \rho_i(h_w - h_i).\end{aligned}$$

Here, λ is the thermal conductivity, and h is the enthalpy.

The law of mass conservation for the dissolved substance has the form

$$\frac{\partial(\nu c)}{\partial t} = D \operatorname{div} \nu \operatorname{grad} c, \tag{1.5}$$

where D is the diffusion coefficient of the salt.

The equations (1.1), (1.3)-(1.5) constitute a system of equations for determining the unknown functions T, P, c, and ν in the two-phase region.

The formulation of the problem with phase transitions contains moving boundaries at which the function ν suffers discontinuity. It is natural to consider water content jumps at which the conditions of continuity of temperature, pressure and impurity concentration are satisfied. In the usual notation we have

$$[T] = 0, \quad [P] = 0, \quad [c] = 0 \tag{1.6}$$

Using the universal relations st a discontinuity, for the mass of the pore content and the dissolved impurity and the energy we obtain

$$m[\nu](1 - \rho_i/\rho_w)\frac{dX}{dt} = [v_w] \tag{1.7}$$

$$m[\nu]c\frac{dX}{dt} + mD[\nu \operatorname{grad} c] = 0 \tag{1.8}$$

$$m[\nu]q\frac{dX}{dt} + [\lambda_f \operatorname{grad} T] = 0 \tag{1.9}$$

Here, X is the position of the water content discontinuity.

Relations (1.6)-(1.9), together with the thermodynamic equilibrium condition (1.1), constitute the complete set of boundary conditions at the moving boundary.

2. Front Model. Supercooling and Superheating

We will consider the process of propagation of a plane thawing front through frozen soil occupying the half-space $x \geq 0$ and in contact at $x = 0$ with aqueous salt solution. The formulation of the problem with a phase transition front in a one-dimensional approximation presupposes the formation of two regions: a thawed region $(0 < x < X(t))$ and a frozen region $(X(t) < x < \infty)$. The frozen region may contain unfrozen water $(\nu = \nu_0 \geq 0)$. In the thawed region $(\nu = 1)$ and the frozen region $(\nu = \nu_0)$ Eqs. (1.3)-(1.5) have the form

$$\frac{\partial T}{\partial t} = a_f \frac{\partial^2 T}{\partial x^2}, \quad \frac{\partial c}{\partial t} = D \frac{\partial^2 c}{\partial x^2}, \quad \frac{\partial P}{\partial t} = \kappa_f \frac{\partial^2 P}{\partial x^2}. \tag{2.1}$$

When $\nu_0 > 0$ in the frozen region the thermodynamic equilibrium condition (1.1) must satisfied. The zone interface $X(t)$ is the thawing front, at which the temperature, salt concentration and pressure continuity conditions (1.6), the thermodynamic equilibrium condition (1.1) and the conditions for moisture content

$$x = X(t): \quad \nu_- = 1, \quad \nu_+ = \nu_0 = \nu_* \tag{2.2}$$

are satisfied. Here, the asterisk denotes the values at the front.

We obtain the mass and the heat balance condition from (1.7)-(1.9) using (1.2) and (2.2).

The initial conditions have the form

$$t = 0: \quad X = 0, T = T_0 = T_f(P_0, c_0), P = P_0, c = c_0 \tag{2.3}$$

At the fixed boundary the soil is in the contact with the salt solution

$$x = 0: \quad T = T^0, c = c^0, P = P^0, T^0 > T_f(P^0, c^0) \tag{2.4}$$

If ν_0 =const and $0 < \nu_0 < 1$, then the problem will be infringed in either direction. We will illustrate this for a self-similar solution of the form

$$T = T(\xi), P = P(\xi), c = c(\xi), X = \gamma t^{1/2}, \xi = x t^{-1/2}, \tag{2.5}$$

assuming that T_0, P_0, c_0, T^0, P^0 and c^0 are constants.

Then the boundary and initial conditions can be written in the form

$$\xi = 0: \quad T = T^0, P = P^0, c = c^0 \tag{2.6}$$

$$\begin{aligned} \xi = \gamma: \quad & T_- = T_+ = T_* = T_f(P_*, c_*), \\ & P_- = P_+ = P_*, c_- = c_+ = c_*, \\ & m(1 - \nu_*)(1 - \rho_i/\rho_w)\gamma/2 + \\ & (P'_- - f_w(\nu_*)P'_+)k/\mu_w = 0, \\ & c_*(1 - \nu_*)\gamma/2 + D(c'_- - \nu_* c'_+) = 0, \end{aligned}$$

$$mq(1 - \nu_*)\gamma/2 = \lambda_f(\nu_*)T'_+ - \lambda_l T'_- \tag{2.7}$$

$$\xi \to \infty: \quad T = T_0, P = P_0, c = c_0 \tag{2.8}$$

In the front model $\nu_* = \nu_0$.

The solutions of the systems of equations in the regions have the form

$$0 < \xi < \gamma: \quad \varphi - \varphi^0 = (\varphi_* - \varphi^0)\frac{erf(\xi/2\omega^{1/2})}{erf(\gamma/2\omega^{1/2})} \tag{2.9}$$

$$\gamma < \xi < \infty: \quad \varphi - \varphi_0 = (\varphi_* - \varphi_0)\frac{erfc(\xi/2\omega^{1/2})}{erfc(\gamma/2\omega^{1/2})}, \tag{2.10}$$

where φ takes the values of T, c, and P, and ω the values of a_l, D, and κ_l and a_f, D, and κ_f in (2.9) and (2.10) respectively. The subscript "l" denotes the thawed region.

The substitution of the solutions (2.9)-(2.10) in the conditions at the moving boundary (2.7) leads to a transcendental equation for determining γ, which was solved numerically for the following values of the parameters:
$\rho_w = 1000$ kg/m^3, $\rho_i = 910$ kg/m^3, $\rho_s = 2000$ kg/m^3, $\lambda_w = 0.58$ W/m K, $\lambda_i = 2.23$ W/m K, $\lambda_s = 2.09$ W/m K, $C_w = 4.19$ kJ/kg K, $C_i = 2.09$ kJ/kg K, $C_s = 0.92$ kJ/kg K, $K_w = 2000$ MPa, $K_i = 5000$ MPa, $K_s = 1000$ MPa, $m = 0.35$, $q = 3.3 * 10^5$ kJ/m^3, $\mu_w = 10^{-3}$ Pa sec, $T_w = 273.15$ K, $P_a = 0.1$ MPa, $\alpha = 66.7$ K, $\eta = 0.0765$ K/MPa, $D = 1.45 * 10^{-9}$ m^2/sec.

The dimensionless variables have the form

$$T_n = \frac{T - T_w}{\tau}, \quad c_n = \frac{\alpha c}{\tau}, \quad P_n = \eta\frac{P - P_a}{\tau},$$

$$T_{fn} = -c_n - P_n, \quad \xi_n = \frac{\xi}{a_w^{1/2}},$$

where $\tau = mq/\rho_w C_w$ and $a_w = \lambda_w/\rho_w C_w$.

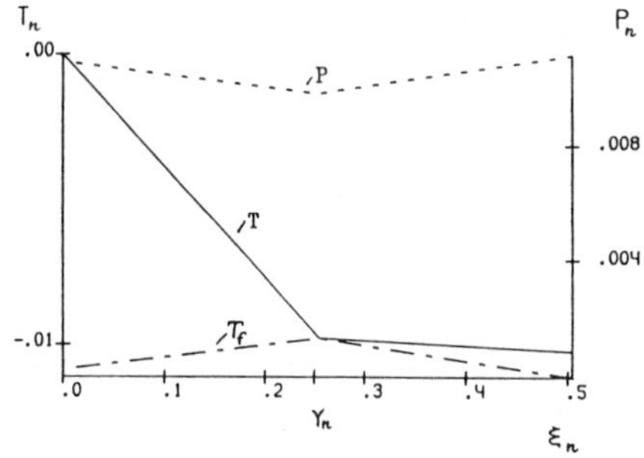

Figure 1. (a)

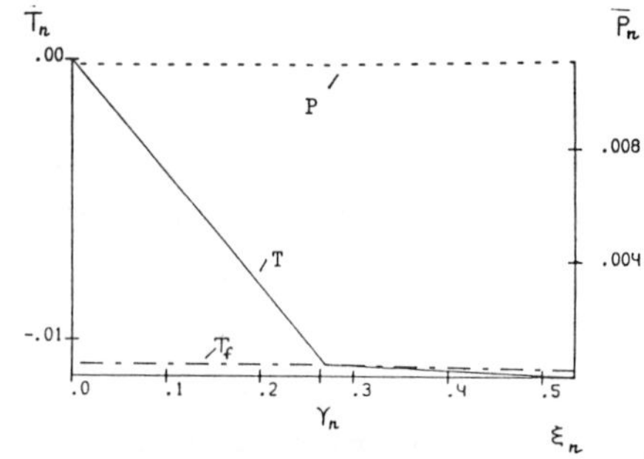

Figure 1. (b)

In Figs. 1 and 2 we have reproduced results of calculating the thawing process in frozen soil containing unfrozen water ($\nu_0 > 0$). They have in common the disturbance of thermodynamic equilibrium in the frozen region. The examples shown in Fig. 1 correspond to the case of a "fresh" frozen soil in contact with fresh water ($c = 0$). Here, $T_0 = 272.65$ K, $P_0 = 6.6$ MPa, $\nu_0 = 0.2$, $T_0 = 273.15$ K, and $P^0 = 4$ MPa; a) $k = 0.2 * 10^{-6}$ μm^2, b) $k = 10^{-5}$ μm^2. As may be seen from the pressure distributions, the fall in pressure leads to a change in the local phase transition temperature and to the infringement of the condition of thermodynamic equilibrium in the frozen region. This may be expressed in the known supercooling effect (when $a_f < \kappa_f$). Thus from Fig. 1b it is clear that the temperature in the frozen region will be lower than the phase transition temperature if the permeability is sufficiently high. In the case of low permeability of the frozen soil ($a_f > \kappa_f$) the disturbance of thermodynamic equilibrium is more often expressed as a superheating effect (Fig. 1a), when the temperature in the frozen region exceeds the phase transition temperature.

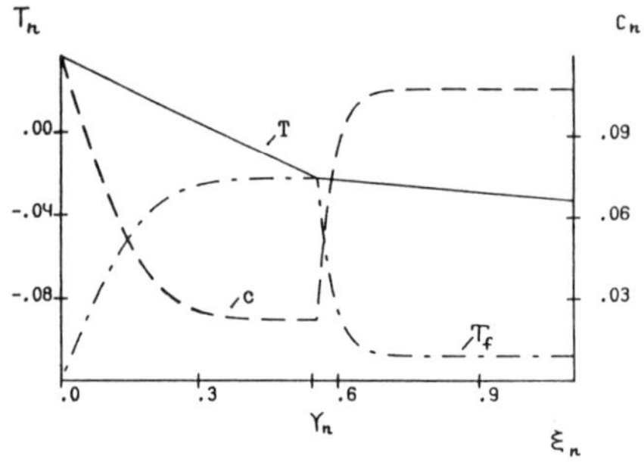

Figure 2.

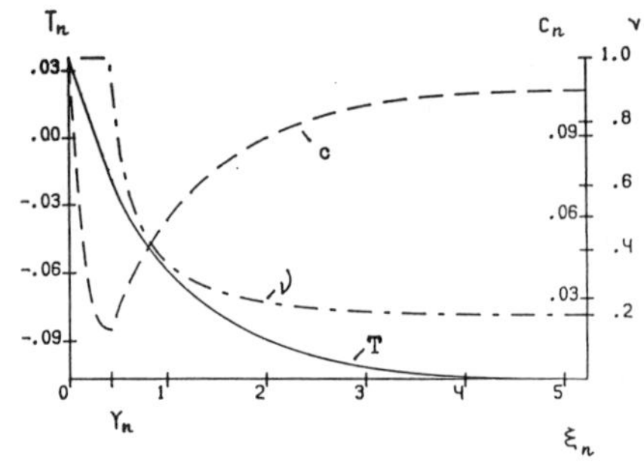

Figure 3.

The calculation results in Fig. 2 correspond to the presence of dissolved salt in the unfrozen water of the frozen soil. Here, $T_0 = 270.15$ K, $c_0 = 0.042$, $P = P_a$, $\nu_0 = 0.2$, $T^0 = 274.15$ K, $c^0 = 0.05$, ($\kappa_f \gg a_f$).

Since the impurity diffusion transport velocity is always less than the conductive heat transport velocity ($D \ll a_f$), the deviation from thermodynamical equilibrium in the frozen region corresponds to superheating, whether the permeability of the porous medium is high or low.

Thus, when $0 < \nu_0 < 1$ and the velocities of the transport processes do not coincide, the results obtained indicate the inconsistency of the front model of the thawing of frozen soil in contact with an aqueous salt solution.

3. Partial Phase Transition Model

In order to construct a noncontradictory solution we will use a model of the two-phase zone in which the phase transition takes place over a spectrum of temperatures. In this case, as in the front model, the mathematical formulation of the problem presupposes the formation of two zones: a thawed zone ($0 < x < X(t)$) and a frozen zone ($X(t) < x < \infty$). The basic difference is that the unfrozen water content of the frozen region is not constant and known, but is unknown function. In the thawed region ($\nu \equiv 1$) equations (2.1) are satisfied. In the frozen zone the conservation laws (1.3)-(1.5) are satisfied, together with the condition of local thermodynamic equilibrium (1.1). At the interface between the thawed and frozen regions $X(t)$ the water content ν changes abruptly from the unknown value $\nu_+ = \nu_*$ to $\nu_- = 1$. On this boundary conditions (1.6)-(1.9) hold. The initial conditions and the conditions at the fixed boundary have the form (2.3)-(2.4).

If the initial and boundary values T_0, P_0, c_0, T^0, P^0 and c^0 are constants, then the problem has a self-similar solution of the form (2.5). In this case the boundary conditions take the form (2.6)-(2.8).

In the thawed zone the solution has the form (2.9). In the frozen zone the basic system of equations has the form:

$$\begin{aligned}
&\lambda_f T'' + T'[m(\lambda_w - \lambda_i)\nu' + (\rho C)_f \xi/2] + \\
&mq\nu'\xi/2 = 0, \\
&D\nu c'' + D\nu' c' + \nu c'\xi/2 + \\
&\nu' c\xi/2 = 0, \quad T = T_f(P, c), \\
&\kappa_f P'' + \frac{kK_f}{m\mu_w}\frac{df_w}{d\nu}\nu' P' + P'\xi/2 + \\
&K_f(1 - \rho_i/\rho_w)\nu'\xi/2 = 0.
\end{aligned} \tag{3.1}$$

System of equations (3.1) was solved numerically. The results of calculations for "fresh" frozen soil in contact with fresh water indicate that on the interval of parameters (pressures, permeabilities) realizable in practice both superheating and supercooling are removed by phase transition of a very small amount of water (ice). This behavior of the solution is attributable to the considerable changes of pressure caused by the change of volume at phase transition, as a result of the weak compressibility of all the components of the mixture - skeleton, ice and water. The result differ little from the front solution, which points to the practical applicability of the front model where there is no dissolved impurity.

To the case of superheating in the front solution as a result of the influence of dissolved salt (Fig. 2) there corresponds a noncontradictory solution with an extended thawing zone (Fig. 3). Here the superheating is removed by the additional thawing of a very considerable amount of ice in the frozen region.

As indicated by examples of the calculation of typical solutions, the direction of the phase transition in the frozen region (partial freezing or thawing) corresponds to the contradiction (supercooling or superheating) detected in the front solution.

Our model of the thawing or frozen soil makes it possible to explain certain effects connected with well drilling in frozen rocks using a water-based drilling fluid, when the thawing and erosion of the rock is much greater than assumed on the basis of the front model. In fact, if the frozen rock contains unfrozen water in which even a small amount of impurity is dissolved, then the thawing process will take place in the regime depicted qualitatively in Fig. 3, i.e. not only will a completely thawed region be formed (as in the front model) but there will also be considerable partial thawing in the extended region. Since in many respects the strenght of the frozen soil is determined by its water content (the ice acts as a cement), the reaching of the critical water content during partial thawing will lead to the collapse and evacuation from the well of incompletely thawed soil.

References

1. N. A. Tsytovitch, "Mechanics of Frozen Soils. General and Applied," [in Russian], Vyssh. Shk., Moscow, 1973.
2. A. G. Kolesnikov, *Modification of the mathematical formulation of the soil freezing problem*, Dokl. Akad. Nauk SSSR **82** (1952), p. 889.
3. G. P. Ivantsov, *Diffusional supercooling in the crystallization of a binary melt*, Dokl. Akad. Nauk SSSR **81** (1951), p. 179.
4. V. T. Borisov, *Crystallization of a binary melt with preservation of stability*, Dokl. Akad. Nauk SSSR **136** (1961), p. 583.
5. V. M. Entov, A. M. Maximov and G. G. Tsypkin, *Formation of a two-phase zone during the crystallization of a mixture in a porous medium*, Dokl. Akad. Nauk SSSR **288** (1986), p. 621.
6. A. M. Maximov and G. G. Tsypkin, *Mathematical modeling of the freezing of a water saturated porous medium*, Zh. Vychisl. Mat. Mat. Fiz. **26** (1986), p. 1743.
7. B. B. Kudryashov and A. M. Yakovlev, "Well Drilling in Frozen Soils," [in Russian], Nedra, Moscow, 1983.
8. N. P. Anisimova, "Cryohydrochemical Characteristics of the Frozen Zone," [in Russian], Nauka, Novosibirsk, 1981.
9. K. Hutter and T. Alts, *Ice and snow mechanics. A challenge to theoretical and applied mechanics*, eds. Niordson and Olhoff, Theoretical and Applied Mechanics. (1985), p. 163, 16th Int. Congr. Proc. Lyngby, 19-25, Aug, 1984, North-Holland, Amsterdam.
10. R. I. Nigmatulin, "Principles of the Mechanics of Heterogeneous Media," [in Russian], Nauka, Moscow, 1978.

An axisymmetric analysis of thermal effects during cementation of femoral prostheses

S. MAZZULLO† M. PAOLINI‡ AND C. VERDI♯

Abstract. We analyse an axisymmetric mathematical model which describes the thermal effects during cementation of a femoral prosthesis. Various numerical simulations illustrate some critical aspects of this implant such as the thermal bone necrosis and the presence of unreacted residual monomer.

1. Introduction. The cementation of hip prostheses with polymethylmethacrylate (PMMA) was introduced less than 30 years ago [9] and rapidly became very popular; today, in fact, more than 300,000 femoral prostheses per year are implanted. On the other hand, the use of cement presents two serious problems, namely: thermal bone necrosis during cementation, because of the relatively high temperature values reached at the bone/cement interface, and toxicity of the cement, because the conversion of monomer into polymer is never 100%.

Geometrically, there are two components to the total hip prostheses: the acetabular and femoral components. The present paper is limited to examine the femoral component. Surgical fixing procedures call for resectioning the femoral head and preparing an adequate medullar cavity into which the stem of the infibulum is cemented (Fig. 1.1).

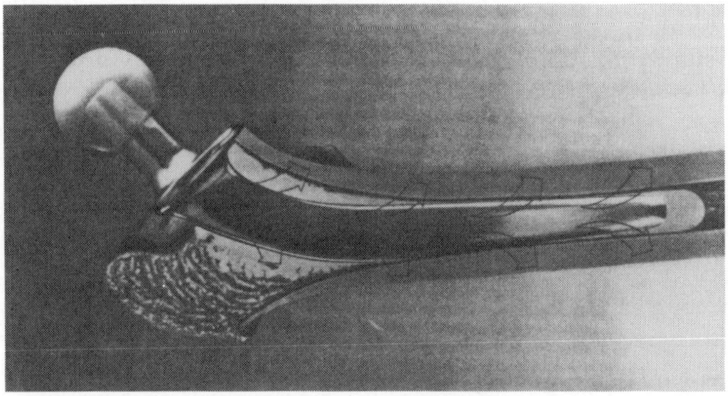

FIGURE 1.1. A femoral prosthesis.

†HIMONT Italia, Centro Ricerche "G. Natta", 44100 Ferrara, Italy.
‡Istituto di Analisi Numerica del CNR, 27100 Pavia, Italy.
♯Dipartimento di Meccanica Strutturale, Università di Pavia, 27100 Pavia, Italy.

Chemically, the acrylic cement belongs to the family of PMMA based, self-hardening acrylic resins. It is prepared in the operating room at the time of surgery, mixing together the liquid and powder components. The liquid contains the monomer (methylmethacrylate, MMA), the polymerization accelerator, and traces of an inhibitor, added to prevent the monomer from polymerizing spontaneously. The powder is composed of small spherical particles of the homopolymer PMMA a few tens of μm in diameter, and it contains the polymerization initiator. For the most common cement in use today, the polymerization time required for the cement to set after the two components have been mixed is approximatively 15 minutes.

Chemical toxicity of the cement is linked to the MMA both during the polymerization, while the femoral cavity is filled, and as unreacted residual monomer which may be present at the end since not the whole monomer is always converted into polymer.

In addition, the polymerization reaction is exothermic and the heat produced is one of the most important parameters in terms of physical toxicity of the cement because it may form bone necrosis at the bone/cement interface.

The parameters that control the temperature of the implant have been the object of research even since the use of cement was introduced in orthopaedic surgery. Since the 1970's, such research, predominantly experimental, has been supported by some mathematical models and numerical simulations [4,5,6]. In particular, the axisymmetric thermal model introduced in [7] is capable of taking into account both the complex geometry of the femoral implant and the chemical/physical properties of the cement. In fact, experimental polymerization kinetics of an actual cement have been used to identify the kinetic parameters as a function of temperature and degree of polymerization. The amount of unreacted residual monomer within the cement has been numerically evaluated, together with an estimate of the thermal bone damage, based on a temperature/exposure time threshold criterion. This simulation has a great clinical significance and represents a useful tool for establishing the optimal operating conditions for the new materials developed in this orthopaedic field.

2. Mathematical Model. The simplified geometry of the femoral implant is indicated in Fig. 2.1. It is a solid with a radial symmetry obtained by rotation around the longitudinal z axis. The cement volume variations are neglected and, for simplicity, all parameters are considered as independent of temperature. Moreover, a perfect thermal contact among the various materials is assumed; this implies continuity of temperature and heat flux at the interfaces. The heat generation and diffusion during the cementation process can thus be described by the Fourier heat equation [2] coupled with a polymerization kinetic equation. Finally, a linear heat transfer with the surrounding medium at a given temperature is assumed at the boundary.

Let $\Omega \subset \mathbf{R}^2$ be the domain indicated in Fig. 2.1 and $(0, T)$ the time interval during which polymerization takes place. Let u denote the *temperature* and w the *degree of polymerization* $(0 \leq w \leq 1)$. Assuming that initial and boundary data are axisymmetric, the solution of the problem will be axisymmetric too. The weak formulation of the problem in the cylindrical coordinates (r, z) is: *find* $u \in L^2(0,T;H^1(\Omega)) \cap H^1(0,T;L^2(\Omega))$ *and*

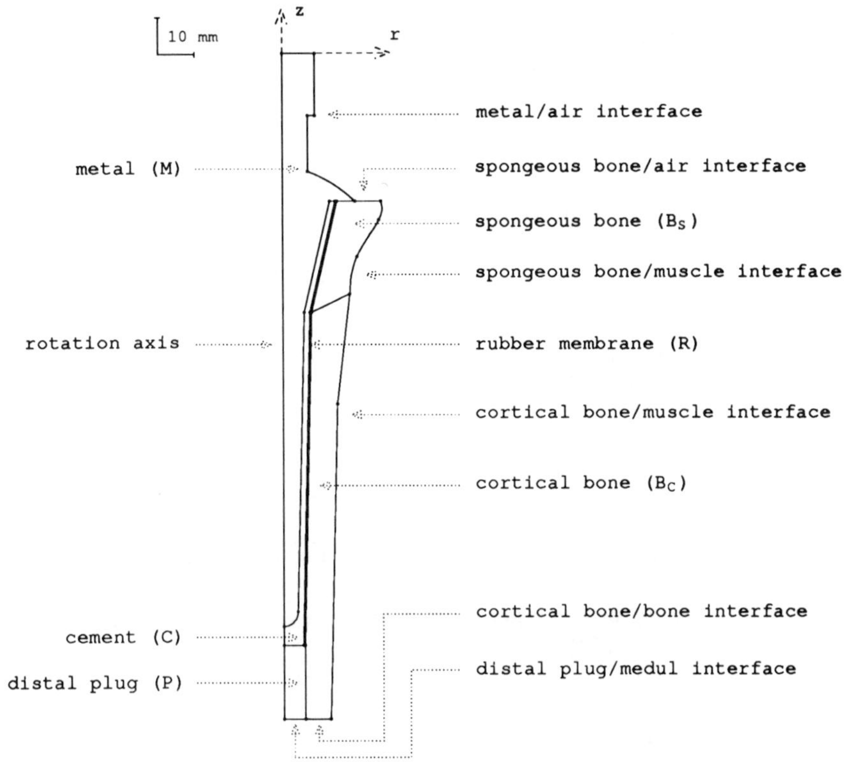

FIGURE 2.1. Domain geometry in cylindrical coordinates.

$w \in L^\infty(\Omega \times (0,T)) \cap H^1(0,T; L^2(\Omega))$ *such that* $u(0) = u_0$, $w(0) = w_0$ *and*, a.e. $t \in (0,T)$,

$$\int_\Omega r\left(\rho c \frac{\partial u}{\partial t} v + k \nabla u \cdot \nabla v\right) + \int_{\partial\Omega} rH(u - u_a)v = \int_C r\rho\lambda \frac{dw}{dt} v, \qquad \forall\, v \in H^1(\Omega), \tag{2.1}$$

$$\frac{dw}{dt} = A(u)P(u,w), \qquad \text{a.e. } (r,z) \in \Omega. \tag{2.2}$$

Parameters ρ, c, k, and λ, are constant in each subdomain and stand for density, specific heat, thermal conductivity, and polymerization enthalpy, respectively. The parameters H and u_a stand for heat transfer coefficient and surrounding temperature, respectively; note that $H = 0$ at $r = 0$ (reflection condition). Finally, u_0 and w_0 stand for initial temperature and degree of polymerization.

REMARK 2.1. Under suitable regularity conditions on the data, the existence and uniqueness of the weak solution as well as a maximum principle for problem (2.1), (2.2) are well known (see, e.g., [10,11]).

3. Polymerization Kinetics. Equation (2.2), that describes the kinetics of polymerization, is basically empirical. The function $A(u)$ acts as a temperature dependent kinetic constant whereas the dimensionless function $P(u,w)$ describes the variation of the degree of polymerization and acts as a shape factor of the kinetics. Experimental data suggest an Arrhenius behaviour for the kinetics constant A, namely

$$A(s) := a \exp\left(-\frac{E}{Rs}\right), \qquad \forall\, s \in \mathbf{R}^+,$$

and the following functional form for the degree of polymerization P

$$P(s_1,s_2) := \frac{\alpha}{w^\star(s_1)} s_2^{1-1/\alpha}[w^\star(s_1)-s_2]^{1+1/\alpha}, \text{ if } s_2 < w^\star(s_1); \quad := 0, \text{ if } s_2 \geq w^\star(s_1),$$

where a, E and $\alpha > 1$ are empirical parameters (see [6,7]) and R is the gas constant. The function $w^\star(u)$ represents the equilibrium conversion of monomer to polymer [1]

$$w^\star(s) := \frac{s}{u_g}, \quad \text{if } s \leq u_g, \qquad := 1, \quad \text{if } s > u_g,$$

where u_g is the glass transition temperature of the cement.

Quantitative description of the polymerization kinetics has required significant efforts, both in theoretical and experimental terms [6]. In fact, although polymerization of PMMA is qualitatively well known, not all kinetic parameters are available for the most commonly used cements [4,5]. Therefore, the decision was made to carry out isothermal polymerization experiments in order to identify the actual kinetic parameters of a commercial cement. Such experiments were carried out at the Himont Italia laboratories in Ferrara using the Howmedica-SIMPLEX P cement.

4. Thermal Bone Necrosis. After temperature values in bone have been calculated, they can be compared to a thermal damage criterion in order to estimate the chances for thermal necrosis. The threshold for thermal damage is obviously time-dependent, because not only the temperature, but also the time during which the tissue is exposed determine thermal bone necrosis [4].

Denoting by $t^\star(\bar{u})$ the exposure time necessary to reach thermal bone necrosis at given temperature $\bar{u}$ = constant, the data reported in [4] suggest the following expression

$$t^\star(s) := M \exp\left(\frac{\mu}{R(s-310)}\right), \qquad \forall\, s > 310.$$

The pre-exponential factor M and the activation energy μ have been identified by linear regression of the Huiskes data [4] (see [7]).

Under nonisothermal conditions, the thermal damage measure η ($\eta = 0$: no damage; $\eta \geq 1$: necrosis) can be estimated by the following additivity rule

$$\eta(r,z) := \int_0^T \frac{dt}{t^\star(u(r,z;t))}, \qquad \text{a.e. } (r,z) \in \Omega.$$

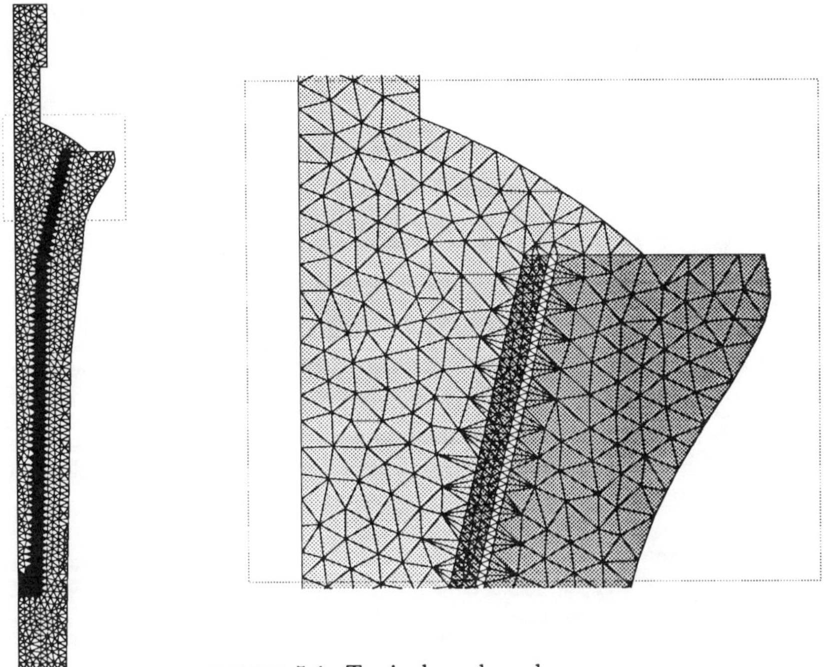

FIGURE 5.1. Typical mesh and zoom.

5. Numerical Approximation. The numerical approximation is accomplished by semi-implicit finite differences in time and finite elements in space. The full discrete scheme amounts to solve a linear positive definite symmetric system preceded by a elementwise algebraic computation at each time step. The proposed algorithm is strictly related to the one introduced in [10].

5.1. Notation. Denote the time step by $\tau := T/N$ and a regular partition of Ω into triangles by $\mathcal{S}_h$ [3, p.132]. Let $\mathcal{S}_h$ be obtained as the union of partitions of the various subdomains of Ω [8] (Fig. 5.1).

Set $\Omega_h := \cup\{S \in \mathcal{S}_h\}$. Let $\mathbf{V}_h^1 \subset H^1(\Omega)$ and $\mathbf{V}_h^0 \subset L^2(\Omega)$ indicate the usual piecewise linear and piecewise constant finite element spaces over $\mathcal{S}_h$. Let $\mathcal{N}_h := \{a_j\}_{j=1}^J$ denote the nodes of $\mathcal{S}_h$, $\{b_m\}_{m=1}^M$ the barycentres of $\mathcal{S}_h$, $\{\varphi_j\}_{j=1}^J$ the canonical basis of $\mathbf{V}_h^1$ and $\{\psi_m\}_{m=1}^M$ the canonical basis of $\mathbf{V}_h^0$. Thus $J := \text{card}(\mathcal{N}_h)$ and $M := \text{card}(\mathcal{S}_h)$. Finally, let $\Pi_h : C^0(\Omega_h) \to \mathbf{V}_h^1$ be the Lagrange interpolation operator.

Let us introduce the following matrices

$$\text{(5.1)} \qquad \mathbf{M} := \left\{ \int_\Omega \rho c r \Pi_h(\varphi_i\varphi_j) dr dz \right\}_{i,j=1,\dots,J}, \qquad \text{mass matrix,}$$

$$\text{(5.2)} \qquad \mathbf{K} := \left\{ \int_\Omega k r \nabla\varphi_i \cdot \nabla\varphi_j dr dz \right\}_{i,j=1,\dots,J}, \qquad \text{stiffness matrix,}$$

$$\text{(5.3)} \qquad \mathbf{B} := \left\{ \int_{\partial\Omega} H r \Pi_h(\varphi_i\varphi_j) d\sigma(r,z) \right\}_{i,j=1,\dots,J},$$

$$\text{(5.4)} \qquad \mathbf{F} := \left\{ \int_{\mathrm{C}} \rho\lambda r \varphi_i \psi_m dr dz \right\}_{i=1,\dots,J; m=1,\dots,M}.$$

Note that matrices $\mathbf{M}$ and $\mathbf{B}$ are diagonal. Set $\mathbf{A} := \mathbf{M} + \tau(\mathbf{K} + \mathbf{B})$. The integrals in Eq.s (5.1) to (5.4) can be easily evaluated elementwise using suitable quadrature rules. The vertex quadrature rule, $\frac{\text{meas}(S)}{3}\sum_{l=1}^3 v(a_{j_l})$ (a_{j_l} vertices of $S \in \mathcal{S}_h$), which is exact for all $v \in \mathbf{P}^1(S)$ [3, p.182], is used for (5.2); the quadrature rule $\frac{\text{meas}(S)}{3}\sum_{l=1}^3 v(\frac{a_{j_l}+a_{j_{l+1}}}{2})$ ($a_{j_4} := a_{j_1}$), which is exact for all $v \in \mathbf{P}^2(S)$, is used for (5.1) and (5.4); finally the integral in (5.3) can be evaluated via the Cavalieri-Simpson rule.

5.2. Approximation Algorithm. Since the initial temperature u_0 is a continuous function with possible exception on the material interfaces, the discrete initial temperature $U^0 \in \mathbf{V}_h^1$ can be defined by $U^0 := \Pi_h u_0$, with the understanding that any intermediate value of u_0 can be taken at the discontinuous nodes. The discrete initial polymer conversion is $W^0 := 0$. The discrete scheme reads as follows: *given discrete functions $U^{n-1} \in \mathbf{V}_h^1$ and $W^{n-1}(t) \in \mathbf{V}_h^0$, for any $1 \le n \le N$ find $U^n \in \mathbf{V}_h^1$ and $W^n(t) \in \mathbf{V}_h^0$ such that*

$$\text{(5.5)} \qquad \begin{aligned} &\int_\Omega r\rho c \Pi_h[(U^n - U^{n-1})\varphi] + \tau \int_\Omega r k \nabla U^n \cdot \nabla\varphi + \tau \int_{\partial\Omega} r H \Pi_h[(U^n - u_a)\varphi] \\ &\qquad = \int_{\mathrm{C}} r\rho\lambda(W^n(t^n) - W^n(t^{n-1}))\varphi, \qquad \forall\, \varphi \in \mathbf{V}_h^1, \end{aligned}$$

$$\text{(5.6)} \qquad \begin{cases} \frac{dW_m^n(t)}{dt} = A(U^{n-1}(b_m))P(U^{n-1}(b_m), W_m^n(t)), \quad \forall\, t \in (t^{n-1}, t^n], \\ W_m^n(t^{n-1}) = W_m^{n-1}(t^{n-1}), \end{cases} \qquad \forall\, 1 \le m \le M,$$

where $t^n := n\tau$ and $W_m^n(t)$ is the value of $W^n(t) \in \mathbf{V}_h^0$ at the mth element of $\mathcal{S}_h$. The equation (5.6), which corresponds to assume an isothermal kinetics on the time interval $(t^{n-1}, t^n]$, can be explicitly integrated giving the solution

$$W_m^n(t) := \begin{cases} W_m^{n-1}(t^{n-1}), & \text{if } W_m^{n-1}(t^{n-1}) \ge w^\star(U^{n-1}(b_m)), \\ w^\star(U^{n-1}(b_m))\frac{Z_m^n(t)}{1+Z_m^n(t)}, & \text{if } W_m^{n-1}(t^{n-1}) < w^\star(U^{n-1}(b_m)), \end{cases}$$

where

$$Z_m^n(t) := \left[(t - t^{n-1})A(U^{n-1}(b_m)) + \left(\frac{W_m^{n-1}(t^{n-1})}{w^\star(U^{n-1}(b_m)) - W_m^{n-1}(t^{n-1})} \right)^{1/\alpha} \right]^\alpha.$$

Equation (5.5) can be written in matrix form as

$$\mathbf{A}U^n = \mathbf{M}U^{n-1} + \mathbf{F}[W^n(t^n) - W^{n-1}(t^{n-1})] + \tau\mathbf{B}(\Pi_h u_a), \tag{5.7}$$

where we have identified piecewise linear and piecewise constant functions with the vector of their nodal and elemental values. Since $\mathbf{A}$ is a symmetric and positive definite matrix, the unique solution to (5.7) can be easily and efficiently computed by a SOR method. An approximate optimal relaxation parameter can be determined in advance so as to accelerate the convergence of this iterative method.

REMARK 5.1. The stability, convergence, and error estimates for the discrete problem (5.5), (5.6) are a straightforward consequence of the result proven in [10].

6. Numerical Simulations. We present three different simulations in order to evaluate the sensitivity of the prosthesis implant to variation in some model parameters (see also [4,6,7]). The prosthesis weight is 210 g and its lenght 155 mm whereas the infibulum diameter ranges from, approximatively, 4 to 13 mm. Thermal and kinetics parameters are collected in [7, Table 5.1 to 5.5]; $T := 900\ s$. The initial temperature is $u_0 = 27\ °C$ in the metal and cement and $u_0 = 37\ °C$ in the bones and plug components. In the passage from the real geometry (Fig. 1.1) to the ideal one (Fig. 2.1), the volumes occupied by the various materials are maintained. The infibulum generally presents grooves which serve to increase the metal/cement contact (see Fig.s 6.1,6.6,6.11, where the cross-section of the infibulum is periodically indented). The time step used in the tests below is $\tau = 5\ s$ and the meshsize is, approximately, 0.5 mm in the cement and 1.5 mm in the remaining materials. In performing the numerical experiments, MKSA units are scaled as follows: $\widetilde{m} = 1\ mm$, $\widetilde{kg} = 22967.0 \times 10^3\ kg$, $\widetilde{s} = 10\ s$, $\widetilde{K} = 100\ K$.

6.1. Test I: Simplest Configuration. Average thickness of the cement is 3.0 mm in the mantle and 10.0 mm at the distal plug (Fig. 6.1). Contact at the bone/cement interface is perfect. Fig. 6.2 shows the isotherms corresponding to the time when the maximum temperature is reached. The maximum (182 $°C$) obviously is achieved within the cement, at the distal position. On the other hand, Fig. 6.3 shows the final polymer conversion isolines. At the distal position the conversion is 100%; it gradually decreases in a medial direction (90-95%) and reaches a minimum at the proximal position (85%). Hence, this configuration presents a considerable amount of unreacted residual monomer throughout the mantle at the cement interface. Fig. 6.4 provides the temperature profiles at the bone/cement interface at subsequent time steps; the diagram on the left indicates the period ranging from 50 to 210 s, the diagram on the right 210 to 900 s. The temperature reaches a maximum (67 $°C$) at the distal position at $t = 210\ s$; moreover it remains high ($> 47\ °C$) throughout almost the entire interface from $t = 195$ to 300 s. Consequently the area of thermal bone necrosis is extended throughout the entire medial and distal cement/bone interface to an average depth of 1.5 mm (Fig. 6.5).

6.2. Test II: Air Bubbles at Cement/Bone Interface. On simulating possible defects which arise when the femoral cavity is filled, Test II introduces some discontinuities in cement/bone thermal contact. It is assumed that the thermal contact is perfect only on some portions of the cement/bone interface, while contact at other adjacent portions is practically nil due to the presence of a thin layer of air which thermally insulates the cement from the adjacent bone (Fig. 6.6). The temperature profiles are now strongly disturbed by the heat flux discontinuity at the interface. The polymerization starts far from the air bubbles because, initially, the bone heats the monomer. Hence, inside the cement, the temperature reaches at $t = 200\ s$ a sequence of maxima corresponding to each portion with perfect contact (Fig. 6.7). After that time, polymerization only continues in correspondence to the air bubbles, where a sequence of maxima ($> 105\ °C$) is reached, giving rise to a complete monomer conversion (Fig. 6.8). Bone necrosis (Fig. 6.10) is practically nil at the air bubble sites in agreement with the bone temperature profiles at the cement/bone interface (Fig. 6.9), which present a sequence of minima corresponding to each air bubble.

6.3. Test III: Rubber Membrane Separating Cement and Bone. This configuration is a proposal to reduce toxic effects of residual monomer and high temperatures. Test II suggests, in fact, that inserting an insulating barrier at the bone/cement interface could have a positive effect, raising the average temperature of the cement and thus coming closer to a complete monomer conversion, without worsening thermal bone damage. Fig.s 6.11 to 6.13 illustrate this case assuming that a 0.5 mm thick membrane is used having thermal properties similar to those of the polyethylene distal plug. Computations show that neither temperature nor conversion profiles are appreciably different from those obtained in Test I. Nevertheless, the thermal damage is markedly lower as one can see by comparing Fig. 6.13 with Fig. 6.5; it could be lowered if membrane thickness is increasing toward the distal position. Besides these interesting results, some functional advantages of a barrier at the bone/cement interface might be: elimination of the lamination and incorporation of blood in the cement; easy revision of the prosthesis; prevention of spreading throughout the body of any monomer which did not react during implantation.

REFERENCES

1. Burnett, G.M. and Duncan, G.L., *High conversion polymerization of vinyl system. I Methylmethacrylate*, Die Makromoleculare Chem. **51** (1962), 154–170.
2. Carslaw, H.S. and Jaeger, J.C., "Conduction of Heat in Solids," Oxford University Press, Oxford, 1959.
3. Ciarlet, P.G., "The Finite Element Method for Elliptic Problems," North-Holland, Amsterdam, 1978.
4. Huiskes, R., "Some Fundamental Aspects of Human Joint Replacement," Acta Orthop. Scand., Supp. 185, Copenhagen, 1979.
5. Jefferis, C.D., Lee, A.J.C., and Ling, R.S.M., *Thermal aspects of self curing PMMA*, J. Bone Joint Surg. **578** (1975), 511-518.
6. Mazzullo, S., Paganetto, G., and Simonazzi, T., *Thermal effects during cementation of an endomedullary infibulum*, in Proc. ECMI 1990, Teubner (to appear).
7. Mazzullo, S., Paolini, M., and Verdi, C., *Numerical simulation of thermal bone necrosis during cementation of femoral prostheses*, (to appear).
8. Paolini, M. and Verdi, C., *An automatic mesh generator for planar domains*, Rivista di Informatica (to appear).
9. Pipino, F., "Il Punto sulla Cementazione degli Impianti Protesici," OIC Medical Press, Firenze, 1987.
10. Verdi, C. and Visintin, A., *Numerical analysis of the multidimensional Stefan problem with supercooling and superheating*, Boll. Un. Matem. It. **1-B** (1987), 795–814.
11. Visintin, A., *Stefan problem with phase relaxation*, IMA J. Appl. Math. **34** (1985), 225–245.

1980 *Mathematics subject classifications*: 92A07,35K60,65N30

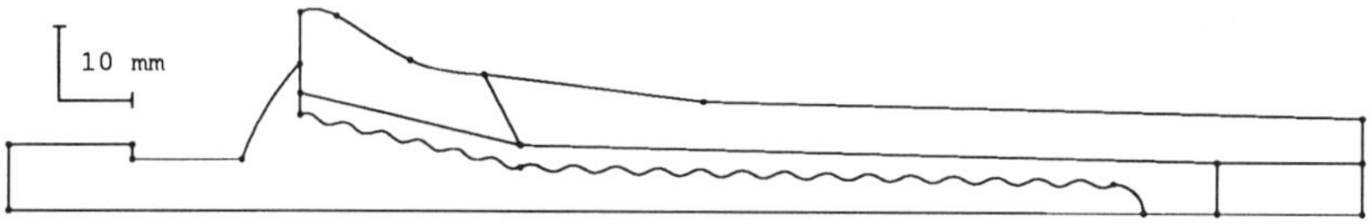

FIGURE 6.1. Test I: domain geometry.

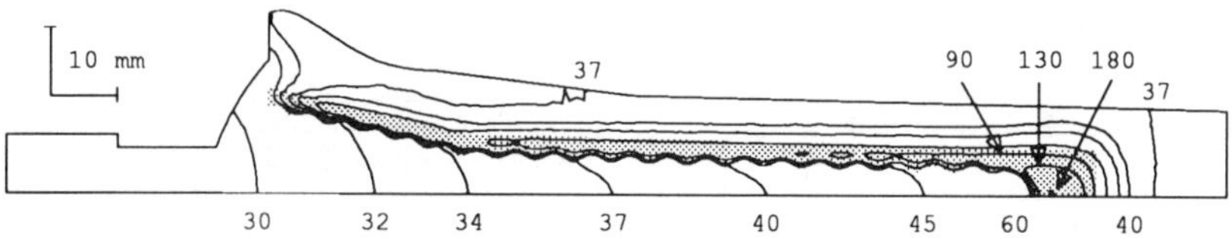

FIGURE 6.2. Test I: isotherms (u [$^\circ C$]) at peak temperature time ($t = 195$ s).

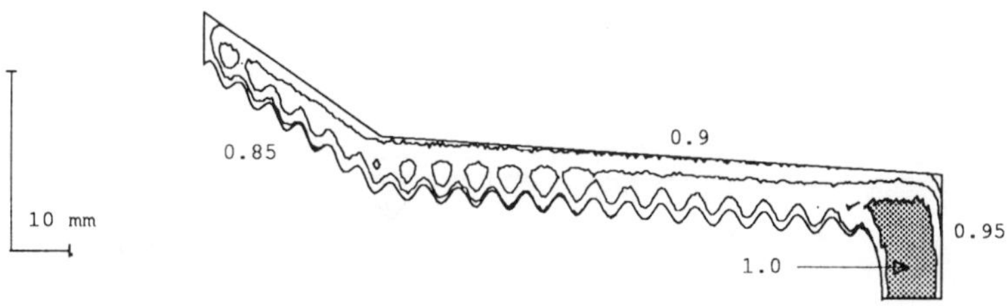

FIG. 6.3. Test I: polymer conversion isolines (w) at final time; r-coord. scaled $\times 3$.

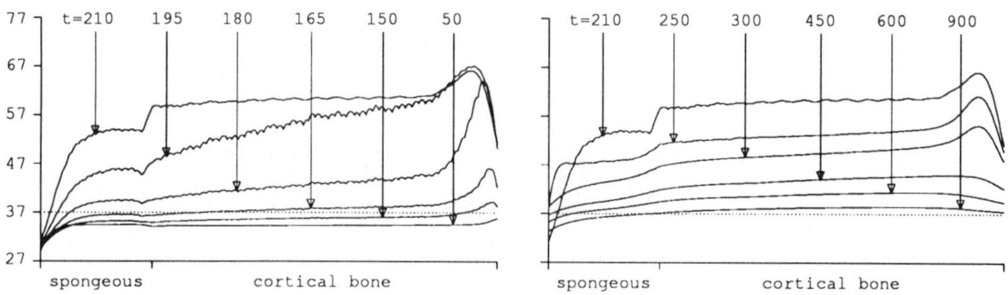

FIGURE 6.4. Test I: cement/bone interface temperature (u [$^\circ C$]).

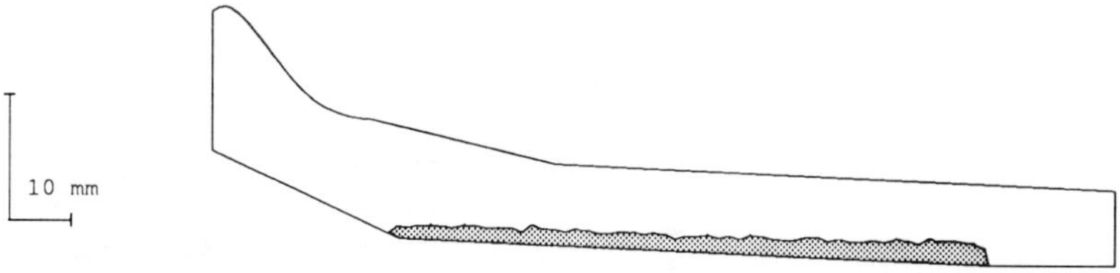

FIG. 6.5. Test I: thermal bone necrosis ($\eta \geq 1$: blackened zone); r-coord. scaled $\times 2$.

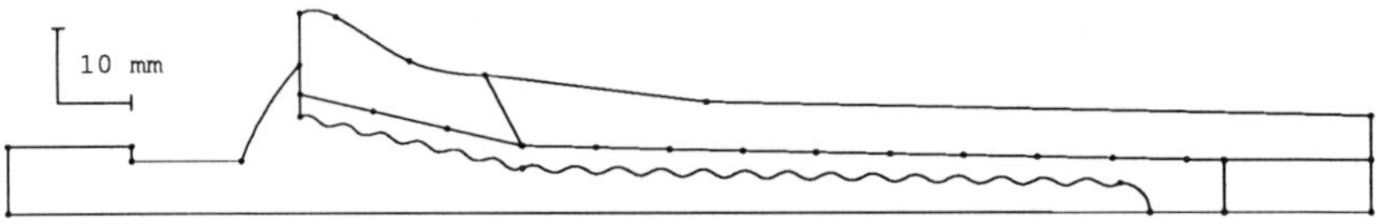

FIGURE 6.6. Test II: domain geometry.

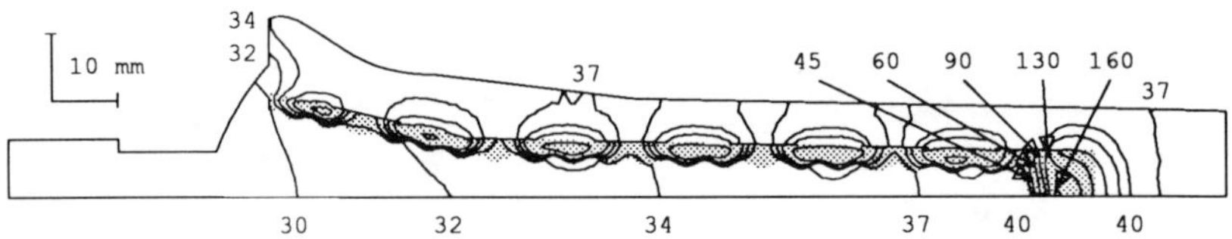

FIGURE 6.7. Test II: isotherms (u [°C]) at peak temperature time ($t = 200$ s).

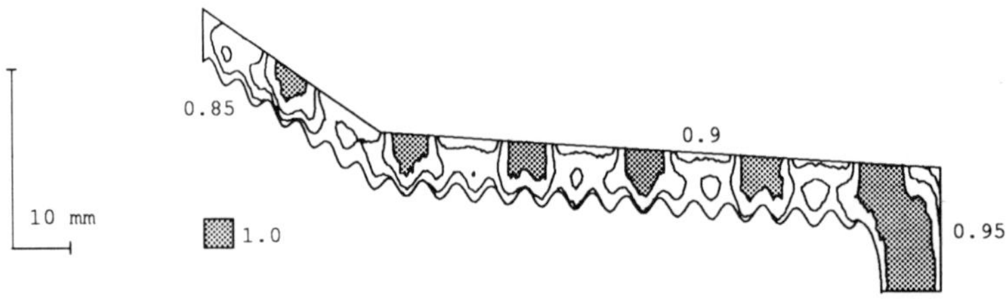

FIG. 6.8. Test II: polymer conversion isolines (w) at final time; r-coord. scaled ×3.

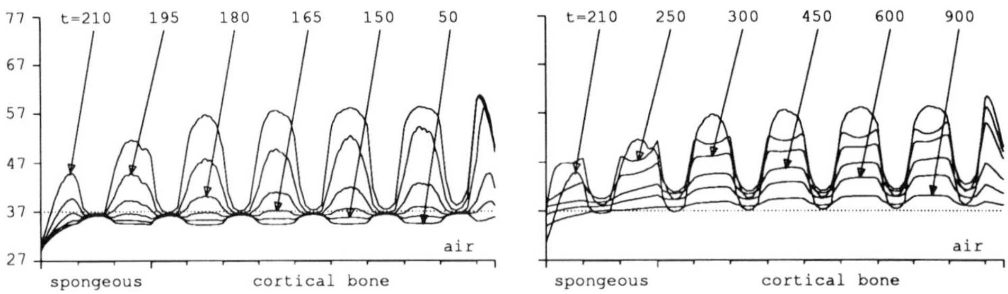

FIGURE 6.9. Test II: cement/bone interface temperature (u [°C]).

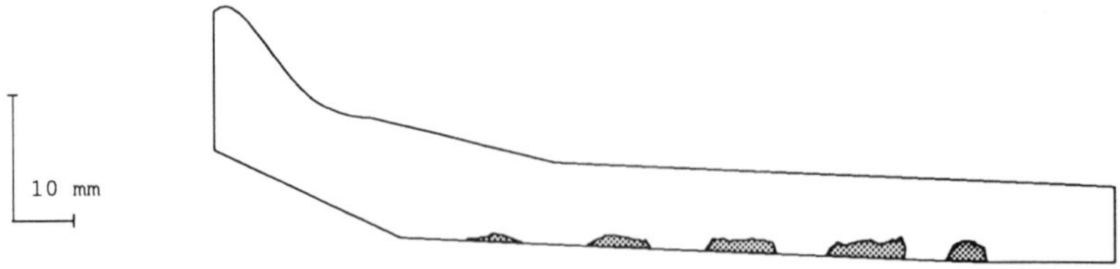

FIG. 6.10. Test II: thermal bone necrosis ($\eta \geq 1$: blackened zone); r-coord. scaled ×2.

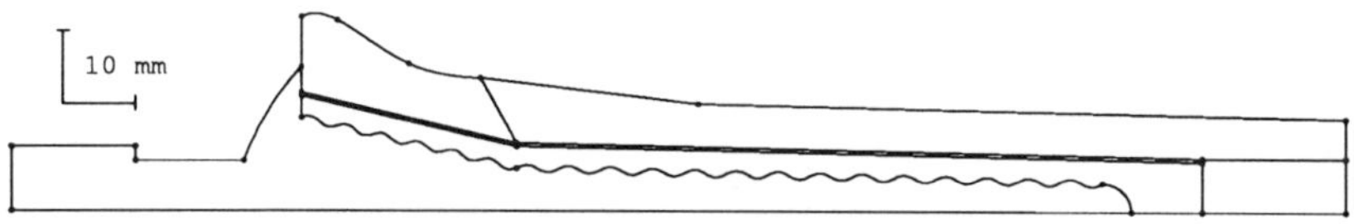

FIGURE 6.11. Test III: domain geometry.

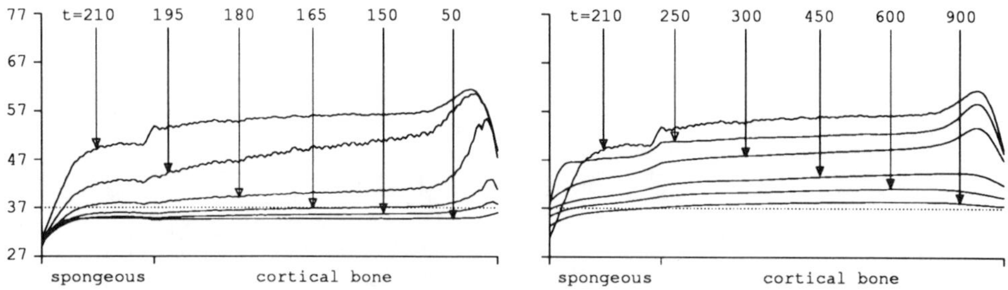

FIGURE 6.12. Test III: rubber membrane/bone interface temperature (u [$^\circ C$]).

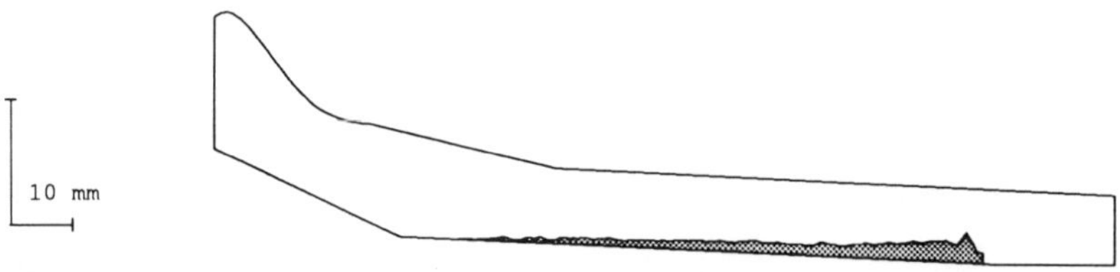

FIG. 6.13. Test III: thermal bone necrosis ($\eta \geq 1$: blackened zone); r-coord. scaled $\times 2$.

Front Tracking of Free Boundaries with Curvature Terms

Gunter H. Meyer

Georgia Institute of Technology
School of Mathematics
Atlanta, Georgia 30332
USA

1. Introduction

Beginning with the one-dimensional one-phase Stefan problem we have applied the method of lines during the past twenty years to a variety of fixed and free boundary problems of increasing size and complexity. One phase reaction-diffusion systems in $\mathbb{R}_2$ with multiple free boundaries, the two-dimensional Stefan problem with a Gibbs Thomson interface condition, and a two-dimensional Stefan problem with a globally defined free boundary condition are among these. We have now assembled a modular general purpose computer code which can be applied to general multi-dimensional reaction-diffusion systems with free boundaries. In particular, it applies to all the problems mentioned above and their analog formulations in $\mathbb{R}_3$.

We shall outline the basic concepts on which this code is based and illustrate its performance for a few multi-dimensional free boundary problems. In particular, we shall present some first numerical experiments with front tracking for the 3-D Stefan problem with a Gibbs-Thomson interface condition. Further details for the 2-D case, including dynamic undercooling, may be found in [5].

2. The numerical method

A standard line-iterative technique is proposed for the numerical solution of reaction-diffusion systems of the form

$$(2.1) \qquad L_i u_i = f_i(t, x, u), \qquad i = 1, \cdots, M$$

where $x = (x_1, x_2, x_3)$ denotes coordinates in an orthogonal coordinate system in $\mathbb{R}_3$ (cartesian, cylindrical, spherical, etc.), and where $u = (u_1, \cdots, u_M)$ stands for the M interacting components. Each operator L_i has the general form

$$(2.2) \qquad L_i = \sum_{j=1}^{3} \frac{\partial}{\partial x_j}\left(k_{ij}\frac{\partial}{\partial x_j}\right) + \sum_{j=1}^{3} b_{ij}\frac{\partial}{\partial x_j} + c_i - d_i\frac{\partial}{\partial t}$$

where all coefficients may be functions of (t, x, u). As we shall see the structure of the algorithm almost automatically provides a linearization of the equations so that it formally is able to cope with non-linear terms. Convergence of the algorithm does, of course, depend crucially on the type of nonlinearities.

The dominant restrictions on our algorithm are of a geometric nature. To begin with, we shall require that the computational domain is $Q_T = \Omega \times [0, T]$ where Ω is a rectangular domain in the chosen coordinate system (a cube, a cylinder, a circular cone, etc.). For definiteness and ease of exposition we shall assume here that Ω is the unit cartesian cube in $\mathbb{R}_3$. With each component u_i there may be associated a free boundary or interface which cuts Q_T. The method proposed here demands that all free boundaries are single-valued surfaces with respect to the same two coordinates. For definiteness we shall assume that the free boundaries allow the representation

$$x_1 = s_{i_\ell}(x_2, x_3, t)$$

where the set $\{i_\ell\}$ indexes those components which have a free boundary. For ease of exposition we shall assume that actually each component has a free boundary so that $i_\ell = i$. The requirement that s_i be a function is a strong limitation on the method because it rules out many interesting free surface shapes.

The statement of problem (2.1) is completed by Dirichlet, Neumann or reflection conditions on $\partial\Omega$ and appropriate initial conditions. Specifically, we shall assume here Dirichlet data on each u_i at $x_1 = 0$ and $x_1 = 1$ and Neumann data at the sides of the cube.

The data on the free boundary may be quite varied and will be written symbolically as

$$g_{ij}(t, x, u, \nabla u, v_i) = 0, \qquad j = 1, 2, 3$$

for the surface associated with u_i. They may be as simple as

$$u_i = \frac{\partial u_i}{\partial n} = 0$$

for obstacle type problems with a free boundary, or as complicated as the Gibbs-Thomson interface relation

$$\sum_{j=1}^{3} \left(k_{j+} \frac{\partial u_+}{\partial x_j} - k_{j-} \frac{\partial u_-}{\partial x_j} \right) = -\lambda v$$

$$u_+ = u_- = -\sigma \nabla \cdot \vec{n}$$

where v is the speed normal to the free boundary $x_1 = s(x_2, x_3, t)$ and n is the normal to it pointing into the liquid phase. Note that in this case there is only one component ($M = 1$) and u_+ and u_- refer to limits at the free boundary coming from the liquid and solid phase, respectively. Not implemented yet is the natural two component system where mass transport is modeled together with the energy transport.

The numerical method for (2.1) is based on a few well established approximations of the continuous problem.

1) The time variable is discretized and all time derivatives in (2.1) and the boundary conditions are replaced by backward difference quotients. An elliptic system of the form (2.1) results for which c_i and f_i are modified to absorb the term $d_i \frac{u_i - u_{i,0}}{\Delta t}$. This discretization method is sometimes referred to as Rothe's method. It is stable computationally and useful for analytic work (see, e.g. [2] and [4]).

2) Retaining x_1 as a continous variable, discretizing x_2 and x_3 and replacing all derivatives with respect to x_2 and x_3 in (2.2) and the boundary conditions by suitable difference quotients we obtain a system of ordinary differential equations of the form

$$(2.3) \qquad L_{i\ell} u_{i\ell} \equiv u''_{i\ell} + b_{i\ell} u'_{i\ell} + c_{i\ell} u_{i\ell} = F_{i\ell}, \quad i = 1, \cdots, M, \quad \ell = 1, \cdots, L$$

where ℓ is an index for a linear ordering of the (x_2, x_3)-mesh points and $F_{i\ell}$ stands for all the terms which are independent of $u_{i\ell}$, such as expressions along ajacent lines, source terms, the solutions at past time levels, etc. This is the well known elliptic method of lines approximation to the system (2.1). It must be noted that in general each equation (2.3) is subject to boundary and interface conditions. Boundary conditions imposed on $\partial\Omega$ transfer simply to the discrete system (2.3). Only free boundary conditions require special attention as will be demonstrated below for the Gibbs Thomson condition.

3) The system (2.3) represents $L \times M$ nonlinear coupled ordinary differential equations. This system is solved iteratively by integrating for a given line successively the M component equations with lagged coefficients and then going to the next line. Always the newest available data is used to evaluate $F_{i\ell}$ and the coefficients $b_{i\ell}$ and $c_{i\ell}$. We sweep through all the lines until all component equations and free boundaries have converged within a prescribed tolerance. In summary, we apply a Gauss-Seidel line iteration. Depending on the structure of the nonlinearities, particularly the type of free boundary conditions, an overrelaxation can help or hurt.

4) Each linear equation (2.3) is a standard two-point boundary value problem with a free interface. Its solution requires a flexible one-dimensional free boundary solver, particularly in view of the complicated interface conditions which can arise from even simple multi-dimensional free boundary problems as seen below. The sweep method known as the Riccati transformation method or also as invariant imbedding is used consistently in our work. A detailed exposition of this method may be found in [5]. Here we only point out that it is based on the affine relationship between the solution $u_{i\ell}$ of (2.3) and its derivative $u'_{i\ell}$ (known as the Riccati transformation)

$$u_{i\ell}(x_1) = R_{i\ell}(x_1) u'_{i\ell}(x_1) + w_{i\ell}(x_1)$$

where $R_{i\ell}$ and $w_{i\ell}$ are solutions of well defined initial value problems for ordinary differential equations and hence may be assumed known, at least numerically. Since the Riccati transformation has to hold on the free boundary it provides an additional free boundary condition which can be used to eliminate algebraically the unknown $u_{i\ell}$

and $u'_{i\ell}$ in favour of a single equation $\varphi_{i\ell}\,(s_{i\ell},\, R_{i\ell}(s_{i\ell}),\, w_{i\ell}(s_{i\ell})) = 0$. Conversely, all roots of the equation $\varphi_{i\ell}(x_1, R_{i\ell}(x_1), w_{i\ell}(x_1)) = 0$ are admissible free boundaries for (2.3).

In summary, we solve multi-component multi-dimensional transient free boundary problems time-implicitly as a sequence of one-dimensional two-point boundary problems with a free interface or boundary. Each equation has the same structure so that the complete solution algorithm consists of repeatedly calling a subroutine for a 1-D solver. Because coupling to the solution along neighboring lines exists only through the source term in (2.3) the method can be parallelized as any other line Gauss-Seidel method, for example through a red-black ordering of the lines.

3. The three-dimensional Stefan problem

Only a thermal model is considered so that $M = 1$ in (2.1). We assume that the heat equation applies to the liquid phase above and the solid phase below the interface $x = s(y, z, t)$. The method of lines approximation corresponding to (2.3) along the line $y = y_i$ and $z = z_j$ is

$$k\,u''_{ij} - \left[\frac{2k}{\Delta y^2} + \frac{2k}{\Delta z^2} + \frac{1}{\Delta t}\right] u_{ij} = F_{ij}(x) \tag{3.1}$$

where

$$F_{ij}(x) = \left[-k\frac{u_{i+1\,j} + u_{i-1\,j}}{\Delta y^2} - k\frac{u_{i\,j+1} + u_{i\,j-1}}{\Delta z^2}\right] - \frac{1}{\Delta t}u_{ij,0}(x)$$

where $u_{ij,0}(x)$ is the solution along the given line from the preceding time step. Let us assume the sides of the box are insulated so that in (3.1)

$$u_{-1j} = u_{2j}, \text{ etc.}$$

where u_{0j} is the solution along the line $y = 0$, $z = z_j$.

We shall assume that $k(x)$ is discontinuous across the interface. The same will be true of u'_{ij}. We shall index limiting values at the interface from above and below with $+$ and $-$.

Let us now turn to the interface condition. The Gibbs-Thomson condition is

$$u_+ = u_- = -\frac{\sigma}{\rho} = -\sigma\nabla\cdot n = -\sigma\frac{(1+s_y^2)s_{zz} + (1+s_z^2)s_{yy} - 2s_y s_z s_{yz}}{(1+s_y^2+s_z^2)^{3/2}} \tag{3.2}$$

$$-k_+\nabla u_+ + k_-\nabla u_- = \lambda\frac{dR}{dt} \tag{3.4}$$

where R is the position vector for a point on the interface $x = s(y, z, t)$. In order to solve (3.1) along a line we need to relate the movement normal to the interface to the movement along the line (y_i, z_j).

We assume that the interface is smooth. Then

$$\frac{dx}{dt} = \frac{\partial s}{\partial y}\frac{dy}{dt} + \frac{\partial s}{\partial z}\frac{dz}{dt} + \frac{\partial s}{\partial t},$$

where $\frac{\partial s}{\partial t}$ is the desired speed along the line. Substitution for $\frac{dR}{dt}$ from (3.4) yields

$$\lambda\frac{\partial s}{\partial t} = k_-\frac{\partial u_-}{\partial x} - k_+\frac{\partial u_+}{\partial x} - s_y\left(k_-\frac{\partial u}{\partial y} - k_+\frac{\partial u}{\partial y}\right) - s_z\left(k_-\frac{\partial u_-}{\partial z} - k_+\frac{\partial u_+}{\partial z}\right). \tag{3.4}$$

When solving (3.1) near a curved interface or boundary one often needs data along adjacent lines from functions which are not computed there. Functions needed in (3.1) are routinely extended C^1-linearly. However, values for u_y and u_z in (3.4) based on such extensions appear to cause instabilities. Furthermore, the approximating expressions do not naturally reduce to the formulation used successfully for the classical Stefan problem when $\sigma = 0$. Instead, we use the tangential derivatives

$$\frac{D}{Dy}u(s(y,z,t),y,z,t) = u_x s_y + u_y$$
$$\frac{D}{Dz}u(s(y,z,t),y,z,t) = u_x s_z + u_z$$

and replace (3.4) by

$$\lambda\frac{\partial s}{\partial t} = k_-(1+s_y^2+s_z^2)\frac{\partial u_-}{\partial x} - k_+(1+s_y^2+s_z^2)\frac{\partial u_+}{\partial x} + (k_+ - k_-)\left(\frac{Du}{Dy}s_y + \frac{Du}{Dz}s_z\right). \tag{3.5}$$

We note that if $k_+ = k_-$ then the tangential derivatives along the free surface drop out. For a realistic test of the Gibbs-Thomson interface condition we shall always set $k_- = 2k_+$. We note also that if $\sigma = 0$ then $u_+ = u_- = 0$ so that the tangential derivatives vanish and we are left with the standard formulation of front tracking for the classical Stefan problem.

If we now use the difference approximations

$$\frac{\partial s}{\partial t} = \frac{s_{ij} - s_{ij,0}}{\Delta t}$$
$$s_y = \frac{s_{i+1\,j} - s_{i-1\,j}}{2\Delta y}, \quad s_z = \frac{s_{ij+1} - s_{ij-1}}{2\Delta z}$$
$$s_{yy} = \frac{s_{i+1\,j} + s_{i-1\,j} - 2s_{ij}}{\Delta y^2}, \quad s_{zz} = \frac{s_{ij+1} + s_{ij-1} - 2s_{ij}}{\Delta z^2}$$

and
$$s_{yz} = \frac{\frac{s_{i+1\,j+1} - s_{i-1\,j+1}}{2\Delta y} - \frac{s_{i+1\,j-1} - s_{i-1\,j-1}}{2\Delta y}}{2\Delta z}$$

and
$$\frac{Du}{Dy}(y_i, z_j) = \frac{u(s_{i+1\,j}) - u(s_{i-1\,j})}{2\Delta y}$$
$$\frac{Du}{Dz}(y_i, z_j) = \frac{u(s_{i\,j+1}) - u(s_{i\,j-1})}{2\Delta z}$$

then it can be verified from (3.2) and (3.5) that the solution u_{ij} is subject to an interface condition of the form

$$u_{ij+}(s_{ij}) = u_{ij-}(s_{ij}) = g_1(s_{ij}) \qquad (3.6)$$
$$g_2(u_{ij+}, u_{ij-}, s_{ij}) = 0$$

where in the Gauss-Seidel iteration all interface data from adjacent lines appear as known quantities during the determination of s_{ij}. Details follow as in the two-dimensional case described in [5].

4. Two numerical experiments

The first example is meant to illustrate the flexibility of the code for tracking a curvature dependent free interface in 3-D. The task is to solve the two-phase Stefan problem for a "hot liquid and cold solid",

$$\nabla \cdot k(u)\nabla u + \beta(\frac{\partial s}{\partial t}, x)\frac{\partial u}{\partial x} - \frac{\partial u}{\partial t} = 0 \qquad (4.1)$$

with the Gibbs-Thomson interface condition (3.2,5) and the boundary conditions

$$u(0, y, z, t) = 2 + \cos(t - y - z)$$
$$u(1, y, z, t) = -2 + \cos(t + y - z).$$

The initial interface is assumed to be

$$s(y, \tau, 0) = 0.5 + 0.3 \cos 2\pi y \cos 3\pi z$$

and the initial temperature is the function which is piecewise linear in x and corresponds to u on the fixed boundaries and to the interface temperature calculated from (3.2) for the initial surface $s(y, z, 0)$. For the coefficients in (4.1) we use

$$\lambda = 1$$

$$k(u_-) = \frac{1}{1 + u^2} \quad \text{and} \quad k(u_+) = 2k(u_-)$$

and

$$\beta(\frac{\partial s}{\partial t}, x) = \begin{cases} \frac{\partial s}{\partial t}(y, z, t)\frac{x}{s(y,z,t)} & x \in [0, s] \\ 0 & x \in [s, 1]. \end{cases}$$

The coefficient becomes a simple function of x when in line iteration k one approximates $\frac{\partial s}{\partial t}$ with

$$\frac{\partial s}{\partial t}(y_i, z_j, t) = \frac{s_{ij}^{k-1} - s_{ij,0}}{\Delta t}.$$

Fig. 1 shows the results obtained with the line iterative method for $\Delta y = \Delta z = 1/20$. For the integration along each line we use a standard trapezoidal rule with $\Delta x = 1/200$.

Fig. 1a shows the initial interface, Fig. 1b the interface after 100 time steps for a coefficient of surface tension of $\sigma = 1$. The smoothing effect of the Gibbs-Thomson term is apparent when one considers that the interface for the classical Stefan problem ($\sigma = 0$) at the same final time is virtually unchanged from the initial surface $s(y, z, 0)$ shown in Fig. 1a.

We remark that the Gibbs-Thomson law in a properly scaled problem is considered without practical importance for a hot liquid-cold solid system.

The second example is the two-phase Stefan problem (3.1,2,5) which will be unstable because of undercooling. The correct physical model should develop dendrites under these circumstances. Growing of numerical dendrites appears to be a difficult task and depends strongly on the scaling of the parameters and the boundary data. We have not succeeded in growing dendrites yet but would like to present some preliminary computational results for tracking the unstable interface in the fully three-dimensional setting.

We assume that the system is subject to the boundary conditions

$$u(0, y, z, t) = -0.2$$
$$u(1, y, z, t) = -0.2$$

and the initial temperatures are constant and equal to the boundary temperature in each phase. The initial interface is $s(y, z, 0) = 0.8$. Below we plot the final interface when the computation breaks down. Fig. 2a shows the interface starting from a flat initial interface when $\sigma = 0$. Fig. 2b shows the interface when the initial interface is perturbed at the center ($s(.5, .5, 0) = .79$) when $\sigma = 0$. Clearly, the instability is a computational effect. Fig. 2c shows the same calculation after a somewhat later time when $\sigma = 0.001$. The instabilities go over two mesh lengths now and may be more than just a numerical effect. Further numerical experiments are in progress.

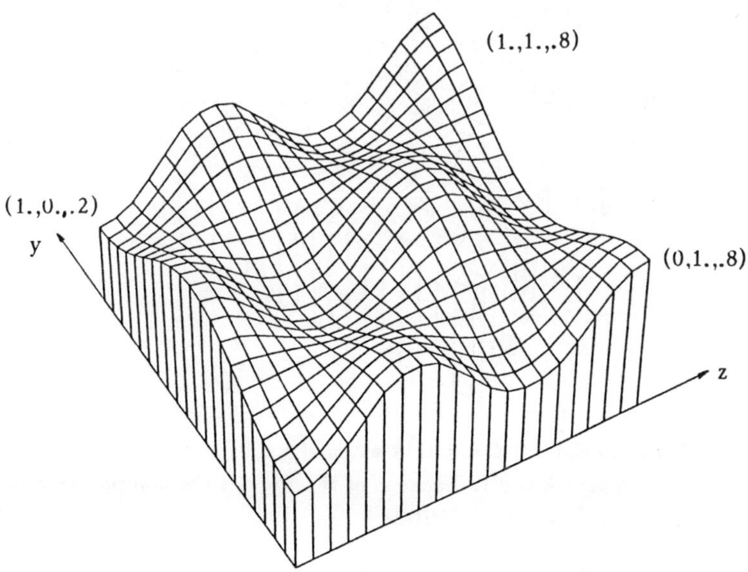

Fig. 1a – Initial interface $x = 0.5 + 0.3 \cos 2\pi y \cos 3\pi z$
Note that the $y - z$ axes are shifted downward from the origin.

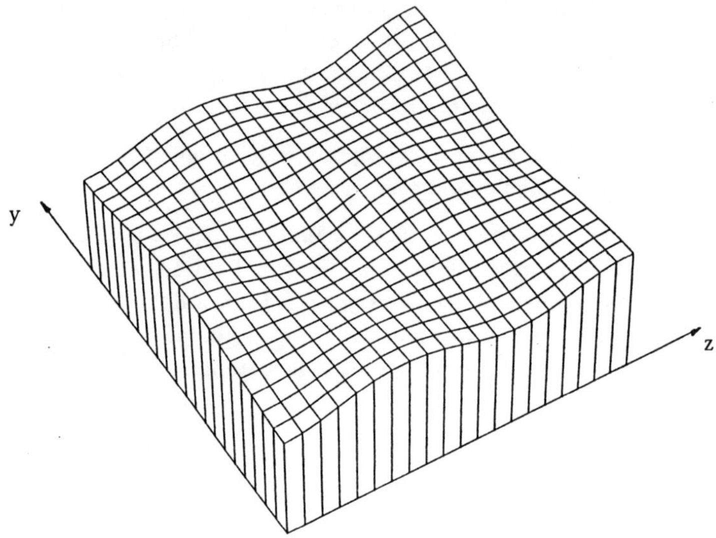

Fig. 1b – Interface for problem (4.1) after 100 time steps with $\Delta t = 10^{-4}$ for $\sigma = 1.0$ The corresponding interface for $\sigma = 0$ is little changed from Fig. 1a.

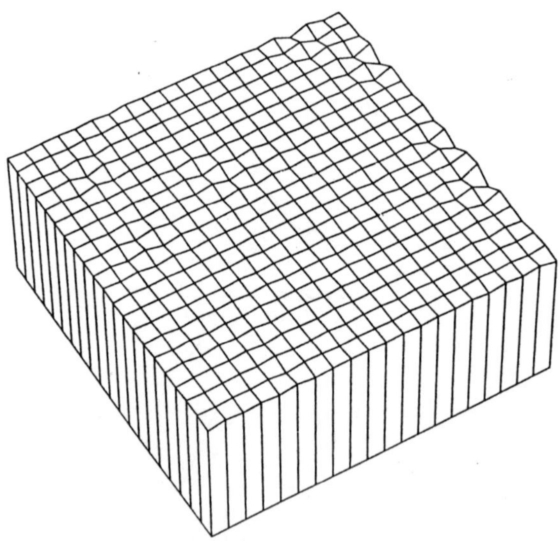

Fig. 2a – Final interface at $t = 0.0149$ when $s(y, z, 0) = 0.8$ and $\sigma = 0$, $k_+ = 1$, $k_- = 2$ and $\lambda = 0.1$. Because of the wiggles the computation could not be continued beyond $t = 0.0149$.

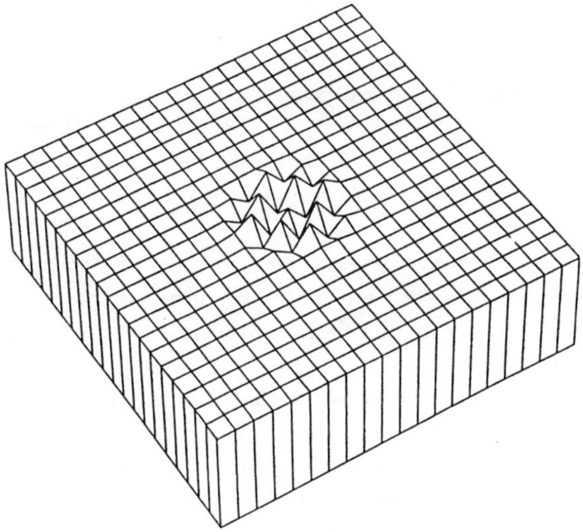

Fig. 2b – Final interface at $t = 0.00265$ when $s(y,z,0) = 0.8$ except for $s(0.5, 0.5, 0) = 0.79$. $\sigma = 0$ and $k_+ = 1$, $k_- = 2$, $\lambda = 0.1$.

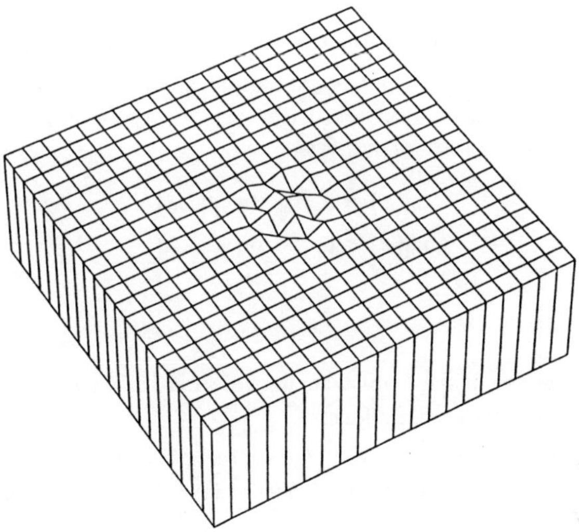

Fig. 2c – Final interface at $t = 0.0031$; data as in Fig. 2b except $\sigma = 0.001$. The smoothing and stabilization due to surface tension is noticeable.

5. Some comments on convergence

At this stage convergence results for the line Gauss-Seidel iteration for the Stefan problem with the Gibbs Thomson interface condition are not available but needed to assure that the observed numerical performance is not a discretization effect. The complexity of the discretized free boundary condition (3.2) and (3.5) so far proved too difficult to handle and only an observed consistency of the computed results with respect to space and time step refinements can be offered.

The second question of convergence of the method of lines approximation to the continuous solution is even more difficult since only preliminary results for the existence of an appropriate weak solution of the Stefan problem with a Gibbs Thomson interface condition are available [3].

However, even for the classical two phase Stefan problem the question of convergence of front tracking is basically unresolved. Only for the one-dimensional case have several numerical methods been analyzed, but with techniques which do not readily extend to the multi-dimensional case (for details see the summary in [1]).

We shall outline here a new method of analysis for the 1-D classical Stefan problem which does not use as strongly the one-dimensional theory of earlier proofs. Whether this analysis is extendable to the multi-dimensional case is open at this time.

We consider Rothe's method for the one-dimensional problem at time $t_n = n\Delta t$:

$$(5.1)\qquad \begin{aligned} &u''(x) - \frac{1}{\Delta t}(u - u_{n-1}) = 0 \qquad x \in (0, s_n) \cap (s_n, 1)\\ &u_+(s_n) = u_-(s_n) = 0\\ &u'_+(s_n) - u'_-(s_n) = -\lambda\frac{s - s_{n-1}}{\Delta t},\\ &u(0) = \alpha(t_n) > 0, \qquad u(1) = \beta(t_n) < 0. \end{aligned}$$

We assume that $u_0(x)$ and s_0 are given, that

$$\begin{aligned} u_0(x) > 0 \qquad &\text{on } [0, s_0)\\ u_0(x) < 0 \qquad &\text{on } (s_0, 1] \end{aligned}$$

and that

$$s_0 \subset (0, 1).$$

We shall prove convergence of the front tracking solution (5.1) to the unique weak solution of the Stefan problem in its enthalpy form

$$(5.2)\qquad \int_0^T \int_0^1 [u(x,t)\varphi_{xx}(x,t) + H(u(x,t)\frac{\partial\varphi}{\partial t}(x,t)]dxdt = 0,$$

at least as long as the free boundary stays away from the fixed lateral boundaries. Here H is the usual enthalpy function

$$H(u) = \begin{cases} u & u < 0 \\ u + \lambda & u > 0 \end{cases}$$

$$H(0) \in [0, \lambda]$$

and φ is arbitrary in $C_0^\infty(Q_T)$.

The numerical solution of (5.1) is straightforward to compute at every time level and will be assumed known exactly (see [4]). Let $\psi(x)$ be any C^2 function on $[0,1]$. Then integration by parts shows that at time level t_n

$$\int_0^1 [u\psi'' - \frac{1}{\Delta t}(u - u_{n-1})\psi] + \lambda \frac{s_n - s_{n-1}}{\Delta t}\psi(s_n) = 0.$$

From the definition of the enthalpy function and the natural front tracking limits

$$\lim_{u \to 0+} H(u) = \lambda, \qquad \lim_{u \to 0-} H(u) = 0$$

follows that the last expression can be written as

$$\int_0^1 [u\psi'' - \frac{H(u) - H(u_{n-1})}{\Delta t}\psi(x)]dx = 0. \tag{5.3}$$

For an arbitrary but fixed $\varphi \in C_0^\infty(Q_T)$ and the sequence $\{u_n\}$ let us define the following functions on Q_T:

$$\left.\begin{aligned} u_N(x,t) &= u_n(x) \\ \varphi_N(x,t) &= \varphi(x, t_{n-1})\alpha_{n-1}(t) + \varphi(x, t_n)\alpha_n(t) \end{aligned}\right\} \quad t \in (t_{n-1}, t_n]$$

where $\alpha_k(t)$ is the usual chapeau function defined on $[0,T]$ and $\Delta t = \frac{T}{N}$ for an arbitrary $N > 0$.

If we substitute u_N and φ_N into (5.2) then the integration over t can be carried out and we obtain

$$\begin{aligned} I_N &\equiv \int_0^T \int_0^1 [u_N(x,t)\varphi_{Nxx}(x,t) + H(u_N(x,t))\frac{\partial \varphi_N}{\partial t}(x,t)]dxdt = \\ &= \sum_{n=1}^N \Delta t \Big[\int_0^1 u_n(\frac{\varphi_n'' + \varphi_{n-1}''}{2}) + H(u_n)\frac{\varphi_n - \varphi_{n-1}}{\Delta t} \Big] dx \end{aligned}$$

where $\varphi_n(x) = \varphi(x, t_n)$. In view of (5.3) we find

$$I_N = \sum_{n=1}^N \Delta t \Big[\int_0^1 (\frac{H(u_n) - H(u_{n-1})}{\Delta t})(\frac{\varphi_n + \varphi_{n-1}}{2}) + H(u_n)\frac{\varphi_n - \varphi_{n-1}}{\Delta t} \Big] dx.$$

Summation by parts yields $\sum_{n=1}^N (H(u_n) - H(u_{n-1}))\varphi_{n-1} = \sum_{n=1}^N -H(u_n)(\varphi_n - \varphi_{n-1})$ because $\varphi_0 = \varphi_N = 0$ for $\varphi \in C_0^\infty(Q_T)$. Thus, for $\varphi_n = \varphi_{n-1} + \varphi_n - \varphi_{n-1}$,

$$I_N = \sum_{n=1}^N \Delta t \frac{1}{2} \int_0^1 (H(u_n) - H(u_{n-1}))\frac{\varphi_n - \varphi_{n-1}}{\Delta t} dx.$$

A second summation by parts yields

$$I_N = -\frac{1}{2}\Delta t \sum_{n=1}^{N-1} \Delta t \int_0^1 H(u_n)\frac{\varphi_{n+1} + \varphi_{n-1} - 2\varphi_n}{\Delta t^2} dx + O(\Delta t)$$

where the remainder term involves H and φ at $t = 0$ and $t = T$. Since $\varphi \in C_0^\infty(Q_T)$ it is clear that $\lim_{N\to\infty} I_N = 0$ provided only a meaning can be given to $\lim_{N\to\infty} H(u_N)$. In order to discuss the convergence of u_N we observe from (5.1) that

$$0 = \int_0^1 [u_n'' - \frac{1}{\Delta t}(u_n - u_{n-1})] u_n dx =$$
$$= u_n(1)u_n'(1) - u_n(0)u_n'(0) - \int_0^1 [u_n'^2 - \frac{u_n - u_{n-1}}{\Delta t} u_n] dx.$$

From the identity [2]

$$2\Delta t \sum_{n=1}^{k} (\frac{u_n - u_{n-1}}{\Delta t}) u_n = u_k^2 - u_0^2 + \Delta t^2 \sum_{n=1}^{k} (\frac{u_n - u_{n-1}}{\Delta t})^2$$

now follows that

$$2\Delta t \sum_{n=1}^{k} \int_0^1 u_k'^2 dx \le \int_0^1 u_0^2 dx + 2\Delta t \sum_{n=1}^{k} [u_n(1)u_n'(1) - u_n(0)u_n'(0)]$$

so that

$$\|u_N\|_{Q_T}^2 + \|\frac{\partial u_N}{\partial x}\|_{Q_T}^2 \le C\{\sum_{n=1}^{N} [u_n(1)u_n'(1) - u_n(0)u_n'(0)] + \int_0^1 u_0^2 dx\}$$

Bounded Dirichlet data α, β on $[0, T]$ imply that u_N, $\frac{\partial u_N}{\partial x} \in L_2(Q_T)$ provided only that

(5.4)
$$\inf \frac{\partial}{\partial x} u_N(0, t) \ge -c > -\infty$$
$$\inf \frac{\partial}{\partial x} u_N(1, t) \ge -c > -\infty$$

uniformly with respect to N. If this is indeed the case then $H(u_N) \in L_2(Q_T)$,

$$\lim_{N\to\infty} I_N = 0$$

and hence

$$\lim_{N\to\infty} \int_0^T \int_0^1 [u_N(x,t)\varphi_{Nxx}(x,t) + H(u_N(x,t))\frac{\partial \varphi_N}{\partial t}(x,t)] dx dt = 0.$$

A priori uniform bounds on $u'_n(0)$ and $u'_n(1)$ can be obtained with typical barrier arguments, at least as long as $s_n \in [\delta, 1-\delta]$ for some $\delta > 0$. For example, it is straightforward to derive conditions on the data under which it follows by induction that on $[0, \delta]$ we have

$$u_n(x) - w_n(x) \geq 0$$

where w_n is the barrier function defined by

$$w_n(x) = \frac{\alpha(t_n)}{g(0)} g(x)$$

with

$$g(x) = (\frac{1}{(x+\delta)^p} - \frac{1}{(2\delta)^p})$$

for a suitable large $p > 0$ so that

$$u'_n(0) \geq w'_n(0).$$

We shall not carry out the calculations here but simply assume that

$$u_N, \frac{\partial u_N}{\partial x} \in L_2(Q_T).$$

It follows from [2] that there exists a subsequence $\{u_N\}$ which converges strongly in $L_2(Q_T)$ and almost everywhere in Q_T to a function $u^* \in L_2(Q_T)$. Define

$$\begin{aligned}
\Omega_+ &= \{(x,t) : u^*(x,t) > 0\} \\
\Omega_- &= \{(x,t) : u^*(x,t) < 0\}. \\
\Omega_0 &= \{(x,t) : u^*(x,t) = 0\}
\end{aligned}$$

From the definition of H it follows that

$$\lim_{N\to\infty} H(u_N) = H(u^*) \quad \text{on } \Omega_+ \cup \Omega_-$$

and

$$\lim_{N\to\infty} H(u_N) \to H^* \quad \text{weakly in } L_2(\Omega)$$

where

$$H^* \subset [0, \lambda] \quad \text{for } x \in \Omega_0$$

because $-\varepsilon \leq u_N(x) \leq \varepsilon$ and $-\varepsilon \leq H(u_N(x)) \leq \varepsilon + \lambda$ for arbitrary $\varepsilon > 0$ and N sufficiently large. Hence

$$\lim_{N_k\to\infty} \int_0^T \int_0^1 [u_N \frac{\partial^2 \varphi}{\partial x^2} + H(u_N)\frac{\partial \varphi}{\partial t}] dx dt = \int_0^T \int_0^1 [u^* \frac{\partial^2 \varphi}{\partial x^2} + H^* \frac{\partial \varphi}{\partial t}] dx dt.$$

Finally, since

$$\int_0^T \int_0^1 [u_n \frac{\partial^2 \varphi}{\partial x^2} + H(u_N) \frac{\partial \varphi}{\partial t}] \, dx dt = I_N + \int_0^T \int_0^1 \{ u_N [\frac{\partial^2 \varphi}{\partial x^2} - \frac{\partial^2 \varphi_N}{\partial x^2}] + H(u_N) [\frac{\partial \varphi}{\partial t} - \frac{\partial \varphi_N}{\partial t}] \} \, dx dt$$

it follows from $I_N \to 0$ and the approximation properties of the chapeau functions that (u^*, H^*) is the enthalpy solution of the Stefan problem. Uniqueness of this solution assures that the sequence $\{u_N\}$ converges as well.

References

[1] J. R. Cannon, *The One-Dimensional Heat Equation*, Addison-Wesley, Reading, Mass., 1984.

[2] O. A. Ladyzenskaja, V. A. Solonnikov and N. N. Ural'ceva, *Linear and Quasilinear Equations of Parabolic*, Translation of Math. Monographs 23, Amer. Math. Soc., Providence, R.I., 1968.

[3] S. Luckhaus, *Solutions of the two-phase Stefan problem with the Gibbs-Thomson law for the melting temperature*, Preprint # 81, University of Bonn, FRG.

[4] G. H. Meyer, *A numerical method for two-phase Stefan problems*, SIAM J. Num. Anal. 8 (1971), 555–568.

[5] G. H. Meyer, *On computing free boundaries which are not level sets*, Proc. 1987 IRSEE Conference, Pitman Research Notes in Mathematics Series 185 (1990), 138–154.

Mixed variational approach for shape optimization in contact problem with prescribed friction

A. MYSLINSKI

System Research Institute
01–447, Warsaw, ul. Newelska 6, Poland

Abstract. This paper deals with a shape optimization problem of an elastic body in unilateral contact with a rigid foundation. The contact with prescribed Coulomb friction occurs at a portion of the boundary of the body. This optimization problem is solved using mixed variational approach where the function satisfying the state inequality and its gradient are selected as independent state variables. Necessary optimality condition is formulated. Conforming finite element method is used to discretize this optimization problem. Convergence of the finite-dimensional approximation is shown. Numerical examples are provided.

Keywords. Shape optimization, elliptic variational inequalities, unilateral contact problem, mixed finite element, convergence of approximation.

Mathematics subject classifications: 35J85, 49A51, 65K10, 65N30

1. INTRODUCTION

This paper is concerned with a shape optimization problem of an elastic body in unilateral contact with a rigid foundation. It is assumed that the contact with prescribed Coulomb friction [3,9] occurs at a portion of the boundary of the body. The equilibrium state of this contact problem is described by an elliptic variational inequality. The existence, uniqueness and the regularity of solution to this variational inequality were investigated in [3,9].

The shape optimization problem for the elastic body in contact consists in finding in a contact region, such shape of the boundary of the domain occupied by the body that the normal contact stress is minimized. It is assumed that the volume of the body is constant as well as that the function describing the boundary of the body is bounded. Moreover this function has bounded second order derivatives.

In literature [6,7,8,13,15] this optimization problem was considered using variational methods where the function satisfying the state inequality was selected as independent state variable. From numerical point of view such selection of the state variable causes that the gradient of the solution to the state inequality is not calculated accurately [14]. To increase accuracy of numerical computations one can apply decomposition approach to solve this optimization problem numerically. In this approach based on Hellinger-Reissner variational principle [2] the function satisfying the state inequality and its gradient are chosen as independent state variables.

In this paper we shall consider the shape optimization for an elastic body in unilateral contact employing this mixed variational approach. Using this approach combined with material derivative method [8,15] we calculate the directional derivative of the cost functional and we formulate necessary optimality condition. Finite element method is used as discretization method and the convergence of the finite-dimensional approximation is shown using the method proposed in [6]. The discretized shape optimization problem is solved numerically. Numerical examples are provided.

2. Contact problem formulation

Consider deformations of an elastic body occupying domain $\Omega = \Omega(v) \subset R^2$ depending on a function v. Domain $\Omega(v)$ has the following geometrical structure

$$\Omega = \Omega(v) = \{(x_1, x_2) \in R^2 : 0 < x_1 < g_1, \quad 0 < v(x_1) < x_2 \leq g_2\} \tag{2.1}$$

where g_1 and g_2 are given positive constants. The boundary Γ of the domain Ω is divided into three disjoint pieces Γ_0, Γ_1 and $\Gamma_2 = \Gamma_2(v)$ described by v. We shall assume that the body is subjected to body forces $f = (f_1, f_2)$. Moreover surface tractions $p = (p_1, p_2)$ are applied along the boundary Γ_1. We shall assume that the body is clamped along a portion Γ_0 of the boundary Γ and that the contact conditions are prescribed on the portion Γ_2 of the boundary Γ.

We denote by $u = (u_1, u_2)$ the displacement of the body and by $\sigma = \{\sigma_{ij}\}$, $i, j = 1, 2$ the stress field in the body. Moreover $u = u(v)$ and $\sigma = \sigma(v)$. Note that throughout the paper we shall use the standard notations and conventions of elasticity [3,9].

In the classical formulation of contact problems one looks for a displacement field u satisfying the equilibrium equations [3,6,7,9] :

$$\partial \sigma_{ij}(x)/\partial x_j + f_i(x) = 0 \quad \text{in } \Omega(v), \quad i, j = 1, 2 \tag{2.2}$$

where the stress tensor σ and the strain tensor $e(u)$ are related by means of the linear Hook's law [3,5] :

$$\sigma_{ij} = c_{ijkl}(x) e_{kl}(u), \quad e_{kl}(u) = 1/2(\frac{\partial u_k}{\partial x_l} + \frac{\partial u_l}{\partial x_k}) \tag{2.3}$$

where the elasticity coefficients $c_{ijkl}, i, j, k, l = 1, 2$ satisfy usual symmetry and ellipticity conditions [3,9]. The following boundary conditions are satisfied :

$$u_i = 0 \qquad \text{on } \Gamma_0\,, \quad i = 1, 2 \tag{2.4)(a}$$

$$\sigma_{ij}(x) n_j = p_i(x), \quad \text{on } \Gamma_1, \quad i, j = 1, 2 \tag{2.4)(b}$$

$$u_2 \geq -v, \quad \sigma_N \geq 0, \quad (u_2 + v)\sigma_N = 0 \qquad \text{on } \Gamma_2 \tag{2.4)(c}$$

$$\sigma_T u_T + |u_T| = 0, \quad |\sigma_T| \leq 1 \quad \text{on } \Gamma_2 \tag{2.4)(d}$$

where σ_N and σ_T are the normal and tangent component of the stress tensor σ to the boundary Γ_2 respectively.

We shall consider the mixed variational formulation of the problem (2.2)-(2.4). Let us introduce :

$$V = \{z \in [H^1(\Omega)]^2 \quad : \quad z_i = 0 \quad \text{on} \quad \Gamma_0, \quad i = 1,2\}$$
$$K = \{z \in V \quad : \quad z_2 \geq -v, \quad \text{on } \Gamma_2\} \tag{2.5}$$

Let us denote

$$S(\Omega) = \{\sigma = \{\sigma_{ij}\}_{i,j=1}^2 \in [L^2(\Omega)]^4 : \sigma_{12} = \sigma_{21}\} \tag{2.6)(a}$$

$$Q(\Omega) = \{\sigma \in S \quad : \quad div\ \sigma \in [L^2(\Omega)]^2\} \tag{2.6)(b}$$

$$L(.,.) : Q \times K \to R$$

$$L(\tau, q) = 1/2 \int_\Omega b_{ijkl}\tau_{ij}\tau_{kl}dx + \int_\Omega \tau_{ij}e_{kl}(q)dx - \int_\Omega fqdx$$
$$- \int_{\Gamma_1} pqds - \int_{\Gamma_2(v)} \tau_T q_T ds \tag{2.7}$$

where $b_{ijkl}, i, j, k, l = 1,2$ are the compliance coefficients satisfying symmetry and ellipticity conditions [3,9]. The mixed variational formulation of the problem (2.2)-(2.4) takes the form

Find the pair $(\sigma, u) \in Q \times K$ satisfying :

$$L(\sigma, q) \leq L(\sigma, u) \leq L(\tau, u) \quad \forall \tau \in Q, \quad q \in K \tag{2.8}$$

There exists a unique solution to the problem (2.8) [3,9]. The necessary optimality conditions characterizing a saddle point of the problem (2.8) take the form [11] :

$$\int_\Omega b_{ijkl}\sigma_{ij}\tau_{kl}dx + \int_\Omega \tau_{ij}e_{kl}(q)dx - \int_{\Gamma_2(v)} \tau_T q_T ds = 0 \quad \forall \tau_{ij} \in Q$$
$$\int_\Omega \sigma_{ij}e_{kl}(\eta)dx - \int_\Omega f\eta dx - \int_{\Gamma_1} p\eta ds - \int_{\Gamma_2(v)} \sigma_T \eta_T ds \geq 0, \quad \forall \eta \in K \tag{2.9}$$

where $i, j, k, l = 1,2$.

In proof of Lemma 5.2 and Theorem 5.1 we shall need the dual variational formulation [3] of the problem (2.2)–(2.4). We employ the dual formulation using the spaces of selfequilibrated tensor fields [2,9,10,16]. In order to do it let us introduce the following space:

$$Q_0(\Omega) = \{\tau \in S \ : \quad \int_\Omega \tau_{ij}e_{kl}(v)\ dx \geq - \int_{\Gamma_2} \tau_N v_N\ ds \quad \forall v \in K\} \tag{2.10}$$

Assume that the tensor field $\sigma^0 \in S$ such that:

(2.11)
$$\int_\Omega \sigma^0_{ij} e_{kl}(v)\, dx - \int_\Omega fv\, dx - \int_{\Gamma_1} pv\, ds - \int_{\Gamma_2} \sigma^0_N v_N\, ds - \int_{\Gamma_2} \sigma^0_T v_T\, ds = 0 \quad \forall v \in V$$

is given. The construction of tensor field σ^0 is discussed in [2,9,10]. By $Q_1(\Omega)$ we denote the space:

(2.12)
$$Q_1(\Omega) = \{\tau \in S \ : \quad \tau \text{ satisfies } (2.11)\}$$

Note that $Q = Q_1 \oplus Q_0$.

The dual variational problem to the problem (2.2)–(2.4) [12] can be written in the form:

$$\text{Find } \epsilon \in Q_0 \text{ such that } \Theta(\epsilon) \leq \Theta(\tau) \quad \forall \tau \in Q_0$$

(2.13)
$$\Theta(\tau) = \frac{1}{2}\int_\Omega b_{ijkl}\tau_{ij}\tau_{kl}\, dx - \int_\Omega b_{ijkl}\tau_{ij}\sigma^0_{kl}\, dx$$

The functional $\Theta(\tau)$ represents complementary energy [2,3] of the body in contact. There exists a unique solution $\epsilon \in Q_0$ to the problem (2.13) and moreover [2,9]:

(2.14)
$$\sigma = \sigma^0 + \epsilon$$

where σ satisfies (2.9).

3. Formulation of the shape optimization problem

Let $\tilde{\Omega} \subset R^2$ be a domain such that for all v : $\Omega(v) \subset \tilde{\Omega}$. Let M be a set :

(3.1)
$$M = \{\phi \in [H^1(\tilde{\Omega})]^2 : \quad \phi \geq 0 \quad \text{on } \tilde{\Omega}\ , \quad \|\phi\|_{H^1(\tilde{\Omega})} \leq 1\}$$

We shall consider domains $\Omega(v)$ depending on a function v from the set U_{ad} defined by :

(3.2)
$$U_{ad} = \{v \in C^{1,1}([0, g_1]) \quad : \quad |\frac{dv}{dx_1}| \leq c_1, \quad \forall x_1 \in [0, g_1], \quad |\frac{d^2v}{dx_1^2}| \leq c_2 \quad \text{a.e. in } (0, g_1), \quad \int_{\Omega(v)} dx = c_3\}$$

where c_1,c_2 and c_3 are given positive constants. The set U_{ad} is assumed to be nonempty. $C^{1,1}([0, g_1])$ [6] denotes the set of Lipschitz continuous functions on $[0, g_1]$ having also

Lipschitz continuous first derivatives. We shall consider the following shape optimization problem :

For given function $\phi \in M$, find function $v \in U_{ad}$ minimizing the cost functional

$$J_\phi(v) = \int_{\Gamma_2(v)} \sigma_N \phi_N ds \tag{3.3}$$

over the set U_{ad}. σ_N is a normal component of the stress field σ satisfying (2.9)-(2.10).

The cost functional (3.3) approximates normal contact stress on the boundary Γ_2, i.e., original boundary flux cost functional [6,13]. Since the shape optimization problem with the boundary flux cost functional is difficult to handle it we modify the original cost functional introducing an auxiliary function ϕ [6,13] and the form (3.3). The shape optimization problem (3.3) consists in finding such boundary $\Gamma_2(v)$ depending on function v that the normal contact stress is minimized. It is assumed that the volume of the body is constant as well as that function v is bounded and has bounded first and second derivatives.

4. Necessary optimality condition

Lemma 4.1: The directional derivative $dJ_\phi(v;k)$ of the cost functional (3.3) for given function $\phi \in M$ with respect to $v \in U_{ad}$ at a point $v \in U_{ad}$ in a direction $k \in U_{ad}$ has the form :

$$\begin{aligned} dJ_\phi(v;k) = & \int_\Gamma [\sigma_{ij} e_{kl}(\phi + w) - f(\phi + w)] k(x_1) n_2 ds - \\ & \int_{\Gamma_1} [(\nabla p(\phi + w) + p \nabla(\phi + w)) k(x_1) + p(\phi + w) D] ds + \\ & E_1(\lambda, u) - E_1(\sigma, \phi + w) - E_2(\sigma, \lambda, u) \end{aligned} \tag{4.1}$$

where

(4.2)

$$E_1(\tau, q) = \int_{\Gamma_2(v)} \{[(\nabla \tau k(x_1))_T - (\bar{N} + \bar{N}^*) \tau_N] q_T + [(\nabla q(k(x_1))_T - (\bar{N} + \bar{N}^*) q_N] \tau_T + \tau_T q_T D\} ds$$

$$E_2(\sigma, \tau, q) = \int_\Gamma b_{ijkl} \sigma_{ij} \tau_{kl} + e_{ij}(q) \tau_{kl}) k(x_1) n_2 ds \tag{4.3}$$

$$D = -n_1 n_2 \frac{dk}{dx_1}, \quad \bar{N} = D(1 - n_1, -n_2), \quad \bar{N}^* \text{ is a transpose of } \bar{N}$$

The stress field $\lambda \in Q$ and the displacement field $w \in V_1$ are solution of the following adjoint system :

$$\int_\Omega (b_{ijkl} \lambda_{ij} \tau_{kl} + e_{ij}(\phi + w) \tau_{kl}) dx - \int_{\Gamma_2(v)} \tau_T (\phi + w)_T ds = 0 \quad \forall \tau \in Q \tag{4.4}$$

(4.5) $$\int_{\Omega} \lambda_{ij} e_{kl}(\eta) dx - \int_{\Gamma_2(v)} \lambda_T \eta_T ds = 0 \quad \forall \eta \in V_1$$

(4.6) $$V_1 = \{z \in V : z_2 = v \quad \text{on B}\}, \quad B = \{x \in \Gamma_2(v) : u_2 = v\}$$

Proof : The material derivative $dJ_\phi(v : k)$ is defined by :

(4.7) $$dJ_\phi(v; k) = \lim_{t \to 0} [J_\phi(v_t) - J_\phi(v)]/t$$

where $v_t = v + tk$. Taking into account that the cost functional (3.3) can be written in the form [3,7,9] :

(4.8) $$J_\phi(v) = \int_{\Omega} \sigma_{ij} e_{kl}(\phi) dx - \int_{\Omega} f \phi dx - \int_{\Gamma_1} p \phi ds - \int_{\Gamma_2(v)} \sigma_T \phi_T ds$$

as well as applying the material derivative method [8,13,15] to transport the cost functional $J_\phi(v_t)$ into a fixed domain $\Omega(v)$ and to calculate the limit (4.7) with $t \to 0$ we obtain (4.1). For details see [11].

Lemma 4.2 : There exist Lagrange multiplier $\mu \in R^3$ such that for all functions $k(x_1) \in U_{ad}$ the following condition holds :

(4.9) $$dJ_\phi(v; k) + \mu_1 \int_{\Gamma} k(x_1) n_2 ds + \mu_2 sgn(\frac{dv}{dx_1}) \frac{dk}{dx_1} + \mu_3 sgn(\frac{d^2 v}{dx_1^2}) \frac{d^2 k}{dx_1^2} \geq 0$$

where $dJ_\phi(v; k)$ is given by (4.1) and the function sgn is defined as follows : $sgn(x) = 1$ for $x > 0$, $sgn(x) = 0$ for $x = 0$, $sgn(x) = -1$ for $x < 0$.

Proof : is standard [1].

5. The finite-dimensional approximation of the shape optimization problem

To discretize optimization problem (3.3) we shall use the conforming finite element method [2]. Let $h > 0$ be a discretization parameter. We shall approximate the set U_{ad} by the set U_{had} [2,6] determined by :

(5.1) $$U_{had} = \{v \in C^1([0, g_1]) : v_{|[\omega_{i-1}, \omega_i]} \in P_1([\omega_{i-1}, \omega_i])\} \cap U_{ad}$$

where $0 = \omega_0 < \omega_1 \cdots < \omega_\kappa = g_1$ is a partition of the segment $[0, g_1]$, $P_1([\omega_{i-1}, \omega_i])$ denotes the set of all linear polynomials of on the segment $[\omega_{i-1}, \omega_i]$. For any $v_h \in U_{had}$ we define:

(5.2) $$\Omega(v_h) = \{(x_1, x_2) \in R^2 : x_1 \in (0, g_1), x_2 \in (v_h(x_1), g_2)\}$$

By $\mathcal{T}_h$ we denote a family of partitions of domain $\Omega(v_h)$ into a triangular elements $O_i \in \mathcal{T}_h$ such that the whole segment $\{(x_1, x_2) : x_1 \in [\omega_{i-1}, \omega_i], x_2 = v_h(x_1)\}$ is the whole side of a triangle $O_i \in \mathcal{T}_h$. It is assumed that the usual requirements [2,9] concerning the mutual position of two triangles belonging to $\mathcal{T}_h(v_h)$ are satisfied. Moreover it is assumed that the family of partitions $\mathcal{T}_h$ of domains $\Omega(v_h)$ is uniformly regular [2] for $h \to 0$ with respect to $v_h \in U_{had}$. By $\Omega_h = \Omega_h(v_h)$ we shall denote the domain $\Omega(v_h)$ with a given partition $\mathcal{T}_h$. Let us introduce the finite dimensional space V_h approximating the space V:

$$V_h = \{z \in [C(\Omega)]^2 \cap V : z_{|O_i} \in [P_1(O_i)]^2, O_i \in \mathcal{T}_h\} \tag{5.3)(a}$$

Moreover we denote by K_h and M_h the sets approximating the sets K and M respectively:

$$\begin{aligned} K_h &= \{z \in V_h \quad : \quad z_{2h} \geq -v_h \text{ on } \Gamma_2(v_h)\} \\ M_h &= \{\phi \in [C(\Omega)]^2 \cap M \quad : \quad \phi_{|O_i} \in [P_1(O_i)]^2, \quad \forall O_i \in \mathcal{T}_h\} \end{aligned} \tag{5.3)(b}$$

Let us introduce the discretization of the dual problem (2.13) using superelement technique [2,9,10]. Let each triangle $O_i \in \mathcal{T}_h$ be divided into 3 subtriangles E_j, $j = 1,2,3$ by connecting the vertices e_j with the center of gravity C. Let us define the following subspaces:

$$\mathcal{A}(E_j) = \{\tau \in S(E_j) \cap [P_1(E_j)]^4 \quad : \quad \text{div } \tau = 0 \text{ in } E_j\} \tag{5.4}$$

Moreover

$$\begin{aligned} \mathcal{B}(O_i) = \{\tau = \{\tau^k\}_{k=1}^3 \quad &: \quad \tau_{|E_j} = \tau^j \in \mathcal{A}(E_j), \\ \tau^j + \tau^{j-1} &= 0 \text{ on } Ce_j, \quad j = 1,2,3, \quad \tau^0 = \tau^3\} \end{aligned} \tag{5.5}$$

$$\begin{aligned} \mathcal{B}_h(\Omega_h) = \{\tau \in S(\Omega_h) \quad &: \quad \tau_{|O_i} \in \mathcal{B}(O_i) \quad \forall O_i \in \mathcal{T}_h, \\ \tau_{|O_i} + \tau_{|O_l} &= 0 \text{ on } O_i \cap O_l, \quad \forall O_i,\ O_l \in \mathcal{T}_h\} \end{aligned} \tag{5.6}$$

$\mathcal{B}_h(\Omega_h)$ is the space of such tensor fields from the space $\mathcal{B}_h(O_i)$ that their boundary tractions are continuous on any interelement boundary. Finally the spaces Q_0 and Q_1 are approximated by the spaces Q_{0h} and O_{1h}, respectively, given by

$$Q_{0h} = \mathcal{B}_h(\Omega_h) \cap Q_0(\Omega_h) \quad Q_{1h} = S(\Omega_d) \oplus \mathcal{B}_h(\Omega_d) \tag{5.7}$$

where Ω_d is a domain such that for all h: $\Omega_d \supset \Omega_h$. The form of the space Q_{1h} follows from the construction of the tensor field σ^0 [2,9,10], i.e., $\sigma^0 = \sigma_1^0 + \sigma_2^0$, $\sigma_1^0 \in S(\Omega_d)$, $\sigma_2^0 \in \mathcal{B}_h(\Omega_d)$. Problem (2.13) is approximated by the following problem:

$$\begin{aligned} &\text{Find } (\epsilon_h \in Q_{0h} \text{ such that} : \Theta_h(\epsilon_h) \leq \Theta_h(\tau_h) \quad \forall \tau_h \in Q_{0h} \\ &\Theta_h(\tau_h) = \frac{1}{2} \int_{\Omega_h} b_{ijkl} \tau_{hij} \tau_{hkl}\, dx + \int_{\Omega_h} b_{ijkl} \tau_{hij} \sigma_{kl}^0\, dx \end{aligned} \tag{5.8}$$

The shape optimization problem (3.3) is approximated by the following finite-dimensional problem:

For given function $\phi_h \in M_h$, find function

$v_h \in U_{had}$ minimizing the cost functional

$$J_{\phi_h}(v_h) = \int_{\Gamma_2(v_h)} \sigma_{hN}\phi_{hN}\, ds \tag{5.9}$$

over the set U_{had}

The pair $(\sigma_h, u_h) \in Q_h \times K_h$ satisfies the following problem approximating the problem (2.9):

$$\int_{\Omega_h} (b_{ijkl}\sigma_{hij} + e_{ij}(u_h))\varphi_{hkl} dx - \int_{\Gamma_h} \varphi_{hT} u_{hT} ds = 0, \quad \forall \varphi_{hij} \in Q_h \tag{5.10}$$

$$\int_{\Omega_h} (\sigma_{hij} e_{kl}(\xi_h) - f\xi_h) dx - \int_{\Gamma_1} p\xi_h ds - \int_{\Gamma_2(v_h)} \sigma_{hT}\xi_{hT} ds \geq 0, \quad \forall \xi_h \in K_h \tag{5.11}$$

It can be shown [2,9] that:

$$\sigma_h = \sigma^0 + \epsilon_h \tag{5.12}$$

where $\sigma_h \in Q_h$, $\epsilon_h \in Q_{0h}$, $\sigma^0 \in Q_{1h}$, and $Q_h = Q_{1h} \oplus Q_{0h}$.
Lemma 5.1 : For given function $\phi_h \in M_h$ and for any $h > 0$ there exists an optimal solution $\hat{v}_h \in U_{had}$ to the problem (5.4).

Proof : is standard [9,12].

In order to show the convergence of the proposed finite-dimensional approximation we shall need the following auxiliary Lemmas :

Lemma 5.2 : Let $v_h \to v$ in $C^1([0, g_1])$ for $h \to 0$. Let $\epsilon \in Q_0$ and $\epsilon_h \in Q_{0h}$ be the solutions of problems (2.13) and (5.8) respectively. Let Ω_d be a domain such that: $\Omega_d \supset \Omega_h$ for all $v_h \in U_{had}$. Let $\tilde{\epsilon}_h$ (resp. $\tilde{\epsilon}$) denote ϵ_h (resp. ϵ) satisfying (5.8) (resp. (2.13)) extended by zero to the domain $\Omega_d \setminus \Omega_h$ (resp. $\Omega_d \setminus \Omega(v)$). Then there exists subsequence $\{h'\}$ of the sequence $\{h\}$ denoted further by $\{h\}$ such for $h \to 0$:

$$\tilde{\epsilon_h} \to \tilde{\epsilon} \quad \text{strongly in } [L^2(\Omega_d)]^4 \tag{5.13}$$

Proof : From boundedness of the sequence $\tilde{\epsilon}_h$ for all $h > 0$ [9,12] follows the existence of an element $\tilde{\epsilon} \in [L^2(\Omega_d)]^4$ and a sequence $\{h'\} \subset \{h\}$ denoted further by $\{h\}$ such that for $h \to 0$ we have :

$$\tilde{\epsilon_h} \to \tilde{\epsilon} \quad \text{weakly in } [L^2(\Omega_d)]^4 \tag{5.14}$$

Setting in (5.11) $\xi_h = w_{kh}$ where w_{kh} is a linear interpolate of suitable chosen smooth function w_k [12] such that $w_{kh} \to \tilde{w}$ as well as taking into account (2.14), (5.12) we can show that $\tilde{\epsilon}_{|\Omega(v)} \in Q_0$. Moreover it is easy to show that $\tilde{\epsilon} = 0$ on $\Omega_d \setminus \Omega(v)$ [12]. Note that the necessary optimality condition for (5.8) takes the form:

$$d\Theta_h(\epsilon_h; \tau_h) \geq 0 \quad \forall \tau_h \in Q_{0h} \tag{5.15)(a}$$

where $d\Theta_h(\epsilon_h; \tau_h)$ is defined by (4.7). Selecting suitable auxiliary tensor τ_h in (5.15)(a) [12] and passing to the limit with $h \to 0$ in (5.8), taking into account (5.14) we obtain

$$\tilde{\Theta}(\epsilon_h) \to \tilde{\Theta}(\epsilon) \tag{5.15)(b}$$

i.e. $\tilde{\epsilon}_{|\Omega(v)} = \epsilon$. From (5.14),(5.15)(a),(b) follows (5.13). For details see [12].

Lemma 5.3 : Let $v_h \to v$ in $C^1([0, g_1])$ for $h \to 0$. Let $u \in K$ be a solution of the primal variational problem to the problem (2.2),(2.4) :

Find $u \in K$ such that :

$$\begin{aligned} &\int_{\Omega(v)} c_{ijkl} e_{ij}(u) e_{kl}(z-u)dx - \int_{\Omega(v)} f_i z_i dx - \\ &\int_{\Gamma_1} p_i(z_i - u_i)ds + \int_{\Gamma_2(v)} (|z_T| - |u_T|)ds \geq 0, \qquad \forall z \in K \end{aligned} \tag{5.16}$$

Let $u_h \in K_h$ be a solution of the discretized problem (5.16) with Ω_h instead of $\Omega(v)$. Then there exists subsequence $\{h'\} \subset \{h\}$ denoted further by $\{h\}$ such that for $h \to 0$:

$$u_h \to u \quad \text{weakly in } [H^1(G_m)]^2 \tag{5.17}$$

for all natural m. The set G_m is given by :

$$G_m(v) = \{(x_1, x_2) \in R^2 : x_1 \in (0, g_1), \quad v(x_1) + \frac{1}{m} < x_2 \leq g_2\} \tag{5.18}$$

Proof : is based on similar arguments as proof of Lemma 5.2. For details see [12] as well as [6, Lemma 7.5].

Taking into account Lemmas 5.2 and 5.3 we are able to prove :

Theorem 5.1 : Let $\hat{v}_h \in U_{had}$ be an optimal solution of problem (5.9). Then each accumulation point of the sequence $\{\hat{v}_h\}$ is an optimal solution of the problem (3.3).

Proof : Since for all $h > 0, U_{had} \subset U_{ad}$ and U_{ad} is compact in the $C^1([0, g_1])$ topology [6] there exists a subsequence $\{\hat{v}_{h'}\} \subset \{\hat{v}_h\}$ denoted further by $\{\hat{v}_h\}$ and an element $\hat{v} \in U_{ad}$ such that for $h \to 0$ we have :

$$\hat{v}_h \to \hat{v} \text{ uniformely in } C^1([0, g_1]) \tag{5.19}$$

From (5.19) as well as Lemmas 5.2 and 5.3 it follows that for $h \to 0$ we obtain

$$\hat{u}_h \to \hat{u} \quad \text{weakly in } [H^1(G_m(\hat{v}))]^2 \tag{5.20}$$

$$\hat{\epsilon}_h \to \hat{\epsilon} \quad \text{strongly in } [L^2(\Omega_d)]^4 \tag{5.21}$$

Moreover from (2.14),(5.12) it follows that the pair $(\hat{\sigma}_h, \hat{u}_h) \in Q_h \times K_h$ satisfies (5.10), (5.11) with $\Omega_h = \Omega_h(\hat{v}_h)$ and the pair $(\hat{\sigma}, \hat{u}) \in Q \times K$ satisfies (2.9) with $\Omega = \Omega(\hat{v})$. Taking into account (5.9) as well as (5.19),(5.20),(5.21) we obtain

$$\liminf_{h\to 0} J_{\phi_h}(\hat{v}_h) \geq J_\phi(\hat{v}) \tag{5.22}$$

Let $v^* \in U_{ad}$ be an arbitrary element and let $v_h \in U_{had}$ be a sequence such that :

$$v_h \to v^* \quad \text{uniformly in} \quad C^1([0, g_1]) \tag{5.23}$$

The existence of such sequence has been shown in [12] and is based on a result in [6]. From (5.9),(5.20),(5.21) as well as (5.22) we obtain :

$$J_\phi(\hat{v}) \leq \liminf_{h\to 0} J_{\phi_h}(\hat{v}_h) \leq J_\phi(v^*) \tag{5.24}$$

what proves that $\hat{v} \in U_{ad}$ is an optimal solution of the problem (5.9).

6. Numerical realization

The discretized shape optimization problem (5.9) was solved numerically. Uzawa algorithm combined with SOR algorithm [5,9] are used to solve the discretized state system (5.10),(5.11). Conjugate gradient method combined with shifted penalty function method [4] are used as optimization methods to minimize the cost functional (5.9) over the set U_{had}.

The computations were carried out for the elastic body consisting of the material characterized by the Poisson's ratio $\nu = 0.29$ and the Young modulus $E = 2.1 \quad 10^{11} Nm^{-2}$. The domain Ω_h is determined by (5.2). For the sake of simplicity, in the computations the set U_{ad} given by (3.2) was approximated by a set of piecewise linear functions [6] with local regularization of the second order at the nodal points of the boundary $\Gamma_2(v_h)$. The boundary Γ_h of the domain Ω_h was divided into three pieces in such a way that the problem (5.9),(5.10),(5.11) is symmetric with respect to the line $x_1 = g_1/2$ [12]. Due to this symmetry in the computations one half of the domain Ω_h was used only. The domain Ω_h is divided into 128 triangular elements. Function $\phi \in M$ defined in (3.1) is selected as $\phi = 1$ on $\tilde{\Omega} \supset \Omega(v_h)$ for all v_h.
The other numerical data are as follows : $g_1 = 8, g_2 = 1, f_i = 0 \quad i = 1,2, p_1 = 0, p_2 = -5.6 \times 10^6$.

Table 1 shows the initial shape S_i and optimal shape S_o of one half of the contact boundary Γ_2. Note [6,7,11,12], that for body with boundary S_i the normal contact stress has its peak in the middle of the contact boundary. For the body with optimal shape boundary

S_o normal contact stress is almost constant and shows very mild increase approaching the middle point of the contact boundary.
The speed of convergence of the proposed algorithm is slow. This speed depends on a proper choice of parameter values in Uzawa and SOR algorithms as well as on accuracy of the computing of the Lagrange multipliers.

x_1	0.0	0.5	1.0	1.5	2.0	2.5	3.0	3.5	4.0
S_i	0.12	0.10	0.08	0.06	0.04	0.02	0.01	0.00	0.00
S_o	0.12	0.08	0.04	0.01	0.00	0.00	0.03	0.06	0.08

Table 1. Initial and optimal shapes of the contact boundary

REFERENCES

[1] J. Céa, "Optimisation.Theorie et Algorithmes," Dunod, Paris, 1971.

[2] Ph. Ciarlet, "The Finite Element Method for Elliptic Problems," North-Holland, Amsterdam, 1978.

[3] G. Duvaut, J.L. Lions, "Les inequations en mecanique et en physique," Dunod, Paris, 1972.

[4] W. Findeisen, J. Szymanowski, A. Wierzbicki,, "Computational Methods of Optimization," in Polish, Polish Scientific Publisher, Warsaw, 1977.

[5] R. Glowinski, M. Fortin, "Augmented Lagrangian Methods : Application to the numerical solution of boundary value problems," North-Holland, Amsterdam, 1983.

[6] J. Haslinger, P. Neittaanmäki, "Finite Element Approximation for Optimal Shape Design. Theory and Applications," J. Wiley and Sons, 1988.

[7] J. Haslinger, P. Neittaanmäki, T. Tihonen, *Shape optimization in contact problems based on penalization of the state inequality*, Aplikace Matematiky 31(1986), 54–77.

[8] E.J. Haug, K.K. Choi, V. Komkov, "Design Sensitivity Analysis of Structural Systems," Academic Press, 1986.

[9] I. Hlavacek, J. Haslinger, I. Necas, J. Lovisek,, "Solving of Variational Inequalities in Mechanics," in Russian, Mir, Moscow, 1986.

[10] I.Hlavacek, *Shape optimization in two-dimensional elasticity by the dual finite element method*, Mathematical Modelling and Numerical Analysis 21(1987), 63–92.

[11] A. Myslinski, *Shape optimization of a contact problem by the dual variational method*, Preprint, 1989.

[12] A.Myslinski, *Mixed finite element approximation of shape optimization in contact problems*, Preprint, 1990.

[13] P. Neittaanmäki, J. Sokolowski, J.P. Zolesio, *Optimization of the domain in elliptic variational inequalities*, Applied Mathematics and Optimization 18(1988), 85–98.

[14] H. Rodrigues, *Shape optimal design of elastic bodies using a mixed variational formulation*, Computer Methods in Applied Mechanics and Engineering 69(1988), 29–44.

[15] J. Sokolowski, J.P. Zolesio, *Shape sensitivity analysis of contact problem with prescribed friction*, Nonlinear Analysis,Theory,Methods and Applications 12(1988), 1399–1411.

[16] J.Sokolowski, *Sensitivity analysis of contact problems with prescribed friction*, Applied Mathematics and Optimization 18(1988), 98-117.

NONSMOOTH PENALTY TECHNIQUES IN CONTROL OF THE CONTINUOUS CASTING PROCESS

TIMO MÄNNIKKÖ and MARKO M. MÄKELÄ

Department of Mathematics, University of Jyväskylä,
Seminaarinkatu 15, SF-40100 Jyväskylä, Finland

Abstract. We introduce a mathematical model which is used to simulate the continuous casting process and to control the secondary cooling water sprays. The main object is to minimize the defects in the final products. The problem is formulated as an optimal control problem where the cost function is constructed according to certain metallurgical criteria and constraints. The temperature distribution of the strand is calculated by solving a nonlinear heat equation with free boundaries between solid and liquid phases.

The state constraints are penalized by using (a) the usual quadratic penalty functions, which are differentiable, and (b) so called exact penalty functions, which are nonsmooth (nondifferentiable). Due to the phase change, the cost function is nonsmooth even in the case of quadratic penalties. Therefore, instead of the classical gradient-based algorithms, we use Proximal Bundle method, which is one of the most efficient methods of nonsmooth optimization.

Some numerical results, calculated with the Cray supercomputer, are also presented.

Keywords. Continuous casting, Free boundary problems, Nonsmooth optimization, Optimal control, Proximal bundle method.

1980 Mathematics subject classifications: 65K10, 65K05.

1. INTRODUCTION

In this paper we consider the simulation and control of the continuous casting of steel. The process can be described as follows: Molten steel is poured down from the tundish into the water cooled mold, where the metal gets a solid shell. After the mold (in the secondary cooling region) the strand is supported by rollers and cooled down by water sprays, so that eventually the solidification is completed. The spray cooling region is further divided into several cooling zones. After the water sprays the strand is cooled down only by radiation. The strand is straightened at the unbending point and in the cutting point it is cut up.

The quality of the product depends on the behavior of the surface temperature and the front of solidification as functions of time; undercooling of the strand can result too long liquid pool, and overcooling can lead to the formation of cracks. Moreover, there must be a smooth transition of the surface temperature, with minimum reheating, as the steel passes from a cooling region to an other. Thus, the secondary cooling plays a major role in the casting process, because the intensity of the water sprays affects highly on the solidification rate.

Measuring the temperature distribution of the strand directly is extremely difficult, and therefore, it is more convenient to calculate the distribution numerically. The main problem in the numerical approximation is that the position of the moving boundary (i.e., the front of solidification) is not known *a priori*, and the position depends on the variables to be solved. The front of solidification is not sharp, but between the solid and liquid phases there exists so called mushy zone, which is considered to be partly solid and partly liquid. Furthermore, there exists a discontinuity at the moving boundary: Due to the effect of latent heat, the temperature gradient across the phase interfaces is discontinuous. We present here a mathematical model which is developed to overcome these difficulties.

2. Calculation of the temperature distribution

Our mathematical model is two dimensional, i.e., the heat conduction to the withdrawal direction is neglected, due to the relatively high withdrawal rate and low thermal conductivity of the steel. Moreover, we assume that the casting speed v remains constant. Hence, the 'age' (or, so called residence time) of a strand cross-section at the distance z is $t = z/v$, so that the withdrawal coordinate axis can be identified with the time axis.

Since the casting speed is constant, the temperature distribution in the mold cannot be controlled with the secondary cooling water sprays. Therefore, we consider only the portion of the machine which begins at the end of the mold (for the calculation of the temperature in the mold we refer to Männikkö [**8**], Männikkö and Mäkelä [**9**]). Furthermore, we omit the portion of the machine after the unbending point. The time events when the cross-section passes the end of the mold, the end of the spray cooling region, the maximum length of the liquid pool and the unbending point are denoted by t_1, t_2, t_3 and t_4, respectively.

Let $\Omega \subset \mathbb{R}^2$ denote the cross-section of the strand. The geometry of Ω can be, e.g., square, rectangle (possibly with rounded corners) or circle. Let $T = T(x,t)$ be the unknown temperature distribution, a function of $x \in \Omega$ and $t \in [t_1, t_4]$.

We use so called enthalpy formulation of the heat equation: Let us define the enthalpy function H and the Kirchhoff's transformation K by

$$H(T) = \int_0^T \left[\rho(\xi)c(\xi) - \rho(\xi)L\dot{f}_S(\xi)\right] d\xi, \qquad K(T) = \int_0^T k(\xi)\, d\xi,$$

where ρ denotes the steel density, c the specific heat, k the thermal conductivity, L the latent heat of the solidification and the function f_S describes the fraction of the solid phase in the mushy zone (the notation $\dot{f}_S$ means the derivative of f_S with respect to temperature).

The temperature dependent quantities ρ, c and k are defined separately in several disjoint temperature intervals, inside which they are assumed to be constants, as is shown in figure 1. The mushy zone is located between the solidus and liquidus temperatures T_S and T_L, and the solid fraction f_S is assumed to vary piecewise linearly there. These assumptions imply that also the enthalpy function H and the Kirchhoff's transformation K are piecewise linear functions.

The temperature distribution T is then obtained by solving the system

$$(1) \qquad \begin{cases} \dfrac{\partial}{\partial t}H(T) = \Delta K(T) & \text{in } \Omega \times]t_1, t_4[, \\ -\dfrac{\partial}{\partial n}K(T) = \begin{cases} h(T - T_{wat}) + \sigma\epsilon(T^4 - T_{ext}^4) \\ \sigma\epsilon(T^4 - T_{ext}^4) \end{cases} & \begin{array}{l} \text{on } \partial\Omega \times]t_1, t_2], \\ \text{on } \partial\Omega \times]t_2, t_4[, \end{array} \\ T(\cdot, t_1) = T_1 & \text{in } \Omega. \end{cases}$$

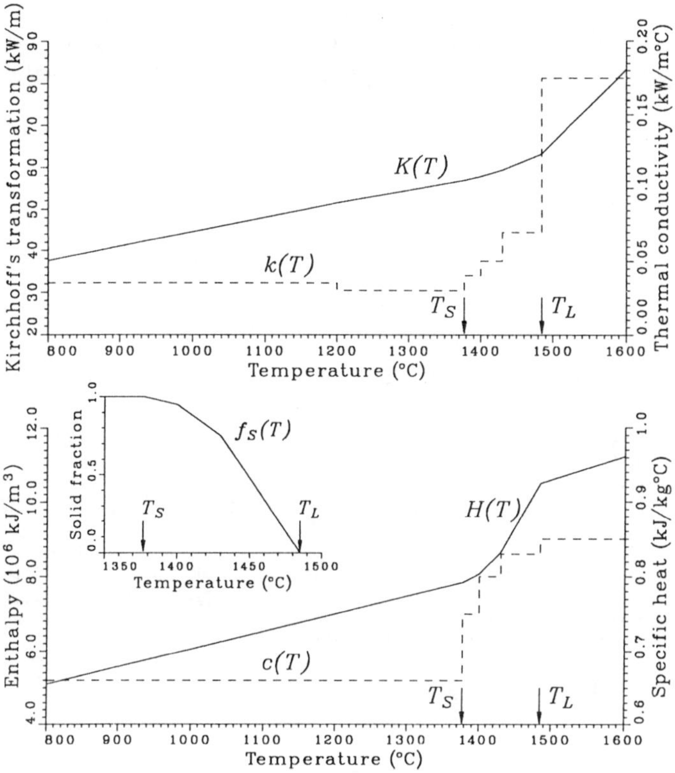

Figure 1. Temperature dependent quantities.

The boundary conditions are defined separately in different cooling regions. On each cooling zone we define a heat transfer coefficient $h = h(x, t)$, which includes the effects of both convection and conduction. The radiative transfer, on the other hand, is governed by the T^4 dependence. Thus, the heat flux in the spray cooling region ($t \in]t_1, t_2]$) consists of the two terms, where T_{wat} denotes the spray water temperature, σ the Stefan-Boltzmann constant, ϵ the emissivity factor and T_{ext} is the temperature of the surrounding environment. In the radiant cooling region ($t \in]t_2, t_4[$) the heat is extracted only by radiation, and hence, we have only the radiative term in that region. Finally, the assumption that we know T_1, the temperature distribution at the end of the mold, gives us the initial condition.

The system (1) is discretized by using the finite element method (FEM) with respect to space and the finite difference method (FDM) with respect to time. Let $\mathcal{T}_d$ be a regular triangulation of Ω, where the grid parameter d denotes the maximum length of the triangle edges. Let x_i, $i = 1, \ldots, N$, denote the nodes of $\mathcal{T}_d$, and let x_i, $i = 1, \ldots, P$, be the nodes on the boundary $\partial\Omega$. The time interval $[t_1, t_4]$ is divided into subintervals with the points $t_1 = t^{K_1} < \cdots < t^{K_4 - 1} < t^{K_4} = t_4$, such that also the time events t_2 and t_3 are among those points (i.e., $t_i = t^{K_i}$ with some K_i). Furthermore, we denote $\Delta t^k = t^k - t^{k-1}$.

The temperature T is approximated by the vector $T^k = (T_1^k, \ldots, T_N^k)$, where T_i^k denotes the value $T(x_i, t^k)$. The heat transfer coefficient h, the enthalpy function H and the Kirchhoff's transformation K are approximated in the same way by the vectors h^k, $H(T^k)$ and $K(T^k)$. Moreover, the nodal values of T_{wat}, T_{ext} and T_1 are assumed to be contained in vectors T^k_{wat}, T^k_{ext} and T_1.

Using the fully implicit scheme in approximating the time derivative of H, we obtain the algebraic system

$$
\begin{aligned}
&T^{K_1} = T_1, \\
&\hat{M}^k H(T^k) + AK(T^k) + \tilde{B}(h^k)T^k + \sigma\epsilon B[T^k]^4 \\
&\qquad = \hat{M}^k H(T^{k-1}) + \tilde{B}(h^k)T^k_{wat} + \sigma\epsilon B[T^k_{ext}]^4, \qquad K_1 < k \le K_2, \\
&\hat{M}^k H(T^k) + AK(T^k) + \sigma\epsilon B[T^k]^4 \\
&\qquad = \hat{M}^k H(T^{k-1}) + \sigma\epsilon B[T^k_{ext}]^4, \qquad K_2 < k \le K_4.
\end{aligned} \tag{2}
$$

Here the $N \times N$-matrices $M = (m_{ij})$ and $A = (a_{ij})$ (the mass and stiffness matrices) are defined by

$$
m_{ij} = \int_\Omega \psi_i \psi_j \, dx, \qquad a_{ij} = \int_\Omega \nabla\psi_i \cdot \nabla\psi_j \, dx,
$$

where ψ_j, $j = 1, \ldots, N$, are the Courant base functions, i.e., ψ_j are piecewise linear functions such that $\psi_j(x_i) = \delta_{ji}$. Moreover, $\hat{M}^k = M/\Delta t^k$, and the matrices B and $\tilde{B}(\cdot)$ are diagonal matrices with diagonal elements

$$
B_{ii} = \begin{cases} d_i, & 1 \le i \le P, \\ 0, & P < i \le N, \end{cases} \qquad \tilde{B}(h)_{ii} = \begin{cases} d_i h_i, & 1 \le i \le P, \\ 0, & P < i \le N, \end{cases}
$$

where d_i denotes the average of the neighboring segment lengths at the node x_i.

Using the implicit function theorem (see Clarke [**1**]) it can be shown that by solving the system (2) we obtain a Lipschitz continuous mapping $h \mapsto T(h)$. Because this system is highly nonlinear we use a combination of a modified successive overrelaxation (SOR) method and a Newton-Raphson method. The Newton-Raphson method is used when we are calculating the temperature on the boundary of the strand. In the interior we use the modified SOR-method, which can handle the phase changes. For more details we refer to Laitinen [4], Laitinen and Neittaanmäki [**6**], Männikkö [**8**].

3. Formulation of the control problem

We define on the boundary of the strand some (smooth) temperature distribution $T_d = T_d(x,t)$, and we want the actual surface temperature to be as near to T_d as possible. Thus, our aim is to minimize the cost function

$$
J(h) = \frac{1}{2} \int_{\partial\Omega \times]t_1, t_4[} (T(h) - T_d)^2 \, ds, \tag{3}
$$

where $T(h) = T(x,t;h)$ denotes the temperature distribution obtained with the heat transfer coefficient $h = h(x,t)$.

For the control we have natural constraints: In each cooling zone there is certain upper limit for the spray water flow rate, and hence, also for h. On the other hand, h includes also the effect of the supporting rollers, and thus, even if the water sprays are switched off, h still has a positive value. Therefore, we have $h_{min} \leq h \leq h_{max}$ with some constants h_{min}, h_{max} (defined separately in each zone), i.e., we have box constraints on the control.

For the state we assign four different constraints; there will be upper and lower bounds for the surface temperature and its change with respect to time, a maximum allowable value for the length of the liquid pool, and a minimum value for the temperature of the strand at the unbending point.

In order to prevent the formation of cracks and shape defects in the products, it is necessary to restrict the surface temperature along the secondary cooling region. Especially, the temperature in the corners of the strand should not be too much lower than in the midfaces. Therefore, we define some upper and lower bounds T_{min} and T_{max} in that region, and we require that

$$T_{min} \leq T \leq T_{max} \quad \text{on } \partial\Omega \times]t_1, t_4[. \tag{4a}$$

Reheating of the surface can generate tensile stresses near the solidification front and can cause internal cracks. On the other hand, excessive cooling of the surface generates tensile stresses on the surface, which also creates cracks. Thus, we use the constraint

$$T'_{min} \leq \frac{\partial T}{\partial t} \leq T'_{max} \quad \text{on } \partial\Omega \times]t_1, t_4[, \tag{4b}$$

where T'_{min} and T'_{max} are some suitable constants.

The length of the liquid pool is restricted by quality requirements and, above all, by safety reasons. When high production rate is desired, the casting speed is increased and then also the pool length increases, but under no circumstances, it may not exceed the cutting point. We want the temperature of the strand to be less than the solidus temperature T_S after the time event t_3, i.e.,

$$T \leq T_S \quad \text{in } \Omega \times]t_3, t_4[. \tag{4c}$$

Unbending of the strand causes both tensile and compressive stresses on the product. To avoid defects, the temperature at the unbending point must be outside the low ductility range of the steel. Furthermore, colder strand causes high stresses also on the rollers, which shortens their life. Therefore, we choose some minimum value T_{duc} for the temperature at that distance, and we have the constraint

$$T_{duc} \leq T(\cdot, t_4) \quad \text{in } \Omega. \tag{4d}$$

The object is now to minimize the cost function (3) subject to the state equation (1), the control constraint $h_{min} \leq h \leq h_{max}$ and the state constraints (4a)–(4d). The discrete form of this problem is the following: We want to minimize

$$J_d^{\Delta t}(h) = \frac{1}{2} \sum_{k=K_1+1}^{K_4} \Delta t^k (T^k - T_d^k)^T B (T^k - T_d^k) \tag{5}$$

subject to the state equation (2), the control constraints $h^k_{min} \le h^k \le h^k_{max}$, $K_1 < k \le K_2$, and the state constraints

$$(6a) \qquad T^k_{min} \le T^k_i \le T^k_{max}, \qquad K_1 < k \le K_4, \quad 1 \le i \le P,$$

$$(6b) \qquad T'_{min} \le \frac{T^k_i - T^{k-1}_i}{\Delta t^k} \le T'_{max}, \quad K_1 < k \le K_4, \quad 1 \le i \le P,$$

$$(6c) \qquad T^k_i \le T_S, \qquad K_3 < k \le K_4, \quad 1 \le i \le N,$$

$$(6d) \qquad T_{duc} \le T^{K_4}_i, \qquad 1 \le i \le N.$$

We handle these constraints by using penalization technique, i.e., each of them is transformed into a penalty term which is added into the cost function. Then the resulting penalized cost function is minimized rather that the original one.

Now the enthalpy function H and the Kirchhoff's transformation K are not differentiable everywhere, as can be seen from figure 1. Therefore, the mapping $h \mapsto T(h)$ is nonsmooth (nondifferentiable), and so is also the cost function $J^{\Delta t}_d$, although it is differentiable almost everywhere (this follows from the fact that $J^{\Delta t}_d$ is Lipschitz continuous).

The nonsmoothness of $J^{\Delta t}_d$ is rather "weak", so it is possible to use some gradient-based method (e.g., the conjugate gradient method) in minimizing $J^{\Delta t}_d$, and still obtain reasonable results. However, it is safer to use some method of nonsmooth optimization. These methods utilize the concept of subgradient, which is a generalization of the gradient for nonsmooth Lipschitz continuous functions $f : \mathbb{R}^n \to \mathbb{R}$. The set of all subgradients of f at some point $x \in \mathbb{R}^n$ is called subdifferential and denoted by $\partial f(x)$. This generalization is a natural one; if the function f is continuously differentiable at x, then gradient $\nabla f(x)$ is the only subgradient, i.e., $\partial f(x) = \{\nabla f(x)\}$. Moreover, we have the following important result: If (x_i) is a sequence of points such that $\nabla f(x_i)$ exists for all i and $x_i \to x \in \mathbb{R}^n$, then

$$(7) \qquad \lim_{x_i \to x} \nabla f(x_i) \in \partial f(x).$$

More detailed theory on nonsmooth analysis can be found in Mäkelä [7].

4. Penalization of the state constraints

4.1. Quadratic penalties. Let C_i, $i = 1, \dots, 4$, denote the sets where the constraints (6a)–(6d) are satisfied, and let P_i, $i = 1, \dots, 4$, denote the projection operators into these sets, respectively. Moreover, we use the notations

$$p^k_1 = T^k - P_1 T^k, \qquad K_1 < k \le K_4,$$
$$p^k_2 = \frac{T^k - T^{k-1}}{\Delta t^k} - P_2\Big(\frac{T^k - T^{k-1}}{\Delta t^k}\Big), \quad K_1 < k \le K_4,$$
$$p^k_3 = T^k - P_3 T^k, \qquad K_3 < k \le K_4,$$
$$p_4 = T^{K_4} - P_4 T^{K_4}.$$

Let us first consider the constraint (6a); the other three are handled in a similar way. The quadratic penalty term for the first state constraint (in discrete form) is

$$J^{\Delta t}_{\varepsilon_1,d}(h) = (g_{\varepsilon_1} \circ T)(h) = \frac{\varepsilon_1}{2} \sum_{k=K_1+1}^{K_4} \Delta t^k (p^k_1)^T B p^k_1,$$

i.e., $J_{\varepsilon_1,d}^{\Delta t}$ is a composite function of g_{ε_1} and $h \mapsto T(h)$. The outer function g_{ε_1} is continuously differentiable with respect to T; the components of the gradient are

$$[\nabla g_{\varepsilon_1}(T)]^k = \varepsilon_1 \Delta t^k B p_1^k, \quad K_1 < k \leq K_4.$$

In this case we have the chain rule (see Mäkelä [**7**])

$$\partial J_{\varepsilon_1,d}^{\Delta t}(h) = [\partial T(h)]^T \nabla g_{\varepsilon_1}(T(h)), \tag{8}$$

i.e., if we found some $\xi \in \partial T(h)$, then we would have $\xi^T \nabla g_{\varepsilon_1}(T(h)) \in \partial J_{\varepsilon_1,d}^{\Delta t}(h)$.

The penalized cost function is now

$$\begin{aligned} J_{\varepsilon,d}^{\Delta t}(h) = J_d^{\Delta t}(h) &+ \frac{\varepsilon_1}{2} \sum_{k=K_1+1}^{K_4} \Delta t^k (p_1^k)^T B p_1^k + \frac{\varepsilon_2}{2} \sum_{k=K_1+1}^{K_4} \Delta t^k (p_2^k)^T B p_2^k \\ &+ \frac{\varepsilon_3}{2} \sum_{k=K_3+1}^{K_4} \Delta t^k (p_3^k)^T M p_3^k + \frac{\varepsilon_4}{2} (p_4)^T M p_4, \end{aligned} \tag{9}$$

where ε_i, $i = 1, \ldots, 4$, are some suitable penalty parameters.

Let h be such that $J_{\varepsilon,d}^{\Delta t}$ is differentiable at h. Then the gradient $\nabla J_{\varepsilon,d}^{\Delta t}$ can be expressed as a function of so called adjoint state, which is the solution of certain adjoint system, deduced from the state equation (cf. Männikkö [**8**], Männikkö and Mäkelä [**9**]). In the case of the cost function (9), the adjoint equation is

$$\begin{aligned} &\dot{H}(T^k)\hat{M}^k W^{k-1} + \dot{K}(T^k) A W^{k-1} + \tilde{B}(h^k) W^{k-1} + 4\sigma\epsilon\tilde{B}([T^k]^3) W^{k-1} \\ &\quad = \dot{H}(T^k)\hat{M}^k W^k + B(T_d^k - T^k) - \varepsilon_1 B p_1^k - \varepsilon_2 \hat{B}^k (p_2^k - p_2^{k+1}), \quad K_1 < k \leq K_2, \\ &\dot{H}(T^k)\hat{M}^k W^{k-1} + \dot{K}(T^k) A W^{k-1} + 4\sigma\epsilon\tilde{B}([T^k]^3) W^{k-1} \\ &\quad = \dot{H}(T^k)\hat{M}^k W^k + B(T_d^k - T^k) - \varepsilon_1 B p_1^k - \varepsilon_2 \hat{B}^k (p_2^k - p_2^{k+1}), \quad K_2 < k \leq K_3, \\ &\dot{H}(T^k)\hat{M}^k W^{k-1} + \dot{K}(T^k) A W^{k-1} + 4\sigma\epsilon\tilde{B}([T^k]^3) W^{k-1} \\ &\quad = \dot{H}(T^k)\hat{M}^k W^k + B(T_d^k - T^k) \\ &\qquad\qquad - \varepsilon_1 B p_1^k - \varepsilon_2 \hat{B}^k (p_2^k - p_2^{k+1}) - \varepsilon_3 M p_3^k, \quad K_3 < k \leq K_4, \\ &\dot{H}(T^{K_4}) M W^{K_4} = -\varepsilon_4 M p_4, \end{aligned} \tag{10}$$

where $W = (W^{K_1}, \ldots, W^{K_4})$ contains the nodal values of the adjoint state, $\hat{B}^k = B/\Delta t^k$, and where we have used the convention $p_2^{K_4+1} = 0$. Moreover, with the notations $\dot{H}$ and $\dot{K}$ we mean the derivatives of H and K with respect to the temperature.

The adjoint equation is linear, and it is solved with the usual SOR-method. The components of $\nabla J_{\varepsilon,d}^{\Delta t}(h)$ are then

$$[\nabla J_{\varepsilon,d}^{\Delta t}(h)]^k = \Delta t^k \tilde{B}(T^k - T_{wat}^k) W^{k-1}, \quad K_1 < k \leq K_2. \tag{11}$$

In smooth (differentiable) points the subgradient coincides with the usual gradient, and, according to (7), in nonsmooth points the subgradient is obtained as a limit of gradients calculated in a converging sequence of smooth points. In practice this is done by calculating the gradient $\nabla J_{\varepsilon,d}^{\Delta t}(h')$ in some smooth point h' which is "sufficiently close" to h.

4.2. Exact penalties. Next we shall introduce so called exact penalty terms. The penalized cost function is now

(12)
$$\begin{aligned} J_{\varepsilon,d}^{\Delta t}(h) = J_d^{\Delta t}(h) &+ \varepsilon_1 \left[\sum_{k=K_1+1}^{K_4} \Delta t^k (p_1^k)^T B p_1^k \right]^{1/2} + \varepsilon_2 \left[\sum_{k=K_1+1}^{K_4} \Delta t^k (p_2^k)^T B p_2^k \right]^{1/2} \\ &+ \varepsilon_3 \left[\sum_{k=K_3+1}^{K_4} \Delta t^k (p_3^k)^T M p_3^k \right]^{1/2} + \varepsilon_4 \left[(p_4)^T M p_4 \right]^{1/2}. \end{aligned}$$

As before, let us consider the constraint (6a). The penalty term for this constraint is

$$J_{\varepsilon_1,d}^{\Delta t}(h) = (g_{\varepsilon_1} \circ T)(h) = \varepsilon_1 \left[\sum_{k=K_1+1}^{K_4} \Delta t^k (p_1^k)^T B p_1^k \right]^{1/2},$$

and now the outer function g_{ε_1} is not differentiable everywhere. We have the following three possibilities:

Case 1. Let h be such that $T = T(h)$ is outside the constraint set C_1. Then g_{ε_1} is continuously differentiable at T and

$$[\nabla g_{\varepsilon_1}(T)]^k = \frac{\varepsilon_1 \Delta t^k B p_1^k}{\left[\sum_{k=K_1+1}^{K_4} \Delta t^k (p_1^k)^T B p_1^k \right]^{1/2}}, \quad K_1 < k \le K_4.$$

Thus, the chain rule (8) holds also in this case.

Case 2. Let h be such that $T = T(h)$ is in the interior of C_1. Then g_{ε_1} is continuously differentiable at T and $\nabla g_{\varepsilon_1}(T) = 0$. The chain rule (8) gives then $\partial J_{\varepsilon_1,d}^{\Delta t}(h) = \{0\}$.

Case 3. Let h be such that $T = T(h)$ is on the boundary of C_1. Then g_{ε_1} is not differentiable at T, but it is convex and $0 \in \partial g_{\varepsilon_1}(T)$. If the constraint set C_1 is chosen such that $h \mapsto T(h)$ is continuously differentiable at the boundary, then we have $0 \in \partial J_{\varepsilon_1,d}^{\Delta t}(h)$.

In all three cases an approximation for a subgradient of $J_{\varepsilon,d}^{\Delta t}$ can be obtained in the same way as earlier, i.e., by solving some adjoint equation: In the case 1 the terms "$\varepsilon_1 B p_1^k$" in (10) are replaced by

$$\frac{\varepsilon_1 B p_1^k}{\left[\sum_{k=K_1+1}^{K_4} \Delta t^k (p_1^k)^T B p_1^k \right]^{1/2}},$$

and in the cases 2 and 3 they are replaced by 0. All the other state constraints are handled in a similar way.

5. Solving the nonsmooth optimization problem

The methods of nonsmooth optimization can be divided into two main classes: subgradient methods and bundle type methods. The basic idea of the former is to replace gradients by subgradients in smooth optimization methods. However, there are still some open questions concerning, e.g., step sizes and stopping criteria. Therefore, we use bundle type methods, whose general idea is the following: Several subgradients from previous iterations are gathered into a bundle, which is used as an approximation of the subdifferential. With the help of this approximation, a search direction is generated, and if the direction is not "good enough", so called null step is performed.

Our algorithm is a modification of the Proximal Bundle method by Kiwiel [**3**] for nonconvex cost functions. Also the Bundle-Trust-algorithm developed by Schramm and Zowe in [**10**] has been applied successfully to our problem. Both of these methods are improved versions of the classical bundle method due to Lemaréchal; they do not need any uncertain line search operation and are not sensitive to the scaling of the cost function.

Our nonconvex nonsmooth optimization problem is to minimize $J^{\Delta t}_{\varepsilon,d}(h)$ subject to $h_{min} \le h \le h_{max}$. We present now a simplified version of our algorithm which is used to solve this problem. For more details we refer to Mäkelä [**7**].

Proximal Bundle Algorithm

(0) Choose an initial control $h^{(0)}$ and an initial weight $\omega^{(0)}$. Calculate a subgradient $\xi^{(0)} \in \partial J^{\Delta t}_{\varepsilon,d}(h^{(0)})$ and initialize the bundle by setting $G^{(0)} := \{\xi^{(0)}\}$. Set $n := 0$ (the iteration counter).

(1) Find a direction $p^{(n)}$ by minimizing

$$\hat{J}_{G^{(n)}}(h^{(n)} + p) + \frac{\omega^{(n)}}{2}\|p\|^2$$

subject to $h_{min} \le h^{(n)} + p \le h_{max}$, where $\hat{J}_{G^{(n)}}$ is a polyhedral approximation of $J^{\Delta t}_{\varepsilon,d}$ at $h^{(n)}$.

(2) If $h^{(n)}$ is acceptable, then stop with the solution $h^{(n)}$; otherwise assign $k^{(n)} := h^{(n)} + p^{(n)}$. If

$$J^{\Delta t}_{\varepsilon,d}(k^{(n)}) < J^{\Delta t}_{\varepsilon,d}(h^{(n)}) - \delta^{(n)}$$

with some $\delta^{(n)} > 0$, then set $h^{(n+1)} := k^{(n)}$ (a serious step); otherwise set $h^{(n+1)} := h^{(n)}$ (a null step).

(3) Calculate a new subgradient $\xi^{(n+1)} \in \partial J^{\Delta t}_{\varepsilon,d}(k^{(n)})$ and update the bundle by $G^{(n+1)} := G^{(n)} \cup \{\xi^{(n+1)}\}$. Choose a new weight $\omega^{(n+1)}$, set $n := n + 1$ and go to step (1).

In step (1) the polyhedral approximation $\hat{J}_{G^{(n)}}$ is generated by using the subgradient bundle $G^{(n)}$ (see Mäkelä [**7**]). After a null step in step (2) there is no decrease in the value of cost function; however, we add one more subgradient into the bundle, which ensures a new and better direction $p^{(n+1)}$ at the next iteration and prevents the algorithm from getting into infinite loop.

In order to save computer memory we use so called subgradient aggregation strategy, which enables us to keep the number of stored subgradients bounded (see Mäkelä [**7**]). To update the weight $\omega^{(n)}$ in step (3) we use safeguarded quadratic interpolation due to Kiwiel [**3**]. We note that the constant choice $\omega^{(n)} \equiv 1$ leads to Kiwiel's generalized cutting plane method, which suffers on the same problems as Lemaréchal's original bundle method.

In the numerical tests we have used the Fortran code PBNCBC (Proximal Bundle method for NonConvex Box Constrained problems) implemented by M. M. Mäkelä, and the quadratic programming problem of step (1) (the direction finding) is solved with the code QPDF4 by K. C. Kiwiel [**2**].

No. of iter.	Quadratic penalties					Exact penalties				
	$J_\varepsilon(h)$	Pen. 1	Pen. 2	Pen. 3	Pen. 4	$J_\varepsilon(h)$	Pen. 1	Pen. 2	Pen. 3	Pen. 4
0	1.0000	21.741	9.0031	0.28194	0.08502	1.0000	21.741	9.0031	0.28194	0.08502
1	0.61034	7.6547	7.8389	0.30920	0.02463	0.68952	7.7081	7.9548	0.29518	0.03030
2	0.43517	3.5093	7.2893	0.08918	0.07656	0.53866	1.8397	7.3710	0.10103	0.07375
3	0.38444	1.5830	6.5179	0.20953	0.02617	0.46371	0.0000	6.8179	0.04304	0.07172
4	0.31365	1.4107	6.1365	0.11696	0.04391	0.45642	0.0000	6.3722	0.0000	0.08197
5	0.30522	1.2704	5.7926	0.06028	0.05546	0.40416	0.0000	5.7931	0.01224	0.05814
10	0.24112	0.0000	3.3892	0.08484	0.03515	0.35789	0.0000	3.5265	0.00714	0.04677
15	0.23567	0.0000	2.7403	0.07532	0.03424	0.34212	0.0000	2.2198	0.0000	0.04616
20	0.23381	0.0000	2.6261	0.05934	0.03728	0.33875	0.0000	1.7448	0.00026	0.04532
25	0.23293	0.0000	2.5860	0.06149	0.03654	0.33572	0.0000	1.4802	0.0000	0.04524
30	0.23226	0.0000	2.6044	0.05676	0.03748	0.33344	0.0000	1.0701	0.0000	0.04569
35	0.23167	0.0000	2.6014	0.06089	0.03652	0.33281	0.0000	1.0017	0.00014	0.04553
40	0.23152	0.0000	2.6040	0.05870	0.03701	0.33236	0.0000	0.9331	0.0000	0.04560
45	0.23130	0.0000	2.6131	0.05593	0.03764	0.33163	0.0000	0.7903	0.0000	0.04565
50	0.23101	0.0000	2.6084	0.05834	0.03705	0.33113	0.0000	0.6950	0.00056	0.04566

Table 1. Convergence of the algorithm.

6. Numerical results

In our example we have a billet, whose cross-section is 100×100 mm^2, and the casting speed v is 2.8 m/min. We assume that the configuration of the casting machine is symmetric, i.e., we restrict the calculation into the lower left quadrant of the cross-section. The values of the temperature dependent material constants are shown in figure 1; the solidus and liquidus temperatures T_S and T_L are 1377 °C and 1485 °C, respectively.

The secondary cooling region consists of six zones, whose lengths are 0.25, 0.55, 0.60, 1.15, 1.10 and 1.50 meters. The minimum values of the heat transfer coefficients are 0.078 kW/m^2°C in zones 1–2, 0.071 kW/m^2°C in zones 3–4 and 0.059 kW/m^2°C in zones 5–6, and the maximum values are 1.234, 1.110 and 0.925 kW/m^2°C, respectively. The unbending point is at the distance 8.50 m (measured from the meniscus level).

The minimum surface temperature T_{min} is defined to be a piecewise linear function, ranging from 1050 °C to 900 °C. Similarly, the maximum surface temperature T_{max} is a piecewise linear function, ranging from 1360 °C to 1200 °C. The maximum reheating and cooling rate on the surface is ± 10 °C/s. The maximum length of the liquid pool is 7.00 m and the minimum temperature T_{min} at the unbending point is 1025 °C. The penalty parameters $\varepsilon_1, \ldots, \varepsilon_4$ are such that all the constraints are (approximately) equally important with the initial cooling, which is chosen such that the control constraints are satisfied, but the state constraints are not.

The test runs have been performed in Cray X-MP EA/432 supercomputer. The dimension of the control h was 325 and the dimension of the state T was 1666. The CPU-time required for 50 iterations was ca. 70 seconds. In Männikkö and Mäkelä [9] also some larger problems have been solved. The values of the cost function are given in table 1. The iteration '0' means the solution with the initial cooling; the cost function is scaled such that it has a value 1 at that point. Also the norms of the penalty terms (without penalty parameters) are given.

7. Conclusion

Nonsmooth penalty techniques has been applied to the control of the secondary cooling in the continuous casting process. A comparison between quadratic and exact penalty functions was made. Numerical tests showed that the exact penalty technique emphasizes the constraints more than the quadratic penalty technique, i.e., in the former the constraints tend to be fulfilled better than in the latter.

References

[1] Clarke, F. H., "Optimization and Nonsmooth Analysis", Wiley-Interscience, New York, 1983.

[2] Kiwiel, K. C., *A Method for Solving Certain Quadratic Programming Problems Arising in Nonsmooth Optimization*, IMA Journal of Numerical Analysis **6** (1986), 137–152.

[3] Kiwiel, K. C., *Proximity Control in Bundle Methods for Convex Nondifferentiable Optimization*, Mathematical Programming **46** (1990), 105–122.

[4] Laitinen, E., "On the Simulation and Control of the Continuous Casting Process", Dissertation, Report 43, University of Jyväskylä, Department of Mathematics, 1989.

[5] Laitinen, E. and Neittaanmäki, P., *On Numerical Solution of the Problem Connected with the Control of the Secondary Cooling in the Continuous Casting Process*, Control-Theory and Advanced Technology **4** (1988), 285–305.

[6] Laitinen, E. and Neittaanmäki, P., *On Numerical Simulation of the Continuous Casting Process*, Journal of Engineering Mathematics **22** (1988), 335–354.

[7] Mäkelä, M. M., "Nonsmooth Optimization: Theory and Algorithms with Applications to Optimal Control", Dissertation, Report 47, University of Jyväskylä, Department of Mathematics, 1990.

[8] Männikkö, T., "A Dual Approach to the State Constrained Optimal Control Problems with an Application to the Continuous Casting of Steel", CSC Research Reports R1/90, Centre for Scientific Computing, Finnish State Computer Centre, 1990.

[9] Männikkö, T. and Mäkelä, M. M., *On the Nonsmooth Optimal Control Problem Connected with the Continuous Casting Process*, in "Advanced Computational Methods in Heat Transfer, Vol. 3: Phase Change and Combustion Simulation", (eds. Wrobel, L. C., Brebbia, C. A. and Nowak, A. J.), Proceedings of the 1st International Conference, Portsmouth, U.K., July 17–20, 1990, Computational Mechanics Publications, Southampton / Springer-Verlag, Berlin–Heidelberg, 1990, pp. 67–78.

[10] Schramm, H. and Zowe, J., "A Version of the Bundle Idea for Minimizing a Nonsmooth Function: Conceptual Idea, Convergence Analysis, Numerical Results", DFG-report 206, Universität Bayreuth, Mathematisches Institut, 1990.

Optimal control for state constrained two-phase Stefan problems

P. NEITTAANMÄKI[1]
D. TIBA[2]

[1] Department of Mathematics
University of Jyväskylä
Seminaarinkatu 15, SF–40100 Jyväskylä, Finland

[2] Institute of Mathematics
Romanian Academy of Science
Bucuresti, Romania

Abstract. We give a new approach to state constrained control problems associated to non-degenerate nonlinear parabolic equations of Stefan type. We obtain uniform estimates for the violation of the constraints.

Keywords. Two-phase Stefan problems, state constraints.

1980 Mathematics subject classifications: 49C10

1. INTRODUCTION

Two-phase Stefan problems arise as models of heat transfer processes involving change of phase, i.e. melting or solidification. Their enthalpy formulation reads as follows:

$$v_t - \Delta y = 0 \quad \text{in } Q, \tag{1.1}$$

$$v \in \beta(y) \text{ in } Q, \tag{1.2}$$

$$\frac{\partial y}{\partial n} = u \quad \text{on } \Sigma, \tag{1.3}$$

$$v(0) = v_0 \quad \text{in } \Omega, \tag{1.4}$$

where Ω is a bounded domain in $\mathbb{R}^N$ with regular boundary Γ, $\Sigma = [0,T] \times \Gamma$, $Q =]0,T[\times \Omega$ and β is a maximal monotone graph in $\mathbb{R} \times \mathbb{R}$ given by

$$\beta(y) = \begin{cases} c_1 y & y < 0, \\ [0, L] & y = 0, \\ c_2 y + L & y > 0. \end{cases} \tag{1.5}$$

Here $L > 0$ is the latent heat, c_1, c_2 are positive coefficients related to the thermal conductivity. We have supposed that $y = 0$ is the phase change temperature and for the sake of simplicity we suppose $c_1 = 1, c_2 \geq 1$.

It is known that, for $u \in L^2(\Sigma)$, $v_0 \in L^2(\Omega)$ and $y_0 = \beta^{-1}(v_0) \in H^1(\Omega)$, there exists a unique solution y of (1.1)–(1.4) and $y \in L^2(0,T;H^1(\Omega)), \beta(y) \in H^1(0,T;H^1(\Omega)^*)$ (see Barbu [**1**]). Moreover, if $u_n \to u$ weakly in $L^2(\Sigma)$ then $y_n \to y$ weakly in $L^2(0,T;H^1(\Omega))$ with y_n, y being the solutions of (1.1)–(1.4) corresponding to u_n, u respectively (Tiba [**12**]).

We associate to the system (1.1)–(1.4), the optimization problem ($y_d \in L^2(\Omega)$ is given):

$$\text{(P)} \qquad \underset{u}{\text{Minimize}} \int_0^T \left\{ \frac{1}{2} \|y - y_d\|^2_{L^2(\Omega)} + \frac{1}{2} \|u\|^2_{H^{-\frac{1}{2}}(\Gamma)} \right\} dt\,,$$

which is relevant in the control of metallurgical processes, in particular in the secondary cooling for the continuous casting of steel, Saguez [**11**], Neittaanmäki, Laitinen [**5**].

From a technological point of view, in order to preserve the quality, it is important to impose in (P) various additional state constraints, Larrecq et al. [**5**]. Neittaanmäki and Laitinen [**9**]. Here, we limit ourselves to the steady state of the constraints

$$(1.6) \qquad y(t,x) \in [-a,a] \quad \text{a.e. in } \Sigma,$$

$a > 0$ given.

The standard treatement of the constraints in the above quoted works is based on their penalization in the cost functional. We propose a different method for state constrained control problems as introduced in [**13**], [**14**]. From a theoretical point of view this provides uniform estimates for the violation of constraints. Numerically, the method is stable and robust to rough initial guesses of the algorithm [**13**]. For the applications of dual approach we refer to Männikkö [**8**].

The outline of the paper is the following: In Section 2 we discuss the two-phase Stefan problems with nonlinear boundary conditions; Section 3 is devoted to an equivalence result between the problem (P) and a singular control problem (P_1); next we analyse the regularization of the problem (P_1) and in the last Section we give a numerical example.

2. Nonlinear boundary conditions

For the sake of subsequent use, we study the the problem

$$(2.1) \qquad v_t - \Delta y = 0 \qquad \text{in } Q,$$

$$(2.2) \qquad v \in \beta(y) \qquad \text{in } Q,$$

$$(2.3) \qquad \frac{\partial y}{\partial n} + \gamma(y) \ni u \qquad \text{in } \Sigma,$$

$$(2.4) \qquad v(0) = v_0 \in \beta(y_0) \text{ in } \Omega,$$

where $\gamma \subset \mathbf{R} \times \mathbf{R}$ is the subdifferential of the indicator function of the interval $[-a,a]$.

We consider the operators $A : H^1(\Omega) \to H^1(\Omega)^*$, $B : H^{-\frac{1}{2}}(\Gamma) \to H^1(\Omega)^*$ given by

$$(2.5) \qquad (Ay, v)_{H^1(\Omega)} = \int_\Omega \operatorname{grad} y \operatorname{grad} v \, dx,$$

$$(2.6) \qquad (Bu, v)_{H^1(\Omega)} = \int_\Gamma uv \, d\sigma, \quad \forall v \in H^1(\Omega)$$

and we denote $\tilde{\beta} \subset H^1(\Omega) \times H^1(\Omega)^*$ the operator generated by β. We notice that the adjoint operator $B^* : H^1(\Omega) \to H^{\frac{1}{2}}(\Gamma)$ is the trace operator.

Formally, the system (2.1)–(2.4) may be written in an abstract form as

$$\tilde{\beta}(y)_t + Ay + B\gamma(B^*y) \ni Bu \quad \text{in } [0,T], \tag{2.7}$$

$$v \in \tilde{\beta}(y)$$

$$\tilde{\beta}(y(0)) \ni v_0. \tag{2.8}$$

Problems of this type were discussed by di Benedetto and Showalter [**2**], but their assumptions are not satisfied here. We establish the following result:

THEOREM 2.1. *Suppose that $u \in W^{1,2}(0,T;H^{-\frac{1}{2}}(\Gamma))$, $v_0 \in L^2(\Omega), y_0 = \tilde{\beta}^{-1}(v_0) \in H^1(\Omega)$, $y_0(x) \in [-a,a]$ a.e. on Ω. There exists at least one solution $y \in L^\infty(0,T;H^1(\Omega)) \cap W^{1,2}(0,T;L^2(\Omega))$ of (2.1)–(2.4), in the sense that*

$$\begin{aligned}&(\beta(y(T)), y(T) - v(T))_{L^2(\Omega)} - (v_0, y_0 - v(0))_{L^2(\Omega)} -\\ &- \int_0^T (\beta(y), y_t - v_t)_{L^2(\Omega)}\, dt + \int_0^T (Ay, y-v)_{H^1(\Omega)}\, dt\\ &\le \int_0^T \int_\Gamma u(y-v)\, d\sigma dt\end{aligned}$$

for any $v \in L^\infty(0,T;H^1(\Omega)) \cap W^{1,2}(0,T;L^2(\Omega))$, $v(t,x) \in [-a,a]$ a.e. on Σ.

REMARK: Generally we cannot write the first three terms as

$$\int_0^T (\beta(y)_t, y - v)_{H^1(\Omega)}\, dt$$

by integration by parts, since we have only that $\tilde{\beta}(y)_t \in L^2(0,T;H^{-1}(\Omega))$.

PROOF OF THEOREM 2.1: We approximate (2.7), (2.8) by

$$\varepsilon(Fy)_t + \tilde{\beta}(y)_t + Ay + B\gamma_\varepsilon(B^*y) \ni Bu \quad \text{in } [0,T], \tag{2.9}$$

$$\tilde{\beta}(y(0)) \ni v_0 \tag{2.10}$$

where $F : H^1(\Omega) \to H^1(\Omega)^*$ is the duality mapping and $\gamma_\varepsilon : L^2(\Gamma) \to L^2(\Gamma)$ is the Yosida approximation of $\tilde{\gamma}$.

The operator $A + B\gamma_\varepsilon B^* : H^1(\Omega) \to H^1(\Omega)^*$ is maximal monotone and bounded and the operator $\varepsilon F + \tilde{\beta} : H^1(\Omega) \to H^1(\Omega)^*$ is maximal monotone, bounded and coercive. We may apply Theorem 1 of di Benedetto and Showalter [**2**] and obtain the existence of a solution $y_\varepsilon \in H^1(0,T;H^1(\Omega))$, $\tilde{\beta}(y_\varepsilon) \in H^1(0,T;H^1(\Omega)^*)$.

We multiply (2.9) by $(y_\varepsilon)_t \in L^2(0,T;V)$ and use the strong monotonicity of $\tilde{\beta}$:

$$\begin{aligned}&\varepsilon \int_0^t \|(y_\varepsilon)_t\|^2_{H^1(\Omega)}\, dt + \int_0^t \|(y_\varepsilon)_t\|^2_{L^2(\Omega)}\, dt + \frac{1}{2}\|y_\varepsilon(t)\|^2_{H^1(\Omega)} -\\ &- \frac{1}{2}\|y_\varepsilon(t)\|^2_{L^2(\Omega)} - \frac{1}{2}\|y_0\|^2_{H^1(\Omega)} + \frac{1}{2}\|y_0\|^2_{L^2(\Omega)} + \int_0^t \int_\Gamma \gamma_\varepsilon(y_\varepsilon)(y_\varepsilon)_t\, d\sigma dt\\ &\le \int_0^t \int_\Gamma u(y_\varepsilon)_t\, d\sigma dt.\end{aligned} \tag{2.11}$$

We have

$$\int_0^t \int_\Gamma \gamma_\varepsilon(y_\varepsilon)(y_\varepsilon)_t \, d\sigma dt = \int_\Gamma i_\varepsilon(y_\varepsilon(t)) \, d\sigma - \int_\Gamma i_\varepsilon(y_0) \, d\sigma \geq -c \tag{2.12}$$

with i_ε the regularization of the indicator function of $[-a,a]$ in $\mathbf{R}$;

$$\begin{aligned} \int_0^t \int_\Gamma u(y_\varepsilon)_t \, d\sigma dt &= \int_\Gamma u y_\varepsilon \, d\sigma \Big|_0^t - \int_0^t \int_\Gamma y_\varepsilon u_t \, d\sigma dt \\ &\leq c\|y_\varepsilon(t)\|_{H^1(\Omega)} + c + c\left[\int_0^t |y_\varepsilon|_{H^1(\Omega)} \, dt\right]^{1/2}. \end{aligned} \tag{2.13}$$

Combining (2.11)–(2.13) we see that $\{y_\varepsilon\}$ is bounded in $L^\infty(0,T;H^1(\Omega))$, $\{(y_\varepsilon)_t\}$ is bounded in $L^2(0,T;L^2(\Omega))$ and $\{\varepsilon^{\frac{1}{2}}(y_\varepsilon)_t\}$ is bounded in $L^2(0,T;H^1(\Omega))$.

We denote $y \in L^\infty(0,T;H^1(\Omega)) \cap W^{1,2}(0,T;L^2(\Omega))$ the weak limit of subsequence of (y_ε) and we remark that $\varepsilon(Fy_\varepsilon)_t \to 0$ strongly in $L^2(0,T;H^1(\Omega)^*)$. As β is a bounded operator, we get that there exists w such that $\beta(y_\varepsilon) \to w$ weakly* in $L^\infty(0,T;L^2(\Omega))$.

We multiply (2.9) by $y_\varepsilon - v$, any $v \in L^2(0,T;H^1(\Omega)) \cap W^{1,2}(0,T;L^2(\Omega))$, $v(t,x) \in [-a,a]$ a.e. on Σ and integrate by parts. We have that $\{\tilde{\beta}(y_\varepsilon(T))\}$ is bounded in $L^2(\Omega)$, so again there is a subsequence of (y_ε) such that $\beta(y_\varepsilon(T)) \to \beta(y(T))$ weakly in $L^2(\Omega)$. We may pass to the limit and obtain the desired conclusion.

□

3. Equivalence

We associate to the problem (P) the problem:

$$(\mathrm{P}_1) \qquad \text{Minimize} \int_0^T \left\{ \frac{1}{2}\|y - y_d\|^2_{L^2(\Omega)} + \frac{1}{2}\|u - w\|^2_{H^{-\frac{1}{2}}(\Gamma)} + \frac{1}{2}\|w\|^2_{H^{-\frac{1}{2}}(\Gamma)} \right\} dt$$

subject to (2.1)–(2.4), where $w \in \gamma(y|_\Gamma)$ is the section which occurs in (2.1)–(2.4).

Since, we ask only that $u \in L^2(0,T;H^{-\frac{1}{2}}(\Gamma))$ it is possible that (2.1)–(2.4) has no solution and we have to interpret the problem (P_1) in the sense of singular control problem, Lions [**6**]. We remark that, by Theorem 2.1, any $u \in W^{1,2}(0,T,H^{-\frac{1}{2}}(\Gamma))$ is admissible for (P_1). Moreover, obviously any u admissible for (P) is also admissible for (P_1) with $w = 0$, i.e. the same cost value.

Although the state system is not necessarily well posed, the next result shows that (P_1) is a well-posed problem and it is equivalent with (P).

Assume that (P) has at least one admissible pair. Then, it yields that (P) has at least one optimal pair, Tiba [**12**].

Theorem 3.1. *Any optimal pair for (P) is optimal for (P_1) with the same optimal value and the converse is also true.*

Proof: Let $[y^*, u^*]$ be a solution of (P). Then $y^* \in [-a,a]$ a.e. on Σ and $0 \in \gamma(B^*y^*)$, that is $[y^*, u^*]$ is admissible for (P_1) with $w^* = 0$, so

$$\inf(\mathrm{P}_1) \leq J_1(y^*, u^*) = J(y^*, u^*) = \inf(\mathrm{P}). \tag{3.1}$$

Here J_1, J denote the cost functionals of (P_1), (P) respectively and $\inf(P_1) \geq 0$.

Consider now a pair $[\hat{y}, \hat{u}]$ admissible for (P_1) and such that

$$J_1(\hat{y}, \hat{u}) \leq J_1(y^*, u^*). \tag{3.2}$$

As $\hat{y}|_\Sigma \in \mathrm{dom}\gamma$, we see that $\hat{y}(t,x) \in [-a, a]$ a.e. on Σ and $[\hat{y}, \hat{u} - \hat{w}]$ ($\hat{w} \in \gamma(B^*\hat{y})$) is an admissible pair for (P). Moreover

$$J(\hat{y}, \hat{u} - \hat{w}) = \int_0^T \left\{ \frac{1}{2}|\hat{y} - y_d|^2_{L^2(\Omega)} + \frac{1}{2}|\hat{u} - \hat{w}|^2_{H^{-\frac{1}{2}}(\Gamma)} \right\} dt \leq J_1(\hat{y}, \hat{u}). \tag{3.3}$$

Combining (3.1)–(3.3) we obtain the existence of optimal pairs in (P_1) and (3.1) is valid with the equality sign. This ends the proof.

□

REMARK: The result of this section may be mainly compared with the work of Bonnans and Tiba [4].

4. Approximation

Due to its singular character, the problem (P_1) is difficult to deal with. However, its regularization has a well posed state system and good approximation estimates are valid.

We define

$$(P_\varepsilon) \qquad \text{Minimize} \int_0^T \left\{ \frac{1}{2}\|y - y_d\|^2_{L^2(\Omega)} + \frac{1}{2}\|u - \gamma_{\varepsilon^2}(y)\|^2_{L^2(\Gamma)} + \frac{1}{2}\|\gamma_{\varepsilon^2}(y)\|^2_{L^2(\Gamma)} \right\} dt$$

subject to

$$\varepsilon(Fy)_t + \beta_\varepsilon(y)_t - \Delta y = 0 \quad \text{in } Q, \tag{4.1}$$

$$\frac{\partial y}{\partial n} + \gamma_{\varepsilon^2}(y) = u \quad \text{in } \Sigma, \tag{4.2}$$

$$y(0) = y_0 \quad \text{in } \Omega. \tag{4.3}$$

We get the existence of a unique solution $y \in H^1(0,T; H^1(\Omega))$ for (4.1)–(4.3) by di Benedetto and Showalter [2]. Therefore any $u \in L^2(\Sigma)$ is admissible for the problem (P_ε).

REMARK: It is possible to take in the definition of (P_1) the norms in $L^2(\Gamma)$ instead of $H^{-\frac{1}{2}}(\Gamma)$, but in this case the set of admissible pairs for (P_1) will be more limited due to the additional constraints $w \in L^2(\Gamma)$.

It is to be expected that (4.1)–(4.3) approximate (2.1)–(2.4) in a certain sense. This may be established, for $u \in W^{1,2}(0,T; L^2(\Gamma))$, by an argument similar to the proof of Theorem 2.1. However, even in this case, nothing may be said about the behaviour of $\gamma_{\varepsilon^2}(\tilde{y}_\varepsilon)$, where $\tilde{y}_\varepsilon$ is the solution of (4.1)–(4.3) corresponding to some $\tilde{u} \in L^2(\Sigma)$. Therefore, in order to carry out considerations, we have to impose the following condition with a theoretical significance:

$$\text{(4.4)} \qquad \begin{aligned}&\text{There is } \tilde{u} \in L^2(\Sigma) \text{ admissible for (P) such that}\\ &\{\gamma_{\varepsilon^2}(\tilde{y}_\varepsilon)\} \text{ is bounded in } L^2(\Sigma).\end{aligned}$$

For elliptic variational inequalities this property is valid under the best regularity results, Brezis [**3**], §I.2, but for two-phase Stefan problems it is not known.

We denote $[y_\varepsilon, u_\varepsilon] \in H^1(0,T;H^1(\Omega)) \times L^2(\Sigma)$ an optimal pair for (P_ε). Its existence may be obtained by estimates similar to [**2**], Theorem 1, since now ε is fixed.

THEOREM 4.1. *Under hypothesis (4.4) there exists $\bar{y} \in L^2(0,T;H^1(\Omega)) \cap L^\infty(0,T;L^2(\Omega))$, $\bar{u} \in L^2(\Sigma)$, $\bar{w} \in L^2(\Sigma)$ such that $y_\varepsilon \to \bar{y}$, $u_\varepsilon \to \bar{u}$, $\gamma_{\varepsilon^2}(y_\varepsilon) \to \bar{w}$ weakly in the above spaces and the pair $[\bar{y}, \bar{u} - \bar{w}]$ is admissible for (P) with $J(\bar{y}, \bar{u} - \bar{w}) \le J(\tilde{y}, \tilde{u})$.*

Moreover, if (4.4) is satisfied by any admissible pair for (P), then $\bar{w} = 0$ and the pair $[\bar{y}, \bar{u}]$ is optimal.

PROOF: We remark that (4.4) and the structure of the cost functional gives that $\{u_\varepsilon\}$ and $\{\gamma_{\varepsilon^2}(y_\varepsilon)\}$ are bounded in $L^2(\Sigma)$ and we prove some supplementary estimates in (4.1)–(4.3).

We multiply (4.1) by $(y_\varepsilon)_t \in L^2(0,T;H^1(\Omega))$ and integrate over $[0,T]$:

$$\text{(4.5)} \qquad \begin{aligned}&\varepsilon \int_0^T \|(y_\varepsilon)_t\|^2_{H^1(\Omega)}\, dt + \int_0^T \|(y_\varepsilon)_t\|^2_{L^2(\Omega)}\, dt + \frac{1}{2}\|y_\varepsilon(T)\|^2_{H^1(\Omega)} - \frac{1}{2}\|y_\varepsilon(T)\|^2_{L^2(\Omega)} -\\ &-\frac{1}{2}\int_\Omega [\operatorname{grad} y_0]^2\, dx + \int_\Gamma i_{\varepsilon^2}(y_\varepsilon(T))\, d\sigma - \int_\Gamma i_{\varepsilon^2}(y_0)\, d\sigma\\ &\le \int_0^T \int_\Gamma u_\varepsilon (y_\varepsilon)_t\, d\sigma dt.\end{aligned}$$

Here, we have used the fact that the approximation β_ε of β may be choosen such that it remains strongly monotone uniformly in ε:

$$\text{(4.6)} \qquad \beta_\varepsilon(y) = y + \lambda_\varepsilon(y),$$

$$\text{(4.7)} \qquad \lambda_\varepsilon(y) = \begin{cases} 0 & y \le 0,\\ \dfrac{y}{\varepsilon} & 0 \le y \le \varepsilon L,\\ my + L - \varepsilon m L & y \ge \varepsilon L,\end{cases}$$

where $m = c_2 - 1 \ge 0$.

The right-hand side in (4.5) may be estimated as follows (c is a generic constant independent of ε):

$$\text{(4.8)} \qquad \begin{aligned}\int_0^T \int_\Gamma u_\varepsilon (y_\varepsilon)_t\, d\sigma dt &\le \int_0^T \|u_\varepsilon\|_{L^2(\Gamma)} \|(y_\varepsilon)_t\|_{L^2(\Gamma)}\, dt\\ &\le c\int_0^T \|u_\varepsilon\|_{L^2(\Gamma)} \|(y_\varepsilon)_t\|_{H^{\frac{1}{2}}(\Omega)}\, dt\\ &\le c\int_0^T \|u_\varepsilon\|_{L^2(\Gamma)} \|(y_\varepsilon)_t\|^{\frac{1}{2}}_{H^1(\Omega)} \|(y_\varepsilon)_t\|^{\frac{1}{2}}_{L^2(\Omega)}\, dt.\end{aligned}$$

Above, we have used the trace theorem in a formal manner since it is necessary to estimate in $H^s(\Omega), s > \frac{1}{2}$, but this will not affect the argument. The interpolation inequality and the trace theorem may be found in Lions-Magenes [7], Ch. I.

From (4.5), (4.8), as $y_0(x) \in [-a, a]$ a.e. Ω, it yields that

$$\begin{aligned} &\varepsilon \int_0^T \|(y_\varepsilon)_t\|^2_{H^1(\Omega)}\, dt + \int_0^T \|(y_\varepsilon)_t\|^2_{L^2(\Omega)}\, dt \\ &\leq c + c \int_0^T \|u_\varepsilon\|_{L^2(\Gamma)} \|(y_\varepsilon)_t\|^{\frac{1}{2}}_{H^1(\Omega)} \|(y_\varepsilon)_t\|^{\frac{1}{2}}_{L^2(\Omega)}\, dt. \end{aligned} \tag{4.9}$$

We apply the Hölder inequality and the boundedness of $\{u_\varepsilon\}$ in $L^2(\Sigma)$:

$$\begin{aligned} &\varepsilon \int_0^T \|(y_\varepsilon)_t\|^2_{H^1(\Omega)}\, dt + \int_0^T \|(y_\varepsilon)_t\|^2_{L^2(\Omega)}\, dt \\ &\leq c\left(1 + \left(\int_0^T \|(y_\varepsilon)_t\|^2_{H^1(\Omega)}\, dt\right)^{3/8} + \left(\int_0^T \|(y_\varepsilon)_t\|^2_{L^2(\Omega)}\, dt\right)^{\frac{3}{4}}\right). \end{aligned} \tag{4.10}$$

But, the expression $x^2 - cx^{\frac{3}{2}}$ has a global minimum on $\mathbf{R}$ and (4.10) yields

$$\varepsilon \int_0^T \|(y_\varepsilon)_t\|^2_{H^1(\Omega)}\, dt \leq c\left(1 + \left(\int_0^T \|(y_\varepsilon)_t\|^2_{H^1(\Omega)}\, dt\right)^{\frac{3}{8}}\right). \tag{4.11}$$

Analysing the variants $\|(y_\varepsilon)_t\|_{L^2(0,T;H^1(\Omega))} \leq 1$ and $\|(y_\varepsilon)_t\|_{L^2(0,T;H^1(\Omega))} > 1$, we get that

$$\varepsilon^{\frac{4}{5}} \|(y_\varepsilon)_t\|_{L^2(0,T;H^1(\Omega))} \leq c, \tag{4.12}$$

that is $\varepsilon(Fy_\varepsilon)_t \to 0$ strongly in $L^2(0,T;H^1(\Omega)^*)$. After a short calculation, we conclude that $\{y_\varepsilon\}$ is bounded in $L^2(0,T;H^1(\Omega)) \cap L^\infty(0,T;L^2(\Omega))$. Then $\{\beta_\varepsilon(y_\varepsilon)\}$ is bounded in $L^\infty(0,T;L^2(\Omega))$ and $\{Ay_\varepsilon\}$ is bounded in $L^2(0,T;H^1(\Omega)^*)$. Writing (4.1)–(4.2) in the form

$$\varepsilon(Fy_\varepsilon)_t + \beta_\varepsilon(y_\varepsilon)_t + Ay_\varepsilon + B\gamma_{\varepsilon^2}(B^* y_\varepsilon) = Bu_\varepsilon, \tag{4.13}$$

we see that $\{\beta_\varepsilon(y_\varepsilon)_t\}$ is bounded in $L^2(0,T;H^1(\Omega)^*)$ too.

Let $[\bar{y}, \bar{u}]$ be the weak limits in $L^2(0,T;H^1(\Omega)) \times L^2(\Sigma)$ of $[y_\varepsilon, u_\varepsilon]$. Multiplying (4.13) by $y_\varepsilon - v$, $\forall v \in L^2(0,T;H^1(\Omega))$, $v(t,x) \in [-a,a]$ a.e. Σ, we may pass to the limit and obtain

$$\begin{aligned} &\int_0^T (\beta(\bar{y})_t, \bar{y} - v)_{H^1(\Omega)\times H^1(\Omega)^*}\, dt + \int_0^T (A\bar{y}, \bar{y} - v)_{H^1(\Omega)\times H^1(\Omega)^*}\, dt \\ &\leq \int_0^T \int_\Gamma \bar{u}(\bar{y} - v)\, d\sigma\, dt, \end{aligned} \tag{4.14}$$

that is $[\bar{y}, \bar{u}]$ satisfies (2.1)–(2.3) in a stronger form than in Theorem 2.1.

For the initial condition (2.4) we remark that $\beta_\varepsilon(y_\varepsilon) \to \beta^0(\bar{y})$ (the minimal section) strongly in $C(0,T;H^1(\Omega)^*)$ and weakly* in $L^\infty(0,T;L^2(\Omega))$. So $\beta_\varepsilon(y_0) \to \beta^0(y_0)$ obviously and in order to that (2.4) is satisfied we have just to add to $\beta_\varepsilon(y_\varepsilon)$ the term $v_0 - \beta^0(y_0)$ which is constant in t and does not modify (4.13).

Denoting $\bar{w} \in L^2(\Sigma)$ the weak limit of $\gamma_{\varepsilon^2}(y_\varepsilon)$it is standard to obtain from (4.14) that the pair $[\bar{y}, \bar{u} - \bar{w}]$ is admissible for (P). Obviously $J(\bar{y},\bar{u}) \leq J(\tilde{y},\tilde{u})$ and the proof is finished. □

REMARK: The meaning of Theorem 2.1 is that by solving the problem (P_ε), which is smooth and unconstrained, one may improve the performance given by the admissible pair $[\tilde{y},\tilde{u}]$.

REMARK: By (4.5) and (4.12) we obtain that $\varepsilon \int_\Gamma i_{\varepsilon^2}(y_\varepsilon(t,x))\,d\sigma$ is bounded and taking into account the definition of i_{ε^2} we get

$$\text{dist}(y_\varepsilon(t,\cdot),[-a,a])_{L^2(\Gamma)} \leq C\varepsilon^{\frac{1}{2}} \tag{4.15}$$

for any $t \in [0,T]$. Uniform estimates in time are specific to the variational inequality approach in state constrained control problems.

References

[1] Barbu, V., "Nonlinear semigroups and differential equations in Banach spaces," Noordhoff, Leyden, 1976.

[2] Di Benedetto, E. and Showalter, R.E., *Implicit degenerate evolution equations and applications*, SIAM J. Math. Anal., No 5 **12** (1981).

[3] Brézis, H., "Problèmes unilatéraux," J. Math. Pures et Appl.51, 1972.

[4] Bonnans, J.F. and Tiba, D., *Equivalent control problems and applications*, in "Control problems for system described by partial diffrential equations and applications," I. Lasiecka, R. Triggiani Eds., L.N.C.I.S. , 97, Springer-Verlag, 1987.

[5] Larrecq, M., Birat, J.P., Saguez, C. and Henry, J., *Optimization of casting and cooling conditions on steel continuous casters; Implementation of strategies on slab and bloom casters*, IRSID, ACI 83 RE 1004, Juillet 1983 (1983), in "paper presented at 3rd PTD-conference, AIME, Pittsburgh,".

[6] Lions, J.L., "Contrôle des systèmes distribués singuliers," Dunod, Paris, 1983.

[7] Lions, J.L. and Magenes, E., "Problèmes aux limites non homogènes et applications," Dunod, Paris, 1968.

[8] Männikkö, T., *Convex and nonconvex duality in optimal control*, University of Jyväskylä, Dept. of Math., Report 49 (1990).

[9] Neittaanmäki, P. and Laitinen, E., *On numerical solution of the problems connected with the control of the secondary cooling in the continuous casting process*, Control: Theory and Advanced Technology **4** (1988), 285–305.

[10] Neittaanmäki, P. and Tiba, D., *A variational inequality approach to constrained control problems for parabolic equations*, Appl. Math. Optim. **17** (1988), 185–201.

[11] Saguez, C., "Thèse," Univ. de Technologie de Compiegne, 1980.

[12] Tiba, D., *Boundary control for a Stefan problem*, in "Optimal control of partial differential equations," K.-H. Hoffmann, W. Krabs Eds., ISNM 68, Birkhäuser, 1984, pp. 229–242.

[13] Tiba, D., *Une approche par inéquations variationelles pour les problèmes de contrôle avec contraintes*, C.R.A.S. Paris, t. 302, Serie 1, No 1 (1986).

[14] Tiba, D. and Tiba, M., *Approximation for control problems with pointwise state constraints*, in "Control and estimation of distributed parameter systems", F. Kappel, K. Kunisch, W. Schappacher Eds., Birkhäuser Verlag (1989), 379–391.

On a free boundary problem of earth dams with separated–variable filtration coefficients

NGO VAN LUOC

Institute of Mathematics
P.O. Box 631 Bo Ho 10000 Hanoi, Vietnam

Abstract. The paper deals with a free boundary problem of a system of earth dams systems with unknown intermediate water levels and separated–variable filtration coefficients. Explicit formulas for the intermediate water levels and an approximate solution by the finite element method are given for the considered problem.

Keywords. Free boundary problems, numerical analysis.

1980 Mathematical subject classifications: 85d:35006, 85g:65007

1. Description of the problem

We consider m earth rectangular dams in the horizontal impervious base (see fig. 1). Suppose that H_0 and H_m are given real numbers, $H_0 > H_m \geq 0$ and H_j is the intermediate water level between j–th and $(j+1)$–th dams. Let $k_j(x,y)$, Γ_j and Q_j be the filtration coefficient, the free boundary, and the filtration discharge of j–th dam D_j, respectively, $j = 1, 2, \ldots, m$.

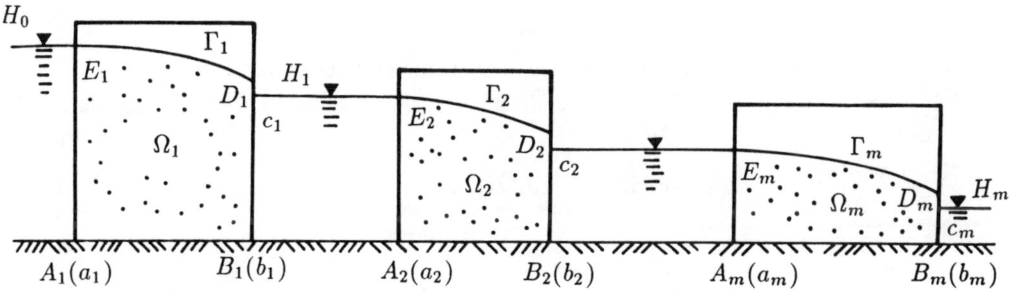

Figure 1

Suppose that the filtration coefficients $k_j(x,y)$ have the following separated–variable form

(1.1) $$k_j(x,y) = k_{1j}(x)k_{2j}(y)\ ,\ j = 1,\dots,m\ ,$$

where

(1.1') $$\begin{aligned} &k_{1j}(x) \in W^{1,2+\mu}(a_j,b_j);\ k_{2j}(y) \in W^{1,2+\mu}(0,H_0), \mu > 0,\\ &k_{1j}(x) \geq \alpha > 0,\ k_{2j}(x) \geq \alpha > 0,\ k'_{2j}(y) \geq 0 \text{ a.e. in } (0,H_0). \end{aligned}$$

Assume that the filtration flow in the dams is stationary. Then the filtration problem of the dam system can be formulated as follows (see [**1**]–[**3**]): find three sequences $\{H_j,\ j = 1,2,\dots,m-1\}$; $\{\Gamma_j,\ j = 1,2,\dots,m\}$ and $\{u_j(x,y),\ j = 1,2,\dots,m\}$ satisfying the conditions

(1.2) $$H_0 > H_1 > \dots > H_{m-1} > H_m,$$

(1.3) $$Q_1 = Q_2 = \dots \qquad = Q_m.$$

If $y = \varphi_j(x)$ is the equation of free boundary Γ_j then $\varphi_j(x)$ is a continuous strictly decreasing function and

(1.4) $$\varphi_j(a_j) = H_{j-1}\ ,\ \varphi_j(b_j) \geq H_j,\ j = 1,2,\dots,m.$$

Put

(1.5) $$\Omega_j = \{(x,y) \in D_j\ ,\ y < \varphi_j(x)\}\ ,\ j = 1,\dots,m.$$

The piezometric head $u_j(x,y)$ belongs to the class $H^1(\Omega_j) \cap C^0(\overline{\Omega}_j)$ and

(1.6) $$\begin{aligned} &\text{div}\ (k_j(x,y)\ \text{grad}\ u_j(x,y)) = 0 \quad \text{(in the sense of distributions)}\\ &u_j\,|_{A_jE_j} = H_{j-1}\ ,\ u_j\,|_{B_jC_j} = H_j,\\ &u_j\,|_{\Gamma_j\cup C_jD_j} = y\ ,\ \frac{\partial u_j}{\partial n}\,|_{\Gamma_j\cup A_jB_j} = 0, \end{aligned}$$

where $\dfrac{\partial}{\partial n}$ indicates the weak normal derivative.

2. Determination of intermediate water levels

It is known from [**2**] that the filtration discharge Q_j of the dam D_j can be calculated by the formula

(2.1) $$Q_j = g_j(H_{j-1}) - g_j(H_j)\ ,\ j = 1,2,\dots,m,$$

where

(2.2) $$g_j(h) = \frac{1}{\lambda_j}\int_0^h k_{2j}(y)(h-y)\,dy, \lambda_j = \int_{a_j}^{b_j} \frac{dx}{k_{1j}(x)}.$$

From (1.2), (1.3) and (2.1) we get the following problem:

Problem A. *Let $g_j(h)$, $j = 1, \dots, m$, be given functions continuous and strictly monotone in the closed interval $[H_m, H_0]$. Find a sequence $\{H_j,\ j = 1, 2, \dots, m\}$ satisfying the condition (1.1) and such that*

$$g_1(H_0) - g_1(H_1) = g_2(H_1) - g_2(H_2) = \dots = g_m(H_{m-1}) - g_m(H_m). \tag{2.3}$$

Theorem 2.1. *Problem A has the unique solution.*

Proof: We begin by showing that Problem A has no more than one solution. Indeed, suppose that Problem A has two solutions: $\{H_j,\ j = 1, \dots, m-1\}$ satisfying the conditions (1.2) and (2.3) and $\{H'_j,\ j = 1, \dots, m-1\}$ satisfying the following conditions:

$$H_0 > H'_1 > \dots > H'_{m-1} > H_m \tag{1.2'}$$

$$\begin{aligned} &g_1(H_0) - g_1(H'_1) = \\ &= g_2(H'_1) - g_2(H'_2) = \dots = g_m(H'_{m-1}) - g_m(H_m). \end{aligned} \tag{2.3'}$$

Put

$$\varepsilon = g_1(H_0) - g_1(H_1)\ ,\ \varepsilon' = g_1(H_0) - g_1(H'_1). \tag{2.4}$$

We shall verify that $\varepsilon = \varepsilon'$. In order to show this we assume the contrary $\varepsilon \neq \varepsilon'$, for instance, $\varepsilon > \varepsilon'$. In view of (2.4) and the monotonicity of the function g_1 we get

$$H_1 < H'_1.$$

Using the last inequality and first $m-1$ equalities in (2.3) and (2.3') we have

$$H_{m-1} < H'_{m-1}. \tag{2.5}$$

On the other hand, from the last equalities in (2.3) and (2.3') it follows

$$H_{m-1} > H'_{m-1}$$

which conflicts with (2.5). Consequently, $\varepsilon = \varepsilon'$. Using this fact, (2.3), (2.3') and the monotone nature of the functions $g_j(h)$ we obtain:

$$H_j = H'_j \quad (j = 1, 2, \dots, m-1).$$

Now we show the existence of solutions of Problem A. Suppose that $x_1 \in [H_m, H_0]$. By virtue of the continuity and strict monotonicity of the functions $g_j(h)$, $j = 1, \dots, m$, there is a sequence of continuous functions $x_j = x_j(x_1)$, $j = 2, \dots, m$ satisfying the relations

$$g_1(H_0) - g_1(x_1) = g_2(x_1) - g_2(x_2) = \dots = g_m(x_{m-1}) - g_m(x_m).$$

It can be verified that the function:

$$f(x_1) = x_m(x_1) - H_m$$

is continuous in $[H_m, H_0]$ and $f(H_0) > 0,\ f(H_m) < 0$. Hence there is at least one value $x_1 = H_1 \in (H_m, H_0)$ such that:

$$f(H_1) = x_m(H_1) - H_m = 0$$

or

$$H_m = x_m(H_1).$$

Put

$$H_j = x_j(H_1)\ ,\ j = 2, 3, \dots, m-1.$$

It is clear that the above constructed sequence $\{H_j,\ j = 1, 2, \dots, m-1\}$ is a solution of Problem A. The proof is complete.

REMARK 2.1. From Theorem 2.1 and the results in [**2**], it follows that the considered filtration problem of the dam system with unknown intermediate water levels has a unique solution (see also [**3**]).

3. Approximate solution

3.1. Suppose that the intermediate water levels can be explicitly calculated. In this case the considered filtration problem of the dam system is decomposed into m separate filtration problems for each dam D_j, $j = 1, \dots, m$. Consequently, we can solve approximatively the filtration problem (1.4)–(1.6) for each dam D_j.

Assume that the filtration coefficients $k_j(x, y)$ depend only on variable x, e.g.,

$$k_j(x, y) = k_{1j}(x)\ ,\ j = 1, 2, \dots, m. \tag{3.1}$$

From (2.1) and (2.2), it follows that:

$$Q_j = \frac{H_{j-1}^2 - H_j^2}{2\lambda_j}\ ,\ j = 1, \dots, m, \tag{3.2}$$

where λ_j is defined by the formula (2.2). The formulas (1.3) now take the form:

$$\frac{H_0^2 - H_1^2}{\lambda_1} = \frac{H_1^2 - H_2^2}{\lambda_2} = \dots = \frac{H_{m-1}^2 - H_m^2}{\lambda_m}. \tag{3.3}$$

From (3.3) it is easily seen that:

$$H_j = \sqrt{H_0^2 - \overline{\lambda}_j(H_0^2 - H_m^2)}, \tag{3.4}$$

where

$$\overline{\lambda}_j = \left(\sum_{i=1}^{j} \lambda_i\right)\left(\sum_{i=1}^{m} \lambda_i\right)^{-1}. \tag{3.5}$$

To solve the problem, it is now enough to find the solution of the filtration problem in each dam D_j.

We introduce the function $g_j(x,y)$ on the boundary ∂D_j of the dam D_j as follows

$$\begin{aligned} g_j(a_j,y) &= \frac{1}{2}(H_j - y)^2 \ , \ x = a_j \ , \ 0 \le y \le H_j, \\ g_j(b_j,y) &= \frac{1}{2}(H_{j+1} - y)^2 \ , \ x = b_j \ , \ 0 \le y \le H_{j+1}, \\ g_j(x,0) &= \frac{1}{2\lambda_j}\left[H_j^2 \int_x^{b_j} \frac{dx}{k_{1j}(x)} + H_{j+1}^2 \int_{a_j}^{x} \frac{dx}{k_{1j}(x)}\right], \\ &\quad y = 0, \ a_j \le x \le b_j. \\ g_j(x,y) &= 0 \text{ in the remaining part of} \partial D_j. \end{aligned} \tag{3.7}$$

Under the hypothesis (3.1), the filtration problem in the dam D_j is reduced to the variational inequality (see [**2**]):

$$\left\{ \begin{aligned} & w_j \in K_j \\ & \int_{D_j} k_{1j}(x) \text{ grad } w_j \text{ grad } (v_j - w_j)\, dxdy \ge \\ & \qquad - \int_{D_j} k_{1j}(x)(v_j - w_j)\, dxdy \qquad \forall \quad v_j \in K_j, \end{aligned} \right. \tag{3.7}$$

where

$$K_j = \left\{ v_j \in H^1(D_j) : v_j|_{\partial D_j} = g_j \ , \ v_j \ge 0 \ \text{ a.e. in } D_j \right\}. \tag{3.8}$$

It can be shown (see [**2**]) that the variational inequality (3.2) has the unique solution w_j of the class $W^{2,2+\mu}(D_j)$ and the triplet

$$\begin{aligned} &\Omega_j = \{(x,y) \in D_j / w_j(x,y) > 0\}, \\ &\varphi_j(x) = \sup\{y \in]0, H_j[/(x,y) \in \Omega_j\} \ , \ x \in]a_j, b_j[, \\ &u_j(x,y) = y - w_{jy}(x,y) \text{ in } \Omega_j \end{aligned} \tag{3.9}$$

gives us the solution of the filtration problem in the dam D_j.

Now we shall construct an approximate solution of the variational inequality (3.7) by the finite element method [**5**], [**6**].

Let $\varphi(h)$ be such a real continuous function that

$$\varphi(h) \to 0 \quad \text{if } h \to 0.$$

We consider a division $\mathcal{F}_h^j$ of D_j in a certain family of triangles $T \in \mathcal{F}_h^j$ having the following properties:
(i) $T \in \mathcal{F}_h^j$, mes $T < \varphi(h)$ and for every h the angles of the triangulars are greater than a strictly positive constant independing on h.
(ii) $T \in \mathcal{F}_h^j \Rightarrow T \subset D_j$,
$T, T' \in \mathcal{F}_h^j \Rightarrow T \cap T' = \emptyset$ or T and T' have a common vertex or a common side.
(iii) If $D_j^h = UT,\ T \in \mathcal{F}_h^j$ then $D_j^h \to D_j$ in the sense that for every compact $E \subset D_j$ the inclusion $D_j^h \supset E$ holds for all h small enough.

Suppose that M is an internal vertex of $T \in \mathcal{F}_h^j$ and $P_1, \dots, P_k$ are vertice having a common side with M. Let w_M denote an affine function on each triangular having the vertex M and $w_M(M) = 1,\ w_M(P_j) = 0,\ i = 1, \dots, k$, and w_M equals zero outside the triangles having the vertex M.

Denote by V_{jh} the linear vector space with the basic vectors w_M. It can be shown that V_{jh} is an internal approximation of the space $V_j = H^1(D_j)$ (see [**5**], [**6**]). We take now as an approximate set of K_j the following convex subset of V_{jh}:

$$K_{jh} = \{v_{jh}/v_{jh} \in V_{jh} : v_{jh} = g_{jh} \text{ on } \partial D_j, v_{jh} \geq 0 \text{ on } D_{jh}\},$$

where g_{ih} is linear interpolation of g_j.

Consider now the variational inequality:

$$\text{(3.10)} \qquad \begin{cases} w_{jh} \in K_{jh} \\ \displaystyle\int_{D_{jh}} k_{1j}(x) \operatorname{grad} w_{jh} \operatorname{grad}(v_{jh} - w_{jh})\, dxdy \geq \\ \qquad \displaystyle -\int_{D_{jh}} k_{1j}(x)(v_{jh} - w_{jh})\, dxdy \quad \forall \quad v_{jh} \in K_{jh}. \end{cases}$$

It is known [**5**] that the variational inequality (3.10) has the unique solution w_{jh}. Put

$$\text{(3.11)} \qquad \begin{aligned} &\Omega_{jh} = \{(x,h) \in D_{jh}/w_{jh}(x,y) > 0\}, \\ &\varphi_{jh}(x) = \sup\{y/(x,y) \in D_{hj}\}\ ,\ a_i < x < b_j, \\ &u_{jh} = y - w_{jh,y}(x,y) \text{ in } D_{hj}. \end{aligned}$$

Then the triplet $\{\varphi_{jh}, \Omega_{jh}, u_{jh}\}$ gives us an approximate solution of the filtration problem in the dam D_j.

THEOREM 3.1. *Assuming the conditions (1), (1'), (i), (ii) and (iii) fulfilled we have*

$$\text{(3.12)} \qquad u_{jh} \to u_j \textit{ strongly in } L^2(D_j).$$

PROOF: From the general internal approximate theorem of variational inequalities [**5**] we have

$$w_{jh} \to w_j \text{ strongly in } H^1(D_j).$$

From this, (3.9) and (3.11) we get (3.12).

REMARK 3.1. By the same way we can obtain an approximate solution of the considered filtration problem in the case where each dam D_j consists of m_{j+1} vertical layers, $j = 1, \dots, m$. Let $a_{j,j-1}$ and $a_{i,j}$ denote the initial point and the end point of the bottom of the dam D_j and

$$a_{j0} = a_j < a_{jl} < \dots a_{j,m_j} < a_{j,m_j+1} = b_j.$$
$$(j = 1, \dots, m)$$

Let k_{jl} be the filtration coefficient of l-th layer in the dam D_j, $l = 1, 2, \dots, m_{j+1}$, $j = 1, \dots, m$. In this case the filtration discharge of the dam D_i is calculated also by the formula (3.2) where

$$\lambda_j = \sum_{l=1}^{m_j+1} \frac{a_{jl} - a_{j-1,l}}{k_{jl}}, \quad j = 1, \dots, m.$$

REMARK 3.2. We can solve approximately the above filtration problem by the difference finite method as in [7].

REMARK 3.3. In the general case the intermediate water levels H_j, $j = 1, 2, \dots, m-1$ must be calculated in the process of solving the problem. In this situation we can get a numerical solution of the filtration problem by applying the iterative method in combination with the finite element techniques as in [4].

REFERENCES

[1]P.Ya. Polubarinova Kochina "The theory of groundwater movement," Princeton University Press, Princeton, N.J., 1962.

[2]Benci V. *On filtration problem through a porous medium*, Vol. 100, Ann. Di Math. Pura ed Appl. Series 4 (1974), 191–204.

[3]Ngo Van Luoc and Ta Hong Quang *A stationary filtration problem for earth dams systems whose filtration coefficients can be separated*, (In Russian), Reports of seminar of I. Vecua Institute of Applied Mathematics, Vol. 20, Tbilisi (1986), 65–69.

[4]Ngo Van Luoc, Ta Hong Quang and Le Kim Luat *An approximate solution of the filtration problem of earth dams systems by the finite element method*, (In Vietnamese), Khoa hoc Tinh toan va Dieu khien, Vol. 1, No. 1 (1985), 21–26.

[5]Glowinski R., Lions J.L. and Tremolierers R. "Analyse numerique des inequations variationnelles," Tome 1 et 2, Dunonod, Paris, 1976.

[6]Ciarlet P.G. "The finite element method for elliptic problems," North–Holland, Amsterdam, 1977.

[7]Baiocchi C., Comicioli V., Guerri L. and Volpi G. *Free boundary problems in the theory of fluid flow through porous media: A numerical approach*, Laboratorio di Analisi Numerica, PAVIA (Italy), Publiazioni **29** (1973), 1–85.

DESIGN AND EFFICIENT IMPLEMENTATION OF AN ADAPTIVE FEM FOR PARABOLIC FBPs

R. H. NOCHETTO† M. PAOLINI‡ AND C. VERDI♯

Abstract. Mesh adaptation is discussed for the two-phase Stefan problem in 2-D. Three local parameters are used to equidistribute interpolation errors in maximum norm for temperature as well as to specify the so-called refined region. An extra parameter is utilized, in the event of mushy regions, to equidistribute L^1-interpolation errors for enthalpy within the mush. Upon failure of certain quality mesh tests, the current mesh is discarded and a new one completely regenerated; consecutive meshes are thus noncompatible. A typical triangulation is coarse away from the discrete interface, where discretization parameters satisfy a parabolic relation, whereas it is locally refined in the vicinity of the discrete interface for the relation to become hyperbolic. A drastic reduction of spatial degrees of freedom is obtained with these highly graded meshes. A suitable interpolation theory for noncompatible meshes quantifies the error introduced by mesh changes and leads to the mesh selection algorithm. The resulting scheme is stable in various Sobolev norms and convergent with an a priori prescribed rate. Binary search techniques on suitable quadtree structured data are used to reach a quasi-optimal computational complexity in several search operations necessary for both mesh generation and interpolation between noncompatible meshes. Several numerical experiments illustrate the superior performance of this method as well as its efficiency in approximating both solutions and interfaces in maximum norm.

1980 Mathematics subject classifications: 65N15,65N30,35R35

1. The Adaptive FEM. Let $\Omega \subset \mathbf{R}^2$ be a convex polygon and $T > 0$ be fixed. Set $\beta(s) := (s-1)^+ - s^-$; β may even be nonlinear on $\mathbf{R}\backslash[0,1]$ [4]. The two-phase Stefan problem consists of finding $\{u, \theta\}$ such that $u_t - \Delta\theta = f(\theta)$, $\theta = \beta(u)$, in $\Omega \times (0,T)$, subject to $\theta = 0$ on $\partial\Omega \times (0,T)$ and $u(0) = u_0$.

Let $\{\mathcal{S}^n\}_{n=1}^N$ denote a set of graded partitions of Ω into triangles, that are shape regular [1, p.132] and weakly acute uniformly with respect to $1 \le n \le N := T/\tau$. The second condition means that for any pair of adjacent triangles the sum of the opposite angles relative to the common side does not exceed π. Given a triangle $S \in \mathcal{S}^n$, h_S stands for its size and verifies $\lambda\tau \le h_S \le \Lambda\tau^{1/2}$, where $0 < \lambda, \Lambda$ are fixed constants. Let $\mathcal{E}^n$ be the set of interelement boundaries of $\mathcal{S}^n$ and $\mathcal{R}^n := \cup\{S \in \mathcal{S}^n : h_S = O(\tau)\}$ indicate the *refined region*. Let $\mathbf{V}^n$ be the space of continuous piecewise linear finite elements over $\mathcal{S}^n$. Let $\Pi^n : C^0(\bar{\Omega}) \to \mathbf{V}^n$ be the usual Lagrange interpolation operator [1, p.94].

†Department of Mathematics and Institute for Physical Science and Technology, University of Maryland, College Park, MD 20742 USA.

‡Istituto di Analisi Numerica del CNR, 27100 Pavia, Italy.

♯Dipartimento di Meccanica Strutturale, Università di Pavia, 27100 Pavia, Italy.

Let $U^0 \in \mathbf{V}^0 := \mathbf{V}^1$ be a suitable approximation to u_0 and $\Theta^0 := \Pi^1[\beta(U^0)]$ [4,5]. Given a mesh $\mathcal{S}^{n-1}$ and a discrete enthalpy $U^{n-1} \in \mathbf{V}^{n-1}$ for any $1 \le n \le N$, the discrete scheme then reads as follows: *select* $\mathcal{S}^n$ *and find* $U^n, \Theta^n \in \mathbf{V}^n$ *such that*

$$(1.1) \qquad \Theta^n = \Pi^n \beta(U^n),$$

$$(1.2) \qquad \hat{U}^{n-1} := \Pi^n U^{n-1}, \qquad \hat{\Theta}^{n-1} := \Pi^n[\beta(U^{n-1})],$$

$$(1.3) \qquad \tau^{-1}\langle U^n - \hat{U}^{n-1}, \chi\rangle^n + \langle \nabla\Theta^n, \nabla\chi\rangle = \langle f(\hat{\Theta}^{n-1}), \chi\rangle^n, \qquad \forall\, \chi \in \mathbf{V}^n,$$

where $\langle \varphi, \chi\rangle^n := \int_\Omega \Pi^n(\varphi\chi)dx$ for all $\varphi, \chi \in C^0(\bar{\Omega})$. The ensuing algebraic system can be written equivalently as:

$$(1.4) \qquad \mathbf{M}^n U^n + \tau \mathbf{K}^n \Theta^n = \mathbf{M}^n(\hat{U}^{n-1} + \tau f(\hat{\Theta}^{n-1}));$$

here $\mathbf{M}^n$ is the mass matrix and $\mathbf{K}^n$ is the stiffness matrix. We have also identified piecewise linear functions with the vector of their nodal values. The interpolation process (1.2) transfers information between two consecutive noncompatible meshes $\mathcal{S}^{n-1}$ and $\mathcal{S}^n$ solely through the nodes of $\mathcal{S}^n$, thus incorporating the interpolation error $U^{n-1} - \hat{U}^{n-1}$, which eventually accumulates in time. The choice of $\mathcal{S}^n$, as described in §§2,3, is dictated by the need to prevent such an effect from compromising accuracy. It is necessary, however, to restrict the number of admissible mesh changes to $O(\tau^{-1/2})$, which in turn is compatible with the mesh selection algorithm of §3. Since (1.1) enforces the constitutive relation $\theta = \beta(u)$ at the discrete level, (1.4) is (strongly) nonlinear and strictly monotone. Its unique solution can be easily and efficiently computed via a nonlinear SOR method [5,7,8].

2. Local Mesh Parameters. To fully describe the adaptive FEM we must indicate how to select the new mesh $\mathcal{S}^n$; this is a crucial task. We will define three local parameters over $\mathcal{S}^{n-1}$ which, conveniently postprocessed [4,5], give rise to a meshsize function $\mathbf{h}^n$ with which $\mathcal{S}^n$ is next generated by the automatic mesh generator of [9].

Since no confusion is possible, we remove the superscripts and simply use the following notation: $\mathcal{S} := \mathcal{S}^{n-1}$, $\hat{\mathcal{S}} := \mathcal{S}^n$, $\mathcal{E} := \mathcal{E}^{n-1}$, $\mathcal{R} := \mathcal{R}^{n-1}$, $\hat{\mathcal{R}} := \mathcal{R}^n$, $U := U^{n-1}$, $\hat{U} := \hat{U}^{n-1}$, $\Theta := \Theta^{n-1}$, $\hat{\Theta} := \hat{\Theta}^{n-1}$ and $F := F^{n-1} := \{x \in \Omega : \Theta^{n-1}(x) = 0\}$ (*discrete interface* or *mushy region*), for $2 \le n \le N$. Set $\mathcal{S}_W := \{S \in \mathcal{S} : S \cap W \ne \emptyset\}$, $\mathcal{E}_W := \{e \in \mathcal{E} : e \subset \partial S, S \in \mathcal{S}_W\}$, $\mathcal{W} := \cup_{S\in\mathcal{S}_W} S$ for any given set $W \subset \bar{\Omega}$.

Note that $\nabla\Theta|_S \in [P^0(S)]^2$ for all $S \in \mathcal{S}$. Set $d_S := |\nabla\Theta|_S|$ and define, for all $e \in \mathcal{E}$, $h_e :=$ length(e) and $D_e := |[\![\nabla\Theta]\!]_e|/h_e$, where $[\![\cdot]\!]_e$ indicates the jump operator across e. Note that these quantities are easy to evaluate in practice. We then introduce the following local parameters away from the interface F:

$$(2.1) \qquad \hat{h}_e := \mu_1 \frac{\tau^{1/2}}{D_e^{1/2}}, \quad \forall\, e \in \mathcal{E}\backslash\mathcal{E}_F; \qquad \hat{h}_S := \mu_2 \frac{\tau^{1/2}}{d_S}, \quad \forall\, S \in \mathcal{S}\backslash\mathcal{S}_F.$$

Set $B :=$ Interior$(\cup\{S \in \mathcal{S}\backslash\mathcal{S}_F : \min_{e\in\mathcal{E}\backslash\mathcal{E}_F : e\subset\partial S}(\hat{h}_S, \hat{h}_e) < \lambda\tau\})$. Note that $\mathcal{B}$, the closure of B, represents the set where the discrete derivatives d_S, D_e are badly-behaved.

At this stage $\mu_1, \mu_2 > 0$ are arbitrary constants which, in practice, result from computational considerations as well as specific properties of the problem at hand. The same comment applies to λ, Λ.

In order to determine a local parameter near the interface, in the absence of mush, we proceed as follows. First, for each piece $F_S := F \cap S$ where $S \in \mathcal{S}_F$, we use a suitable discretization of the Stefan condition to approximate the velocity V_S of F_S, namely,

$$V_S := (\nabla\Theta|_{S_1} - \nabla\Theta|_{S_2}) \cdot \nu, \tag{2.2}$$

where $S_1, S_2 \in \mathcal{S}$ belong to each phase, are displayed on the direction ν (unit vector normal to F) and satisfy $\operatorname{dist}(S_i, S) \geq h_S$ $(i = 1, 2)$; see [4, §§3,4]. We next consider a cone $\mathcal{C}_S$ of axis ν, vertex at S, opening $\pi/2$ and height $\mu_3 V_S \tau^{1/2}$ as being the region most likely to contain the evolution of $F_S := S \cap F$ for at least $O(\tau^{-1/2})$ time steps. This is so because $\hat{\mathcal{S}}$ must meet the quality tests of §3 during that number of time steps. The local parameter associated with the interface is thus defined by (see [4, §§3,4; 5, §6.2.5])

$$\hat{h}_{F_S} := \tau \min\{\max(\lambda, V_S), M\}. \tag{2.3}$$

The above two new constants $\mu_3 > 0$ and $M \geq \lambda$ are arbitrary at this stage. Same rules of selection as for the previous four constants apply; μ_3 may depend on n.

We consider now the case of discrete mushy regions, which are a striking manifestation of degeneracy in that the underlying PDE becomes $u_t = f(0)$, as least formally. They may also be produced by the numerical method, as in the Ex. III of §6. A *discrete mushy region* $\mathcal{M}$ is defined as the union of all triangles $S \in \mathcal{S}$ such that $\Theta|_S$ vanishes. We say that $\mathcal{M}$ is *degenerate* on a side $e \subset \Gamma := \partial\mathcal{M}$ if

$$\operatorname{osc}_e(U) < 1 \qquad \text{and} \qquad d_S \leq \mu_4 h_e, \quad \forall\, S \in \mathcal{S}_e, \tag{2.4}$$

where $\mu_4 > 0$ is a suitable constant and $\operatorname{osc}_e(U)$ is the oscillation of U in the set $\cup_{S \in \mathcal{S}_e} S$, which is easy to calculate because U is piecewise linear. Let Γ_D denote the union of all those e's and set $\Gamma_N := \Gamma \backslash \Gamma_D$, which stands for the nondegenerate part of Γ. The condition (2.4) implies that discrete second derivatives are uniformly bounded across Γ_D. Set $I := (F \backslash \mathcal{M}) \cup \Gamma_N$, which represents the *nondegenerate interface*, namely, the union of the sharp interface and the nondegenerate part Γ_N of Γ. Note that $\nabla U|_S \in [P^0(S)]^2$ and set $D_S := |\nabla U|_S|$ for all $S \in \mathcal{S}$. We then define the following local parameter to determine the local meshsize within the mush:

$$\hat{h}_S := \tau \max\left[\lambda, \min\left(\Lambda^\star, \frac{\mu_5}{D_S^{1/3}}\right)\right], \qquad \forall\, S \in \mathcal{S}_{\mathcal{M}} \backslash \mathcal{S}_{\Gamma_N}, \tag{2.5}$$

where $\mu_5 > 0$ and $\Lambda^\star \geq \lambda$ are suitable constants; see [4, §S4; 5, §3]. We also need a substitute for (2.2) for all sides $e \subset \Gamma_N$. Consider $S_1, S_2 \in \mathcal{S}$ as in (2.2) and set

$$V_e := \frac{(\nabla\Theta|_{S_1} - \nabla\Theta|_{S_2}) \cdot \nu}{\operatorname{osc}_e(U)}. \tag{2.6}$$

3. Mesh Selection Algorithm. The initial mesh $\mathcal{S}^1$ is built via (2.1), (2.3), and (2.5), with the required pointwise information extracted from θ_0 and u_0. Assuming now that we have a mesh $\mathcal{S}$, we would like to discuss the various tests to be performed on the computed solution $\{\Theta, U\}$ to either accept or discard $\mathcal{S}$.

The first test consists of checking whether the discrete interface I is within the refined region $\mathcal{R}$ or not. In the event I escapes from $\mathcal{R}$, we say that the test has failed. Note that only the nondegenerate boundary Γ_N of $\mathcal{M}$ must belong to $\mathcal{R}$ whereas $\mathcal{M}$ may exit $\mathcal{R}$. Rejection of $\mathcal{S}$ is mostly dictated by failure of this test (see §6).

The second test ascertains that interpolation errors are still equidistributed correctly:

$$(3.1) \qquad h_e \leq \mu_1^\star \, \hat{h}_e, \quad \forall\, e \in \mathcal{E}\backslash(\mathcal{E}_F \cup \mathcal{E}_B); \qquad h_S \leq \mu_2^\star \, \hat{h}_S, \quad \forall\, S \in \mathcal{S}\backslash(\mathcal{S}_F \cup \mathcal{S}_B);$$

here $\mu_1^\star, \mu_2^\star > 1$ are suitable constants. This rules out the possibility of an excessive refinement induced by large discrete derivatives. However, the new local meshsize might be much smaller than the current one, if influenced by the refined region $\hat{\mathcal{R}}$. This test fails at least once in all examples of §6.

The third test finally verifies whether or not the truncation error in time matches the meshsize near the interface. Since the interface velocity may vary substantially during an $O(\tau^{-1/2})$ period of time, thus making (2.3) inadequate as a truncation error indicator, we enforce the constraints (see [4, §§3,4]):

$$(3.2) \qquad \mu_3^- \, \hat{h}_{F_S} \leq h_S \leq \mu_3^+ \, \hat{h}_{F_S}, \qquad \forall\, S \in \mathcal{S}_I;$$

here $\mu_3^- < 1 < \mu_3^+$ are suitable constants. The Ex. II in §6, for instance, makes (3.2) fail.

If any one of the above tests fails, then the current mesh $\mathcal{S}$ is rejected as well as the solution $\{\Theta, U\}$, which is overwritten with the previously computed solution. A new *graded* mesh $\hat{\mathcal{S}}$ with the following properties is then generated. To preserve the constraint $h_{\hat{S}} \geq \lambda\tau$, we must keep $\mathcal{S}_B$ fixed because discrete derivatives are badly-behaved. In addition we must not modify $\mathcal{S}_I$, because this would cause an inadmissible interpolation error for U [4, §§3,4]. Hence,

$$(3.3) \qquad S \in \hat{\mathcal{S}}, \qquad \forall\, S \in \mathcal{S}_B \cup \mathcal{S}_I,$$

is the first restriction on $\hat{\mathcal{S}}$. The second one reads

$$(3.4) \qquad \lambda\tau \leq h_{\hat{S}} \leq \min_{\substack{S' \in \mathcal{S}_I : \mathcal{C}_{S'} \cap \hat{S} \neq \emptyset \\ e \in \mathcal{E}\backslash(\mathcal{E}_B \cup \mathcal{E}_F) : e \cap \hat{S} \neq \emptyset \\ S \in \mathcal{S}\backslash(\mathcal{S}_B \cup \mathcal{S}_I) : S \cap \hat{S} \neq \emptyset}} \left(\Lambda\tau^{1/2}, \hat{h}_{F_{S'}}, \hat{h}_e, \hat{h}_S\right), \qquad \forall\, \hat{S} \in \hat{\mathcal{S}}.$$

This accounts for the equidistribution of interpolation errors for both Θ and U as well as the definition of refined region $\hat{\mathcal{R}}$, which satisfies $F \subset \hat{\mathcal{R}}$. The effective implementation of (3.4) will be discussed in §5.

Keeping all triangles of $\mathcal{S}_B \cup \mathcal{S}_I$ fixed is nearly the best we can do in a general setting. For computational purposes, however, it is always preferable to remove the contraint (3.3). This is feasible whenever I is smooth [4, §S4.1]. The entire mesh can thus be regenerated, on replacing (2.1) by

$$(3.5) \quad \hat{h}_e := \max\left(\lambda\tau, \mu_1 \, \frac{\tau^{1/2}}{D_e^{1/2}}\right), \ \forall\, e \in \mathcal{E}\backslash\mathcal{E}_F; \quad \hat{h}_S := \max\left(\lambda\tau, \mu_2 \, \frac{\tau^{1/2}}{d_S}\right), \ \forall\, S \in \mathcal{S}\backslash\mathcal{S}_F.$$

Both strategies are equivalent for well-behaved interfaces [4,5]. The latter is used in §6.

4. Theoretical Issues. We now comment on the heuristic idea behind (2.1). Let $\zeta : \mathbf{R}\backslash\{0\} \to \mathbf{R}$ be a smooth nonlinear function; examples relevant to our study are $\zeta(s) = \beta^{-1}(s)$ and $\zeta(s) = s^2$. The definition (2.1) is so devised that the local pointwise interpolation error corresponding to $\zeta(\Theta)$ satisfies $\hat{h}_e^2 D_e + \hat{h}_S^2 d_S^2 = O(\tau)$. Since this error accumulates in time, we impose a restriction to the maximum number of mesh changes, namely $O(\tau^{-1/2})$, for the final error to be $O(\tau^{1/2})$. We notice that second derivatives D_e (first derivatives d_S) may blow up without violating $\hat{h}_e \geq \lambda\tau$ ($\hat{h}_S \geq \lambda\tau$) as far as $D_e \leq (\mu_1/\lambda)^2\tau^{-1}$ ($d_S \leq (\mu_2/\lambda)\tau^{-1/2}$). This is consistent with the expected values of D_e and d_S as heuristics and numerical experiments indicate [3,4,5]. They also suggest that

$$\sum_{e\in\mathcal{E}} h_e^2 D_e \leq C, \tag{4.1}$$

with $C > 0$ independent of τ, that we further assume for each mesh change. Such a *structural* assumption is a discrete analogue of $\Delta\theta \in L^\infty(0,T; M(\Omega))$, which is known to hold for the continuous problem; $M(\Omega)$ stands for the space of finite regular Baire measures in Ω. In the event of mushy regions, for each mesh change we also assume that

$$\|\nabla U\|_{L^1(\Omega)} \leq C \sum_{S\in\mathcal{S}} h_S^2 D_S \leq C, \qquad \text{length}(\Gamma) \leq C, \tag{4.2}$$

which is consistent with numerical evidence. The first condition in (4.2) is valid for the continuous problem.

A general interpolation theory between noncompatible meshes is developed in [4, §5]. This, in conjunction with (3.1), (4.1), and (4.2), yields

$$\|\Theta - \hat{\Theta}\|_{L^\infty(\Omega)} \leq C\tau, \quad \|\nabla(\Theta - \hat{\Theta})\|_{L^2(\Omega)} \leq C\tau^{1/2}, \quad \|U - \hat{U}\|_{L^1(\Omega)} \leq C\tau. \tag{4.3}$$

Since meshes $\mathcal{S}$ and $\hat{\mathcal{S}}$ are noncompatible, we cannot expect a pointwise error estimate for $\nabla\Theta$ to hold. In fact, consider the refinement case for which $\|\nabla(\Theta - \hat{\Theta})\|_{L^\infty(\hat{\mathcal{S}})} \leq C \max_{e\in\mathcal{E}_{\hat{\mathcal{S}}}} h_e D_e$ [4, §5]. This yields $\|\nabla(\Theta - \hat{\Theta})\|_{L^\infty(\hat{\mathcal{S}})} = O(1)$ provided $D_e = O(h_e^{-1})$, as expected to happen near the nondegenerate interface I.

Since all meshes $\mathcal{S}^n$ are weakly acute, the *discrete maximum principle* is valid. This serves to exploit monotonicity properties of the problem at hand which in turn compensate for the lack of regularity. As a consequence of (4.3), we have the following natural *a priori estimates* for the discrete problem [4, §6]:

$$\max_{1\leq n\leq N} \|U^n\|_{L^\infty(\Omega)} + \max_{1\leq n\leq N} \|\Theta^n\|_{L^\infty(\Omega)} \leq C. \tag{4.4}$$

$$\sum_{n=1}^{N} \|U^n - \hat{U}^{n-1}\|_{L^2(\Omega)}^2 + \sum_{n=1}^{N} \tau\|\nabla\Theta^n\|_{L^2(\Omega)}^2 \leq C. \tag{4.5}$$

$$\sum_{n=1}^{N} \tau^{-1}\|U^n - \hat{U}^{n-1}\|_{L^2(\Omega\backslash\mathcal{R}^n)}^2 + \max_{1\leq n\leq N} \|\nabla\Theta^n\|_{L^2(\Omega)} \leq C, \tag{4.6}$$

$$\max_{1\leq n\leq N} \|U^n - \hat{U}^{n-1}\|_{L^1(\Omega)} \leq C\tau. \tag{4.7}$$

The leftmost term in (4.5) is a discrete-time $H^{1/2}$-estimate that accounts for the global behavior of U^n which, in the limit, is discontinuous. The corresponding term in (4.6) states, instead, a discrete-time H^1-regularity away from the interface F^n, where U^n and Θ^n are equivalent variables. The a priori estimate (4.7) is a discrete analogue of $u_t \in L^\infty(0,T;M(\Omega))$, but still a bit weaker than the structural assumption (4.1). We stress the need for stability estimates in nonenergy spaces such as (4.4) and (4.7) as they play a relevant role in the error analysis.

The error analysis is based upon (4.3) to (4.7) and a quasi-optimal pointwise error estimate for the Laplace operator on highly graded meshes satisfying $\max_{S\in\mathcal{S}^n} h_S \leq C \min_{S\in\mathcal{S}^n} h_S^\gamma$ for $0 < \gamma \leq 1$ [4, §S3]; $\gamma = 1/2$ is this context. If the number of mesh changes is limited to $O(\tau^{-1/2})$, then we have [4, §7]:

$$\|e_u\|_{L^\infty(0,T;H^{-1}(\Omega))} + \|e_\theta\|_{L^2(0,T;L^2(\Omega))} \leq C\tau^{1/2}|\log\tau|^{7/2}. \tag{4.8}$$

For the practical range of time steps τ, the logarithm above plays no significant role. The restriction on the number of mesh changes accounts for the accumulation of the interpolation error $U^{n-1}-\hat{U}^{n-1}$, which is $O(\tau)$. The major novelty here is to be interpreted in terms of properly distributed spatial degrees of freedom (DOF): for well-behaved discrete interfaces, only DOF$=O(\tau^{-3/2})$ are necessary for an $O(\tau^{1/2})$ global accuracy, as opposed to quasi-uniform meshes that require DOF$=O(\tau^{-2})$ [2,7].

DOF can be rendered quasi-optimal, namely $O(\tau^{-1})$, at the expense of more frequent mesh changes and the use of a (local) L^2-projection operator instead of Π^n to transfer information between consecutive meshes. See [6] for details.

5. Computational Issues. The routine TEST verifies the admissibility of the current mesh $\mathcal{S}^{n-1}$. First, the algorithm checks whether the discrete interface I^{n-1} lies in the interior of the refined region $\mathcal{R}^{n-1}$ (TEST=**OK**) or not. In the event I^{n-1} escapes from $\mathcal{R}^{n-1}$ (TEST=**FAIL**), the computed solution U^{n-1} is discarded and the previous one recovered; $\mathcal{S}^{n-1}$ is then rejected. To prevent the program from performing a useless time step, triangles along $\partial\mathcal{R}^{n-1}$ (blackened elements in Fig 6.2) alert that an imminent remeshing must be done (TEST=**ALERT**). The second and third test in turn verify whether (3.1) and (3.2) are valid (TEST=**OK**) or not.

If TEST=**OK**, then $\mathcal{S}^n := \mathcal{S}^{n-1}$ is selected; otherwise a new mesh has to be generated. The expected local meshsize, extracted from the tests above, is stored in a piecewise constant function $\check{\mathbf{h}}^n$ defined on a fixed auxiliary uniform square mesh $\mathcal{Q}$ of size $O(\tau^{1/2})$. This function is postprocessed by the routine H_DEFINE, which constructs another piecewise constant function $\mathbf{h}^n$ satisfying $\mathbf{h}^n|_R \leq \check{\mathbf{h}}^n|_P$ for all $P \in \mathcal{Q}$ such that $\mathrm{dist}(P,R) \leq \mathbf{h}^n|_R$. The automatic mesh generator MESH of [9] next uses $\mathbf{h}^n$ to produce an adequate (weakly acute) triangulation $\mathcal{S}^n$, namely one verifying the compatibility constraint: $h_S \leq \check{\mathbf{h}}^n(x)$ for all $x \in S$, where S is any element in $\mathcal{S}^n$.

The FE code was written in C-language, on a VAX 8530 VMS 5.1, because of the need to avoid very large static memory space allocations and also use *quadtrees*. Such data structures are in essence a convenient organization of a given finite set of points of $\mathbf{R}^2$, that in turn allows several search operations to be performed with logarithmic complexity. They are essentially to find, insert and remove a point, to find a nearest point to a given one and to find all points that belong to a given set. Quadtrees are then used in both the advancing front algorithm of MESH, that starting from the fixed boundary invades Ω, and the nontrivial interpolation process $\hat{U}^{n-1} = \Pi^n U^{n-1}$ carried out by INTERPOLATION. Implementation details can be found in [5,9]. A schematic flow chart of the program is as follows:

$n = 1$; do (while $n \leq N$)	
{H_DEFINE; MESH	(defines $\mathbf{h}^n$ and generates $\mathcal{S}^n$)
MATRIX	(computes $\mathbf{M}^n$ and $\mathbf{K}^n$)
INTERPOLATION	(computes $\hat{U}^{n-1} = \Pi^n U^{n-1}$)
do {SOR; $n = n+1$} while (TEST=**OK** & $n \leq N$)	(computes U^n and Θ^n)
if (TEST=**FAIL**) {$n = n-1$; SOL_UPDATE}}	(retrieves U^{n-1})

The main advantage of our refinement strategy is its computational simplicity and efficiency, as CPU times for the various routines reveal; see §6. In particular a mesh data structure is eliminated as soon as the interpolation process has been carried out, thus releasing the corresponding memory allocation. On the contrary, enrichment/coarsening procedures require a delicate data structure to keep track of successive mesh changes, which in turn seems to be very sensitive to the number of refinement levels. For strongly graded meshes, such as those here, this becomes a critical issue. The computational complexity of the various tasks is ($J^n :=$ number of nodes of $\mathcal{S}^n$): H_DEFINE, MATRIX, TEST and SOL_UPDATE $\rightarrow CC_n = O(J^n)$; MESH and INTERPOLATION $\rightarrow CC_n = O(J^n \log J^n)$; SOR $\rightarrow CC_n = O((J^n)^{4/3} \log N)$. Note that CC_n for both MESH and INTERPOLATION is *quasi-optimal.*

6. Numerical Experiments. Several numerical experiments were performed to illustrate the superior performance of our Adaptive FEM (AM) [3,4,5] with respect to the standard one with a fixed mesh (FMM) [2,7,8]. The first experiment corresponds to the evolution of a smooth interface, the second example illustrates the formation of a cusp whereas the last one shows the evolution of a mushy region that eventually becomes a sharp interface. In presenting the numerical results, we have employed the following notation: J :=average number of nodes, $E_\theta^\infty := \|\theta - \Theta\|_{L^\infty(Q)}$, scaled $\times 10^2$, E_I^∞ :=distance between continuous and discrete interfaces, scaled $\times 10^2$, $\mathbf{t}$:= total CPU time in seconds and $\mathbf{t}_{\mathrm{H}}$, $\mathbf{t}_{\mathrm{MESH}}$, $\mathbf{t}_{\mathrm{MAT}}$, $\mathbf{t}_{\mathrm{TEST}}$, $\mathbf{t}_{\mathrm{INT}}$, $\mathbf{t}_{\mathrm{SOR}}$:=CPU time of H_DEFINE, MESH, MATRIX, TEST, INTERPOLATION, SOR, respectively, in seconds. For details we refer to [5].

6.1. *Example I: Oscillating Interface.* This is a classical two-phase Stefan problem with an interface that moves up and down. Here $\Omega := (0,5) \times (-0.5, 4.5)$, $T := \pi/1.25$ and $x^2 + (y - \sin(1.25t))^2 = 1$ is the exact interface. This example is an extremely difficult test for our numerical method, because the velocity normal to the interface exhibits a significant variation along the front. Table 6.1 shows the CPU time distribution for AM; $\|\theta\|_{L^\infty(Q)} \approx 13.38$. Table 6.2 compares $\mathbf{t}$ with the final pointwise accuracy for both AM and FMM. A drastic improvement is observed here as well as in Figs 6.2 and 6.3, which exhibit the location of discrete and exact interfaces for both AM and FMM, respectively.

6.2. *Example II: Formation of a Cusp.* This a two-phase problem with unknown exact solution and $\Omega := (-2,4) \times (0,5)$, $T := 1$. A cusp is expected to develop at $(0,0)$ as numerical simulation corroborates. Fig 6.4 shows the discrete interface for a number of time steps for both AM and FMM, whereas the cusp formation is depicted in Fig 6.5.

N	J	E_θ^∞	E_I^∞	t_H	t_{MESH}	t_{MAT}	t_{TEST}	t_{INT}	t_{SOR}
40	339	10.7	5.83	7.1	16.3	1.8	6.9	1.6	15.6
60	592	7.42	5.01	14.7	38.6	3.8	17.1	4.6	46.3
80	818	5.17	3.26	25.1	68.4	6.6	24.7	8.9	99.3
120	1406	3.92	2.66	51.7	149.7	13.7	58.2	21.0	284.9
160	2110	3.44	2.32	70.8	221.5	20.6	105.3	34.2	609.3
240	3631	2.58	1.72	150.8	534.4	48.9	221.3	89.2	1855.9

TABLE 6.1. Example I: Adaptive Method.

Adaptive Method				Fixed Mesh Method			
$N \times J$	E_θ^∞	E_I^∞	t	$N \times J$	E_θ^∞	E_I^∞	t
40×339	10.7	5.83	50	100×1812	12.4	6.88	292
60×592	7.42	5.01	126	150×4107	7.78	5.65	919
80×818	5.17	3.51	235	200×7361	6.31	3.53	2264

TABLE 6.2. Example I: Comparison of Pointwise Accuracy.

6.3. *Example III: Evolution of a Mushy Region.* This is a two-phase Stefan problem with an initial mushy region expanding in the solid phase. The enthalpy in the mush increases so as to cause the spontaneous appearance of a liquid phase in its interior. Such a phase then expands faster than the mushy zone, which eventually disappears for the interface to become sharp and the problem a classical one. The mushy region is determined by $s_1(t) := \max(t-0.25, 0)$ and $s_2(t) := \max(0.5(t+0.25), t-0.25)$ with $0 < t < T := 1$. The problem is solved in $\Omega := (0,5) \times (0,1)$ without taking any advantage of its 1-D structure. We can thus compare the true interfaces $x = s_1(t)$ and $x = s_2(t)$ with the computed ones as illustrated in Fig 6.6. Pointwise accuracy is now comparable for both methods, but AM is certainly faster (see Table 6.3) and provides a better approximation of the nondegenerate interface $s_1(t)$; here $\|\theta\|_{L^\infty(Q)} \approx 6.13$.

Adaptive Method				Fixed Mesh Method			
$N \times J$	E_θ^∞	E_I^∞	t	$N \times J$	E_θ^∞	E_I^∞	t
80×506	9.09	5.47	173	80×1396	9.27	9.53	180
160×1385	1.15	4.36	884	160×5216	1.67	4.39	1485

TABLE 6.3. Example III: Comparison of Pointwise Accuracy.

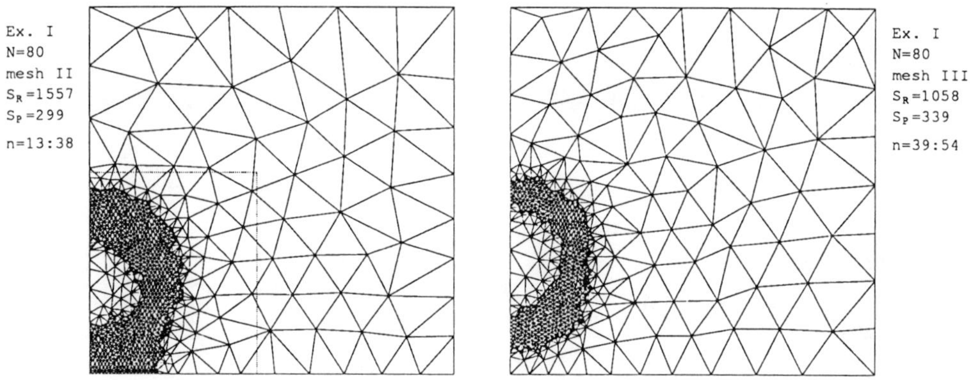

FIGURE 6.1. Example I (AM, $N = 80$): Two Consecutive Meshes.

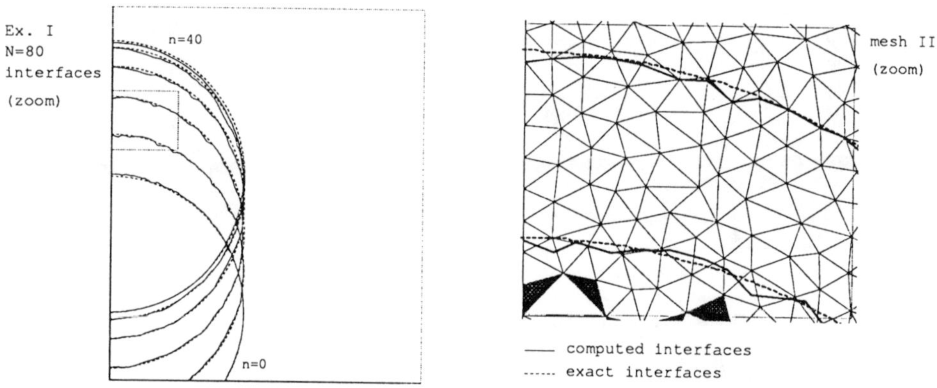

FIGURE. 6.2. Example I (AM, $N = 80$): Interfaces at $n = 8k$ $(0 \leq k \leq 5)$; zoom of Mesh II.

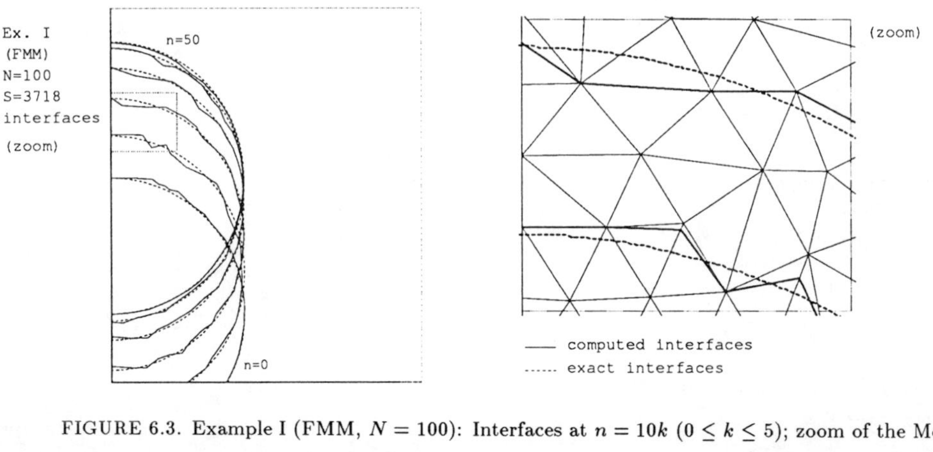

FIGURE 6.3. Example I (FMM, $N = 100$): Interfaces at $n = 10k$ $(0 \leq k \leq 5)$; zoom of the Mesh.

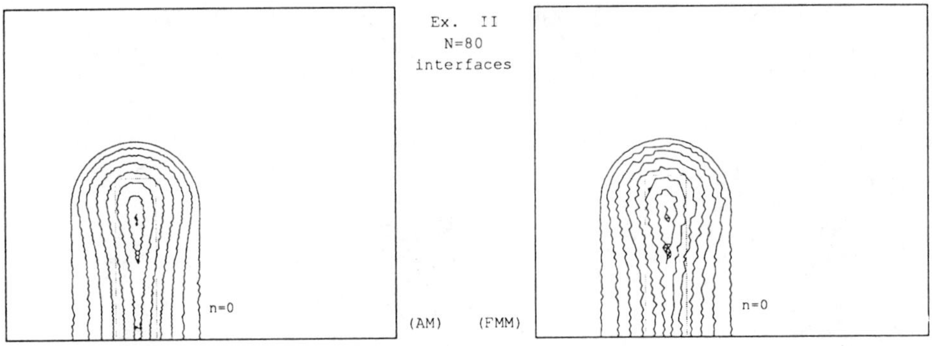

FIGURE 6.4. Example II (AM (FMM), $N = 80$): Interfaces at $n = 0, 10, 20, 30, 40, 50, 60, 67(68)$.

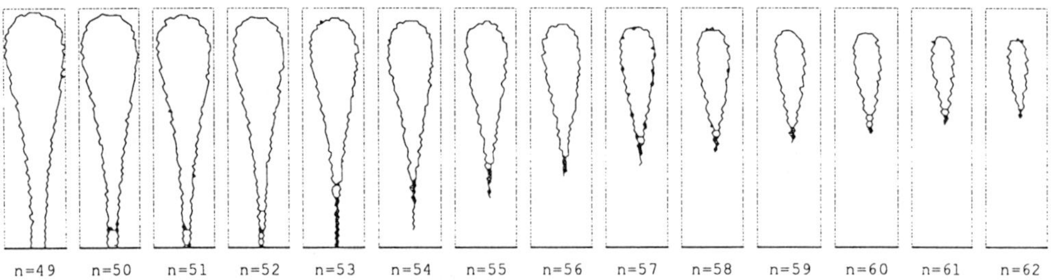

FIGURE 6.5. Example II (AM, $N = 80$): Cusp Formation (zoom).

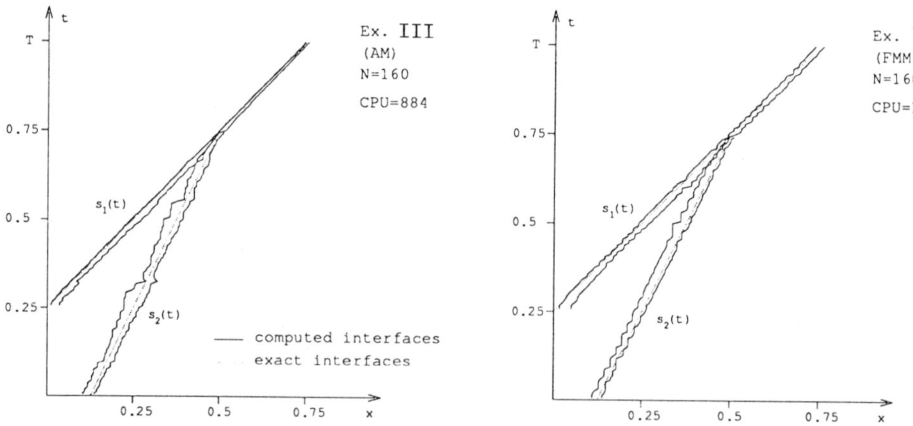

FIGURE 6.6. Example III (AM and FMM, $N = 160$): Interfaces $x = s_1(t)$ and $x = s_2(t)$.

References

1. P.G. Ciarlet, "The finite element method for elliptic problems," North Holland, Amsterdam, 1978.
2. C.M. Elliott, *Error analysis of the enthalpy method for the Stefan problem*, IMA J. Numer. Anal. **7** (1987), 61–71.
3. R.H. Nochetto, M. Paolini and C. Verdi, *Selfdaptive mesh modification for parabolic FBPs: theory and computation*, "in Proceedings Free boundary value problems with special respect to their numerical treatment and optimal control," Birkhäuser, Stuttgart, 1990, pp. 181–206.
4. R.H. Nochetto, M. Paolini and C. Verdi, *An adaptive finite element method for two-phase Stefan problems in two space dimensions. Part I: Stability and error estimates*, Math. Comp. (to appear).
5. R.H. Nochetto, M. Paolini and C. Verdi, *An adaptive finite element method for two-phase Stefan problems in two space dimensions. Part II: Implementation and numerical experiments*, SIAM J. Sci. Statist. Comput. (to appear).
6. R.H. Nochetto, M. Paolini and C. Verdi, *Quasi-optimal mesh adaptation for two-phase Stefan problems in 2D*, "in Computational Mathematics and Applications," Istituto di Analisi Numerica del C.N.R., 730, Pavia, Italy, 1989, pp. 313–326.
7. R.H. Nochetto and C. Verdi, *Approximation of degenerate parabolic problems using numerical integration*, SIAM J. Numer. Anal. **25** (1988), 784–814.
8. M. Paolini, G. Sacchi and C. Verdi, *Finite element approximations of singular parabolic problems*, Int. J. Numer. Meth. Eng. **26** (1988), 1989–2007.
9. M. Paolini and C. Verdi, *An automatic mesh generator for planar domains*, Rivista di Informatica (to appear).

A Domain Decomposition Technique Applied to a Free Surface Seepage Problem

C.A. PAPADOPOULOS and J. M. SLOSS
Department of Mathematics
University of California, Santa Barbara, Calif. 93106

J. C. BRUCH Jr.
Department of Mechanical and Enviromental Eng.
University of California, Santa Barbara, Calif. 93106

Abstract

A domain decomposition technique for a free boundary seepage problem of flow through a porous dam with a toe drain is considered. An iterative procedure is proposed that reduces the problem to a sequence of problems on each subdomain, one which includes the free boundary and is described by a variational inequality and the other which includes the remainder of the problem and is described by a second-order elliptic equation. A relaxation is performed at the subdomain interfaces at each iteration. Numerical results are presented.

1. Introduction

Consider the following free boundary value problem on the open bounded connected set D in R^2: Find $\{w, \Omega\}$, $w(x_1, x_2) \in K$, $\Omega \in D$ such that

$$Lw = F(x_1, x_2)\chi_\Omega \quad \text{in } D,\ F > 0 \tag{1}$$

$$a(s)w + b(s)\frac{\partial w}{\partial x_1} + c(s)\frac{\partial w}{\partial x_2} = 0 \quad \text{on } \partial D$$

with

$$Lw = -\sum_{i,j=1}^{2} \frac{\partial}{\partial x_i}(a_{ij}(x_1, x_2)\frac{\partial w}{\partial x_j}) + \lambda w,\ \ \lambda > 0 \tag{2}$$

where $\{a_{ij}\}$ are symmetric, bounded, and piecewise smooth and such that $\sum_{i,j=1} a_{ij}\xi_i\xi_j \geq M\,|\xi|$, $M > 0$ for all $\xi = (\xi_1, \xi_2) \in R^2$, a,b,c are piecewise smooth, K is a convex set and $\chi_\Omega = 1$ on Ω, $\chi_\Omega = 0$ on $D \setminus \Omega$.

Examples of this arise in the filtration of a liquid through a porous dam. It is the purpose of this paper to discuss an algorithm for the solution of this problem when D can be decomposed into subregions. The free boundary value subregion of the problem has simple boundary conditions and geometry while the more complex boundary conditions can be relegated to the other regions. The algorithm involves solving successive subproblems on the subregions and relating these subproblems across the common boundaries.

Domain decomposition for solving free boundary value problems, on which the domains overlap, using an iteration technique has been used in Crank [2]. Decomposition methods (not free boundary value) in which the data passes from one region to the next through the boundary have been considered in Marini and Quarteroni [5], [6] and Funaro et al. [3].

2. Method

To describe the method consider homogeneous Dirichlet data and decompose D into two non-overlapping regions with common boundary Γ.

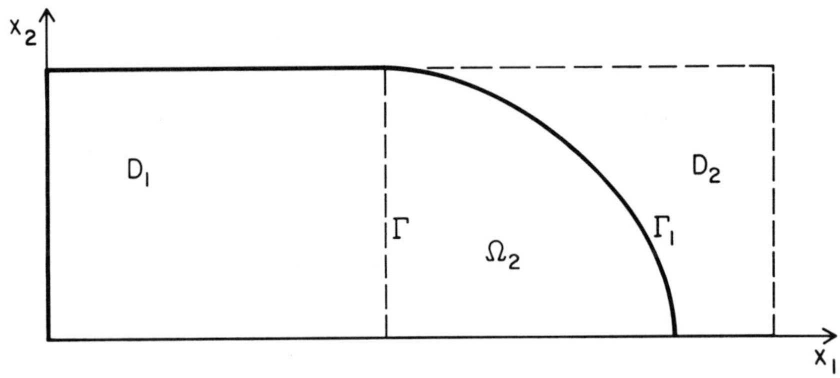

Figure 1: Theoretical Domain Decomposition.

Let $\Phi = \{v\,|_\Gamma\!: \ v \in H^1(D)\}$. For $\tilde{\phi} \in H^{1/2}(\Gamma)$ let $R_k : H^{1/2}(\Gamma) \to H^1(D_k)$ $k = 1,2$ extend $\tilde{\phi}$ as solutions of:

$$a_k(R_k\tilde{\phi}, v) = 0 \quad \forall v \in H^1(D_k), \ \ v = 0 \text{ on } \partial D \cap \partial D_k, \ k = 1,2 \tag{3}$$

where

$$a_k(w,v) = \int_{D_k} [\sum_{i,j=1}^{2} a_{ij} \frac{\partial w}{\partial x_j}\frac{\partial v}{\partial x_i} + \lambda wv] dx_1 dx_2, \ k = 1,2 \tag{4}$$

Let $\Omega_2 = \Omega \cap D_2$ and consider:

Problem I: Let $g \in H^{1/2}(\Gamma)$, $g \geq 0$ on Γ, and

$$H_{ad}^{(2)} = \{v : v \in H^1(D_2), \ v = 0 \text{ on } \partial D \cap \partial D_2, \ v = g \text{ on } \Gamma, \ v \geq \sigma g \text{ on } D_2\} \tag{5}$$

where $\sigma : H^{1/2}(\Gamma) \to H^1(D_2)$ such that if $g \in H^{1/2}(\Gamma)$, then $\sigma g = g$ on Γ, $\sigma g = 0$ on $\partial D \cap \partial D_2$, $\sigma g \geq 0$ on D_2.
Strong Form: Find $\{w_2, \Omega_2\}$ such that

$$Lw_2 = F\chi_{\Omega_2},\ w_2 \in U_{ad}^{(2)}(g) \cap H^2(D_2),\ \Omega_2 = \{(x_1, x_2) \in D_2 : w_2(x_1, x_2) > 0\}$$

Variational Form: Find $w_2 \in U_{ad}^{(2)}(g)$ such that

$$a_2(w_2, v - w_2) \geq (F, v - w_2)_2 \quad \forall v \in U_{ad}^2(g) \tag{6}$$

in which

$$(\tilde{f}, \tilde{g})_k = \int_{D_k} \tilde{f}\tilde{g}\, dx_1 dx_2,\ k = 1,2$$

Problem II Let

$$U_{ad}^{(1)} = \{v : v \in H^1(D_1), v = 0 \text{ on } \partial D \cap \partial D_1\}$$

Strong Form: Let $h \in H^2(D_1)$, find $w_1 \in U_{ad}^{(1)} \cap H^2(D_1)$ such that

$$Lw_1 = F \text{ in } D_1, \frac{\partial w_1}{\partial \eta_1} = \frac{\partial h}{\partial \eta_1} \in H^{1/2}(\Gamma), \tag{7}$$

where η_1 is the exterior normal to D_1 on Γ
Variational Form: Let $h \in H^1(D_1)$, find $w_1 \in U_{ad}^{(1)}$ such that

$$\begin{aligned} a_1(w_1, v - w_1) = \quad & (F, v - w_1)_1 \quad -a_2(w_2, R_2\gamma_0(v - w_1)) \\ & + \int_{\Omega_2} FR_2\gamma_0(v - w_1)dx_1dx_2\ \forall v \in U_{ad}^{(1)} \end{aligned} \tag{8}$$

in which $\Omega_2 = \{(x_1, x_2) \in D_2 : h(x_1, x_2) > 0\}$

Theorem 1 *If $\{w_2, w_1\}$ with $w_2 \in U_{ad}^{(2)}(w_1)$ solves the variational form of problems I and II, respectively, with $h = w_2$, and $g = w_1$ on Γ and in addition w_2 and w_1 are sufficiently regular, then*

$$w = \begin{cases} w_1 & \text{in } D_1 \\ w_2 & \text{in } D_2 \end{cases}$$

gives a solution of

$$Lw = F\chi_\Omega \text{ in } D \text{ with } w \geq 0 \text{ in } D \text{ and } w = 0 \text{ on } \partial D$$

With suitable regularity assumptions, it can be shown that the variational form and the strong form are equivalent.

3. Iterative Scheme

Let $g^1 \in \Phi$, $g^1 \geq 0$ be given. For $n \geq 1$ construct $w_2^n \in H^1(D_2), w_1^n \in H^1(D_1)$ by:

$$\begin{aligned} U_{ad}^{(2)}(g^n) = \{v : v \in H^1(D_2), v &= 0 \text{ on } \partial D \cap \partial D_2, \\ v &= g^n \text{ on } \Gamma, v \geq \sigma g^n \text{ on } D_2\} \end{aligned}$$

(in practice σg^n dies off quickly as we move away from Γ e.g. less than a given tolerance). Find $\{w_2^n, \Omega_2^n\}$, $w_2^n \in U_{ad}^{(2)}(g^n)$, and $\Omega_2^n = \{(x_1, x_2) : w_2^n(x_1, x_2) > 0\}$ such that

$$a_2(w_2^n, v - w_2^n) \geq (F, v - w_2^n)_2 \quad \forall v \in U_{ad}^{(2)}(g^n) \tag{9}$$

and find $w_1^n \in U_{ad}^{(1)}$ such that

$$\begin{aligned} a_1(w_1^n, v - w_1^n) &= (F, v - w_1^n)_1 - a_2(w_2^n, R_2\gamma_0(v - w_1^n)) \\ &+ \int_{\Omega_2^n} F R_2 \gamma_0(v - w_1^n) dx_1 dx_2 \end{aligned} \tag{10}$$

where

$$g^{n+1} = \gamma_0(w_2^{(n+1)}) = \theta_n \gamma_0(w_1^n) + (1 - \theta_n) g^n \tag{11}$$

with $0 < \theta_n \leq 1$.

Theorem 2 *Assume $\exists \theta_{min} > 0$ such that $\theta_n \geq \theta_{min} \quad \forall n \geq 1$. If the sequence $\{\gamma_0 w_2^n\}$ converges as $n \to \infty$, then the whole sequence $\{w_2^n, w_1^n\}$ converges to the solution, $\{w_2, w_1\}$ of the free boundary-value problem I and the free boundary-value problem II.*

4. Example Problem

Considered here is the steady, two-dimensional seepage through a variable shaped dam with a toe drain (see Fig. 2). In Baiocchi [1] the problem of a dam with arbitrary shape on an impermeable, horizontal base separating two reservoirs is formulated using quasi-variational inequalities and efficient and rigorous algorithms are given for obtaining numerical results. In order to simplify the problem, several assumptions are made. First, the soil in the flowfield is taken to be homogeneous and isotropic. Second, capillary and evaporation effects are neglected. Third, the flow follows Darcy's Law.

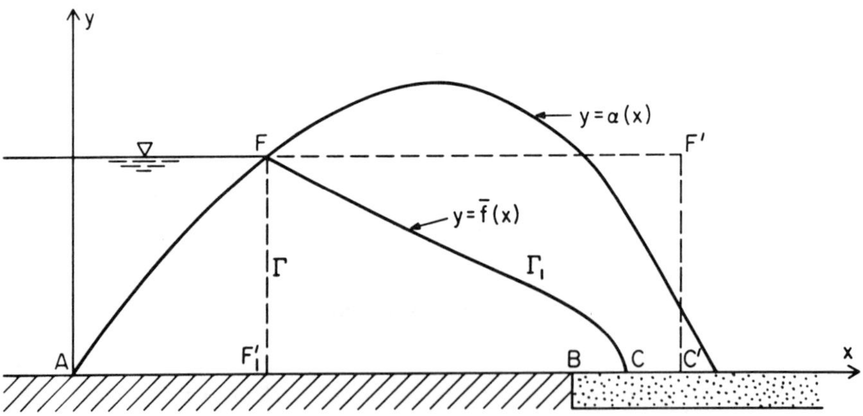

Figure 2: Flow problem and solution domains.

Since a free surface problem is being considered, the free surface location is not known a priori. However, on the free surface two boundary conditions hold: (1) $\phi = ky$; and (2) $\psi =$ constant; or equivalently for (2) $\phi_\eta = 0$, where η is the outward normal direction, ϕ is the velocity potential, and ψ is the stream function. On the remainder of the boundaries, either Neumann or Dirichlet data are given. Let $\Gamma_1 = \{(x,y) : x_F < x < x_C,\ y = \bar{f}(x)\}$ be the free surface which is the boundary line between wet and dry soil. It should be noted that x's and y's having letter subscripts on them designate the x-distance and y-distance to that lettered point, respectively. Furthermore, k (the permeability) will be set equal to 1 without loss of generality.

Thus the following quantities need to be found: $y = \bar{f}(x)$ (the function describing the shape of the free surface Γ_1); Ω, (the seepage domain); $\phi(x,y) = \frac{p}{\rho g} + y$, where p is the pressure anywhere in the flowfield, ρ is the density of the fluid and g is the acceleration constant; $\psi(x,y)$; and q (the flowrate through the flowfield). The function $\bar{f}(x)$is to be defined and smooth on its interval of existence. Furthermore, it is strictly decreasing on this interval and must satisfy

$$\bar{f}(x_F) = y_F,\ \bar{f}(x_C) = 0,\ \frac{d\bar{f}(x_F)}{dx} = -\frac{1}{\alpha'(x_F)} \text{ and } \frac{d\bar{f}(x_C)}{dx} = -\infty$$

The functions $\phi(x,y)$ and $\psi(x,y)$ are defined on $\bar{\Omega}$ and are to be in $H^1(\Omega) \cap C^0(\bar{\Omega})$. Further, for the problem shown in Fig. 2:

$$\begin{aligned}
\Omega &= \{(x,y) : 0 < x \le x_F,\ 0 < y < \alpha(x);\ x_F < x < x_C,\ 0 < y < \bar{f}(x)\} \\
\phi_x &- \psi_y = 0 \text{ and } \phi_y + \psi_x = 0 \text{ in } \Omega \\
\phi &= y_F \text{ on } \widehat{AF} \\
\phi &= 0 \text{ on } [BC] \\
\psi &= q \text{ on } [AB] \\
\psi &= 0 \text{ on } \Gamma_1 \text{ [i.e., curve } (x, \bar{f}(x))] \\
\phi &= y \text{ on } \Gamma_1
\end{aligned} \tag{12}$$

Let the solution domain Ω be extended to the known region $D = \{(x,y) : 0 < x \le x_F,\ 0 < y < \alpha(x);\ x_F < x < x_{C'},\ 0 < y < y_F\}$ in Fig. 2. Then extend ϕ and ψ continuously to be defined on $\bar{D}$ by setting

$$\tilde{\phi}(x,y) = \begin{cases} \phi(x,y) & \text{in } \bar{\Omega} \\ y & \text{in } \bar{D} - \bar{\Omega} \end{cases}$$

and

$$\tilde{\psi}(x,y) = \begin{cases} \psi(x,y) & \text{in } \bar{\Omega} \\ 0 & \text{in } \bar{D} - \bar{\Omega} \end{cases} \tag{13}$$

This yields

$$\begin{aligned}
\tilde{\phi}_x - \tilde{\psi}_y &= 0 \text{ in } D, \\
\tilde{\phi}_x + \tilde{\psi}_y &= \chi_{D-\bar{\Omega}} \text{ in } D
\end{aligned} \tag{14}$$

in the sense of distributions where $\chi_{D-\bar{\Omega}} = 1$ in $D - \bar{\Omega}$, $\chi_{D-\bar{\Omega}} = 0$ in Ω .

Next define a new dependent variable w using the Baiocchi transformation

$$w(P) = \int_{\widehat{FP}} -\tilde{\psi}dx + (y - \tilde{\phi})dy, \tag{14}$$

where $\widehat{FP}$ is a smooth path in D joining F to P in D in Fig. 2. The integration is independent of the path due to (13). If (11) holds, then for all w in $H^2(D) \cap C^1(\bar{D})$:

$$\Delta w = \chi_\Omega \text{ in } D \tag{15}$$

$$\begin{aligned} w_y &= y - y_F \text{ on } \widehat{AF} \\ w &= (q^2/6) + q(x_B - x) \text{ on } [AB] \\ w_y &= 0 \text{ on }]BC[\\ w &= 0 \text{ in } \bar{D} - \bar{\Omega} (\text{in particular on } \Gamma_1); \\ w &> 0 \text{ in } \Omega \; (w \geq 0 \text{ in } D) \end{aligned} \tag{16}$$

Hence,

$$w(x,y) \geq 0, \; 1 - \Delta w(x,y) \geq 0, \; w(1 - \Delta w) = 0 \text{ in } D.$$

If a w is found satisfying (15) subject to the conditions (16), then the following quantities can be obtained:

$$\begin{aligned} \Omega &= \{(x,y) : (x,y) \text{ in } D, \; w > 0\} \\ \text{graph } \bar{f} &= \partial\Omega - \partial D \equiv \text{ points of } \partial\Omega \text{ not in } \partial D \\ \phi &= y - w_y \text{ in } \Omega \\ \psi &= -w_x \text{ in } \Omega \\ q &= \psi(x,0) \text{ on } [AB] \end{aligned} \tag{17}$$

4.1. Decomposed Problem

The region D is decomposed into the subsets $D_1 = \{(x,y) : 0 < x < x_{F_1'}, 0 < y < \alpha(x)\}$ and $D_2 = \{(x,y) : x_{F_1'} < x < x_{C'}, 0 < y < y_F\}$ with the boundary of D given by ∂D and the interface between D_1 and D_2 given by $\Gamma = \{(x,y) : x = x_F, 0 < y < y_F\}$. See Funaro et al. [3]. If w_1 denotes the restriction of w to D_1 and w_2 the one to D_2, then (15) and (16) can be equivalently written in the following split form:

$$\Delta w_1 = 1 \text{ in } D_1 \tag{18}$$

$$(w_1)_y = y - y_F \text{ on } \widehat{AF} \tag{19}$$

$$w_1 = \left(\frac{q^2}{6}\right) + q(x_B - x) \text{ on } [AF_1'] \tag{20}$$

$$w_1 = w_2 \text{ on } \Gamma \tag{21}$$

$$\frac{\partial w_1}{\partial x} = \frac{\partial w_2}{\partial x} \text{ on } \Gamma \tag{22}$$

$$\Delta w_2 = \chi_\Omega \text{ in } D_2 \tag{23}$$

$$w_2 = \left(\frac{q^2}{6}\right) + q(x_B - x) \text{ on } [F_1'B] \tag{24}$$

$$(w_2)_y = 0 \text{ on } [BC] \tag{25}$$

$$w_2 = 0 \text{ in } \bar{D}_2 - \Omega \text{ (in particular on } \Gamma_1 \text{)} \tag{26}$$

The following iterative procedure similar to that stated in Section 3 is now given for this problem. Let $w_2^1 = g^1$ be a given on Γ. We consider the two sequences of functions w_2^n and w_1^n, $n \geq 1$ satisfying, respectively, the problems:

$$\Delta w_2^n = \chi_\Omega \text{ in } D_2 \tag{27}$$

$$w_2^n = \left(\frac{q^2}{6}\right) + q(x_B - x) \text{ on } [F_1'B] \tag{28}$$

$$(w_2^n)_y = 0 \text{ on } [BC] \tag{29}$$

$$w_2^n = 0 \text{ in } \bar{D}_2 - \Omega \tag{30}$$

$$w_2^n = g^n \text{ on } \Gamma \tag{31}$$

and

$$\Delta w_1^n = 1 \text{ in } D_1 \tag{32}$$

$$(w_1^n)_y = y - y_F \text{ on } \widehat{AF} \tag{33}$$

$$w_1^n = \left(\frac{q^2}{6}\right) + q(x_B - x) \text{ on } [AF_1'] \tag{34}$$

$$\frac{\partial w_1^n}{\partial x} = \frac{\partial w_2^n}{\partial x} \text{ on } \Gamma \tag{35}$$

where

$$g^{n+1} = \theta w_1^n + (1-\theta) g^n \text{ on } \Gamma \text{ for } n \geq 1 \tag{36}$$

4.2. Numerical Scheme and Results

An iteration scheme to solve the problem given by (27) - (36) will now be presented. It is a modified version of that stated in Section 3 and will be designated in particular by using the superscript iteration numbers in parentheses. The D_1 and D_2 regions will be discretized and the problem solved using a finite difference successive over-relaxation scheme with projection.

The flowrate through the flowfield, Ω, is also an unknown a priori. Thus, in addition to the inner iterations to solve for w for a given q, there is also an outer iteration on the q to determine the flowrate. A compatibility condition is necessary for this outer iteration. The condition used herein is similar to that given by Sloss and Bruch [7], i.e.,

$$f_h(q^{(r)}) = (w_2(x_F, y_F - \Delta y))_{q^{(r)}} - \frac{\Delta y^2}{2}, \; r = 0, 1, 2, \ldots \tag{37}$$

Then $f_h(q^{(r)}) = 0$ represents a compatibility condition, which if imposed on the set of solutions $(w_1)_{q,h}$ and $(w_2)_{q,h}$ (one for every q), permits the determination of a unique $\bar{q}$ such that $(w_1)_{\bar{q},h}$ and $(w_2)_{\bar{q},h}$ will be a solution of (27) - (31) and (32) - (35), respectively, as well as satisfy (37). Due to the monotonicity of $f_h(q^{(r)})$ in (37), the secant method is used to approximate the root.

The numerical example to be investigated (one solved by Sloss and Bruch [7]) using the previously given approach has the following data: $\alpha(x) = x$, $y_F = 30$ ft; $x_F = 30$ ft; $x_B = 60$ ft; $x_{C'}$, which should be greater than $\left(x_B + \frac{q}{2}\right)$, (see Harr [4], Sloss and Bruch [7]); $q^{(0)} = 15$ ft^3/sec per foot depth normal to the plane of the flow; $q^{(1)} = 16$ ft^3/sec per foot depth normal to the plane of the flow; and $\Delta x = \Delta y = 2.5$ ft.; with stopping error estimates:

$$\max_{i,j}\left|(w_1)^{(n+1)}_{q^{(r)},i,j} - (w_1)^{(n)}_{q^{(r)},i,j}\right| < \epsilon_1(\text{similar for iterates of } w_2) \tag{38}$$

and

$$\left|f_h(q^{(r)})\right| < \epsilon_2 \tag{39}$$

The basic numerical scheme consists in choosing initial guessed values for $(w_1)^{(1)}_{q^{(0)},i,j}$ and $(w_2)^{(1)}_{q^{(0)},i,j}$ in D_1 and D_2 equal to zero, respectively, as well as equal to zero on Γ. The i and j are the row and column mesh point numbers, respectively. The first iteration pass (which consists in evaluating the algorithm given in (40) and (41) once at each mesh point) is performed in D_2 using the Dirichlet data boundary condition (31) with $(w_2)^{(1)} = g^{(1)} = 0$ and $(w_1)^{(1)} = 0$ in (36) which can be written as

$$w_2^{(n+1)} = \theta w_1^{(n)} + (1-\theta)w_2^{(n)} \text{ on } \Gamma$$

or in discretized notation as

$$(w_2)^{(n+1)}_{q^{(r)},i,1} = \theta(w_1)^{(n)}_{q^{(r)},i,NC1} + (1-\theta)(w_2)^{(n)}_{q^{(r)},i,1}, \text{ on } \Gamma,\ 1 \le i \le NR$$

where NC1 is the number of columns in D_1 and NR is the number of rows. The basic numerical algorithm used in D_2 is

$$(w_2)^{(n+1/2)}_{q^{(r)},i,j} = \frac{(\Delta x)^2(\Delta y)^2}{2[(\Delta x)^2+(\Delta y)^2]}\left\{\frac{1}{(\Delta x)^2}\left[(w_2)^{(n)}_{q^{(r)},i-1,j} + (w_2)^{(n+1)}_{q^{(r)},i+1,j}\right] + \frac{1}{(\Delta y)^2}\left[(w_2)^{(n)}_{q^{(r)},i,j-1} + (w_2)^{(n+1)}_{q^{(r)},i,j+1}\right] - 1\right\} \tag{40}$$

$$(w_2)^{(n+1)}_{q^{(r)},i,j} = \max\left\{0, (w_2)^{(n)}_{q^{(r)},i,j} + \bar{\alpha}\left[(w_2)^{(n+1/2)}_{q^{(r)},i,j} - (w_2)^{(n)}_{q^{(r)},i,j}\right]\right\} \tag{41}$$

where $\bar{\alpha}$ is the relaxation parameter taken equal to 1.85.

For the first iteration pass (which consists in evaluating the basic algorithm once at each mesh point) in D_1 the Neumann boundary condition (35) is used along Γ. This shows up in the basic numerical scheme in D_1 (which is similar to (40) and (41) with w_1 replacing w_2) using

$$(w_1)^{(n+1)}_{q^{(r)},i,NC1+1} = (w_1)^{(n)}_{q^{(r)},i,NC1-1} - \left\{3(w_2)^{(n+1)}_{q^{(r)},i,1} - 4(w_2)^{(n+1)}_{q^{(r)},i,2} + (w_2)^{(n+1)}_{q^{(r)},i,3}\right\} \tag{42}$$

This iteration scheme which consists in evaluating the basic algorithm once at each mesh point with interchange of data on Γ after each pass proceeds until (38) is satisfied for the inner iteration. $f_h(q^{(0)})$ is then evaluated and checked against ϵ_2. If (39) is not satisfied, $q^{(1)}$ is used along with the values of $(w_1)_{q^{(0)},i,j}$ and $(w_2)_{q^{(0)},i,j}$ just obtained as starting values to make another set of inner and outer iterations. If $f_h(q^{(1)})$ does not satisfy (39), $q^{(0)}$, $q^{(1)}$, $f_h(q^{(0)})$, and $f_h(q^{(1)})$ are used to obtain $q^{(2)}$ from the secant method. This procedure is then repeated until all error criteria, (38) and (39), are satisfied, as well as the equivalence of the values from each region on Γ.

Tables I and II list the computational and iteration information for the example. Since the number of iterations will depend upon the parameter θ, numerical experiments were performed to determine the best value. Table I lists those results where the word 'Iterations' in the Table stands for the total number of iterations to obtain convergence.

Table I. Iteration Information Obtained by Varying θ

θ	0.025	0.050	0.055	0.060	0.065	0.075	0.085	0.100
Iterations	976	481	450	449	453	458	467	479

The results in Table II were obtained using $\theta = 0.06$, $\epsilon_1 = 0.01$ and $\epsilon_2 = 0.01$. Also shown in Table II are the results obtained by Sloss and Bruch [7] solving for w throughout the whole problem without any decomposition. In a comparison between the results for the free surface location obtained by Sloss and Bruch [7] and those of the present method, they both gave exactly the same results, i.e., the same first mesh points to have a value of zero as you proceed vertically for fixed x's (for one x the present method gave a free surface location one mesh point higher than the result of Sloss and Bruch [7]).

Table II. Computational and Iteration Information for Example

	$q^{(r)}$		$f_h(q^{(r)})$		n	
r	Sloss and Bruch [7]	Present	Sloss and Bruch [7]	Present	Sloss and Bruch [7]	Present
0	15.00000	15.00000	47.13327	51.50678	134	123
1	16.00000	16.00000	59.45287	64.87255	95	97
2	11.17412	11.14637	2.23226	2.25730	114	109
3	10.98586	10.97139	0.27792	0.23439	74	73
4	10.985909	10.95112	-0.00152	0.00326	51	74
5						
					468	449

The iteration approach presented (a modified version of that given in Section 3 and designated by the superscript iteration numbers in parentheses) passes from one region, D_2, to the other, D_1, interchanging data along Γ after *each* iteration (i.e., one pass through the mesh points with the algorithm). The approach given in Section 3 designated by the superscript notation without parentheses was also tried in which the problem in region D_2 was solved first to convergence. Data was then interchanged on Γ and the problem in region D_1 was solved. The error criterion (39) was then checked and was found not to be satisfied. Data was again transferred through Γ and the right hand region, D_2, solved again. This pattern was repeated until all the error criteria were met. There were roughly two and one half times as many iterations needed for this latter approach over the former in addition to a change in the θ-value to 0.475.

References

[1] C. Baiocchi. Free boundary problems in the theory of fluid flow through porous media. In *Proc. Int. Congr. Math.*, pages 237–243, Vancouver, 1975.

[2] J. Crank. *Free and Moving Boundary Problems.* Clarendon Press, Oxford, England, 1984.

[3] D. Funaro, A. Quarteroni, and P. Zanolli. An iterative procedure with interface relaxation for domain decomposition methods. *SIAM J. Numer. Anal.*, 25:1213–1236, 1988.

[4] M.E. Harr. *Groundwater and Seepage.* McGraw-Hill, New York, 1962.

[5] L.D. Marini and A. Quarteroni. An iterative procedure for domain decomposition methods: a finite element approach. In R. Glowinski, G.H Golub, and J. Periaux, editors, *Domain Decomposition Methods for Partial Differential Equations*, SIAM, Philadelphia, PA, 1988.

[6] L.D. Marini and A. Quarteroni. A relaxation procedure for domain decomposition methods using finite elements. *Numer. Math*, 55:575–598, 1989.

[7] J. M. Sloss and J.C. Bruch Jr. Free surface seepage problems. *J. Eng. Mech Div. Proc.*, ASCE 104, EM5:1099–1111, 1978.

Numerical investigation of soliton generation by a moving region of surface pressure

B.E. Protopopov

Lavrentyev Institute of Hydrodynamics
Siberian Division of the USSR Academy of Science
Novosibirsk 630090, USSR

Abstract. This work is devoted to numerical investigation of the process of soliton generation by a moving disturbance. The model of a potential flow of ideal incompressible fluid is used, which doesn't require both amplitude and steepness of waves under consideration to be small, as other applicable approximate models do. This allows the considered phenomenon to be described more precisely and also some information about validity of numerical results, based on approximate models, to be obtained.

Keywords: Wave generation, soliton, potential flow, numerical analysis, free boundary.

Mathematics subject classifications: 76B, 65M

1. Introduction

A forcing disturbance, such as a surface pressure distribution, moving with a transcritical velocity, can generate, periodically, a succession of solitary waves, advancing upstream of the disturbance in procession. This phenomenon was firstly simulated numerically by Wu & Wu [**1**] with use of the so-called generalized Boussinesq (g–B) equations. The model takes into account both nonlinear and dispersive effects (the mechanism of the phenomenon may be treated as a well-balanced interplay of these effects), yielding the adequate qualitative picture of the process. But some questions about validity of quantative results arise because of the approximate character of the model, constructed with some assumptions on smallness of both nonlinearity and dispersion. The other applicable model, the forced Korteweg–de Vries equation [**2**], possesses less generality because it is further simplification of the g–B model. Some analysis of applicability of the models mentioned above has been carried out in [**3**], where one can find the comparison of the numerical results, obtained within the framework of both models, and the experimental data in comparison with the numerical ones in the case of the moving bottom topography.

In this work the phenomenon of soliton generation is considered in the frames of the potential flow model, which is more general with respect to the above-mentioned approximate models, held for weakly nonlinear and weakly dispersive long waves. Except the potential model, the the g–B equations have been applied for the phenomenon simulation in order to estimate the applicability region of these equations by comparison of numerical results, based on different models.

The author wishes to express his thanks to Dr. I.V. Sturova for her continuous support of the work.

2. Mathematical formulation

At every moment of time t the domain occupied by fluid is assumed to be a curvelinear quadrangle $Q(t) = \{0 \le x \le l,\ -h \le y \le \eta(x,t)\}$ in the coordinate system $0xy$ with axis $0x$ directed along the surface of undisturbed fluid and axis $0y$ pointed vertically upwards. The fluid motion is due to the action of the surface pressure distribution

$$p(x,t) = p_0(\xi) = \begin{cases} \frac{1}{2}p_m(1+\cos\pi\xi), & |\xi| \le 1, \\ 0, & |\xi| > 1, \end{cases} \tag{2.1}$$

where $\xi = x - X(t)$ is the local coordinate, $X(t)$ defines the movement of the middle point $\xi = 0$ of the pressure region, p_m is the maximum value of $p_0(\xi)$. Here and further, the dimensionless variables are used only, in which the half–length of the pressure domain, the gravitational acceleration and the fluid density are equal to unity.

Both models, which are used here, contain two equations of evolutionary type, the former describes the transformation of the surface elevation $\eta(x,t)$ in time, the latter is necessary for the velocity field evolution to be found. These equations can be written as

$$\eta_t + v = 0, \tag{2.2}$$

$$q_t + s_x = 0 \tag{2.3}$$

with functions $v(x,t)$, $q(x,t)$, $s(x,t)$ defined below. Here and henceforth, subscripts will be used to denote partial derivatives. In addition to the equations written above, the initial data must be imposed

$$\eta = \eta_0(x), \quad q = q_0(x) \quad \text{at } t = 0, \tag{2.4}$$

as well as the relations between η, v, q, s (containing time t as a parameter only) must be stated to complete the system.

For the potential flow model these relations are

$$q = u, \tag{2.5}$$

$$s = \frac{1}{1+\eta_x^2}\left(\frac{1}{2}\left(u^2 - v^2\right) + \eta_x uv\right) + \eta + p, \tag{2.6}$$

where $u(x,t)$ and $v(x,t)$ mean, respectively, the tangential and normal (interior) components of fluid velocity on the free surface, both times $\sqrt{1+\eta_x^2}$. In this case equation (2.5) becomes the usual kinematic condition on the free boundary and (2.6) is the dynamic condition (the momentum equation, written along the free surface in terms of tangential and normal components). Dependence of v on η and u is complicated enough and may be expressed with the help of the so-called normal derivative operator $N(\eta,\varphi)$, acting on the free-surface elevation $\eta(x,t)$ and the potential boundary value $\varphi(x,t)$, the latter being defined as

$$\varphi(x,t) = \varphi_0(t) + \int_0^x u(\xi,t)\,d\xi, \tag{2.7}$$

with an arbitrary function $\varphi_0(t)$. The operator $N(\eta, \varphi)$ acts as follows

$$v = N(\eta, \varphi) = \eta_x \Phi_x - \Phi_y \quad \text{on} \quad y = \eta(x,t), \tag{2.8}$$

where $\Phi(x, y, t)$, the velocity potential, is the solution of the elliptic problem:

$$\begin{aligned} &\Phi_{xx} + \Phi_{yy} = 0 && \text{in } Q(t), \\ &\Phi_x = 0 && \text{on } x = 0,\ x = l, \\ &\Phi_y = 0 && \text{on } y = -h, \\ &\Phi = \varphi && \text{on } y = \eta(x,t). \end{aligned}$$

To overcome some difficulties, caused by one of the fluid domain boundaries being described by the unknown function $\eta(x,t)$, we rewrite the system of equations in terms of new space coordinates (x, z), where $z = (\eta - y)/(\eta + h)$. Such transformation replaces the fluid domain $Q(t)$ by a constant reactangle $\Pi = \{0 \le x \le l,\ 0 \le z \le 1\}$. The elliptic problem may be rewritten now as follows:

$$U_x + V_z = 0 \quad \text{in } \Pi, \tag{2.9}$$

$$U = 0 \quad \text{on } x = 0,\ x = l, \tag{2.10}$$

$$V = 0 \quad \text{on } z = 1, \tag{2.11}$$

$$\Phi = \varphi \quad \text{on } z = 0, \tag{2.12}$$

where the following symbols have been introduced:

$$U(x,z,t) = \alpha\Phi_x + \beta\Phi_z, \qquad V(x,z,t) = \beta\Phi_x + \gamma\Phi_z, \tag{2.13}$$

$$\alpha(x,t) = \eta + h, \qquad \beta(x,z,t) = (1-z)\eta_x, \qquad \gamma(x,z,t) = (1+\beta^2)/\alpha, \tag{2.14}$$

The condition (2.8) is replaced by

$$v = V \quad \text{on } z = 0. \tag{2.15}$$

In the case of the g–B model, the system of equations (2.2)–(2.4) has been completed in a more simple way [**1**]:

$$q = w - \frac{1}{3}h^2 w_{xx}, \tag{2.16}$$

$$w = 0 \quad \text{on } x = 0,\ x = l, \tag{2.17}$$

$$s = \frac{1}{2}w^2 + \eta + p, \qquad v = \left[(\eta + h)w\right]_x, \tag{2.18}$$

where $w(x,t)$ means the water–layer depth–averaged x–component velocity of the fluid. The relative simplicity of the g–B model (equations (2.2)–(2.4), (2.16)–(2.18)), in comparison with the potential flow model (equations (2.2)–(2.7), (2.9)–(2.15)), has been achieved due to the following limitations of amplitude a and length λ of waves investigated [**1**]:

$$\delta_1 = a/h \ll 1, \quad \delta_2 = h/\lambda \ll 1, \quad \delta_1 = \mathcal{O}(\delta_2^2). \tag{2.19}$$

3. Numerical method

The problem has been solved numerically with the finite–difference method. A second–order accurate Crank–Nikolson discretization of evolutionary equations (2.2), (2.3) has been carried out

$$\eta^{n+1,k+1} = \eta^n - \frac{\tau}{2}\left(v^{n+1,k} + v^n\right), \tag{3.1}$$

$$q^{n+1,k+1} = q^n - \frac{\tau}{2}\left(s_x^{n+1,k} + s_x^n\right), \tag{3.2}$$

where τ is a time step, the first superscript denotes a time step number, the second one is an iteration number. The iterative procedure is necessary at every time step because of scheme implicity and nonlinearity of the relations, connecting η, v, q, s.

The appropriate scheme for solving the elliptic problem has been constructed by analogy with that from [4]

$$\frac{\Phi^{k+\frac{1}{2}} - \Phi^k}{\omega} = U_x^{k+\frac{1}{2}} + V_z^k, \qquad \frac{\Phi^{k+1} - \Phi^{k+\frac{1}{2}}}{\omega} = V_z^{k+1} - V_z^k,$$

where ω is an iteration parameter (the first superscript, the time step number, has been omitted). U, V and Φ may be connected in accordance with the relations

$$U = \left(\Phi_x + \beta V\right)/\gamma, \qquad V = \left(\Phi_z + \beta U\right)/\alpha,$$

derived from (2.13), (2.14). So, the scheme, in its complete form, looks like

$$I. \quad \Phi^{k+\frac{1}{2}} - \omega U_x^{k+\frac{1}{2}} = \Phi^k + \omega V_z^k, \tag{3.3}$$

$$U^{k+\frac{1}{2}} = \left(\Phi_x^{k+\frac{1}{2}} + \beta^{k+1} V^k\right)/\gamma^{k+1}, \tag{3.4}$$

$$U^{k+\frac{1}{2}} = 0 \qquad \text{on } x = 0, \quad x = l; \tag{3.5}$$

$$II. \quad \Phi^{k+1} - \omega V_z^{k+1} = \Phi^{k+\frac{1}{2}} - \omega V_z^k, \tag{3.6}$$

$$V^{k+1} = \left(\Phi_z^{k+1} + \beta^{k+1} U^{k+\frac{1}{2}}\right)/\alpha^{k+1}, \tag{3.7}$$

$$\Phi^{k+1} = \varphi^{k+1} \qquad \text{on } z = 0, \tag{3.8}$$

$$V^{k+1} = 0 \qquad \text{on } z = 1. \tag{3.9}$$

In both models the derivatives with respect to space coordinates are discretized with use of the central differences only, providing second–order approximations. This becomes possible if the nodes of the computational grid are placed in the so–called "chess order". At points $x_{i-\frac{1}{2}}$, where x_ν is defined as νh_1 ($h_1 = l/m_1$ is a grid step in the x–direction, m_1 is integer), the nodes $\eta_{i-\frac{1}{2}} = \eta(x_{i-\frac{1}{2}}, t)$, $v_{i-\frac{1}{2}}$, $s_{i-\frac{1}{2}}$ ($i = 1, \ldots, m_1$) are placed. Between these points the nodes q_i ($i = 1, \ldots, m_1 - 1$) lie. Also at points x_i, but including the boundary points of the interval $[0, l]$, the nodes u_i or, in dependence on the model used, w_i ($i = 0, \ldots, m_1$) are placed.

In the potential flow model the elliptic problem (3.3)–(3.9) is calculated on the grid, consisted of the nodes $\Phi_{i-1/2,j-1} = \Phi(x_{i-1/2}, z_{j-1}, t)$ $(i = 1, \dots, m_1;\ j = 1, \dots, m_2)$, U_{ij-1} $(i = 0, \dots, m_1;\ j = 1, \dots, m_2)$, $V_{i-1/2,j-1/2}$ $(i = 1, \dots, m_1;\ j = 0, \dots, m_2)$, where $z_\nu = \nu h_2$, $h_2 = 1/(m_2 - 0.5)$ is the grid step in the z–direction, m_2 is integer. After the appropriate finite differences have been substituted instead of space coordinate derivatives, in accordance with, for example,

$$(\Phi_x)_{ij} \approx \left(\Phi_{i+1/2,j} - \Phi_{i-1/2,j}\right) \Big/ h_1,$$

the solving of system (3.3)–(3.9) is reduced to reversing a succession of tridiagonal matrices.

The iterative procedure continues until the following condition is achieved

$$\|U_x + V_z\|_{c_h} < \varepsilon,$$

where $\varepsilon > 0$ is a given number, small enough, and $\|f\|_{c_h}$ means $\max_{i,j} |f_{ij}|$.

In the case of the g–B model the elliptic part of the problem, expressed by equation (2.16) with boundary condition (2.17), is simple enough for its finite–difference realization to be omitted.

4. Results

The calculations were carried out for the case of a channel with a length $l = 75$ and a depth $h = 1$. The movement of the disturbance is defined by

$$X(t) = \begin{cases} x_0 & \text{for } t \leq 0, \\ x_0 + ct & \text{for } t > 0, \end{cases}$$

with the starting point $x_0 = 2$ and the constant value of the velocity $c = 1$, which is critical for the chosen depth: $Fr = c/\sqrt{h} = 1$. Until the beginning of the surface pressure movement, the fluid is assumed to be at rest, that means

$$\eta_0(x) = -p_0(x - x_0), \qquad q_0(x) = 0.$$

The numerical results, obtained for the case of the potential flow model, with the pressure value $p_m = 0.2$ and the grid parameters $m_1 = 375$, $m_2 = 10$, $\tau/h_1 = 0.5$, are presented in Figures 1, 2. In the former the wave profile evolution is shown. Here the lower curve represents the configuration of the fluid surface at moment $t = 0$, every next curve, upwards the Figure, is the wave profile for the next moment of time, with a constant time increment $\Delta t = 10$, up to the moment of the calculation stop $t = 60$. For every moment of time the position of the pressure distribution on the fluid surface is denoted by two vertical short lines on the corresponding curve. This Figure gives a general picture of the wave generation process, when a succession of solitary waves, advancing upstream of the disturbance, is formed, while a wave train develops downstream of an ever elongating stretch of a uniformly depressed water surface immediately behind the disturbance.

Development of the solitary waves can be seen from Figure 2. Here the curve 1 represents the amplitude $a_1(t)$ of the first soliton or, more presicely, the local maximum of the surface elevation before the disturbance, the curve 2 shows the velocity of movement of this maximum $v_1(t)$, i.e. the time derivative of its horizontal coordinate. At some moment of time the second solitary wave becomes distinguishable, its amplitude $a_2(t)$ and velocity $v_2(t)$ are shown by the curves 3 and 4, respectively. The dashed line represents the wave resistance, defined as (see [**1**])

$$r(t) = \int_0^l p\eta_x \, dx.$$

The birth of the i–th ($i = 1, 2, \dots$) soliton is accompanied by nonmonotonous behavior of the corresponding curve $a_i(t)$, sudden increase of $v_i(t)$ and the next maximum of the function $r(t)$. The maximum points of $r(t)$ are reasonable to be considered as the moments of the corresponding soliton appearance. Every separated soliton moves with a nearly constant velocity, while its amplitude is increasing (with slowing–down the growth).

The basic characteristics of the process in dependence on the pressure value p_m are reflected in Figures 3, 4. These Figures also make it possible to watch the dynamics of divergence of the numerical results, obtained in different models, with increase of p_m, i.e. with intensification of nonlinear effects (with growth of the parameters δ_1, δ_2 from (2.19)). In Figure 3 the wave resistance $r(t)$ is shown, calculated for $p_m = 0.2$ (a) and $p_m = 0.1$ (b). The solid line 1, as well as the neighbouring dashed and dotted lines, correspond to calculations within the framework of the potential flow model, the rest of curves are obtained with use of the g–B equations. The solid curves represent the numerical results for the case of the grid step $h_1 = 0.2$, the dashed curves are obtained with $h_1 = 0.4$ and the dotted ones correspond to $h_1 = 0.1$. In all cases the relation $\tau/h_1 = 0.5$ and the z–coordinate step $h_2 = 2/19$ are invariable.

The frequency of the first soliton appearance $\omega_1 = 2\pi/t_1$, the soliton amplitude $a_{11} = a_1(t_1)$ at moment t_1 of its birth and the maximum value of the wave resistance $r_1 = r(t_1)$, calculated with use of the potential model, are presented in Figure 4 by points 1, 2, 3, respectively. Points 4, 5, 6 show the same parameters, but obtained with use of the g–B approximation. One can see that in the case $p_m = 0.2$ the approximate model, in comparison with more general potential one, diminishes essentially the values of ω_1 (by 25 %), a_{11} (by 35 %) and r_1 (by 43 %). With decrease of p_m the disagreement of the numerical results becomes less, and in the case $p_m = 0.1$ the relative difference of the parameters mentioned amounts 11 %, 16 %, 28 %, respectively.

Providing a more pronounced response of water to the surface pressure, the potential model is also more "sensitive" to the variation of the grid size, as one can see from Figure 3, where the wave resistance, calculated with different grids, is presented. Moreover, the dependence of the numerical results on the grid size increases essentially with increasing the pressure value p_m, i.e. with intensifying the nonlinear effects. This is, probably, due to the fact that $p_m = 0.2$ lies in vicinity of some critical value of p_m, for which the flow becomes unstable (wave breaking for $p_m > 0.15$ was also observed experimentally [**3**]), that makes the problem solution to depend essentially on numerical viscosity.

5. Summary

The numerical algorithm has been developed to calculate nonlinear water waves within the framework of the potential flow model. The algorithm is effective enough to be applied to such complicated problem, as soliton generation by a moving disturbance, which has been investigated earlier with use of weakly nonlinear, weakly dispersive models only. The use of the potential model has not brought any new principal features in the general picture of the phenomenon, but has permitted to correct the basic characteristics of the process. In particular, the greater values of both soliton generation frequency and soliton amplitudes have been obtained. Disagreement of the numerical results, based on the potential model and on the g–B approximation, increases with increasing the pressure amplitude and becomes essential for still moderate values of p_m. Only for pressure values, small enough ($p_m < 0.1$), an accurate numerical simulation of the phenomenon is possible with use of a simple approximate model.

References

[1] Wu D.M. and Wu T.Y., *Three-Dimensional Nonlinear Long Waves Due to Moving Surface Pressure*, Proc. 14th Symp. on Naval Hydrodynamics, Michigan, (1982).

[2] Wu T.Y., *Generation of upstream advancing solitons by moving disturbances*, J. Fluid Mech. **184** (1987), 75–99.

[3] Lee S.J., Yates G.T. and Wu T.Y., *Experiment and analyses of upstream-advancing solitary waves generated by moving disturbances*, J. Fluid Mech. **199** (1989), 563–593.

[4] Douglas J. and Rachford H.H., *On the numerical solution of heat conduction problems in two and three space variables*, Transactions of the Amer. Math. Soc. **82, N 2** (1956), 421–439.

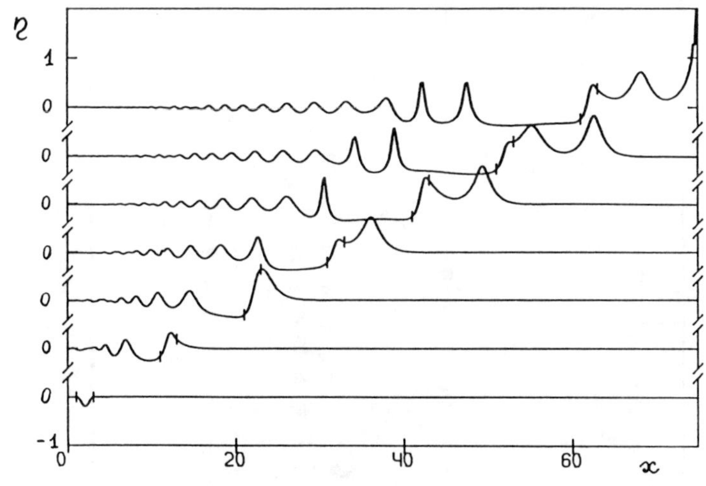

Figure 1. The free-surface elevation η at different moments of time $t = 0, 10, 20, \ldots, 60$.

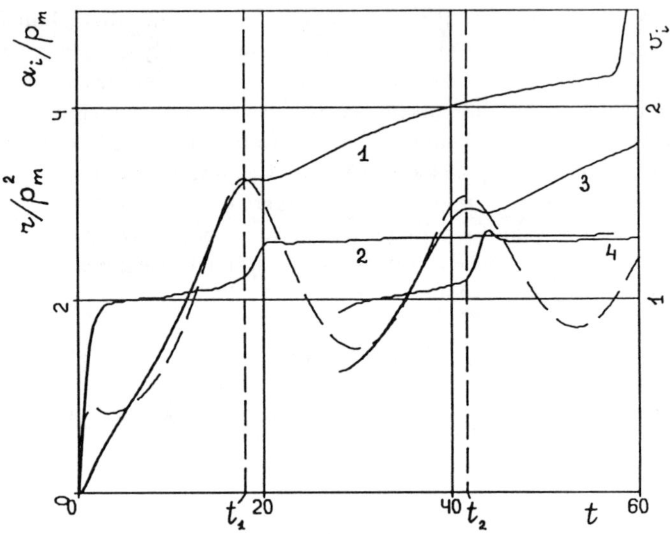

Figure 2. Amplitude a_i (curves 1,3) and velocity v_i (curves 2,4) of i–th soliton ($i = 1, 2$); wave resistance $r(--)$.

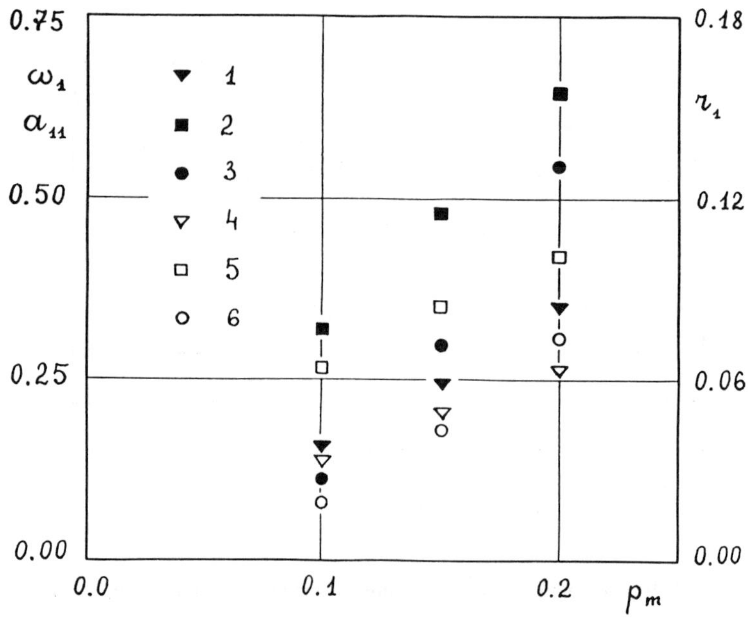

Figure 4. The soliton generation frequency $\omega_1 = 2\pi/t_1$ (points 1,4), the soliton amplitude $a_{11} = a_1(t_1)$ (points 2,5), the wave resistance maximum $r_1 = r(t_1)$ (points 3,6), based on the potential model (1–3) and the Boussinesq approximation (4–6).

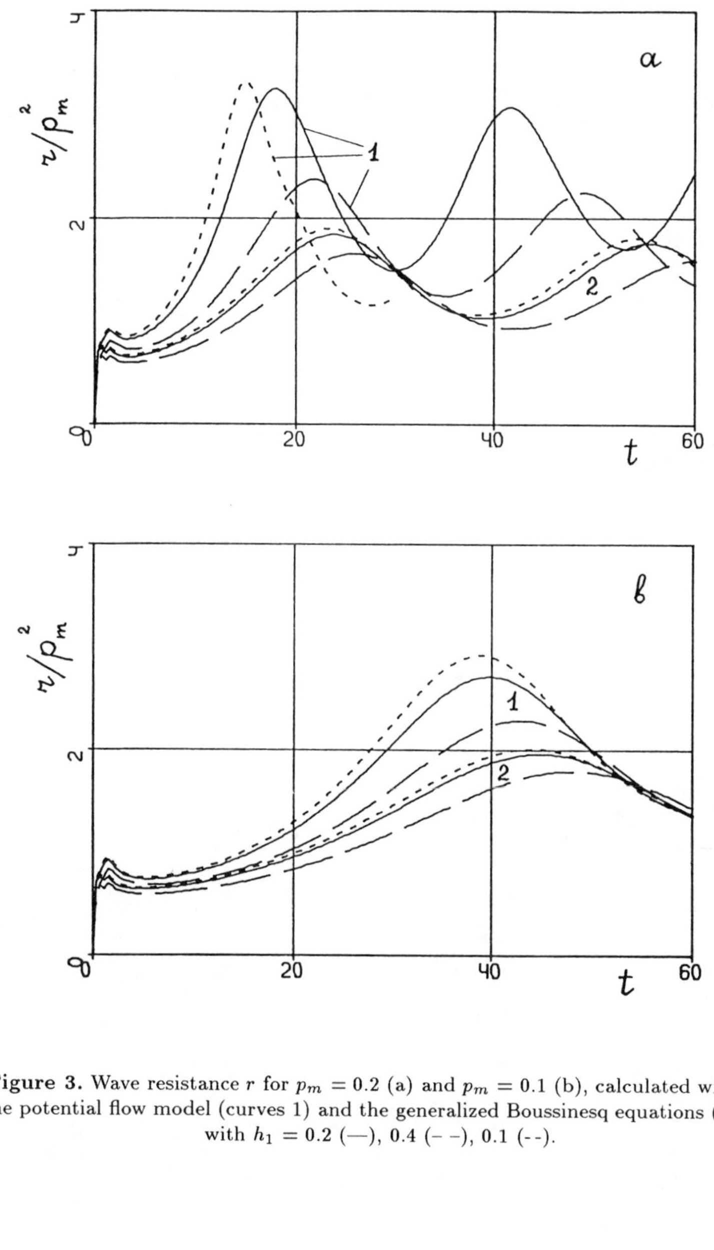

Figure 3. Wave resistance r for $p_m = 0.2$ (a) and $p_m = 0.1$ (b), calculated with use of the potential flow model (curves 1) and the generalized Boussinesq equations (curves 2) with $h_1 = 0.2$ (—), 0.4 (– –), 0.1 (- -).

Eigenfrequencies of a viscous, incompressible fluid with a capillary free boundary

R.M.S.M. Schulkes and C. Cuvelier

Department of Mathematics
Delft University of Technology
P.O. Box 356, 2600 AJ Delft
The Netherlands

Joint Research Center
Ispra I-21020, Varese
Italy

Abstract. Oscillations of a viscous, incompressible liquid with a capillary free-boundary are studied by means of numerical techniques. Starting from the static equilibrium configuration of the system we study small oscillations of the system about this equilibrium. A finite-element discretization in conjunction with an inverse-iteration procedure is used for the calculation of the eigenmodes of the system.

1. Introduction

Fluid oscillations in a micro-gravity environment occur frequently nowadays, see Walter [6]. Specific examples are fluids in liquid propellant tanks of spacecraft and fluids in experimental set-ups which benefit from the absence of gravity, like e.g. processes involving liquid bridges. A thorough understanding of the dynamic behaviour of the fluid is essential for a number of reasons. Regarding fluids in propellant tanks it is important to avoid nutation frequencies which are close to the eigenfrequencies of the fluid since this can lead to so-called fluid-slosh instabilities, see e.g. Abramson [1]. In processes involving liquid bridges it is essential to avoid the breakup of the liquid bridge. Spacecraft almost always experience vibrations due to operating equipment or actions of the crew. These vibrations can lead to the rupture of the liquid bridge when frequencies of vibrations are near the eigenfrequencies of the liquid bridge.

The nature of a micro-gravity environment implies that forces other than the gravitational force are important. For fluids with a free surface this means that capillary (or surface tension) forces play an important role. Both the static and the dynamic behaviour of the free liquid surface is in that case quite different from that on earth. The difficulty of performing micro-gravity experiments on earth means that it is desirable to be able to model the fluid motion in a micro-gravity environment by means of computational techniques.

In this paper we show how the problem of small oscillations of a viscous, incompressible fluid with a capillary free-boundary may be solved numerically. First of all we calculate the equilibrium shape of the capillary free boundary. We then consider small perturbations of the system with respect to this equilibrium configuration. The equations governing the small fluid motion are written in a variational formulation. Then it is shown how, by means of the finite-element technique in conjunction with an inverse-iteration procedure, the eigenmodes of the problem can be determined.

2. Equilibrium capillary surface

Consider the liquid-gas interface of a liquid partly filling a container. Due to the mutual interactions of liquid particles having a non-zero resultant on the interface there is a pressure jump across the interface. This pressure jump is proportional to the total curvature of the interface as expressed by the well-known Laplace-Young equation

$$\alpha\left(\frac{1}{R_1}+\frac{1}{R_2}\right)=\Delta p. \tag{1}$$

Here α is the coefficient of surface tension and R_1, R_2 are the principal radii of curvature of the interface. A force balance argument on the line of intersection of the container wall leads to the boundary condition in which the so-called contact-angle condition is specified, namely

$$\mathbf{n}_S \cdot \mathbf{n}_\Gamma = -\cos\delta \tag{2}$$

see figure 1. When the total volume of fluid is fixed the equations (1) and (2) are to be suplemented by the volume constraint viz.

$$\int_\Omega dx = V_f \tag{3}$$

where V_f is the volume of the fluid.

The shape of the liquid-gas interface are determined by equations (1)-(3). In the case of a rotationally symmetric capillary surface equation (1) is a second order, non-linear ordinary differential equation. Solving this equation is complicated by the fact that the domain of solution is, in general, not known a priori - it has to be found as part of the solution. In order to be able to determine this geometrical unknown an extra boundary condition is prescribed in addition to the contact angle condition, namely, the condition of intersection of the free-surface and the container wall.

Only a global outline of the solution procedure for this capillary free-boundary problem is given. For details of the method and its application to the capillary free-boundary problem the reader is referred to Schulkes and Cuvelier [4] and the review article of Cuvelier and Schulkes [2]. First of all we assume that some initial estimate of the geometrical unknown is given. The boundary conditions at the free boundary are then expanded about this estimate to yield a new boundary condition which is essentially is linear combination of the original conditions. This procedure leads to a problem in which the geometrical unknowns are reduced to the free boundary itself. An iteration procedure for subsequent updates of the free-boundary estimate follows naturally from the expansion. The solution procedure is now as follows. The non-linear differential equation is solved (iteratively, using e.g. a Newton procedure) on the estimated domain subject to the new boundary condition. The estimate of the domain is then updated and the differential equation is solved on the new domain. Repeat this nested iterative procedure until convergence is attained.

In figure 2 we show the shape of the capillary surface in various rotating containers and different angular velocities

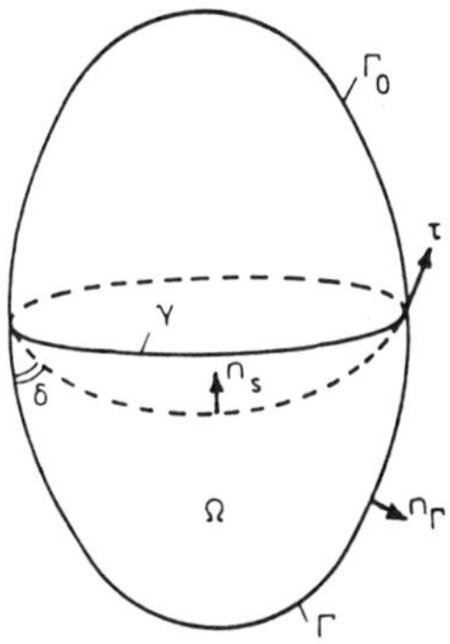

Figure 1: Schematic diagram.

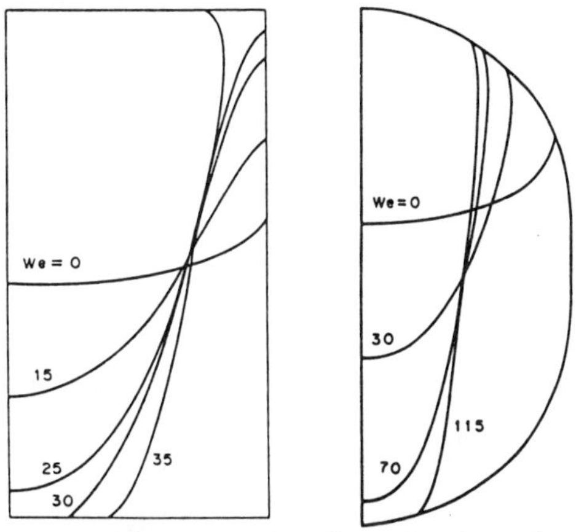

Figure 2: Capillary free-boundary shapes for various rotation speeds.

3. Equations of motion and variational formulation

Consider a rotationally symmetric domain Ω which is occupied by a viscous, incompressible fluid of density ρ and viscosity μ. The (rotationally symmetric) free surface is denoted by S and the rigid boundary of the container wall is denoted by Γ. We assume that the z-axis is the symmetry axis of the system and the the system may be rotating about this symmetry axis with the angular velocity ω. The gravitational force is directed along the negative z-axis. The equations which determine the motion of the fluid in a coordinate frame rotating with angular velocity $\boldsymbol{\omega}$, are the Navier-Stokes equations subject to the incompressibility constraint and suitable boundary and initial conditions. Solving these non-linear equations is beyond the scope of this paper. Therefore we linearize the equations with respect to the configuration of the system in the static state and consider only small perturbations relative to this configuration. The linearized equations in dimensionless form will be stated below, for a derivation of these equations the reader is referred to Schulkes and Cuvelier [5]. The governing equations in the body of the fluid are

$$\left.\begin{array}{l}\dfrac{\partial \mathbf{u}}{\partial t} + 2\sqrt{We}\,\hat{\mathbf{k}} \times \mathbf{u} + \nabla p = Oh\nabla^2 \mathbf{u} \\ \nabla \cdot \mathbf{u} = 0\end{array}\right\} \quad \text{in } \Omega, \tag{4}$$

where $\mathbf{u} = (u_r, u_\theta, u_z)$ is the fluid velocity, p the pressure and $\hat{\mathbf{k}}$ a unit vector directed along the z-axis. We have introduced the dimensionless numbers $We = \rho\omega^2 L^3/\alpha$ (L is a length scale, α is the coefficient of surface tension) termed the Weber number and $Oh = \mu/\sqrt{\rho\alpha L}$ termed the Ohnesorge number. The gradient and Laplace operators take on their respective forms in cylindrical coordinates owing to the rotational symmetry.

The boundary condition on the rigid container wall is given by the usual no-slip condition characteristic of viscous flows, namely

$$\mathbf{u} = 0 \quad \text{on } \Gamma, \tag{5}$$

and on the capillary free surface S we have

$$\left.\begin{aligned} &\sigma_\tau = 0 \\ &\sigma_n = -(Bo\hat{\mathbf{k}}\cdot\mathbf{n}_S - \frac{1}{R_1^2} - \frac{1}{R_2^2} - We(\hat{\mathbf{k}}\times\mathbf{R})\cdot(\hat{\mathbf{k}}\times\mathbf{n}_S))\eta + \frac{1}{r}\frac{\partial}{\partial s}(r\frac{\partial\eta}{\partial s}) \\ &u_n = \frac{\partial\eta}{\partial t} \end{aligned}\right\} \quad \text{on } S, \tag{6}$$

$$\frac{\partial\eta}{\partial s} = 0 \quad \text{on } \Gamma\cap S, \tag{7}$$

and the symmetry conditions

$$u_r = 0,\ \ u_\theta = 0,\ \ \sigma_\tau = 0,\ \ \frac{\partial\eta}{\partial s} = 0 \ \text{ at } \ r = 0. \tag{8}$$

In the above equations R_1 and R_2 are the principal radii of curvature of S, s is a curvilinear coordinate parallel to S, $\eta(\mathbf{x},t)$ denotes a small normal displacement of the free surface S relative to the static configuration and $\mathbf{R}$ denotes the position vector of the static free surface relative to some origin. The dimensionless number $Bo = \rho g L^2/\alpha$ is termed the Bond number. We have used the notation

$$\sigma_n = (\boldsymbol{\sigma}\cdot\mathbf{n})\cdot\mathbf{n},\ \ \sigma_\tau = (\boldsymbol{\sigma}\cdot\mathbf{n})\cdot\boldsymbol{\tau},$$

for the normal and tangential stresses respectively where $\mathbf{n}$ and $\boldsymbol{\tau}$ denote unit normal and tangential vectors and

$$\boldsymbol{\sigma} = -p\mathbf{I} + Oh(\nabla\mathbf{u} + \nabla\mathbf{u}^T)$$

denotes the Cauchy stress tensor. Due to the rotational symmetry all quantities are independent of the azimuthal coordinate. In general u_θ will be non-zero only when $We \neq 0$, i.e. when the Coriolis force is non-zero.

Since we are interested in the eigenmodes of the system we assume that all time-dependent quantities exhibit a temporal behaviour of the form $e^{\lambda t}$. Here λ is in general some complex quantity of which the real part (usually negative) characterizes the damping of oscillations and the imaginary part characterizes the oscillatory behaviour of the fluid motion. Our aim is to solve equations (4)-(8) by means of the finite-element discretization technique. To that end the problem is written in variational form, namely:

> find $\mathbf{u}$ and p such that for all suitably smooth functions $\mathbf{v}$ and q the following equations are satisfied
>
> $$\int_\Omega(\lambda\mathbf{u}\cdot\mathbf{v} + 2\sqrt{We}\hat{\mathbf{k}}\times\mathbf{u}\cdot\mathbf{v} - p\nabla\cdot\mathbf{v})r\,dx \ + Oh\,a(\mathbf{u},\mathbf{v}) + \frac{1}{\lambda}b(\mathbf{u},\mathbf{v}) = 0, \tag{9}$$

$$\int_{\Omega} q(\nabla \cdot \mathbf{u}) r dx = 0,$$

where the bilinear form $b(\mathbf{u}, \mathbf{v})$ is given by

$$b(\mathbf{u}, \mathbf{v}) = \int_{S} \left[(Bo\hat{\mathbf{k}} \cdot \mathbf{n}_S - \frac{1}{R_1^2} - \frac{1}{R_2^2} - We(\hat{\mathbf{k}} \times \mathbf{R}) \cdot (\hat{\mathbf{k}} \times \mathbf{n}_S)) u_n v_n + \frac{\partial u_n}{\partial s} \frac{\partial v_n}{\partial s} \right] r ds.$$

Note that the boundary conditions have been employed and that η has been eliminated from the equations by means of the kinematic conditions on S. The functional $a(\mathbf{u}, \mathbf{u})$ is proportional to the rate of dissipation of energy in the liquid. Problem (9) defines a boundary-value problem for the determination of the spectral parameter λ.

4. Numerical solution of the spectral problem

The spectral problem, as defined by equation (9) will be discretized using a finite-element procedure. The fact that the pressure does not appear in the incompressibility constraint poses some numerical difficulties. This problem is eliminated by means of a penalty function approach, see Cuvelier et al. [3]. Application of the standard finite-element technique yields the discrete equivalent of the momentum equation, viz.

$$\lambda \mathbf{M}\tilde{\mathbf{u}} + 2\sqrt{We}\mathbf{C}\tilde{\mathbf{u}} - \mathbf{L}^T\tilde{\mathbf{p}} + Oh\mathbf{A}\tilde{\mathbf{u}} + \frac{1}{\lambda}\mathbf{B}\tilde{\mathbf{u}} = 0,$$

and of the (penalized) incompressibility constraint

$$\epsilon \mathbf{D}\tilde{\mathbf{p}} = -\mathbf{L}\tilde{\mathbf{u}},$$

where ϵ is some small penalty parameter (typically $\epsilon \leq 10^{-6}$). The vectors $\tilde{\mathbf{u}}$ and $\tilde{\mathbf{p}}$ contain the velocity and pressure unknowns in the nodal points. Since the matrix $\mathbf{D}$ is non-singular, it may be inverted to express the pressure unknowns in terms of the velocity unknowns. Substituting for $\tilde{\mathbf{p}}$ in the momentum equation yields the quadratic eigenvalue problem

$$(\lambda^2\mathbf{M} + \lambda\mathbf{S} + \mathbf{B})\tilde{\mathbf{u}} = 0, \tag{10}$$

where the following substitution has been made

$$\mathbf{S} = 2\sqrt{We}\mathbf{C} + \frac{1}{\epsilon}\mathbf{L}^T\mathbf{D}^{-1}\mathbf{L} + Oh\mathbf{A}.$$

Before solution methods for eigenvalue problem (10) can be considered it is important to realise that generally only a very small number of eigenvalues are important. Generally one is interested only in the lowest anti-symmetric eigenmodes of the system. Calculating the whole of the spectrum would then be a wasteful exercise. This is even beside the fact that general purpose eigenvalue routines like the QZ-algorithm generally break down when the order of the matrices becomes too large. In our calculations we found that an Inverse-Iteration procedure was quite effective to calculate selected eigenvalues. For details of the Inverse-Iteration procedure applied to the quadratic eigenvalue problem (10) we refer to Schulkes and Cuvelier [5].

5. Numerical results

Let us first consider eigenmodes of a liquid in a rigid, non-rotating tank. In particular we consider the geometry of a propellant tank used in a TV-SAT satellite. The parameters are given the values $Oh = 10^{-3}$ and $Bo = 100$. The shape of the static capillary free-surface has been calculated for given values of Bo and fill-fraction and for a contact angle $\delta = \pi/2$. In Table 1 we show the eigenfrequencies of the lowest two eigenmodes for various fill-fractions. Note that $\mathrm{Im}(\lambda)$ is strongly dependent on the fill fraction of the propellant tank. In figure 3

fill fraction	λ_1	λ_2
0.95	-0.24+44.7i	-0.72+82.9i
0.70	-0.26+22.5i	-0.35+45.1i
0.50	-0.29+41.0i	-0.61+77.3i

Table 1: First and second eigenmode of fluid in a TV-SAT tank for various fill fractions.

we show streamlines for the first and second eigenmode for two different fill-fractions.

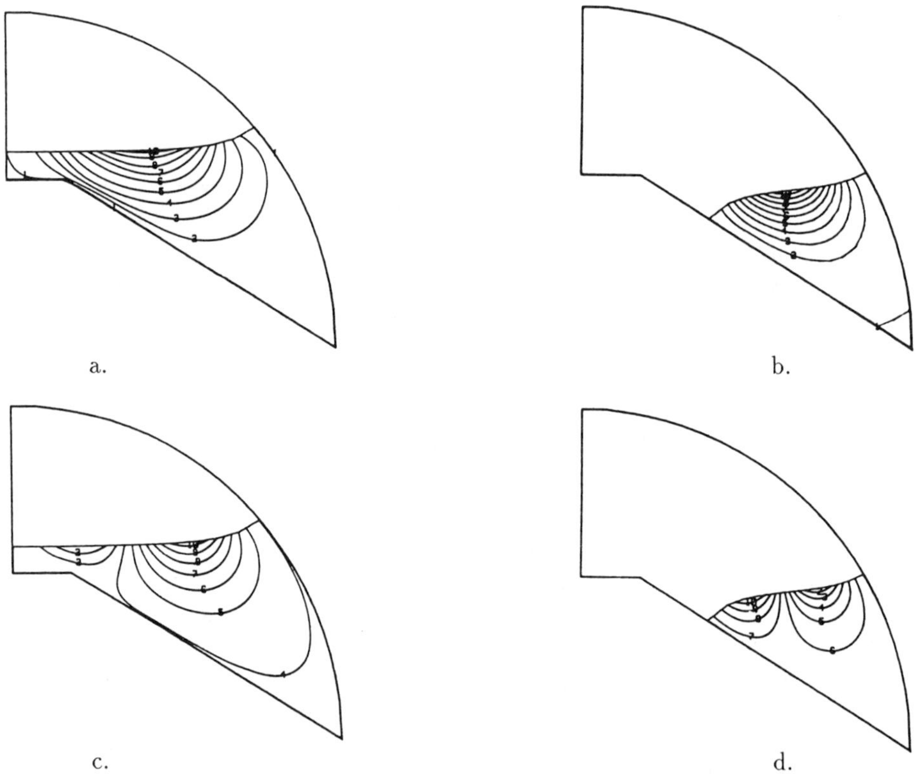

Figure 3: Streamlines of the fluid flow in a TV-SAT tank for the first (a,b) and second (c,d) eigenmodes with $Bo = 100$, $\delta = \pi/2$ and fill fractions 0.75 (a,c) and 0.5 (b,d).

Next we consider oscillations of a rotating liquid bridge. We consider a liquid bridge anchored between two circular discs with radii $R = 0.5$ and $R = 0.75$ separated a distance 1. The volume of fluid between the discs is 0.35π and we set the parameter values $Bo = 5$ and $Oh = 0.1$. It was found that no stable static configuration is possible for $We > 7.3$, i.e. surface tension forces could not balance centrifugal forces for values of We exceeding $We = 7.3$. In Figure 4 we show vector plots of some free-surface and internal (rotation induced) oscillation modes for the case $We = 7.0$.

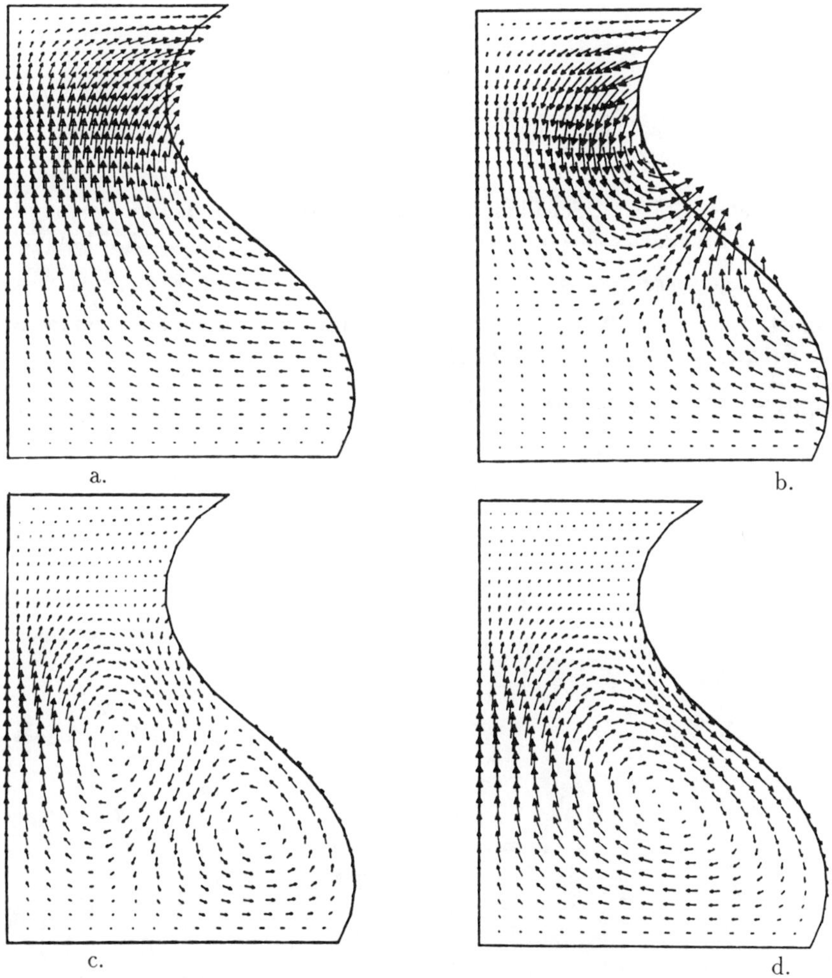

a. b. c. d.

Figure 4: Vector plots of the first (a) and second (b) free-surface modes and of two internal modes (c,d) for the parameter values $Bo = 0.5$, $Oh = 0.1$ and $We = 7.0$.

Concluding remarks

We have shown how the problem of small oscillations of a viscous, incompressible fluid with a capillary free boundary can be solved numerically. The finite-element approach in conjunction with an inverse-iteration procedure provide an efficient way of calculating eigenmodes of the system. The finite-element approach is particularly usefull because complicated geometries do not pose a significant problem and Neumann boundary conditions are dealt with in a natural way.

REFERENCES

[**1**] N.H. Abramson (ed.), "The dynamic behavior of liquids in moving containers", *NASA SP*-106 (1966).

[**2**] C. Cuvelier and R.M.S.M. Schulkes, *Some numerical methods for the computation of capillary free boundaries governed by the Navier-Stokes equations*, SIAM Review **32**(3) (1990).

[**3**] C. Cuvelier, A. Segal and A.A. van Steenhoven, "Finite-element methods and the Navier-Stokes equations", Reidel, Dordrecht (1986).

[**4**] R.M.S.M. Schulkes and C. Cuvelier, *An efficient method for the computation of static meniscus configurations*, Acta Astronautica **19**(8) (1989), 699-705.

[**5**] R.M.S.M. Schulkes and C. Cuvelier, *On the computation of normal modes of a rotating, viscous, incompressible fluid with a capillary free boundary*, Comp. Meth. Appl. Mech. Engng. (1990), to appear.

[**6**] H.U. Walter (ed.), "Fluid sciences and material sciences is space. A European perspective", Springer-Verlag (1987).

The Stefan problem for a hyperbolic heat equation

N.V. Shemetov

Lavrentyev Institute of Hydrodinamics
Siberian Division of the USSR Academy of Sciences
Novosibirsk 630090, USSR

Abstract. The Stefan problem with the time relaxation of Cattaneo are considered. It has a finite speed of propagation for the temperature. In this paper we prove the existence of the weak solution of the relaxed Cattaneo–Stefan problem and show that the weak solutions of this problem converge to the weak solution of the Stefan problem.

Keywords. Stefan problems, time relaxation, hyperbolic equation, parabolic equation, Glimm's scheme, approximate solution, error estimates, weak solution, admissibility condition.

1980 Mathematics subject classifications: 35L60, 35R35

1. Introduction

The classical theory of conduction of heat is based on the conservation of energy law

$$\frac{\partial e}{\partial t} + \operatorname{div} q = 0 \tag{1}$$

and on the classical Fourier heat-conduction law

$$q(t) = -\nabla T(t)$$

where q is the heat flux. The internal energy e is related to the temperature T via the constitutive equation

$$e = e(T) \quad (\text{or } T = T(e)), \tag{2}$$

where $T(s)$ is a nondecreasing function in $\mathbb{R}$.

The main paradox of this theory is infinite speed of propagation of the temperature. We may get over it by the time relaxation of Cattaneo

$$\tau q_t(t) + q(t) = -\nabla T(t), \qquad \tau \geq 0 \tag{3}$$

The resulting system (1)-(3) is then hyperbolic and yields a finite speed of propagation for T.

Recently, there has been great interest in studying the properties of the system (1)-(3) for melt problems. The authors of [**1,2,3**] have required that at a melt interface, the temperature of both the solid and liquid phase is at the melt temperature. This requirement leads to mathematical difficulties such as unsolvability of this problem with some initial and boundary data.

In the paper [**4**] the system (1)-(3) is considered in a weak sense, hence only the Rankine-Hugoniot relations are fulfiled on the melt interface. The correctness of such formulation of the melt problem with constant initial and boundary data is shown there. In accordance with the idea of the paper [**4**] the authors of [**5**] has shown the existence and uniqueness of a smooth solution of a one-phase hyperbolic Stefan problem.

We should note that other interesting formulations of the hyperbolic Stefan problem have been analysed in [**6,7,8**] and the numerical approximation for this problem has been considered in [**9**].

We prove the existence of the weak solution of the hyperbolic Stefan problem (1)-(3) with a "monotone" initial data and show convergence of the weak solutions of the problem (1)-(3) to the weak solution of the Stefan problem.

2. Mathematical formulation

The Cauchy problem is considered in the region $Q = \{(x,t) | x \in \mathbf{R}, 0 \le t \le T^*\}$ for the system of differential equations

$$
\begin{aligned}
&e_t + q_x = 0, \qquad \tau q_t + q + T_x(e) = 0, \quad (x,t) \in Q \\
&e(x,0) = e_0(x), \quad q(x,0) = q_0(x), \qquad x \in \mathbf{R}
\end{aligned} \tag{4}
$$

where e and T are linked by the constitutive equation $T = T(e)$. The function $T : \mathbf{R} \to \mathbf{R}$ is assumed to satisfy the conditions:

1) $T = T(s)$ is continuous and has a piece-continuous derivative that has a finite number of points of discontinuity on a finite interval.
2) $T'(s) \ge 0$ for all $s \in \mathbf{R}$.

We assume that $(q_0, e_0)(x)$ satisfy the following conditions

a) $(q_0, e_0)(x)$ are bounded functions;
b) $e_0(x)$ is monotone and for any x_1, $x_2 \in \mathbf{R}$ the following inequality

$$\sqrt{\tau}|q_2 - q_1| \le \left| \int_{e_1}^{e_2} (T'(y))^{\frac{1}{2}} dy \right|$$

is fulfilled, where $(q_i, e_i) = (q_0, e_0)(x_i)$, $i = 1, 2$.

We call some notations introduced in [**10**] (see also [**11**]):

$BV(Q)$ - the space of function of bounded variation;
$F(q,e)$ - the set of jump's points of a function $(q,e) \in BV(Q)$;
H_1 - the one-dimensional Hausdorff measure;
$l_a(q,e)(x,t)$ is the "approximate limit" of a function $(q,e) \in BV(Q)$ at $(x,t) \in Q$ on the vector a;
$n = n(x,t)$ - the Federer's normal to $F(q,e)$ at a point (x,t);
$(q_+, e_+) = l_n(q,e)$, $(q_-, e_-) = l_{-n}(q,e)$.

DEFINITION. *A weak solution of the problem (4) is the restricted function $(q,e) \in BV(Q)$ which satisfies the following equations*

$$\begin{aligned} &\int_Q (\tau q f_t - qf + T(e)f_x)dxdt + \int_{-\infty}^{+\infty} \tau q_0(x)f(x,0)dx = 0 \\ &\int_Q (eg_t + qg_x)dxdt + \int_{-\infty}^{+\infty} e_0(x)g(x,0)dx = 0 \end{aligned} \tag{5}$$

where $f,g \in C_0^1(Q) = \{s(x,t) \in C^1(Q) | \mathrm{supp}\ s \subseteq Q\}$ and for H_1 - almost everywhere points of the set $F(q,e)$ the admissibility condition is fulfilled, that is

1. *if $q_- > q_+$, then $W(e) \geq T(e)$ for $e \in [e_-, e_+]$ if $e_+ > e_-$;*
   for $e \in [e_+, e_-]$ if $e_+ < e_-$.
2. *if $q_- \leq q_+$, then $W(e) \leq T(e)$ for $e \in [e_-, e_+]$ if $e_+ > e_-$;*
   for $e \in [e_+, e_-]$ if $e_+ < e_-$.

where $W(e) = \frac{(T(e_+) - T(e_-))(e - e_-)}{(e_+ - e_-)} + T(e_-)$.

THEOREM 1. *Let $T = T(e)$ has the properties 1), 2) and the initial data $(q_0, e_0)(x)$ satisfy the conditions a), b), then the Cauchy problem (4) has a weak solution $(q,e)(x,t)$ and for it the following estimates are fulfilled*

$$\sqrt{\tau}|q(x,t)| < C, \quad (x,t) \in Q; \quad \sqrt{\tau}\,\mathrm{Var}\ q(:,t) < C, \quad t \geq 0$$

$$\int_{-\infty}^{+\infty} |(q,e)(x,t_2) - (q,e)(x,t_1)|dx < (\frac{C}{\sqrt{\tau}}|t_2 - t_1|, C|t_2 - t_1|), \quad t_1, t_2 \geq 0 \tag{6}$$

$e(x,t)$ is a monotone bounded function of x for fixed t. Here Var $q(:,t)$ is the variation of q in $x \in \mathbf{R}$ for fixed t, and the constant C is independent on x,t and τ.

From Theorem 1 we easily can get

THEOREM 2. *Let $\{(q^\tau, e^\tau)\}$ be a set of the weak solutions of the problem (4) with initial data $(q_0, e_0)(x)$ satisfying the properties a),b) and the constitutive equation $T = T(e)$ satisfying 1), 2). Then there exists a sequence e^{τ_i} converging to e almost everywhere in Q when $\tau_i \to 0$. The function $e(x,t)$ is a weak solution of the Stefan problem*

$$e_t - (T(e))_{xx} = 0, \quad (x,t) \in Q; \quad e(x,0) = e_0(x), \quad x \in \mathbf{R}.$$

The function $e(x,t)$ is a monotone bounded function of x.

The homogeneous system corresponding to the system (4) has the form

$$\begin{aligned} &e_t + q_x = 0, \qquad \tau q_t + T(e)_x = 0, \quad (x,t) \in Q \\ &e(x,0) = e_0(x), \quad q(x,0) = q_0(x), \qquad x \in \mathbf{R} \end{aligned} \tag{7}$$

Then we consider the case when $e(x)$ is a monotone increasing function.

3. Approximation of the initial data and the constitutive equation

Let $x_1, x_2 \in \mathbf{R}$, $x_1 \le x_2$ and $f = f(x)$ be a function defined on $\mathbf{R}$. We denote by $Df(x_1, x_2)$ and $Df^*(x_1, x_2)$ the closed convex hulls of the sets $\{(x,y)|y \ge f(x), x_1 \le x \le x_2\}$ and $\{(x,y)|y \le f(x), x_1 \le x \le x_2\}$. We determine the functions

$$b(x, x_1, x_2, f) = \min\{y|(x,y) \in Df(x_1, x_2)\}$$
$$b'(x, x_1, x_2, f) = \max\{y|(x,y) \in Df^*(x_1, x_2)\}$$

Lemma 1. *Let $f = f(x)$ be a monotone increasing function, and $x_1 \le \cdots \le x_i \le \cdots \le x_s$, then we have*

$$\sum_{i=1}^{s-1} [(f(x_{i+1}) - f(x_i))(x_{i+1} - x_i)]^{\frac{1}{2}} \le [(f(x_s) - f(x_1))(x_s - x_1)]^{\frac{1}{2}}$$

Lemma 2. *Let the conditions of Lemma 1 be satisfied and $f \in C^1[x_1, x_s]$, then*

$$\int_{x_1}^{x_s} (f'(y))^{\frac{1}{2}} dy \le \sum_{i=1}^{s-1} [(f(x_{i+1}) - f(x_i))(x_{i+1} - x_i)]^{\frac{1}{2}}.$$

The proofs of Lemma 1 and 2 are omitted.

Claim 1. *There exists a sequence of piece-linear functions T_h satisfying conditions 1), 2) and such ones that*

$$|T_h(e) - T_h(e')| < C|e - e'|$$
$$|T(e) - T_h(e)| < Ch, \quad e, e' \in [e_0(-\infty), e_0(+\infty)], \tag{8}$$

$$\int_{e_0(-\infty)}^{\pm\infty} (T_h'(y))^{1/2} dy = \pm\infty \tag{9}$$

where $h = 2^{-N}$, $N = 1, 2, \ldots$. Here after, C is a constant independing from h, x, t, τ. There exists a sequence of piece-constant functions $(q_0^h, e_0^h)(x)$, which converge to $(q_0, e_0)(x)$ almost everywhere on $\mathbf{R}$ when $h \to 0$. The functions $(q_0^h, e_0^h)(x)$ and $T(e)$ satisfy the following conditions:

A) $e_0(-\infty) \le e_0^h(x) \le e_0(+\infty)$, $\max\{q_0^h(x)|x \in \mathbf{R}\} < C$

B) *If $x_1, x_2 \in \mathbf{R}$, $x_1 < x_2$, then*

$$e_1 \le e_2$$

$$-\int_{e_1}^{e_2} [b'(y, e_1, e_2, T_h)]^{\frac{1}{2}} dy \le \sqrt{\tau}(q_1 - q_2) \le \int_{e_1}^{e_2} [b_*'(y, e_1, e_2, T_h)]^{\frac{1}{2}} dy$$

where $(q_i, e_i) = (q_0^h, e_0^h)(x_i)$.

Proof: We determine a sequence

$$(q_0^h, e_0^h)(x) = \begin{cases} (q_0, e_0)(-\infty), & x \le -N \\ (q_0, e_0)((m+1)h), & mh < x \le (m+2)h, m - \text{ even}, \\ & -M \le m \le M-2, M = h^{-1}N \\ (q_0, e_0)(+\infty), & x > N \end{cases} \tag{10}$$

We denote the values of the function $e_0^h(x)$ by $\{a_i | i = 1, \dots, k, e_0(-\infty) = a_1 < \dots < a_i < \dots < a_k = e_0(+\infty)\}$. Let us divide each interval $[a_i, a_{i+1}]$ into h^{-1} equal parts and add the points of discontinuity of the function $T = T(e)$ to the points of this partition. The set of all these points is a finite, let us denote them by $\{b_j\}$. We determine the sequence $\{T_h(e)\}$ of piece-linear monotonically increasing functions with joins the points $(b_j, T(b_j))$. From Lemma 2 it is obvious that the functions $T_h(e)$ and (q_0^h, e_0^h) satisfies the statements of Suggestion 1.

In the sections 4,5,6 the parameter h of the functions $T_h(e)$ and $(q_0^h, e_0^h)(x)$ will be omitted for the sake of simplicity.

4. The Riemann problem for the system (7)

The Riemann problem is the Cauchy problem (7) with the initial data

$$(q_0, e_0)(x) = \begin{cases} (q_1, e_1), & x \le 0 \\ (q_r, e_r), & x > 0 \end{cases} \tag{11}$$

where (q_1, e_1), (q_r, e_r) are constants.

In this section we give a brief description of the method of construction of the weak solution suggested in [**12,13**].

It is well-known that if $(q, e)(x, t)$ satisfies (7) at all points of smoothness and has a piece-smooth line of discontinuity in the plane (x, t), then it is a weak solution only when it satisfies the Rankine-Hugoniot relations along each line of discontinuity $x = x(t)$:

$$\tau x'(q_+ - q_-) = (T_+ - T_-), \quad x'(e_+ - e_-) = (q_+ - q_-)$$

and on the line $x = x(t)$ the admissibility condition are fulfilled for the points (q_+, e_+), (q_-, e_-). Here $(q_\pm, e_\pm, T_\pm) = (q(x \pm 0, t), e(x \pm 0, t), T(x \pm 0, t))$.

Let us take

$$R(e, e_1) = \begin{cases} 1/\sqrt{\tau} \int_{e_1}^{e} [b'(y, e_1, e, T)] dy, & e_1 \le e, \\ 1/\sqrt{\tau} \int_{e_1}^{e} [b'_*(y, e, e_1, T)] dy, & e_1 \ge e. \end{cases}$$

and define the functions $F^\pm(e, e_1, q_1) = -q_1 \mp R(e, e_1)$. By virtue of equality (9), it follows that $R(e, e_1) \to \pm\infty$ as $e \to \pm\infty$, then for two arbitrary prescribed points (q_1, e_1), (q_r, e_r) the curves $F^+(e, e_r, q_r)$, $F^-(e, e_1, q_1)$ are interacted each other. It should be noted that the intersection may be over a whole segment since the function $T = T(e)$ can have a domain of constancy. Hence, let us pass from the curves $F^\pm$ considered on the plane (q, e) to those on the (q, T)- plane as follows: let us take that

$$G^\pm(T, e_1, q_1) = F^\pm(O_1(T), e_1, q_1)$$

$$O_1(T) = \begin{cases} \min\{e | e \ge e_1, T(e) = T\}, & \text{if } T \ge T(e_1) \\ \max\{e | e \le e_1, T(e) = T\}, & \text{if } T \le T(e_1) \end{cases} \tag{12}$$

CLAIM 2. *For any two points* (q_1, e_1), (q_r, e_r) *there exists a single point* $(\bar{q}, \bar{T})$ *such that* $\bar{q} = G^-(\overline{T}, e_1, q_1) = G^+(T, e_r, q_r)$.

CLAIM 3. *If* $q_1 = F^+(e_1, e_r, q_r)$, *the Riemann problem (7), (11) has a weak solution of the form* $(q,e)(x,t) = (q,e)(\frac{x}{t})$ *and such that* $(q,e)(x,t) = (q_1, e_1)$ *at* $\frac{x}{t} \leq \varepsilon$ *for a certain value of* $\varepsilon \geq 0$. *Moreover, if* $x_1 \leq x_2$, *then for each* $t > 0$ *we have* $(e(x_2,t) - e(x_1,t))(e_r - e_1) \geq 0$.

PROOF: We consider the case when $e_1 < e_r$. For the sake of simplifcity let us introduce the notation $b(e) = b(e, e_1, e_r, T)$. Since $b'(e)$ exists everywhere except at a finite number of points, we define it additionally at these points so that it could be continuous from the left. A graph of the function $b = b(e)$ on the interval (e_1, e_r) exhibits inflections in a finite sequence of points e_i, $i = 1, \ldots, k$, $e_l = e_1 < \cdots < e_i < \cdots < e_k = e_r$. The solution is defined as follows:

$$(q,e)(x,t) = \begin{cases} (q_1, e_1), & [b'(e_1+0)]^{\frac{1}{2}} \geq \frac{x}{t}, \\ (q_i, e_i), & [b'(e_i-0)]^{\frac{1}{2}} < \frac{x}{t} \leq [b'(e_i+0)]^{\frac{1}{2}} \\ (q_r, e_r), & [b'(e_r-0)]^{\frac{1}{2}} < \frac{x}{t}, \end{cases} \tag{13}$$

where $q_i = q_r + \frac{1}{\sqrt{T}} \int_{e_r}^{e_i} [b'(y)]^{\frac{1}{2}} dy$. It is obvious that $(q,e)(x,t)$ is the weak solution, satisfying the statements of Claim 3.

CLAIM 4. *If* $q_r = F^-(e_r, e_1, q_1)$, *then the Riemann problem (7), (11) has a weak solution of the form* $(q,e)(x,t) = (q,e)(\frac{x}{t})$ *and such that* $(q,e)(x,t) = (q_r, e_r)$ *at* $\frac{x}{t} > \varepsilon$ *for a certain value of* $\varepsilon \leq 0$. *Moreover, if* $x_1 \leq x_2$, *then for each* $t > 0$ *we have* $(e(x_2,t) - e(x_1,t)(e_r - e_1) \geq 0$.

SUGGESTION 5. *For any given points* (q_l, e_l), (q_r, e_r) *the Riemann problem has the weak solution of the form*

$$(q,e)(x,t) = (Q,E)(\frac{x}{t}, (q_l, e_l), (q_r, e_r)).$$

PROOF: From Claim 2 it follows that there exists a point $(\bar{q}, \overline{T})$ such that $\bar{q} = G^+(\overline{T}, q_r, e_r) = G^-(\overline{T}, q_1, e_1)$. Then in accordance with Claim 3 there exists the solution $(\overline{Q}, \overline{E})(x,t)$ of the problem (7),(11) with the initial data

$$(q_0, e_0)(x) = \begin{cases} (\bar{q}, O_r(\overline{T})), & x \leq 0 \\ (q_r, e_r), & x > 0 \end{cases}$$

that $(\overline{Q}, \overline{E})(\frac{x}{t}) = (\bar{q}, O_r(\overline{T}))$, when $\frac{x}{t} \leq \varepsilon_1$, $\varepsilon_1 \geq 0$. In accordance with Claim 4 there exists the solution $(\tilde{Q}, \tilde{E})(x,t)$ of the problem (7),(11) with the initial data

$$(q_0, e_0)(x) = \begin{cases} (\bar{q}, O_1(\overline{T})), & x > 0 \\ (q_l, e_1), & x \leq 0 \end{cases}$$

that $(\tilde{Q}, \tilde{E})(\frac{x}{t}) = (\bar{q}, O_l(T))$, when $x/t > \varepsilon_2$, $\varepsilon_2 \leq 0$. The function

$$(Q,E)(\frac{x}{t}) = \begin{cases} (\overline{Q}, \overline{E})(\frac{x}{t}), & x \leq 0 \\ (\tilde{Q}, \tilde{E})(\frac{x}{t}), & x > 0 \end{cases}$$

is the weak solution of the Riemann problem.

5. The Glimm's difference scheme

To prove the existence of solution of our problem, we use Glimm's scheme [**14,15**]. Let us choose mesh steps to be equal to h in x-axis and equal to s in t-axis satisfying the condition

$$\frac{h}{s} \geq \max\{(T'(e))^{\frac{1}{2}} | e \in [e_0(-\infty), e_0(+\infty)]\} \tag{14}$$

The relation $\frac{h}{s}$ is kept to fixed, i.e. s is proportional to h (Note that $h = 2^{-N}$, $N = 1, 2, \dots$). For each interger $n > 0$, we define $Y_n = \{m | m-$ integer, $m + n-$ even, $-(M + n + 2) \leq m \leq M + n, M = Nh^{-1}\}$. Let us suppose that on the line $t = ns$, $x \in \mathbb{R}$ the approximate solution $(q, e)(x, t)$ of the problem (4) has the constant values such that

$$(q, e)(x, ns) = \begin{cases} (q_0, e_0)(-\infty), & x \leq -(M+n)h \\ (q_{n,m}, e_{n,m}), & mh < x \leq (m+2)h, \quad m \in Y_n \\ (q_0, e_0)(+\infty), & x > (M+n)h \end{cases}$$

Let us set $z_{n,m} = (q_{n,m}, e_{n,m})$ and describe the procedure of construction $(q, e)(x, t)$ within the band $ns \leq t < (n+1)s$ in accordance with the known values $z_{n,m}$ and subsequent choice of constant values $z_{n+1,m}$ at $t = (n+1)s$. According to Claim 5, there exists solution $(\tilde{q}, \tilde{e})(x, t) = (Q, E)(\frac{x-mh}{t-ns}; z_{n,m}, z_{n,m+2})$, $t > ns$ of the Riemann problem for the system (7) with the initial data

$$(\hat{q}, \hat{e})(x, ns) = \begin{cases} z_{n,m}, & x \leq mh \\ z_{n,m+2}, & x > mh \end{cases}$$

Further it is shown that if the initial data for the time $t = ns$ satisfy the condition $e_0(-\infty) \leq \tilde{e}(x, ns) \leq e_0(+\infty)$, then for all $(x, t) \in R * [ns, (n+1)s)$ this inequality is fulfilled. Discontinuities, appearing as the result of discontinuity decay at the points (mh, ns) do not intersect, as it is seen from the condition (14) and the proof of Claims 3,4. Within the band $(x, t) \in R * [ns, (n+1)s)$ we have that

$$(q, e)(x, t) = (Q, E)(\frac{x - mh}{t - ns}; z_{n,m}, z_{n,m+2}), \quad m \in Y_n \tag{15}$$

is the exact weak solution of the system (7) with piece-constant initial data and piece-linear function $T(e)$. Let us define the approximate solution $(q, e)(x, t)$ of the problem (4) in the band

$$(q, e)(x, t) = (\tilde{q}(x, t)\left(1 - \frac{t - ns}{\tau})\right), \tilde{e}(x, t)), \quad (x, t) \in R * [ns, (n+1)s) \tag{16}$$

Let us choose an arbitrary point $x_{n+1,m}$ on each mesh interval $(m-2)h < x \leq mh$, $m \in Y_{n+1}$ at $t = (n+1)s$, then define

$$z_{n+1,m} = (q, e)(x_{n+1,m}, (n+1)s - 0), \tag{17}$$

and

$$(q,e)(x,(n+1)s) = \begin{cases} (q_0,e_0)(-\infty), & x \le -(M+n+1)h \\ (q_0,e_0)(+\infty), & x > (M+n+1)h \end{cases} \tag{18}$$

The equalities (17), (18) determine recurrently the values $\{z_{n,m}\}$ for each $n = 1,2,\dots,$ if the sequences $x_{n,m}$ are prescribed. Noted that a specification of the points $x_{n,m}$ is equivalent to a specification of the points $a_{n,m} = \frac{(x_{n,m}-(m-2)h)}{2h}$ of the interval $[0,1]$. This set is denoted by $a = \{a_{n,m}\}$. It may be considered as a point of the infinite-dimensional space $A = \prod_{m\in Y_n, n\ge 1}[0,1]$. The approximate solution $(q,e)(x,t,h,a)$ is defined by the relations (16)-(18).

CLAIM 6. *Let $(q,e)(x,t,h,a)$ be the approximate solution of the problem (4) with the initial data satisfying the conditions a), b), then*

A1) $e_0(-\infty) \le e(x,t,h,a) < e_0(+\infty)$

B1) *For any choice of the point $a \in A$ and any $x_1 < x_2$:*

$$e_1 \le e_2$$

$$-\int_{e_1}^{e_2} [b'(y,e_1,e_2,T)]^{\frac{1}{2}}\,dy \le \sqrt{\tau}(q_1-q_2) \le \int_{e_1}^{e_2} [b'_*(y,e_1,e_2,T)]^{\frac{1}{2}}\,dy, \tag{19}$$

where $(q_i,e_i) = (q,e)(x_i,t,h,a)$.

The proof of Claim 6 is based on the following two lemmas:

LEMMA 3. *If inequalities (19) are fulfilled in the plane (q,e) between the pairs (q_1,e_1), (q_2,e_2) and (q_2,e_2), (q_3,e_3) then (19) are fulfilled also between the pairs (q_1,e_1), (q_3,e_3).*

COROLLARY. *Let e_2^1, e_2^2 belong to a interval of constance of the function $T = T(e)$ and inequalities (19) are fulfilled in the plane (q,e) between the pairs (q_1,e_1), (q_2,e_2) and (q_2,e_2), (q_3,e_3) then (19) are fulfilled also between the pairs (q_1,e_1), (q_3,e_3).*

The proof of Lemma 3 and its Corollary are omitted.

LEMMA 4. *The solution of the problem (7), (11) with the initial data satisfying the conditions a), b), satisfies the properties A1),B1).*

PROOF: In accordance with Claim 2 there exists a point $(\bar{q},\overline{T})$ such that $\bar{q} = G^+(\overline{T},e_r,q_r)$ $= G^-(\overline{T},e_1,q_1)$. Let us show that $T_1 \ge \overline{T} \ge T_r$. Let $q_r \le q_1$ (the case when $q_1 < q_r$ is considered in a similar way), then

$$\sqrt{\tau}(q_l-q_r) \le \int_{e_l}^{e_r} [b'_*(y,e_l,e_r,T)]^{\frac{1}{2}}\,dy.$$

(1) Let us suppose $\overline{T} > T_1 \le T_r$, i.e. $\bar{e} = O_1(\overline{T}) = O_r(\overline{T}) < e_1 \le e_r$, therefore

$$0 \le \sqrt{\tau}(-q_r+q_1) = \int_{e_1}^{\bar{e}} [b'(y,e_1,\bar{e},T)]^{\frac{1}{2}}\,dy + \int_{e_1}^{\bar{e}} [b'(y,e_r,\bar{e},T)]^{\frac{1}{2}}\,dy < 0.$$

which is a contradiction

(2) Let us suppose that $T_1 \le T_r < \overline{T}$, i.e. $e_1 \le e_r < \bar{e} = O_1(\overline{T}) = O_r(\overline{T})$, therefore

$$\sqrt{\tau}(-q_r + q_1) = \int_{e_1}^{\bar{e}} [b'_*(y, e_l, \bar{e}, T)]^{\frac{1}{2}}\, dy + \int_{e_1}^{\bar{e}} [b'_*(y, e_r, \bar{e}, T)]^{\frac{1}{2}}\, dy >$$

$$\int_{e_1}^{\bar{e}} [b'_*(y, e_1, \bar{e}, T)]^{\frac{1}{2}}\, dy > \int_{e_1}^{e_r} [b'_*(y, e_1, e_r, T)]^{\frac{1}{2}}\, dy$$

which is also absurd.

From Claims 3,4 and the construction of the Riemann problem $(q,e)(x,t)$ it follows that the function $e(x,t)$ is monotone in x, since $e_1 \le O_1(\overline{T}) \le O_r(\overline{T}) \le e_r$. At the points (x_1,t), (x_2,t), $0 < x_1 < x_2$, let the solution take the values $(q_k, e_k) = (q,e)(x_1,t)$, $(q_j, e_j) = (q,e)(x_2,t)$ related by the equality (see (13)):

$$\sqrt{\tau}(-q_j + q_k) = \int_{e_k}^{e_j} [b'(y, O_r(\overline{T}), e_k, T)]^{\frac{1}{2}}\, dy = \int_{e_k}^{e_j} [b'(y, e_k, e_j, T)]^{\frac{1}{2}}\, dy$$

The latter equality follows from geometrical considerations and from the fact that e_k, e_j are the peaks of the graph of the function $b(y) = b(y, O_r(\overline{T}), e_r)$. From these inequalities it follows the fulfilment of the inequalities (19) when $x > 0$ (similarly when $x < 0$). If $O_1(\overline{T}) = O_r(\overline{T})$, then the statement follows from Lemma 3, and when $O_1(\overline{T}) \ne O_r(\overline{T})$ it follows from the Collary of Lemma 3.

PROOF OF COLLARY 6: It would be sufficient to show that if the properties A1), B1) are fulfilled at $t = ns$, then they are fulfilled at $ns < t \le (n+1)s$ too. Within the time interval $(ns, (n+1)s)$ the approximate solution $(q,e)(x,t,h,a)$ are defined by the formulaes (see (15), (16))

$$(q,e)(x,t) = (\tilde{q}(x,t)(1 - \frac{t - ns}{\tau}, \tilde{e}(x,t)). \tag{20}$$

The function $(\tilde{q},\tilde{e})(x,t)$ represents a superposition of the solutions of the Riemann problem (7), (11). Hence, in accordance with Lemmas 3, 4, $(q,e)(x,t)$ has the properties A1), B1). Since the functions $(q,e)(x,t,h,a)$ and $(\tilde{q},\tilde{e})(x,t)$ are related by (20), then it is easy to prove that within the region $ns < t < (n+1)s$, $x \in \mathbf{R}$, the function $(q,e)(x,t,h,a)$ has the properties too. When $t = (n+1)s$ the fulfilment of these properties follows from Lemma 3 since the statement of new initial data is equivalently to "omitting" some intermediate values available in the approximate solution at $t \in (ns, (n+1)s)$.

CLAIM 7. *Let $(q,e)(x,t,h,a)$ be the approximate solution of the problem (4). Then $e(x,t,h,a)$ is a monotone increasing function and*

$$e_0(-\infty) < e(x,t,h,a) < e_0(+\infty), \qquad (x,t) \in Q$$

$$\sqrt{\tau}\max\{q(x,t,h,a) \mid x \in \mathbf{R}\} < C, \qquad \sqrt{\tau}\ \mathrm{Var}\ q(:,t,h,a) < C \qquad \textit{for any } t > 0$$

$$\int_{-\infty}^{+\infty} |\,(q,e)(x,t_2) - (q,e)(x,t_1)\,|\, dx < \left(\frac{C}{\sqrt{\tau}}\,|\,t_2 - t_1\,|, |\,t_2 - t_1\,|\right), \quad t_1, t_2 > 0. \tag{21}$$

PROOF: The inequalities (21) follow from Claim 6 and the following remarks:

1. Note that the inequalities

$$\left.\begin{array}{l}\displaystyle\int_{e_1}^{e_2}[b'(y,e_1,e_2,T)]^{\frac{1}{2}}\,dy\\ \displaystyle\int_{e_1}^{e_2}[b'_*(y,e_1,e_2,T)]^{\frac{1}{2}}\,dy\end{array}\right\}\le[T(e_2)-T(e_1))(e_2-e_1)]^{\frac{1}{2}}$$

are a consequence of Lemma 1. Using the definition of the variation of a function and Lemma 1 gives

$$\sqrt{\tau}\ \mathrm{Var}\ q(:,t,h,a)\le[(T(e_0(+\infty))-T(e_0(-\infty)))\,(e_0(+\infty)-e_0(-\infty))]^{\frac{1}{2}}\,.$$

The bound of q follows from the obvious inequality

$$|\,q(:,t,h,a)\,|<\ \mathrm{Var}\ q(:,t,h,a)+|\,q_0(-\infty)\,|\qquad\text{for any } x\in\mathbf{R}.$$

2. Since the approximate solution (q,e) has a bounded velocity of propagation of discontinuities within the interval $[ns,(n+1)s]$ and is a piece-constant function of the bounded variation, then integration gives the desired estimates (21).

6. PROOF OF THEOREM 1

Let us consider the region $Q_{mn}=\{(x,t)\,|\,mh\le x\le(m+2)h, ns\le t\le(n+1)s\}$. In this region the approximate solution $(q,e)(x,t,h,a)$ are defined by (16)-(18). The region Q_{mn} is divided into the subregions $Q^1_{mn}=\left\{(x,t)\in Q\,|\,[b'(e_l+0)]^{1/2}\ge\frac{x}{t}\right\}$, $Q^{j+1}_{mn}=\{(x,t)\in Q_{mn}|[b'(e_j-0)]^{1/2}<\frac{x}{t}\le[b'(e_j+0)]^{1/2}\},(j=1,\dots,k)$, $Q^{k+2}_{mn}=\{(x,t)\in Q_{mn}|[b'(e_r-0)]^{\frac{1}{2}}<\frac{x}{t}\}$. In these regions the function $(\tilde q,\tilde e)(x,t)$ has constant values (see (13)) and on the lines $\frac{x}{t}=[b'(e_j-0)]^{\frac{1}{2}}$ the Rankine-Hugoniot conditions are fulfilled. Hence in each region Q^j_{mn}

$$\tau q_t(x,t)+q(x,t)+T(e(x,t))_x=-\tilde q(x,t)\frac{t-ns}{\tau},\quad e_t(x,t)+q_x(x,t)=0$$

and on the line $\frac{x}{t}=[b'(e_j-0)]^{\frac{1}{2}}$

$$x'\tau\,[q]-[T(e)]=x'\,[\tilde q]\,(t-ns),\quad x'\,[e]-[q]=-\,[\tilde q]\,\frac{t-ns}{\tau}\tag{22}$$

Integrating the first equality of (22) in the region Q^j_{mn} and then adding over j we get the equality:

$$\begin{aligned}0=&\{\sum_{j=1}^{k+2}\int_{Q^j_{mn}}(\tau q_t+q+T(e)_x)f\,dxdt\}+\{\sum_{j=1}^{k+2}\int_0^s((\tau[q]-[T(e)])f)_{x=\xi_j t}dx+\\&+\int_{\partial Q_{mn}}\{qf\,dx-T(e)f\,dt\}+\int_{Q_{mn}}(\tau qf_t-qf+T(e)f_x)dxdt\}=\\&=J_1+J_2+J_3+J_4,\quad f\in C_0^1(Q),\quad \xi_j=[b'(e_j-o)]^{\frac{1}{2}}.\end{aligned}$$

From (21), (22) we have that $|J_1| < Ch\max\{|q|\,|(x,t)\in Q_{mn}\}$, $|J_2| < Ch^2\,\mathrm{Var}\{q(:,t)|mh \le x \le (m+2)h\}$. Since the functions $q(x,t)$, $e(x,t)$ and variation of these functions are restricted in Q, then we have

$$(23)\qquad \int_Q (\tau q f_t - qf + T(e)f_x)dxdt + \int_R \tau q_0 f(x,0)dx = \delta(q,f,h,a) + O(h),$$

where $\delta(q,f,h,a) = \sum_{n=1}^{\infty} \delta^n(q,f,h,a)$,

$$\delta^n(q,f,h,a) = \int_{-\infty}^{+\infty} \tau(q(x,ns-0,h,a) - q(x,ns+0,h,a))f(x,0)dx$$

Let us consider δ as a function of the variable a. According to Kolmogorov's theorem of mathed distributions, we may introduce a countably additive measure defined on A. Then according to Glimm's theorem [**14**], there exists a sequence $h_i \to 0$ such that $\delta(h_i,a) \to 0$ almost everywhere in A. In accordance with a well-known theorem of function theory, from (21) it follows that the set of the functions $(q,e)(x,t,h,a)$ contains a subsequence $(q,e)(x,t,h_i,a)$ that converges almost everywhere in Q and also in $L_2(Q)$ as h_i/too. Hence using these results we get the fulfilment of Theorem 1. Note that the function $(q,e)(x,t)$ satisfies the admissibility condition. Note also that for H_1 -almost everywhere points of the set $F(q,e)$ the following relations

$$n_t(q_+ - q_-) = n_x(T_+ - T_-), \quad n_t(e_+ - e_-) = n_x(q_+ - q_-), \quad n_x > 0$$

are fulfilled (see [**13,14**]), where $n = (n_t, n_x)$ - the Federer's normal to $F(q,e)$ (see Definition of the weak solution). Since the functions $(q,e)(x,t,h,a)$ satisfy the inequality (19), then the limit function $(q,e)(x,t)$ satisfies (19) too. From Lemma 1 we see that the inequality (19) is true only when the admissibility condition is true.

References

[1] L. de Socio, G. Guatieri, *A hyperbolic Stefan problem*, Quart.Appl.Math. **41** (1983), 51 - 87.

[2] A.Solomon, V.Alexiades, D.Wilson, J.Drake, *On the formulation of hyperbolic Stefan problems*, Quart.Appl.Math. **43** (1985), 295 - 304.

[3] B. D'Acunto, *Non-Fourier Ablation*, 1, Ricerche di Mathematica **37** (1988), 121–132.

[4] J. M. Greenberg, *A hyperbolic heat transfer problem with phase changes*, IMA J. of Applied Mathematics **38** (1987), 1–21.

[5] A. Friedman, Hu Bei, *The Stefan problem for a hyperbolic heat equation*, 1, J. of Math.Anal. and Appl. **37** (1989), 249–279.

[6] A. Visintin, *Stefan problem with phase relaxation*, IMA J. of Applied Mathematics **34** (1985), 225–245.

[7] R. E. Showalter, N. J. Walkington, *A hyperbolic Stefan problem*, Quart. Appl. Math. **45** (1987), 769 - 781.

[8] R. H. Nochetto, C. Verdi, *Approximation of multidimensional Stefan-like problems via hyperbolic relaxation*, Calcolo **25** (1989).

[9] S. Mazzulo, M. Paolini, C. Verdi, *Polymer Crystallization and Processing: Free boundary problem and their Numerical Approximation*, Mathematical Engineering in Industry **2 No. 3** (1989), 219–232.

[10] A. I. Volpert, *The Spaces BV and quasi-linear equations*, N 2, Matem. Sburnik **73** (1967), 255 – 302.

[11] E. Giusti, *Minimal surfaces and functions of bounded variation*, Monographs in Mathematics, Boston **80** (1986).

[12] Leibovich L., *Solutions of the Riemann problem for hyperbolic systems of quasilinear equations without convexity conditions*, N 1, Math. Anal. Appl. **45** (1974), 232 – 257.

[13] Gavriluk S. L., *Problem of arbitrary discontinuoty decay in media with nonmonotonic equation of state*, Preprint N 10, Inst. of Math. Novosibirsk. (1984).

[14] J. Glimm, *Solutions in the large for nonlinear hyperbolic systems of eguations*, Comm. Pure Appl. Math. **18** (1965), 697 – 715.

[15] Ying Lung-An, Wang Ching-Hua, *Global solutions of the Cauchy problem for a nonhomogeneous quasilinear hyperbolic system*, Comm. Pure Appl. Math. **33** (1980), 579 – 597.

International Series of Numerical Mathematics, Vol. 99, © 1991 Birkhäuser Verlag Basel

Numerical method for free-surface hydrodynamical problems

PETER J. SHOPOV

Laboratory of Numerical Methods, Institute of Mathematics
P.O. Box 373, 1113 Sofia, Bulgaria

Abstract. A numerical method for free surface hydrodynamical problems is presented. It is based on FEM in Lagrangian approach and is of divergence-free type. It is developed for unsteady Navier-Stokes equations for systems involving multiple deformable interfaces of liquid-gas or liquid-liquid type. The surface tension is considered as an example of surface force. Special attention is paid on problems with pressure and stress boundary conditions and dynamic contact lines. A new approach for mathematical modelling of problems with contact angles is proposed and tested. Comparisons with experiments are presented, which confirms the consistency of this approach and of the numerical method.

1. INTRODUCTION

Free surface hydrodynamics is important for many problems in science and technology. In the class of considered problems the role of the free surface is played by a deformable liquid-fluid interface. For example the dynamics and stability of jets, films, drops, bubbles and the cavitation phenomena belong to this class. A great number of experimental studies is devoted to such problems as well as many theoretical investigations based mainly on analytical methods under various restrictions. They yield many interesting results but mainly of qualitative character due to the high nonlinearity and complexity of these problems. Numerical methods have to be employed to obtain more complete and quantitative results.

The main goal of the presented numerical method is to provide an universal tool for solving viscous hydrodynamical problems with simple and multiple free boundaries. It is designed to be used in fluid mechanics and in software for engineering problems. Some attention is paid to nonstandard boundary conditions and geometries in the fixed domain case; pressure and stress boundary conditions, multiply connected domains and with many inlets and outlets, flows in branched channels and in presence of filtrating walls. Such problems can be treated also in the case of multiphase flow.

We try to incorporate as broad range of transient problems as possible. The problems involving liquid-fluid-solid and liquid-liquid-fluid dynamic contact lines are included in the scope of this numerical method as well as one, two and three phase flows and changes in the topology of the triangulation during the computations.

At present we consider only 2D plane and axisymmetric problems, which is connected mainly with the modest productivity of the available computers. The numerical method is of divergence-free type and the number of unknowns in the linear systems is comparatively small. This is connected mainly with the way the linear systems are solved and could be substituted by an other numerical procedure, if it is preferable due to some reasons. The Lagrangian approach is chosen as a base of the time integration due to its high flexibility and the simplified treatment of the convection.

The earliest numerical methods for viscous free surface hydrodynamics belong to the class of finite difference methods in velocity-pressure approach. Interesting problems have been solved by marker and cell method [**1**] and its Lagrangian variant [**2**]. An other related important tool is volume of fluid method [**3**], which appears lately. This group of methods posses many virtues but the surface tension approximation is not very reliable and the treatment of complicated geometries needs some additional efforts. These methods are designed and employed mainly for high speed computers and dense grids.

The second group consists of finite difference methods based on a transformation of the unknown domain to a standard one. This approach provides better description of the surface tension and the opportunity to work in a nice domain. It is usually applied in velocity-stream function variables. This approach yields many reliable results for basic problems of free-surface hydrodynamics [**4**]-[**8**]. A typical feature of such methods is that codes based on them are applicable for a restricted class of problems, because they depend on the transformation. This made them a good tool for specialized packages.

The third group consists of finite element methods in velocity-pressure approach [**10**]. They are very flexible and universal, which make them particularly suitable for packages. For steady problems mainly Eulerian approach is employed [**10**]. The totally linearized version [**11**] seems to provide a especially fast procedure for determining the position of the free surface in the stedy state case. In the unsteady case some complications arise in the description of the motion of the free surface and mesh nodes in Eulerian approach, which are settled in [**12**] and used successfully in many computations e.g. [**13**]. Lagrangian methods are more rarely used perhaps due to the complications with the grid redefinition.

Here we present a divergence-free Lagrangian method [**14**]-[**19**], which could be associated with this group. Numerical modelling of dynamic contact lines seems to be not considered yet, perhaps because its mathematical modelling is not very clear. The unsteady pressure driven motion of fluids with free boundaries in divergence-free approach is not studied too, up to author's knowledge.

In the next section the mathematical formulation of the considered problems is given, followed by a description of the numerical method. In the penultimate section numerical examples are presented for transient motion of bubbles, drops, A and B-type multiple drops, engulfment problems, motion of liquid in capillaries, transient pressure driven motion of a drop in a tube, hydrodynamical interaction of two deformable bubbles near a rigid interface (a doubly connected free surface problem), followed by discussions and conclusions about this numerical method.

2. Mathematical model

Consider for simplicity two unmixable liquids occupying the domains $\Omega_i(t)$ with an deformable interface between them Γ_i and one gas phase (see Fig.1). The incompressible Navier-Stokes equations are used to describe the motion of liquids

$$\frac{Dv^{(1)}}{Dt} = \mathrm{div}\Pi v^{(1)} - \mathrm{grad}p^{(1)} + F^{(1)} \; ; \; \mathrm{div}v^{(1)} = 0 \tag{2.1}$$

(2.2) $$\lambda \frac{Dv^{(2)}}{Dt} = \text{div}\Pi v^{(2)} - \text{grad}p^{(2)} + F^{(2)} \; ; \; \text{div}v^{(2)} = 0$$

where $\Pi v^{(1)} = \text{Re}^{-1} Dv^{(1)}$; $\Pi v^{(2)} = \eta \text{Re}^{-1} Dv^{(2)}$, $D_{i,j} v^{(s)} = \frac{1}{2}(\partial v^{(s)}_{i,j} + \partial v^{(s)}_{j,i})$, $v(u, v)$ is the velocity, $\frac{D}{Dt} = \partial_t + (v.\nabla)$, $F^{(s)}$ is the vector of the body forces for s-th liquid, $\lambda = \varrho_2/\varrho_1$, $\eta = \mu_2/\mu_1$, $\text{Re} = \frac{U_0 l \varrho_1}{\mu_1}$, U_0 is the reference velocity and l is the reference length. We also consider this equations in 2D axisymmetric case, when they have a modified form.

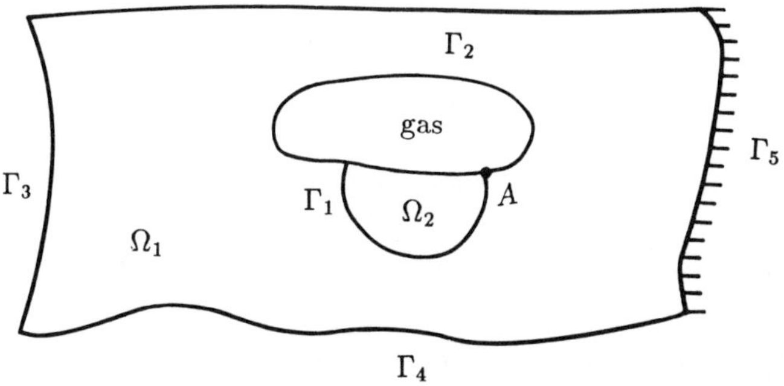

Figure 1.

For the free surfaces Γ_i with equations $S_i(x, t) = 0$ we shall write the standard kinematic condition

(2.3) $$\frac{DS_i}{Dt} = 0 \; .$$

On the liquid-liquid free surfaces Γ_1 the standard boundary conditions (B.C.) are

(2.4) $$\Pi v^{(1)}.n - \Pi v^{(2)}.n + (p^{(2)} - p^{(1)})n - R_1|_{\Gamma_1} = 0 \; ; v^{(1)} - v^{(2)}|_{\Gamma_1} = 0$$

where n is the unit outward normal to Ω_1 and R_1 is the vector of surface forces at Γ_1. If we take in (2.4) the unit outward normal to Ω_2 then the vector R_1 has to be taken with opposite direction.

At the gas-liquid interface the B.C. (2.4) reads

(2.5) $$\Pi v^{(1)}.n + (p_0 - p^{(1)})n - R_2|_{\Gamma_2} = 0$$

where n is the unit outward normal to Ω_2, R_2 is the vector of the surface force at Γ_2 and p_0 is the pressure in gas phase.

Usually p_0 is taken to be constant or as a function of the volume V of the gas phase, which reads for an isothermal process as follows

(2.6) $$p_0(t) = p(t_0) + \frac{V(t_0)}{V(t)} \; .$$

At infinity and at the rigid boundaries the standard no-slip conditions are applied

$$v|_{\Gamma_3} = v_g \ , \tag{2.7}$$

where v_g is a known function.

This condition ensures the mass conservation of the liquid in $\Omega_i(t)$, if it is applied to the entire $\partial\Omega_i$ except the free boundary.

The pressure or stress B.C. are used at inlets, outlets and sometimes at infinity

$$p = p_{\mathrm{out}}|_{\Gamma_4} \ , v.\tau = 0|_{\Gamma_4} \ \text{or} \ \ -\sigma_{n,n} = \alpha|_{\Gamma_4} \ , -\sigma_{n,t} = \beta|_{\Gamma_4} \tag{2.8}$$

where p_{out} , α, β are functions. In the case of internal problems the function β is not always known and this leads to some minor complications [**19**].

If the walls are permeable, the filtration B.C. are used

$$v_n = c(-\sigma_{n,n} - p_{\mathrm{out}})|_{\Gamma_4} \ , v.\tau|_{\Gamma_4} = 0 \ , c \geq c_0 > 0 \ . \tag{2.9}$$

The conditions (2.8) and (2.9) do not ensure the mass conservation of the liquid in $\Omega_i(t)$ and hence of the volume occupied by the gas phase. Such situation occurs e.g. when modelling bubble collapse, when pressure B.C. are applied at the infinity.

Initial conditions for the velocity and the position of the free boundaries are required

$$v|_{t=0} = v_0 \ , S_i|_{t=0} = S_{i,0} \ , i = 1,2 \ . \tag{2.10}$$

In general, the numerical method can be applied for any specification of body and surface forces. But here we consider only the gravity and surface tension as examples of body and surface forces, respectively

$$F_s = \mathrm{grad} H_s \ ; H_1 = -Fr^{-1} y \ ; Fr = \frac{U_0^2}{gl} \ , H_2 = \lambda H_1 \ , s = 1,2 \tag{2.11}$$

$$R_1 = \frac{1}{We}\left(\frac{1}{R_1} + \frac{1}{R_2}\right)\bar{n} \ ; We = \frac{U_0 \varrho l}{\sigma_{1,2}} \ ; R_2 = \zeta R_1 \ , \zeta = \frac{\sigma_{2,3}}{\sigma_{1,2}} \ . \tag{2.12}$$

The gravity force is supposed to act in the opposite direction to the axis y, R_1 and R_2 are the two main radii of curvature, g is the gravitational acceleration and $\bar{n}$ is the unit normal pointing to the center of the curvature, $\sigma_{i,j}$ is the surface tension coefficient at the interface $\Omega_i \cap \Omega_j$.

If contact points A (see fig.1) of the two liquid-liquid-fluid of liquid-fluid-solid interfaces exist, additional information is required to complete the boundary condition. We use a surface force balance type condition [**18**] which includes infinite forces. For liquid-liquid-fluid contact line it reads

$$\gamma_A(v) = (\tau_{12}\sigma_{12} + \tau_{13}\sigma_{13} + \tau_{23}\sigma_{23}).\delta(A) + \\ 0.5[(n_{12} + n_{13}).\Pi v^{(1)} + (n_{21} + n_{23}).\Pi v^{(2)} + (n_{31} + n_{32}).\Pi v^{(3)}]|_A = 0, \tag{2.13}$$

where τ_{ij} is the unit tangential vector to $\Gamma_{ij} = \Omega_i \cap \Omega_j$ at point A; n_{ij} is the unit normal vector to Γ_{ij} directed into Ω_j; δ is Dirac's δ-function for $\Gamma_1 \cup \Gamma_2$.

Remark 1. If the velocity is discontinuous at such point A, then the viscous part of the stress tensor $\Pi^{(i)}$ contains a delta function too. All finite terms in the condition (2.13) have not to be considered, because their contribution is negligible.

For a liquid-fluid-solid contact line, we have to impose only the tangential component (with respect of the solid interface) of the equation (2.13), completed with the standard unpermeability condition

$$\gamma_A(v).\tau|_A = 0 \ , v.n|_A = 0 \tag{2.14}$$

Evidently the velocity in the point A at the moving contact line is discontinuous in this case.

Measuring of the surface tension coefficient σ_{13} and σ_{23} at the fluid-solid interfaces is practically very difficult and the values for them are not available. So it is interesting to mention that the knowledge of the contact angle α at static contact line provides enough information for (2.14). Indeed, if the rigid surface is C^1 -smooth, then from follows in the static case (2.14)

$$\tau_{12}\sigma_{12} + \tau_{13}\sigma_{13} + \tau_{23}\sigma_{23} = \tau_{12}(\sigma_{12} - \sigma_{23}) + \tau_{13}\sigma_{13} = 0 \ . \tag{2.15}$$

If we know the contact angle α then the difference between both surface tensions coefficients $\sigma_{12} - \sigma_{23}$ can be computed from (2.15) which is all that we need to implement (2.14).

3. Numerical method

The principle of virtual power for the above described problem is

$$(\lambda Dv/Dt, \sigma v) + (\Pi(v), D(\sigma v)) + c^{-1}\int_{\Gamma_5} v_n\,\sigma v_n\,ds + (p, div(\sigma v)) \tag{3.1}$$

$$= \sum \langle R_i, \sigma v\rangle_{\Gamma_i} + \langle p_0, \sigma v_n\rangle_{\Gamma_2} - \langle p_{out}, \sigma v_n\rangle_{\Gamma_4 \cup \Gamma_5} - \langle \beta, \sigma v_\tau\rangle_{\Gamma_4} + (F, \sigma v) + \varphi(\sigma v)$$

$$(div\,v, \sigma p) = 0; \tag{3.2}$$

where the scalar products are taken in $\Omega(t) = \sum_{i=1}^{2} \Omega_i(t)$, the functions are defined in $\Omega(t)$ using their definition in $\Omega_i(t)$ e.g. $\lambda = 1$ in $\Omega_1(t)$ and λ in $\Omega_2(t)$

$$\varphi(\sigma v) = (\tau_{12}\sigma_{12} + \tau_{13}\sigma_{13} + \tau_{23}\sigma_{23})(A).\sigma v(A) \text{ or} \tag{3.3}$$

$$\varphi(\sigma v) = (\tau_{12}\sigma_{12} + \tau_{13}\sigma_{13} + \tau_{23}\sigma_{23}).n(A)\,\sigma v.n(A) \tag{3.4}$$

The form (3.3) refers to the case of liquid-liquid-fluid contact line and (3.4) to liquid-fluid-solid one.

If we posses a predictor for $\hat{\Omega}_i = \Omega_i(\hat{t})$ than we could use e.g. fully implicit scheme for the full time derivative and to solve (3.1) by means of FEM. It results in a method with direct tracking of the free boundary, which consists of finite element sides. In this way we obtain v_h and construct a corrector for $\Omega_i(\hat{t})$. The systems of FEM are of the type

$$AU + B^T P = F,\ BU = G \tag{3.5}$$

We use a second order 9 node biquadratic velocity quadrilateral isoparametric finite element with linear pressure in local variables (ξ, ν), see **[19]** and the references therein. This seems to be the best finite element for Navier-Stokes equations. A number of other second order FE are included in our codes but this one yields the best results **[19]**. Of course, the numerical method could work with other FE too. The first order FE **[22]** deserves also special attention, although some problems could arise with the approximation of the free boundary in this case.

$$v_h = \sum U_i \Phi_i,\ p_h = \sum P_k \Pi_k \tag{3.6}$$

The approximation of the interfaces is only continuous but not C^1-smooth and hence R_i from (2.12) is a delta function in the junction points B of FE sides a_i. Hence besides the usual integrals $\langle R_i, \sigma v\rangle_{\Gamma_i}$ in (3.1) , we have to take into account an irregular part, which corresponds to this delta function. It turns out to be a penalty term which acts to keep the junction angles near to Π **[14]**, **[15]**.

$$\langle R_i, \sigma v\rangle_{\Gamma_i}(B) = 2(We_i)^{-1}\zeta_i \sin\beta\,(\sigma v.n)(B)\,\Gamma(B), \tag{3.7}$$

where $n = (n^+ + n^-)/\|n^+ + n^-\|^{-1}$, $\sin\beta = (1 - (n.n)^2)^{1/2}$ and $\Gamma(B)$ is presented only in the axisymmetric case.

This apparatus appears to be very good and the main part of the examples presented in the next chapter are calculated with it. But it is easy to see that it does not control directly the smoothness of the boundary in the points at the line of symmetry for axisymmetric problems and this reflects badly on the efficiency of the computations. So we have developed another one, which is based on the direct calculation of $\langle R_i, \sigma v\rangle_{\Gamma_i na_s}$.

For it we need the modules of the surface tension force at the three points P, which are calculated drawing a circumference through the point P and the two neighboring points at the interface Γ_i. In this way the angles at the junction points are included implicitly. The comparisons of the both techniques for the surface tension shows that they yields the same results but the second one is a bit better in the axisymmetric case.

Let's say how integrals $\langle R_i, \sigma v\rangle_{\Gamma_i} na_s$ are computed. The free surface approximation consists of parabolas through three points. The sphere is the unique stable shape in quiescent liquid in weightlessness for any We and p_0. We want this property to hold exactly for discrete models. It is fullfilled if the module of the surface tension is computed at a curve composed by circular segments through the three points but the integration is performed along the original curve. This approximation is used to ensure that for the spherical shape we have no spurious bending. If it is not so this error can grow considerably for small Weber numbers.

It is interesting to mention that the contribution of the contact line boundary conditions (3.3) or (3.4) is of the same form as the smoothness penalty term (3.7).

If the interface is considerably deformable the explicit Euler method for (2.3) yields a good predictor $x^p(\hat{t})$ for the position of the mesh nodes $x(t)$.

$$x^p(\hat{t}) = x(t) + \tau v^p(t) + O(\tau^2),\ v^p(t) = v(x(t), t). \tag{3.8}$$

At present moment a fully implicit scheme is employed for (3.1) to obtain $\hat{v}^c$. The symmetric scheme and Geer's method can be used too and are in process of programming. As a corrector for (3.8) we use the implicit Euler schemes

$$x^c(\hat{t}) = x(t) + \tau\hat{v}(x(t), t). \tag{3.9}$$

$$x^c(\hat{t}) = x(t) + 0.5\tau(\hat{v}(x(\hat{t}), t)) + (\hat{v}(x(t), t) \tag{3.10}$$

The second possibility posses a truncation error $O(\tau^3)$ and has proved experimentally to be better. Although the total accuracy is always $O(\tau)$ due to the first order time approximation of (3.1) the corrector (3.9) does not conserve well the mass of the particle. In some experiments up to 30 % of the mass is lossed in this way, when if (3.10) is employed the looses for the same problem are only 0.5% [**17**].

The control of the smoothness of Γ_i is also applied. If the $\max\beta$ is larger then a given value, the time integration step is rejected out and τ is decreased.

Automatic choice of τ is developed on the basis of exactness and smoothness control [**15**]. The free surface in the presence of the surface tension is very sensitive to non-smooth deformations and τ changes sometimes between 10^{-5} and 0.5.

If the predictions are recognized to be good, only one solution of the system for v is needed per time step. So the consistency of the predictor step (3.8) is quite important.

Real interfaces belong at least to C^1. Hence from (3.8-10) follows that v_n belongs also to C^1. This additional information can be used to filtrate the truncation error in the normal component of the velocity v_n, which is responsible for exact evaluation of Γ_i [17]. Our package is provided with optional usage of C^1 cubic parametrical splines for this purpose. This yields the same result as without it, but the program runs several times faster.

The systems (3.5) are solved in two steps [23]. First they are decomposed to the form

$$\tilde{A}\tilde{U} = \tilde{F},\ (\tilde{\tilde{U}}, P) = \tilde{C}(\tilde{U}) + \tilde{G},\ U = \tilde{U} \cup \tilde{\tilde{U}}, \tag{3.11}$$

which holds after a change of the variables. This decomposition is performed out through operations on local matrices and the system (3.11) is assembled directly. This technique is close to the divergence-free approach.

The systems (3.12.a) are positive definite and symmetric and are solved using Gauss type method or iterative methods. They correspond to finite elements in the system of internal variables $\tilde{U}$.

$$\tilde{v}_h = \sum \tilde{U}_i \tilde{\Phi}_i \tag{3.12}$$

where the vector of variables consists of the two velocity components and the stream function Ψ at vertices and circulations C_k at finite element sides a_k, $C_k = \int_{a_k} (v, \tau)\, d\gamma$, where $d\gamma = ds$ in 2D plane case and $d\gamma = r ds$ in the axisymmetric one.

Some problems arises in the case of multiply connected domains for numerical methods employing the stream function. Our method and packages are able to treat such problems in a standard way preserving the positive definiteness of the matrices [19]. Examples of free-surface problems in multiply connected domains are presented in the next section.

The pressure could be calculated using v_h by marching procedure and the numerical method is equivalent to a velocity-pressure finite element method [23].

A typical feature of Lagrangian methods is that a grid redefinition is required when the mesh becomes too deformed. In our method the regridding is performed in four steps [17]:

(i) Define a new conforming triangulation τ_h with nodes $\{A_i\}$.

(ii) For every A_i find FE e'_j from the old triangulation τ'_h so that $A_i \in e'_j$.

(iii) Find $v(A_i) = v_{h,e'}(A_i)$ using the old velocity field at $\tau_{h'}$.

(iv) So we construct the new velocity field v_h at τ_h. It has to be discretely divergence-free i.e. to satisfy (3.2). We shall use it as an initial condition and in this case the violation of (3.2) leads to spurious results at least for small times.

In general this condition is violated for the new velocity field on τ_h. Hence we have to construct a discretely divergence-free approximation $\tilde{v}_h$ of v_h. For our method the velocity field is used as initial condition for internal variables. Hence it is always discretely solenoidal at τ_h. But its construction from v_h is not uniquely defined. The primitive variable velocity field $\tilde{v}_h$, corresponding to the internal variable one, will differ from v_h.

At present we use more or less a standard mesh generator based on the macroelements to define the new meshes. It is connected with the great variety of problems that we study, which needs different regridding algorithms. Now fully automatic regridding is in development for particular problems.

An Eulerian variant of the method is also under development, which is designed for solving problems with liquid-fluid-solid dynamic contact lines. The solution of such problems is singular near the contact points and hence the grid redefinition looses its accuracy in this zone. Of course, other additional efforts on special grid refinement and using of special functions to handle the singularity are to be put in action to get good accuracy in this case.

4. Numerical examples

In this section we shall present some numerical examples to give a feeling for the scope of the applications of this method. In these examples the particles are moving under buoyancy if something else is not stated. As reference length is taken the equivalent radius of the particle and as reference velocity - the Stokes velocity of a rigid spherical particle with the same equivalent radius and zero density. If the reason for the motion is the gravity, then the Eötvös number is the convenient measure for the deformability of the interface.

$$Eo = 18We/Re \tag{4.1}$$

4.1. Unsteady motion of bubbles.

There exist many basic hydrodynamical questions connected with the velocity, shape and stability of bubbles and their interaction with each other or interfaces. For example even unsteady motion of a bubble in unbounded liquid is not studied yet [**24**]. There are many results for stationary motion of bubbles but it is not clear in which conditions they could be used, e.g. how long time passes after separation of a bubble from the nozzle till the stationary velocity is achieved.

The rise of a bubble to a deformable liquid-liquid interface is studied using this method [**17**],[**25**].

An example of free-surface problem in a doubly connected domain is the rise of two bubbles to a rigid wall, 2D plane case. The numerical results for $Re = 9$, $We = 40$, $Fr = 2$, $d = 2$, $t = 0, 0.8, 1.6$ are presented on Fig. 2.

Fig. 2

4.2. Rise or coalescence of drops.

The rise of deformable bubbles or drops towards a deformable liquid-liquid interface is considered using this method in [**17**],[**25**] and the unsteady motion of type-A compound drop in [**26**]. The coalescence of two drops in presence of a rigid wall is shown on Fig. 3 for $Re_1 = 9$, $Re_2 = 6$, $We = 2.2$, $Fr = 0.44$, $\lambda = 0.2$.

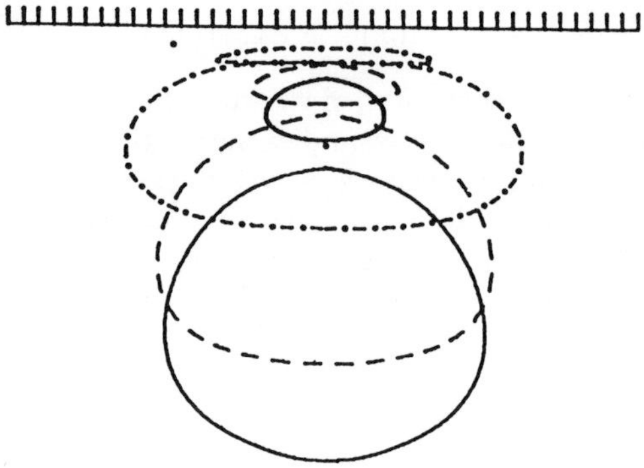

Fig. 3

4.3. Problems with dynamic contact angles.

Problems with liquid-fluid-solid contact lines are important e.g. for capillary motion, local analysis of flows in porous media and coating technology. To test our method we consider the dynamics of the liquid and the free surface due to a change in the contact angle. Liquid in a capillary is supposed to be with initially flat surface i.e. with contact angle is $\Pi/2$. This initial condition does not agree with the boundary condition (2.14) because the coefficients σ_{ij} generate another contact angle. The evolution in time of the free surface is presented on Fig. 4 for $Re = 1$, $We = 1$, $(\sigma_{13} - \sigma_{23})/\sigma_{12} = cos(\Pi/4)$, $t = 0,\ 0.6,\ 5.4$ and $(\sigma_{13} - \sigma_{23}/\sigma_{12} = cos(\Pi/6)$, $t = 0,\ 0.5,\ 4.5$.

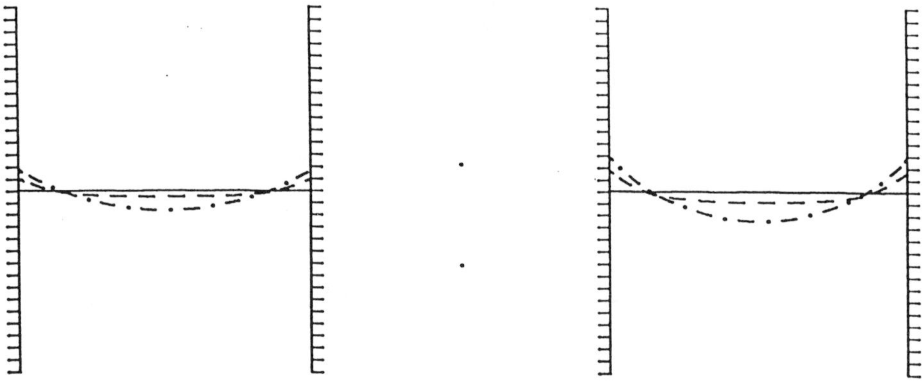

Fig. 4

The comparison with natural experiments (their Fig. 8 a., frame 3) of **[27]** in the liquid-liquid-fluid case and our numerical experiment is presented on Fig. 5. The coincidence is very good, which proves the consistency of the mathematical model.

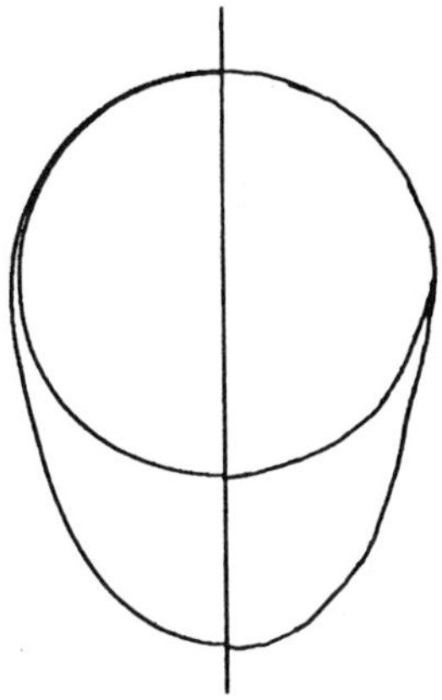

Fig. 5

4.4. Problems with pressure and filtration boundary conditions.

The unsteady motion of a drop in a tube due to constant pressure gradient is presented on Fig. 6 for $Re_1 = 0.19$, $Re_2 = 1$, $We = 3$, $a_0 = 0.914$ (equivalent radius), $l_{channel} = 6$, $\Delta p = 24$. Initially the drop has been spherical.

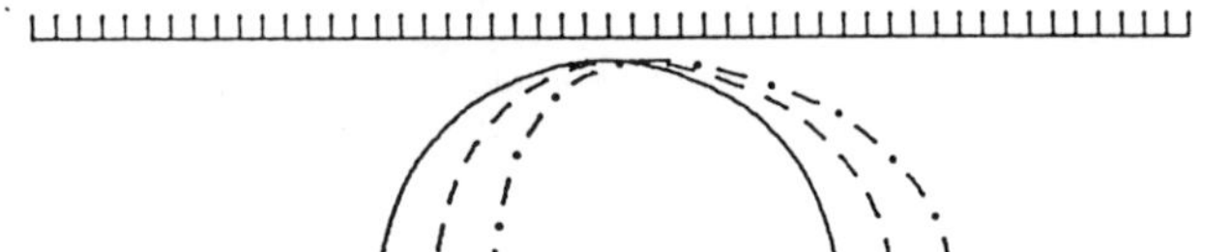

Fig. 6

More numerical examples are presented in [**19**], [**20**].

5. Conclusions

In this study a numerical method of divergence-free type for viscous hydrodynamics with simple or multiple free boundaries is presented. This technique is rather universal and capable to solve various problems of multiphase flow. This is illustrated in the numerical examples. The pressure and filtration boundary conditions are in the scope of the method, which enables the solution of pressure driven free surface problems as well as in domains with many inlets and outlets (e.g. in branched channels).

We pay also special attention to problems with contact lines, for which mathematical modelling is not very clear. A new approach to treat this is proposed, which is easily included in this numerical method. All obtained numerical results are in very good qualitative agreement with the existing experiments and theories. The quantitative coincidence with natural experiments in liquid-liquid-fluid case are clearly excellent. This approach is clearly promising for the liquid-fluid-solid case too, but up to our opinion, the use of the Eulerian approach would be better in this case, because the solution is very irregular near the contact point and the grid redefinition looses accuracy.

The next steps are planned: (i) Eulerian and Eulerian-Lagrangian codes, (ii) automatic adjustment of the grid, (iii) multigrid and multilevel, (iv) iterative methods.

References

[1] F. H. Harlow and J. E. Welch, *Numerical calculations of time dependent viscous incompressible flow of fluid with free surface*, Phys. Fluids **8** (1965), 2182–2189.

[2] C. W. Hirt, J. L. Cook and T. D. Butler, *A Lagrangian method for calculating of incompressible fluid with free surface*, J. Comput. Phys. **5** (1970), 214–222.

[3] C. W. Hirt and B. D. Nichols, *Volume of fluid (VOF) method for the dynamics of free boundaries*, J. Comput. Phys. **39** (1981), 201–226.

[4] V. J. Rivkind, G. M. Ryskin and G. A. Fishbein, *Motion of a spherical drop in viscous flow*, (in Russian), J. Eng. Physics. **20** (1971), 1023–1038.

[5] V. J. Rivkind, *Steady motion of deformable viscous drop*, Zap. Naucn. Sem. Leningrad. Otdel. Mat. Inst. Steklov (LOMI) **84** (1983), 220–243.

[6] C. I. Christov and P. Volkov, *Numerical investigation of the steady viscous flow past a resting deformable bubble*, J. Fluid Mech. **158** (1984), 341–364.

[7] G. M. Ryskin and L. G. Leal, *Numerical solution of free-boundary problems in fluid mechanics*, J. Fluid Mech. **148** (1984), 1–35.

[8] I. S. Kang and L. G. Leal, *Numerical solution of axisymmetric, unsteady free-boundary problems at finite Reynolds number. I. Finite difference scheme and its application to the deformation of a bubble in a unaxial straining flow*, Phys. Fluids **30** (1987), 1929–1940.

[9] F. Shokoohi and H. G. Elrod, *Numerical investigation of the disintegration of liquid jets*, J. Comp. Phys. **71** (1987), 324–342.

[10] C. Cuvelier, A. Segal and A. A. van Steenhoven, "Finite element methods and Navier-Stokes equations," D. Reidel Publishing Company, Dordrecht, Boston, Lancaster, Tokyo, 1986.

[11] N. P. Kruyt, C. Cuvelier, A. Segal and J. van Zanden, *A total linearization method for solving viscous free boundary flow problems by the finite element method*, Int. J. Numer. Meth. Fluids **8** (1988), 351–363.

[12] D. L. Lynch, *Unified approach to simulation on deforming elements with application to phase change problems*, J. Comp. Phys. **47** (1982), 387–411.

[13] R. Keunings, *An algorithm for the simulation of transient viscoelastic flows with free surface*, J. Comp. Phys. **62** (1986), 199–220.

[14] P. J. Shopov and P. D. Minev, *Numerical solution of viscous hydrodynamic problems with free boundaries*, University Annual Applied Mathematics (in Bulgarian) **22** (1986), 211–220.

[15] P. J. Shopov, *Numerical method for free-surface hydrodynamical problems*, Comp. rend. Acad. bulg. Sci. **41** (1988), 37–41.

[16] P. J. Shopov, P. D. Minev, I. B. Bazhlekov, Z. D. Zapryanov, *Hydrodynamical interaction of a deformable bubble with a rigid wall at moderate Reynolds numbers*, (in print), J. Fluid Mech..

[17] P. J. Shopov, P. D. Minev, I. B. Bazhlekov, *Numerical method for Unsteady Viscous Hydrodynamical Problems with free Boundaries*, (in print), Int. J. Num. Meth. Fluids.

[18] I. Bazhlekov, P. J. Shopov, *Mathematical and numerical modeling of dynamic contact lines*, (in print), Comp. rend. Acad. bulg. Sci..

[19] P. J. Shopov, J. Jordanov, *Numerical solution of Stokes equations with pressure boundary conditions*, submitted to J. Comput. Physics..

[20] P. J. Shopov, J. Jordanov, *Numerical method for free surface viscous hydrodynamics with pressure boundary conditions*, (in preparation).

[21] P. J. Shopov, I. Bazhlekov, *Numerical modelling of problems with dynamic liquid-liquid-fluid and liquid-liquid-solid contact lines*, (in preparation).

[22] P. J. Shopov, *Isoparametric divergence-free finite element for simulation of incompressible fluid flow*, (in Russian), Serdica **10** (1984), 316–321.

[23] P. J. Shopov, *Condensation method for hydrodynamic problems*, (in Russian), Serdica **10** (1984), 198–205.

[24] P. J. Shopov and P. D. Minev, *Numerical modelling of the unsteady motion of bubbles and drops in unbounded viscous fluid*, submitted to J. Theoretical and Comput. Fluid Dynamics.

[25] P. J. Shopov and P. D. Minev, *Interaction of bubbles and drops with a deformable interface*, (in preparation for J. Fluid Mech.).

[26] P. J. Shopov and I. B. Bazhlekov, *Unsteady motion of type-A compound drop in unbounded liquid*, (in print), Mech. Res. Commun..

[27] Y. H. Mori, *Configurations of gas-liquid two-phase bubbles in immiscible liquid media*, Int. J. Multiphase Flow **4** (1978), 383–396.

FDM approximation of variational inequalities with an application to injection moulding

JÖRG STEINBACH

Sektion Mathematik, Technische Universität Chemnitz
PF 964, Chemnitz 9010, Germany

Abstract. This paper is devoted to the numerical solution of variational inequalities, which are used to simulate the injection moulding process of a plastic melt into a mould cavity.

1. INTRODUCTION

The Hele–Shaw flow theory is frequently applied by engineers for modelling the mould filling process (see e.g. [**1**]). Then a free boundary problem for the pressure ρ can be derived from the Navier–Stokes equations. From the mathematical point of view it is useful to transform this problem into variational inequalities by means of the Baiocchi transformation $u(x,t) = \int_0^t \rho(x,t')\,dt'$.

$$\text{(1.1)}\qquad \begin{aligned} &\text{Find } u(t) \in K = \{w \in H^1(\Omega) : w \geq \phi = 0 \text{ in } \Omega\} \\ &a(t; u(t), v - u(t)) \geq (f(t), v - u(t)) + \int_0^t b(t'; u(t'), v - u(t))\,dt' \\ &\text{for all } v \in K, t \in S = [0,T] \end{aligned}$$

with the bilinear forms $a(t; v(t), w) = \int_\Omega [k(x,t) \operatorname{grad} v(x,t) \operatorname{grad} w(x) + (qv)(x,t)w(x)]\,dx$ and $b(t; v(t), w) = \int_\Omega [\frac{\partial k}{\partial t}(x,t) \operatorname{grad} v(x,t) \operatorname{grad} w(x)]\,dx$. The domain $\Omega \subset \mathbb{R}^2$ represents the lay-flat of the midsurface of the cavity and T is the mould filling time. The spaces $H^m(\Omega)$ denote the Sobolev spaces $W_2^m(\Omega)$ for $m \geq 0$. The function k depends on the viscosity η of the plastic melt and on the thickness d of the cavity, where $d \ll \operatorname{diam} \Omega$ is assumed. The term f is a function of the abundance of the sources (the so-called gates) and q is a constant with $q \geq q_0 > 0$.

Provided the viscosity is a constant or a function of space variables only, we obtain elliptic inequalities, because the bilinear form b is vanishing in (1.1). In the more general case $\eta = \eta(\vartheta(x,t))$ (ϑ – temperature) we have to solve a nonlinear system consisting of the inequality (1.1) and the following heat equation.

$$\text{(1.2)}\qquad \rho c \left(\frac{\partial \vartheta}{\partial t} + \sum_{j=1}^{2} \overline{v}_j \frac{\partial \vartheta}{\partial x_j} \right) - \frac{\partial}{\partial z}(\lambda \frac{\partial \vartheta}{\partial z}) = \eta \dot{\gamma}^2 \,,$$

where $x = (x_1, x_2) \in \Omega$, z -the axis perpendicular to the domain Ω, $\overline{v}_j$ -the component of the mean velocity field according to the x_j axis ($j = 1, 2$), ρ -the density, c -the heat capacity, λ -the heat conductivity and $\dot{\gamma}$ -the shear rate. The equation (1.2) balances the heat convection in flow direction, the heat conduction in the direction of the z axis and the frictional heat.

For a more detailed derivation of this mathematical model we refer to [**16**]. The main aim of the computer aided simulation of the injection moulding process consists in the prediction of the filling pattern (flow fronts).

2. Elliptic variational inequality

In this section we consider the following elliptic inequality.

$$\begin{aligned} &\text{Find } u \in K = \{v \in H^1(\Omega) : v \geq \phi \text{ in } \Omega,\ v = g_1 \text{ on } \Gamma_1\} \\ &a(u, v-u) \geq \langle \Phi, v-u \rangle \qquad \text{for all } v \in K, \end{aligned} \tag{2.1}$$

where Ω denotes a bounded open subset of R^2 with the smooth boundary $\Gamma = \partial\Omega = \Gamma_1 \cup \Gamma_2 \cup \Gamma_3$. The continuous positive definite bilinear form a and the continuous bounded functional Φ are defined as

$$a(v, w) = \int_\Omega (k \operatorname{grad} v \operatorname{grad} w + qvw)\, dx + \int_{\Gamma_3} \varkappa vw\, ds$$

$$\langle \Phi, v \rangle = \int_\Omega fv\, dx + \int_{\Gamma_2 \cup \Gamma_3} gv\, ds.$$

A detailed investigation of the analytical properties of the solution is published e.g. in [**2**], [**3**], [**6**], [**10**], [**11**] or [**15**]. For generalities on the approximation of the inequality (2.1) from the numerical point of view see [**4**], [**6**], [**7**] and [**12**].

For the numerical solution we suggest the following strategy consisting of separate steps.
(i) Triangulation. We use a flexible approximation of the domain Ω by irregular networks formed by triangles and/or rectangles. The grid $\overline{\omega} = \omega \cup \gamma$ ($\gamma = \gamma_1 \cup \gamma_2 \cup \gamma_3$ -the discrete boundary) is the set of all nodes of the given network.
(ii) Discretization of the inequality (2.1) by means of the finite difference method (FDM). We construct a finite difference inequality by means of the balance method (perpendicular bisector method). This method is motivated from the physical point of view.

$$\begin{aligned} &\text{Find } y \in K_h = \{v \in L_2(\overline{\omega}) :\ v(x) \geq \phi(x) \text{ for } x \in \overline{\omega},\ v = g_1 \text{ for } x \in \gamma_1\} \\ &(\Lambda y, v-y) \geq (\Phi_h, v-y) \text{ for all } v \in K_h\ , \end{aligned} \tag{2.2}$$

where $L_2(\overline{\omega})$ is a discretization of the space $L_2(\Omega)$. Here (Λ, y, v) and Φ_h denote the finite difference approximation of the bilinear form and the functional in (2.1).
(iii) Replacement of the discrete inequality (2.2) by a discrete penalty problem. This penalty problem is represented by a nonlinear system of equations.

$$\begin{aligned} &\text{Find } y_\varepsilon \in L_2(\overline{\omega}),\quad y_\varepsilon(x) = g_1(x) \text{ for } x \in \gamma_1 \\ &(\Lambda y_\varepsilon, v) + \varepsilon^{-1}((y_\varepsilon - \phi)^-, v) = (\Phi_h, v) \text{ for all } v \in L_2^0(\overline{\omega})\ , \end{aligned} \tag{2.3}$$

where $L_2^0(\overline{\omega}) = \{v \in L_2(\overline{\omega}) : v(x) = 0 \text{ for } x \in \gamma_1\}$ and $(v-\phi)^- = \min\{0, v-\phi\}$.
(iv) Solution of the system (2.3) by an iteration method. After a finite number of iteration steps the exact solution of the discrete penalty problem is reached and at each iteration step one has to solve a linear system of equations.

Details of this concept and the proves of the following results can be found in [**8**] and [**15**]. For the difference between the solutions of the problems (2.2) and (2.3) the estimate $\|y - v_\varepsilon\|_{1,\overline{\omega}} \le C\frac{\varepsilon}{h}$ holds in a discrete W_2^1 -norm on the grid $\overline{\omega}$, where h denotes the discretization parameter. Under the assumption $u \in K \cap H^2(\Omega)$ for the regularity of the solution of problem (2.1) we deduce the estimate $\|u - v\|_{1,\overline{\omega}} \le Ch$ for the error between the solutions of (2.1) and (2.2). Consequently, we obtain the convergence $\|u - v_\varepsilon\|_{1,\overline{\omega}} \le Ch$ for the solutions of (2.1) and (2.3) coupling the penalty and the discretization parameters by $\varepsilon \le h^2$. Analogous results are also valid for the FEM (see e.g. [**10**]).

3. Analytical properties of evolutionary inequalities

A detailed investigation of inequalities of the type (1.1) from the analytical point of view is performed in [**13**], [**14**] and [**15**]. We want to give a short survey about the results of these studies. Let us first consider an abstract evolutionary inequality.

$$\text{Find } u \in \Re_1 = \{w \in C(S,V) : w(t) \in K \text{ for all } t \in S = [0,T]\}$$

$$\tag{3.1} \begin{aligned} &\langle A(t)u(t), v - u(t)\rangle \ge \langle f(t), v - u(t)\rangle + \\ &+ \langle \int_0^t (Bu)(t')\,dt', v - u(t)\rangle \qquad \text{for all } v \in K \text{ and } t \in S, \end{aligned}$$

where V denotes a real Hilbert space, $C(S,V)$ the space of the abstract continuous functions $u \in (S \to V)$ and $L_2(S,V)$ the space of measurable abstract functions $u \in (S \to V)$ with $\int_S \|u(t)\|_V{}^2\,dt < \infty$ (for the theory of these spaces see [**5**] or [**9**]). Finally we assume $K \subseteq V$ to be a convex and closed subset and $K \ne \emptyset$.

For the existenceheorem we need the following assumptions. The operator $A(t) \in (V \to V^*)$ is radial-continuous for all $t \in S$ i.e. the mapping $[0,1] \ni \alpha \to \langle A(t)(u + \alpha v), v\rangle$ is continuous for all fixed u, $v \in V$, $t \in S$. The function $t \to A(t)x$ is a mapping from $S \to C(S,V^*)$ for all $x \in V$ (V^* -the dual space of V). Further let $A(t)$ for all $t \in S$ be strong monotone with a constant $0 < m \ne m(t)$.

Let the mapping $B \in (L_2(S,V)) \to L_2(S,V^*))$ be Lipschitz-continuous with a constant L and for f is assumed $f \in C(S,V^*)$.

Theorem 1. *Under these assumptions the problem (3.1) is uniquely solvable. For solutions $u_i = u_i(f_i)$ $(i = 1,2)$ there holds the estimate*

$$\|u_1 - u_2\|_{C(S,V)} \le M\|f_1 - f_2\|_{C(S,V^*)} \qquad \text{with } M = M(L,m,T)\,.$$

This theorem is proved in [**15**] by means of the Banach fixed point theorem and the Gronwall inequality.

In the sequel we replace the abstract operators A and B by continuous bilinear forms a and b and the space V by $V = H_0^1(\Omega)$ (closure of $\overset{\circ}{C}{}^\infty$ in $H^1(\Omega)$), where $\Omega \subset \mathbb{R}^n$ is a bounded domain with a smooth boundary. We use the penalty method for the investigation of these problems.

$$\begin{aligned} &\text{Find } u \in \Re_1 = \{w \in C(S, H_0^1(\Omega)) : w(t) \in K \text{ for all } t \in S\} \\ &a(t; u(t), v - u(t)) \geq (f(t), v - u(t)) + \int_0^t b(t'; u(t'), v - u(t))\, dt' \\ &\text{for all } t \in S \text{ and } v \in K = \{w \in H_0^1(\Omega) : w \geq \phi \text{ in } \Omega\}. \end{aligned} \tag{3.2}$$

$$\begin{aligned} &\text{Find } u_\varepsilon \in C(S, H_0^1(\Omega)) \\ &a(t; u_\varepsilon(t), v) + \varepsilon^{-1}((u_\varepsilon(t) - \phi)^-, v) = (f(t), v) + \int_0^t b(t'; u_\varepsilon(t'), v)\, dt' \\ &\text{for all } v \in H_0^1(\Omega) \text{ and } t \in S. \end{aligned} \tag{3.3}$$

The bilinear forms are defined as $a(t; u(t), v) = \int_\Omega [k_a(x,t) \operatorname{grad} u(x,t) \operatorname{grad} v(x) + (qu)(x,t)v(x)]\, dx$ and $b(t; u(t), v) = \int_\Omega k_b(x,t) \operatorname{grad} u(x,t) \operatorname{grad} v(x)\, dx$.

By means of the shift theorem for elliptic equations (i.e. for the solution of $a(w, v) = (f, v)$ for all $v \in H_0^1(\Omega)$ it holds $w \in H^2(\Omega) \cap H_0^1(\Omega)$) and the Rothe mothod (semidiscretization in time, see e.g. [**9**]) we obtain the regularity $u_\varepsilon \in C(S, H_0^1(\Omega)) \cap L_2(S, H^2(\Omega))$ for the solution of (3.3). For the difference of the solutions of (3.2) and (3.3) we derive $\|u - u_\varepsilon\|_{C(S,H^1(\Omega))} \leq C\varepsilon^{\frac{1}{2}}$. Finally we deduce the regularity $u \in C(S, H_0^1(\Omega)) \cap L_2(S, H^2(\Omega))$ for the solution of (3.3).

REMARK 1. *Without difficulties we can consider problems with nonhomogeneous Dirichlet boundary conditions instead of homogeneous Dirichlet conditions. It is also possible to perform an extension of this theory to boundary conditions of the Neumann type, which are more suitable for the description of the injection moulding process than Dirichlet conditions (see problem (1.1)). Problems with time dependent obstacle functions $\phi = \phi(x,t)$ are also treated in [**15**].*

4. NUMERICAL TREATMENT OF EVOLUTIONARY INEQUALITIES

In this section we consider the numerical solution of the inequality (3.2) for the case $k_b = \frac{\partial k_a}{\partial t}$ and $q = q(x)$ which is typical for the injection moulding process. We use Dirichlet boundary conditions. Extensions to Neumann and also mixed conditions and also to time dependent obstacle function ϕ are possible. In what follows we need for the FDM approximation additional to the space grid $\overline{\omega}$ also the division $\overline{\omega}_\tau = \{t_k = k\tau,\ k = 0, \ldots, N\}$, $N\tau = T$ of the time interval $S = [0, T]$. By y^k we denote the values of the grid function $y^k(x) = y(x, t_k)$ for $x \in \overline{\omega}$ and $t_k \in \overline{\omega}_\tau$. We formulate the discrete inequality.

$$\text{Find } y^k \in K_h = \{v \in L_2(\overline{\omega}) : \ v(x) \geq \phi(x) \text{ for } x \in \overline{\omega}, \ v = 0 \text{ for } x \in \gamma\}$$

$$(\Lambda^k y^k, v - y^k) \geq (f^k, v - y^k) + \sum_{i=0}^{k-1}((\Lambda^{i+1} - \Lambda^i)y^i, \ v - y^k) \tag{4.1}$$

$$\text{for all } v \in K_h \text{ and } k = 0, \dots, N,$$

where Λ^i denotes a positive definite elliptic difference operator weighted with respect to t_i and t_{i+1}, which represents an approximation of the continuous operator.

For the solution of the evolutionary problem (3.2) we use the same strategy (four steps) as described in section 2 for the elliptic inequality. Note that the problem (4.1) represents a discrete elliptic inequality for all $k = 0, \dots, N$. Especially for $k = 0$ the problem (4.1) is identical with the (2.2) elliptic inequality as described in section 2.

For the investigation of (4.1) we use the following penalty problem.

$$\text{Find } y_\varepsilon^k \in L_2^0(\overline{\omega}) = \{v \in L_2(\overline{\omega}) : v = 0 \text{ for } x \in \gamma\}$$

$$\begin{aligned} &(\Lambda^k y_\varepsilon^k, v) + \varepsilon^{-1}((y_\varepsilon^k - \phi)^-, v) = (f^k, v) + \\ &+ \sum_{i=0}^{k-1}((\Lambda^{i+1} - \Lambda^i)y_\varepsilon^i, v) \qquad \text{for all } v \in L_2^0(\overline{\omega}) \text{ and } k = 0, \dots, N. \end{aligned} \tag{4.2}$$

We want to give some properties of the problems (4.1) and (4.2). For a detailed investigation we refer to [**15**]. The problems (4.1) and (4.2) are uniquely solvable because of the positive definiteness of the finite difference operators Λ^i $(i = 0, \dots, N)$. Provided f is an increasing grid function with respect to the time we also obtain increasing solutions of (4.1) and (4.2) with respect to the time. This property reflects the physical behaviour of the injection moulding process, too.

For an error analysis concerning the solutions of (3.2) and (4.2) we combine the following two estimates. Under the regularity assumption $u \in C(S, H_0^1(\Omega)) \cap C(S, H^2(\Omega)) \cap C^1(S, C^{0,1}(\Omega))$ we obtain the estimate

$$\|u - y\|_{C(1,\overline{\omega})} \leq C_1 h + C_2 \tau,$$

for the difference between the solutions of (3.2) and (4.1), where $\|\cdot\|_{C(1,\overline{\omega})}$ denotes a discrete approximation of the norm in the space $C(S, H^1(\Omega))$. For the penalty error between the solutions of (4.1) and (4.2) there holds the estimate $\|y - y_\varepsilon\|_{C(1,\overline{\omega})} \leq C_3 \varepsilon^{\frac{1}{2}}$.

Hence coupling the discretization and penalty parameters by $\varepsilon \leq h^2$ and $h \sim \tau$ we obtain the following convergence result for the solutions of the problems (3.2) and (4.2) $\|u - y_\varepsilon\|_{C(1,\overline{\omega})} \leq Ch$.

We propose the following iteration method for the solution of the penalty problem (4.2).

$$\Lambda^k z_n^k + \varepsilon^{-1} r(z_{n-1}^k)(z_n^k - \phi) = f^k + \sum_{i=0}^{k-1}(\Lambda^{i+1} - \Lambda^i) y_\varepsilon^i \tag{4.3}$$

for $x \in \omega$, $z_n^k = 0$ for $x \in \gamma$, $k = 0, \dots, N$, $n \geq 0$, $z_{-1}^k \in L_2^0(\overline{\omega})$ arbitary, y_ε^i the solutions of (4.2) for $i < k$.

By $r(v)$ we denote the term $r(v) = \begin{cases} 0 \text{ for } v \geq \phi \\ 1 \text{ for } v < \phi \end{cases}$. We mention that for $k = 0$ the iteration method (4.3) is identical with the method described in section 2 (step (*iv*)). We may to deduce the following relations for the solutions of (4.2) and (4.3)

$$z_0^k(x) \leq z_1^k(x) \leq \dots \leq z_n^k(x) \leq \dots \leq y_\varepsilon^k(x) \text{ for all } x \in \overline{\omega}.$$

Further, the iteration process requires only a finite number of steps to arrive at the exact solution of (4.2). This fact motivates the use of the solutions of (4.2) y_ε^i $(i = 0, \dots, k-1)$ for the computation of z_n^k $(k = 1, \dots, N)$ in the iteration method (4.3). The necessary number m $(m \geq 1)$ of steps to reach $z_{m-1}^k = y_\varepsilon^k$ $(k = 0, \dots, N)$ depends essentially on the difference between the sets $\omega^+(y_\varepsilon^k)$ and $\omega^+(z_{-1}^k)$ $(\omega^+(v) = \{x \in \omega : v(x) > \phi(x)\})$. Hence the choice $z_{-1}^{k+1}(x) = y_\varepsilon^k(x)$ for $x \in \overline{\omega}$ and $k = 0, \dots, N-1$ is suitable. If additional information is available (e.g. the abundance of the gates for injection moulding process) it is useful to determine z_{-1}^{k+1} by an extrapolation of y_ε^k $(k = 0, \dots, N-1)$. Finally we consider some results of the computer aided simulation of the injection process by means of the solution of the system (1.1), (1.2) for the plastic product 'cover plate'. By using the Arrhenius law $\eta(\vartheta) = \eta(\vartheta_0)\exp(c(\vartheta^{-1} - \vartheta_0^{-1}))(\eta(\vartheta_0)$ and c -constants dependent on the plastic, see [**1**], is given a relation between the viscosity and the temperature. We determine a mean temperature by integrating the equation (1.2) with respect to the the thickness d and dividing ot by d. In order to solve the system (1.1), (1.2) for every $t_k \in \overline{\omega}_\tau$ we perform the following iteration process. We start with the temperature $\vartheta(t_{k-1})$, compute the viscosity by the Arrhenius law and determine $u(t_k)$ by means of the inequality (1.1). Then we compute the pressure and the velocity and determine the new temperature by means of the problem (1.2). This process is repeated one or two times. In Figure 1 and 2 are shown the results of computations for the 'cover plate' with a constant and a discontinuous (along the rectangle) thickness. The flow fronts for $t = 0.3$ s (3), $t = 0.6$ s (6), $t = 0.9$ s (9) and $t = 1.1$ s (11) as well as the temperature and the pressure for $t = 1.1$ s are presented in each case. In Figure 2 we recognize the qualitative agreement between the results of computer simulations and the experiment. For further computational results we refer to [**15**].

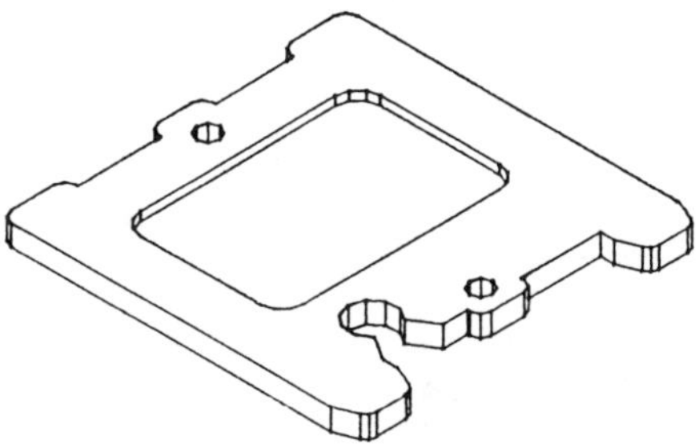

geometry of the
cover plate

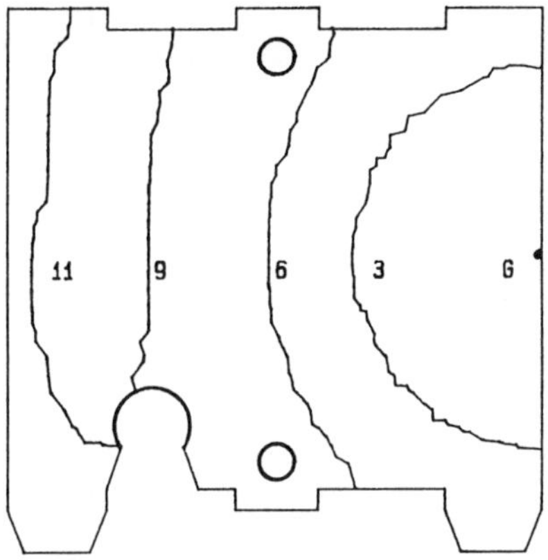

some flow fronts

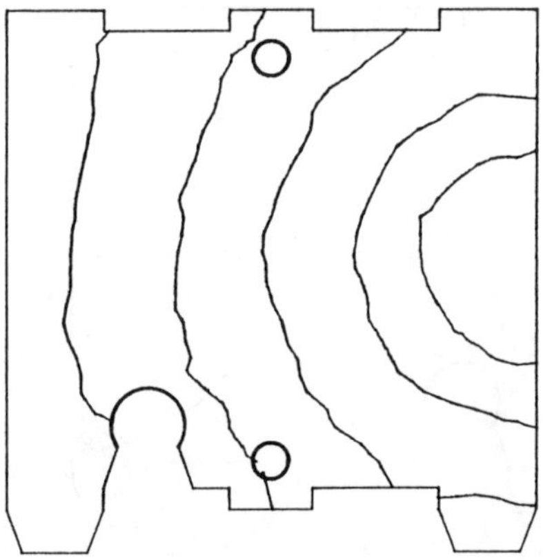

$t = 1.1\,\mathrm{s}$, course isotherms

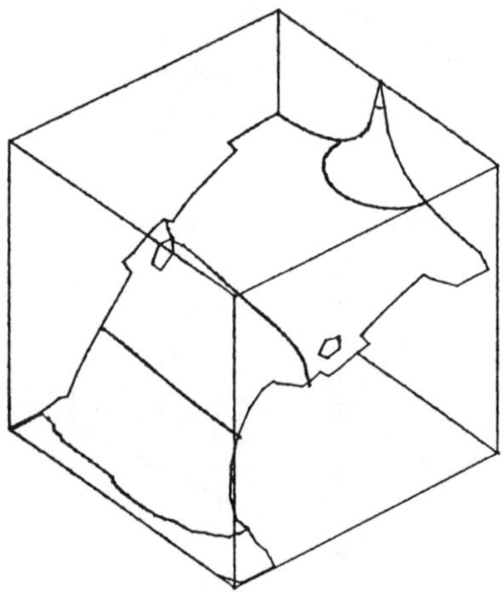

$t = 1.1\,\mathrm{s}$, hill of the pressure

Fig. 1 Cover plate with constant thickness non-isothermal computation, mould filling time $= 1.2\,\mathrm{s}$

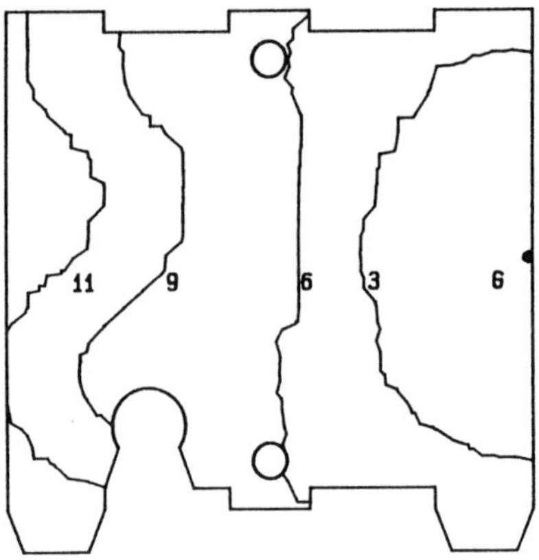

some flow fronts

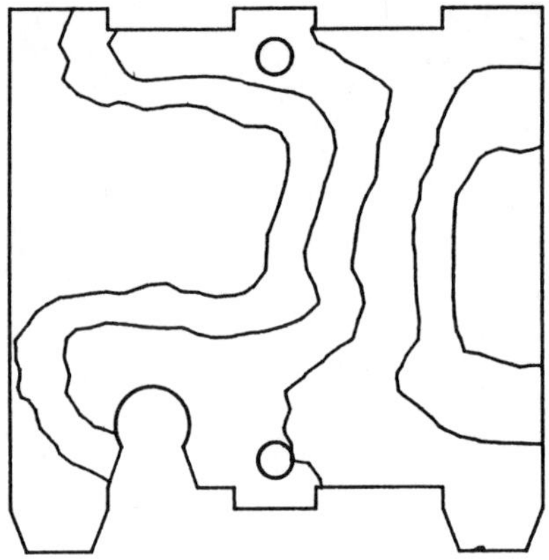

$t = 1.1\,\mathrm{s}$, course of isoterms

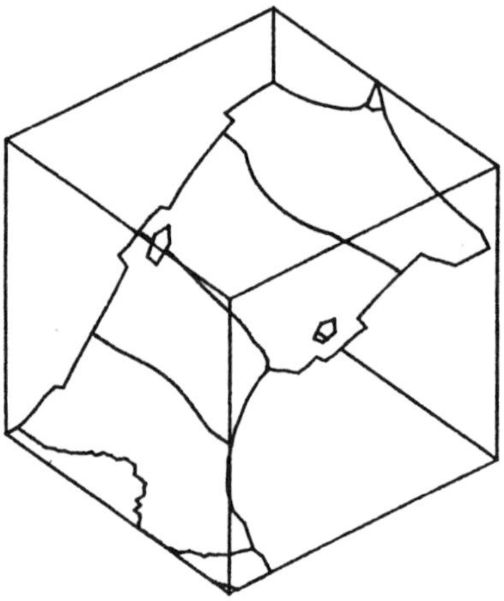

$t = 1.1\,\mathrm{s}$, hill of the pressure

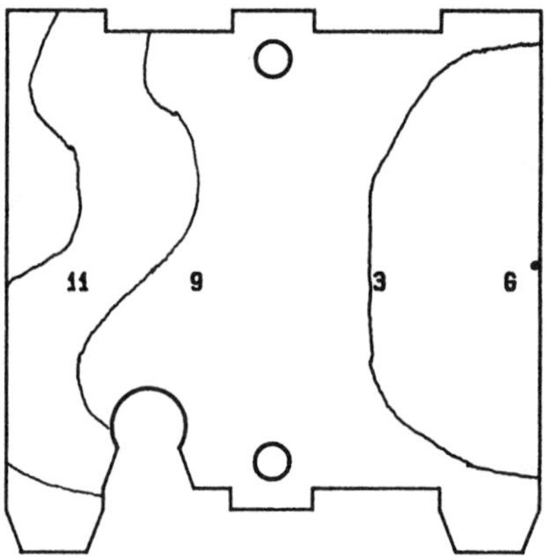

real filling pattern
from the experiment

Fig. 2 Cover plate with discontinuous in thickness (2.5 mm, 1.5 mm) non-isothermal computation, mould filling time = 1.2 s

References

[1] Austin, C., White, J.W., *Filling of mold cavities, the injection molding process*, in "Computer aided engineering for injection molding," (ed. Bernhardt E.C.) Carl Hanser Verlag, München, 1983.

[2] Bensoussan, A., Lions, J.L., "Applications of variational inequalities in stochastic control," North-Holland Publishing Company, Amsterdam, 1982.

[3] Bensoussan, A., Lions, J.L., "Contrôle impulsionnel et inéquations quasivariationnelles," Dunod–Bordas, Paris, 1982.

[4] Brezzi, F., Hager, W.W., Raviart, P.A., *Error estimates for the finite element solution of variational inequalities, Part I–Primal theory*, Numer. Math. **28** (1977), 431–443.

[5] Gajewski, H., Gröger, K., Zacharias, K., "Nichtlineare Operatorgleichungen und Operatordifferentialgleichungen," Akademie - Verlag, Berlin, 1974.

[6] Glowinski, R., "Numerical methods for nonlinear variational problems," Tata institute of fundamental research, Bombay, Springer-Verlag, 1980.

[7] Glowinski, R., Lions, J.L., Tremolieres, R., "Analyse numérique des inéquations variationelles," Dunod-Bordas, Paris, 1976.

[8] Hartwig, K.H., Weinelt, W., *Numerische Lösung linearer elliptischer Variationsungleichungen mittels FDM*, WSR der TH K. -M. -St. **8** (1985).

[9] Kačur, J., "Method of Rothe in evolution equations," Teubner - Text 80, Leipzig, 1985.

[10] Kinderlehrer, D., Stampacchia, G., "An introduction to variational inequalities and their applications," Academic Press, New York, 1980.

[11] Lions, J., "Quelques méthodes de résolution des problèmes aux limites non linéaires (Russian)," Dunod, Gauthier-Villars, Paris, 1969.

[12] Scholz, R., *Numerical solution of the obstacle problem by the penalty method*, Computing **32** (1984), 297–306.

[13] Steinbach, J., *Existenzsätze für eine Klasse von evolutionären Variationsungleichungen*, WZ der TU K. -M. -St. **30** 1 (1988), 22–26.

[14] Steinbach, J., *Untersuchungen zu evolutionären Variationsungleichungen*, WZ der TU K. -M. -St. **31** 2 (1989), 257–262.

[15] Steinbach, J., "Numerische Lösung elliptischer und evolutionärer Variationsungleichungen mittels Differenzenverfahren," Thesis TU K. -M. -St., 1990.

[16] Weinelt, W., Hartwig, K.H., *Zur mathematischen Modellierung von Spritzgießprozessen*, WZ der TU K. -M. -St. **28** 2 (1986), 153–160.

A linear approach for the nonlinear distributed parameter identification problem

XUE–CHENG TAI[1,2]
PEKKA NEITTAANMÄKI[1]

[1] University of Jyväskylä, Department of Mathematics
Seminaarinkatu 15, 40100 Jyväskylä, Finland

Abstract. In identifying the nonlinear distributed parameters we propose an approach, which enables us to identify the nonlinear distributed parameters by just solving linear problems. In this approach we just need to identify linear parameters and then recover the nonlinear parameters from the identified linear parameters. An error estimate for the finite element approximation is derived. Numerical tests are also presented.

Keywords. Distributed parameter systems, nonlinear equations, identification, inverse problems, nonlinearity, approximation, finite element method.

1980 Mathematics subject classifications: 49D15, 65J15, 65N30, 93B30

1. INTRODUCTION

In this paper we shall consider the nonlinear elliptic system:

$$(1.1) \qquad \begin{cases} -\nabla \cdot (a(u)\nabla u) = f \text{ in } \Omega \\ a(u)\dfrac{\partial u}{\partial n} = g \text{ on } \partial\Omega \end{cases}$$

and the nonlinear parabolic system:

$$(1.2) \qquad \begin{cases} u_t - \nabla \cdot (a(u)\nabla u) = f \text{ in } \Omega \times [0,1] \\ a(u)\dfrac{\partial u}{\partial n} = g(\cdot, t) \text{ on } \partial\Omega \times [0,1] \\ u(x,0) = u_0(x) \text{ in } \Omega\ . \end{cases}$$

Our problem is that we know some kind of observation of the state u and then we want to recover the nonlinear parameter $a(u)$. This kind of problems have important applications, for example, in biology [**2**], industrial heat conduction problems [**1,10**], chemical reaction modelling, air and water pollution control problems, underground water and oil-exploration [**3**]. For the computation of the identification of the nonlinear parameters as in (1.1) and (1.2) there already exist many experimental results [**1–5,10**]. In paper [**4**], the finite element method was used to identify the nonlinear distributed parameters. In this paper

[2] Permanent address: Institute of Systems Science Academia Sinica, Beijing 100080, P.R. China

we also use the finite element method (or so called Galerkin method) to identify the nonlinear parameter, but we regard the nonlinear parameter as a linear spatially varying parameter and then identify it. By using the proposed method we can essentially reduce the difficulty in identifying the nonlinear distributed parameters and save essentially the CPU time needed in the computing.

For simplicity of the theoretical analysis, we assume Ω is an open bounded domain in $\mathbb{R}^2$ with a Lipschitz boundary, the state u and the parameter $a(u)$ are scalar functions. In §3 we will give the convergence proof only for the elliptic system (1.1). We can easily see from the proofs that analogical estimate remains valid for parabolic system (1.2).

We assume that we know a distributed observation for u in Ω and we want to identify parameter $a(u)$. The distributed observation is only necessary for the theoretical analysis. In the numerical experiment, we can also handle the point observation. In order to identify parameter $a(u)$, the fit–to–data output–least–square method is always used, i.e., we solve the following problem to identify the parameters:

$$(\mathsf{P}) \qquad \begin{cases} \text{Find } a^*(\cdot) \in Q \text{ such that} \\ J(a^*) = \min\limits_{\tilde{a} \in Q} \{ J(\tilde{a}) \equiv \int_\Omega |u(\tilde{a}) - z|^2 \, dx \} \,, \end{cases}$$

where Q is the set of admissible parameters which contains some a priori information about the identified parameter, z is the observation for u and $u(\tilde{a})$ is the solution of (1.1) with a corresponding parameter $\tilde{a}(\cdot)$.

The standard approach to solve (P) numerically by the finite element method reads

$$(\mathsf{P}_h) \qquad \begin{cases} \text{Find } a_h^*(\cdot) \in Q_h \text{ such that} \\ J_h(a_h^*) = \min\limits_{\tilde{a}_h \in Q_h} J_h(\tilde{a}_h) \equiv \int_{\Omega_h} |u_h(\tilde{a}_h) - z|^2 \, dx \,, \end{cases}$$

where $u_h(\tilde{a})$ is the finite element solution of (1.1) corresponding to the parameter $\tilde{a}_h(\cdot)$ and Q_h is the set of discrete admissible parameters which is in a finite element space.

The nonlinear parameter identification problem (P_h)is in practice quite time consuming to solve. Namely every function evaluation means solving the nonlinear system (1.1). Moreover, the definition of Q_h may be quite troublesome due to the dependence of u.

We shall propose another approach in this paper. By denoting

$$(1.3) \qquad b(x_1, x_2) = a(u(x_1, x_2)) \,,$$

we can write (1.1) as

$$(1.4) \qquad \begin{cases} -\nabla(b\nabla u) = f \\ b\dfrac{\partial u}{\partial n} = g \,. \end{cases}$$

So instead of identifying parameter $a(u)$ from (1.1) we will identify parameter $b(x)$ from (1.4) and then recover parameter $a(\cdot)$ from (1.3) as $b(x)$ and $u(x)$ are known. Therefore, in the computing instead of solving (P_h) numerically, we solve the following minimization problem

$$(\mathsf{IP}_h) \qquad \begin{cases} \text{Find } b_h(\cdot,\cdot) \in M_h = M \cap T^h \text{ such that} \\ J_h(b_h) = \min\limits_{\tilde{b}_h \in M_h} \{J_h(\tilde{b}_h) \equiv \int_\Omega |u_h(\tilde{b}_h) - z|^2 \, dx\} \,, \end{cases}$$

where $u_h(\tilde{b}_h) \in S^h$ is the solution of

$$\int_\Omega \tilde{b}_h \nabla u_h(\tilde{b}_h) \nabla v_h \, dx = \int_\Omega f v_h \, dx + \int_{\partial\Omega} g v_h \, ds \quad \forall v_h \in S^h \tag{1.5}$$

with the compatibility condition

$$\int_\Omega u_h(\tilde{b}_h) \, dx = \int_\Omega z \, dx \,. \tag{1.6}$$

Let us notice that (1.5) is a linear equation with parameter $\tilde{b}_h$. Above T^h and S^h are the finite dimensional subspaces for $L^2(\Omega)$ and $H^1(\Omega)$, respectively, and M is the admissible set for the linear parameter $\tilde{b}(x)$.

In the computing, we also put the following constraint into problem (IP_h) (which follows from Lemma 2.1).

$$\frac{\partial}{\partial x_1} \tilde{b}_h \frac{\partial}{\partial x_2} u = \frac{\partial}{\partial x_2} \tilde{b}_h \frac{\partial}{\partial x_1} u. \tag{1.7}$$

This constraint can be taken as a penalty term into the cost function J_h. From Lemma 2.1 below, we will see that the constraint is just used to guarantee the identified parameter b_h is not a multi-valued function when it is regarded as a function of u. We assume that $z = u$, i.e. there is no observation error.

We want to emphasize here that the proposed method not only works for the identification of the parameters $a(u)$ in (1.1) and (1.2), but it also works for the identification of other parameters that are functions of the state u.

2. Preliminaries

For a nonnegative integer k we shall denote by $W^{k,p}(\Omega)$ the usual Sobolev space of functions defined on Ω with norms

$$\|u\|_{k,p,\Omega} = \left\{ \sum_{|j|=0}^{k} \|D^j u\|^p_{L^p(\Omega)} \right\}^{1/p}, \quad 1 \le p < \infty \text{ and } \|u\|_{k,\infty,\Omega} = \sum_{j=0}^{k} \|D^j u\|_{L^\infty(\Omega)}.$$

We further denote by $H^k(\Omega)$ the space $W^{k,2}(\Omega)$ and the norm of $H^k(\Omega)$ by $\|u\|_{k,\Omega}$.

We shall use the notation $(\cdot,\cdot)$ to denote the L^2 -inner product and $\langle \cdot,\cdot \rangle$ to denote L^2 -inner product on $\partial\Omega$. As from (1.1) we can see the state u is related to the parameter $a(\cdot)$ by the variational equation

$$(a(u)\nabla u, \nabla v) = (f,v) + \langle g, v \rangle \quad \forall v \in H^1(\Omega). \tag{2.1}$$

We assume the solution u of this equation exists and is unique. As usual we shall require that $(f,1)+\langle g,1\rangle=0$, $f\in L^2(\Omega)$, $g\in L^2(\partial\Omega)$.

We use the fit-to-data technique and the finite element method in our approach. In order to define the finite dimensional approximation spaces, we let $\mathcal{T}_h$, $0<h<1$, be a family of triangulations of $\bar{\Omega}$. If the boundary is curved, we shall use triangles at the boundary with one edge replaced by a segment of the boundary. We assume the family $\{\mathcal{T}_h\}$ is regular and quasi-uniform. For a fixed integer $r\geq 1$ we then define

$$S_h^r=\{v\in C^0(\overline{\Omega}): v\,|_T\in P_r \quad \forall T\in \mathcal{T}_h\},$$

where P_r is the space of polynomials of degree less or equal r.

In order to get an error estimate for the identified parameter, we propose the following assumptions on the state u: There exists a constant vector $\vec{v}$ and a constant $\delta>0$ such that

$$\text{(A1)}\qquad \nabla u\cdot\vec{v}\geq\delta>0 \quad \forall \quad x=(x_1,x_2)\in\Omega.$$

The physical meaning of this hypothesis is that there is always some flow in the $\vec{v}$ direction. This assumption is essential to our analysis, but does not appear to be necessary in practical computations. In the case where $|\nabla u|$ may vanish at some points, for example, in the maximum or minimum points, see Remark 3.1 for possible extensions.

In the following, we give a technical lemma which gives the explanation of the constraint (1.7). The proof is based on elementary calculus, see [**9**, p.276], for example.

LEMMA 2.1. *For two given functions $d(x_1,x_2)$ and $w(x_1,x_2)$, if w satisfies the condition (A1), then the necessary and sufficient condition for the existence of a function $c(\cdot)$ such that*

$$d(x_1,x_2)=c(w(x_1,x_2)) \tag{2.2}$$

is given by

$$\frac{\partial}{\partial x_1}d\frac{\partial}{\partial x_2}w=\frac{\partial}{\partial x_2}d\frac{\partial}{\partial x_1}w. \tag{2.3}$$

Moreover, if d and w have kth order continuous derivatives at a point (x_1^0,x_2^0), then $c(\cdot)$ also have kth order continuous derivatives at $w_0=w(x_1^0,x_2^0)$.

3. Error estimate for the identified parameter

In this section, we will derive an error estimate for our approach in identifying the nonlinear paramerer. In the analysis, we take $T_h=S_h^r$, $S^h=S_h^{r+1}$ and

$$M=\{\phi:\ \phi\in L^\infty(\Omega),\ 0<\lambda^{-1}<\phi<\lambda \text{ a.e. in } \Omega\}. \tag{3.1}$$

We also assume the state u and the parameter a satisfy the following regularity property:

$$\text{(A2)}\qquad u\in W^{r+2,\infty}(\Omega),\quad a\in H^{r+1}(\mathbf{R}),\ \text{and } 0<\lambda^{-1}<a(u)<\lambda \text{ a.e. in } \Omega.$$

So f and g satisfy some corresponding regularity conditions. In the error estimate, we will always use C to indicate a generic constant which is independent of h.

If $b_h(\cdot,\cdot)$ is the solution of ($\mathbf{IP}_h$) which also satisfies (1.7), then from Lemma 2.1 we see that there exists a function $a_h(\cdot) : [u_{\min}, u_{\max}] \to \mathbf{R}$ such that

$$b_h(x_1, x_2) = a_h(u(x_1, x_2)). \tag{3.2}$$

Here the subscript h of $a_h(\cdot)$ is just used to indicate that $a_h(\cdot)$ is related to h. It does not mean that $a_h(\cdot)$ belongs to some finite element spaces. In any element b_h is infinitely differentiable, so a_h has the same regularity as u.

With the hypotheses as in (A1) and (A2) we can prove the following theorem.

THEOREM 3.1. *If $u(\cdot,\cdot)$ and $a(\cdot)$ satisfy (A1) and (A2), and if the finite element spaces are taken as $T^h = S_h^r$, $S^h = S_h^{r+1}$, then the identified parameter $a_h(\cdot)$ in (3.2) satisfies the following error estimate*

$$\left(\int_\Omega |a(u) - a_h(u)|^2 \, dx\right)^{1/2} \leq Ch^{r+1}. \tag{3.3}$$

Before the proof of Theorem 3.1 we state two technical lemmas.

LEMMA 3.1. *Under condition (A1), if $|u_x| + |u_y| \neq 0$ a.e. in Ω, then the parameter $a(\cdot)$ is uniquely identifiable.*

PROOF: Suppose there are two parameters $a_1(\cdot)$ and $a_2(\cdot)$ satisfying (2.1). Substracting the equations corresponding to these two parameters from each other, we can get

$$\int_\Omega (a_1(u) - a_2(u))\nabla u \cdot \nabla v \, dx = 0 \quad \forall v \in H^1(\Omega). \tag{3.4}$$

Taking $v(x) = \int_0^{u(x)} (a_1(s) - a_2(s)) \, ds$ we obtain from (3.4) that

$$\int_\Omega |a_1(u) - a_2(u)|^2 |\nabla u|^2 \, dx = 0. \tag{3.5}$$

As $|u_x| + |u_y| \neq 0$ a.e. in Ω, we have $a_1(u) = a_2(u)$ a.e. in Ω.

REMARK 3.1. In assumption (A1) we suppose $\nabla u \cdot \vec{v} \geq \delta > 0$ for a constant vector $\vec{v}$. In the case that $|u_x| + |u_y|$ vanishes at some point in the domain, we have proved in [**13**] for a linear parameter $a(x)$ in a two point boundary value problem that the identified parameter $a_h(x)$ obtained by using the fit-to-data technique and the finite element method satisfies the error estimate

$$\|(a(x) - a_h(x))(|u_x| + h|u_{xx}| + \ldots + h^r|u^{(r+1)}|)\|_{L^\infty} \leq Ch^{-1/2}(h^{r+1} + \frac{\varepsilon}{h}). \tag{3.6}$$

Here ε is an observation error, r is the order of the finite element space and h is the mesh size. This estimate should also be true for our identified nonlinear parameter $a_h(\cdot)$ as in (3.2). The bottleneck in the proof for such an estimate as (3.6) is Lemma 2.1. If we can prove Lemma 2.1 without condition (A1), then we can prove that our identified parameter $a_h(\cdot)$ in (3.2) also satisfies the same error estimate as (3.6) with the L^2-norm in the left hand side. Such a kind of estimates has also been proved for linear parameter in two point boundary problems in [**8,12**].

LEMMA 3.2. *Let the assumptions of Theorem 3.1 be valid. Let $u_h(\tilde{b}_h)$ be defined by (1.5), (1.6) and let u be the solution of (2.1), then we have for all h small enough*

$$\inf_{\tilde{b}_h \in M_h} \|u_h(\tilde{b}_h) - u\|_{0,\Omega} \le Ch^{r+2}, \tag{3.7}$$

where the constant C is independent of h, but depends on $\|a\|_{r+1}$, $\|u\|_{r+2}$.

The proof is similar to the proof in [**6**, Lemma 3 ,p. 540] and is omitted here.

PROOF OF THEOREM 3.1: Let b_h be the solution of ($\mathbf{IP}_h$) and define $w_h = u_h(b_h)$, where $u_h(b_h)$ means a solution of (1.5), (1.6) with the corresponding parameter b_h. Consequently, by using (1.5) and (3.2) we see

$$(a_h(u)\nabla w_h, \nabla v_h) = (f, v_h) + \langle g, v_h\rangle \quad \forall v_h \in S^h\ . \tag{3.8}$$

By (2.1) and (3.8)

$$((a(u) - a_h(u))\nabla u, \nabla v_h) = (a_h(u)\nabla(w_h - u), \nabla v_h) \quad \forall v_h \in S^h. \tag{3.9}$$

Therefore

$$\begin{aligned} ((a(u) - a_h(u))\nabla u, \nabla v) &= ((a(u) - a_h(u))\nabla u, \nabla(v - v_h)) \\ &\quad + (a_h(u)\nabla(w_h - u), \nabla v) + (a_h(u)\nabla(w_h - u), \nabla(v_h - v)) \\ &\quad \forall v \in H^1(\Omega), \quad v_h \in S^h. \end{aligned} \tag{3.10}$$

Let

$$v = \int_0^u (a(s) - a_h(s))\, ds.$$

Then $\nabla v = (a(u) - a_h(u))\nabla u$. Define v_h as the L^2-projection of v into S^h. Then by using a kick-back technique, we can obtain the following inequality:

$$\|(a(u) - a_h(u))\nabla u\|_{0,\Omega}^2 \le C\|\nabla(v - v_h)\|_{0,\Omega}^2 + C\|a_h(u)\nabla(w_h - u)\|_{0,\Omega}^2. \tag{3.11}$$

As $w_h = u_h(b_h)$ and b_h is the solution of ($\mathbf{IP}_h$) we have

$$\|w_h - u\|_{0,\Omega} = \inf_{\tilde{b}_h \in M_h} \|u_h(\tilde{b}_h) - u\|_{0,\Omega} \le Ch^{r+2}, \tag{3.12}$$

which follows from Lemma 3.2. Choosing u_I as the interpolation of u in S_h, we get by the inverse properties of S_h^{r+1}

$$\begin{aligned} \|\nabla(w_h - u)\|_{0,\Omega} &\le \|\nabla(u - u_I)\|_{0,\Omega} + \|\nabla(u_I - w_h)\|_{0,\Omega} \\ &\le \|\nabla(u - u_I)\|_{0,\Omega} + Ch^{-1}\|u_I - w_h\|_{0,\Omega} \\ &\le \|\nabla(u - u_I)\|_{0,\Omega} + Ch^{-1}\|u_I - u\|_{0,\Omega} + Ch^{-1}\|u - w_h\|_{0,\Omega} \\ &\le Ch^{r+1} + Ch^{-1}\cdot Ch^{r+2} = Ch^{r+1}. \end{aligned} \tag{3.13}$$

By standard approximation theory [7] we have

$$\|\nabla(v-v_h)\|_{0,\Omega}=\sum_{T\in\mathcal{T}_h}\|\nabla(v-v_h)\|_{0,T}\le Ch^{r+1}\sum_{T\in\mathcal{T}_h}\|v\|_{r+2,T}. \tag{3.14}$$

We define Θ_h to be the L^2-projection of $a(u)$ into $T^h = S_h^r$. As $\Theta_h - a_h(u) \in T^h = S_h^r$ and by the definition of v, $\nabla v = (a(u) - a_h(u))\nabla u$, we obtain

$$\begin{aligned}\|v\|_{r+2,T} &\le \|u\|_{r+2,\infty,T}\|a(u)-a_h(u)\|_{r+1,T}\\ &\le \|u\|_{r+2,\infty,T}(\|a(u)-\Theta_h\|_{r+1,T}+\|\Theta_h-a_h(u)\|_{r,T})\\ &\le \|u\|_{r+2,\infty,T}(\|a(u)-\Theta_h\|_{r+1,T}+Ch^{-r}\|\Theta_h-a_h(u)\|_{0,T}).\end{aligned} \tag{3.15}$$

Above we use the inverse property for $\Theta_h - a_h(u) = \Theta_h - b_h \in T^h$. As $\|a(u)-\Theta_h\|_{r+1,T} \le \|a(u)\|_{r+1,T} + \|\Theta_h\|_{r,T} \le C$ we find by (3.14) and (3.15) that

$$\begin{aligned}\|\nabla(v-v_h)\|_{0,\Omega} &\le Ch^{r+1}+Ch\|\Theta_h-a_h(u)\|_{0,\Omega}\\ &\le Ch^{r+1}+Ch\|\Theta_h-a(u)\|_{0,\Omega}+Ch\|a(u)-a_h(u)\|_{0,\Omega}\\ &\le Ch^{r+1}+Ch\|a(u)-a_h(u)\|_{0,\Omega}.\end{aligned} \tag{3.16}$$

Substituting (3.16) and (3.13) back into (3.11), we get

$$\|(a(u)-a_h(u))\nabla u\|_{0,\Omega}^2 \le Ch^{2(r+1)}+Ch^2\|a(u)-a_h(u)\|_{0,\Omega}^2+Ch^{2(r+1)}. \tag{3.17}$$

As u satisfies (A1) we see that there exists a constant $C_0 > 0$ such that

$$|u_x|^2+|u_y|^2 > C_0 > 0 \text{ in } \Omega.$$

Therefore for $Ch < C_0/2$ we get from (3.17)

$$\|a(u)-a_h(u)\|_{0,\Omega}^2 \le Ch^{2(r+1)}.$$

This completes the proof.

REMARK 3.2. Similar proof can be carried also in three dimensional case that for given functions $b(x,y,z)$, $u(x,y,z)$,if u satisfies a condition similar to (A1), then the necessary and sufficient condition for the existence of a function $a(\cdot)$ such that $b(x_1,x_2,x_3) = a(u(x_1,x_2,x_3))$ is $b_{x_1}u_{x_2} = b_{x_2}u_{x_1}$, $\quad b_{x_3}u_{x_1} = b_{x_1}u_{x_3}$ and $b_{x_3}u_{x_2} = b_{x_2}u_{x_3}$

REMARK 3.3 The error estimate in Theorem 3.1 is also true for the identification of the parameters in the parabolic system (1.2). If $a_h(\cdot)$ is the identified parameter for $a(\cdot)$ by solving the corresponding discrete problem ($\mathbf{IP}_h$) for the parabolic problem (see Example 4.2.), then the identified parameter satisfies the following error equation

$$((a(u)-a_h(u))\nabla u,\nabla v_h)=(a_h(u)\nabla(w_h-u),\nabla v_h)+(\frac{d}{dt}(w_h-u),v_h).$$

Here we only consider the semidiscrete case and w_h is defined similarly as in the proof of Theorem 3.1. By using the error estimate for the parabolic equations as in [**11**], we can prove the following error estimate is true for the parabolic system:

$$\left(\int_0^1 \int_\Omega \mid a(u) - a_h(u) \mid^2 \, dx \, dt\right)^{1/2} \leq C h^{r+1} . \tag{3.18}$$

4. Numerical tests

In the computing, we will use bi-cubic B-spline functions as the approximation for the parameter. We use a uniform mesh.

Example 4.1 Consider the following two dimensional nonlinear elliptic system.

$$\begin{cases} -\nabla \cdot (a(u)\nabla u) + u = f \text{ in } \Omega \\ a(u)\dfrac{\partial u}{\partial n} = g \text{ on } \partial\Omega . \end{cases} \tag{4.1}$$

Let $\Omega = (0,1)\times(0,1)$. According to the proposed method, instead of identifying parameter $a(u)$ from (4.1), we shall identify a linear parameter $b(x_1, x_2) = a(u(x_1, x_2))$. We will use the multigrid method for solving the obtained linear problems numerically (subroutines D03EDF and D03EEF of the NAG subroutine library). The cost function is taken as:

$$J_{h,\mu}(b) = \int_\Omega |u_h(b_h) - z|^2 \, dx + \mu \int_\Omega |u_{x_1} b_{hx_2} - u_{x_2} b_{hx_1}|^2 \, dx .$$

Here μ is the penalty parameter. The minimization of the cost function $J_{h,\mu}$ will be performed by the quasi-Newton method (subroutine DBCONF of the IMSL subroutine library). In this example, we take the test functions as follows: $u = e^{x+y^2}$,

$$a(u) = \begin{cases} 4 \quad \text{for } u \leq 1.5 \\ 3 + u \quad \text{for } 1.5 \leq u \leq 5.5 \text{ and} \\ 8.5 \quad \text{for } u \geq 5.5 \end{cases}$$

and the corresponding f, g are obtained from (4.1). Let $z = u$ be the observation and we try to recover the parameter $a(u)$. We take $h_1 = 1/32$ as the mesh size for u_h (uniform mesh), and $h_2 = 1/5$ as the mesh size for $b_h(x)$ in both the x_1 and x_2 directions. Figures 4.1–4.2 show the identified parameters with two different penalty values.

Example 4.2. Consider the following nonlinear parabolic system

$$\begin{cases} u_t = (a(u)u_x)_x + f(x,t), \quad (x,t) \in (0,1) \times (0,1) \\ u(x,0) = u_0(x), \quad x \in (0,1) \\ u(0,1) = u(0,t) = 0, \quad t \in (0,1) . \end{cases} \tag{4.3}$$

This model describes the heat conduction process in a heated media whose conductivity depends on the temperature [**1,10**]. Our goal is to identify the heat conductivity parameter

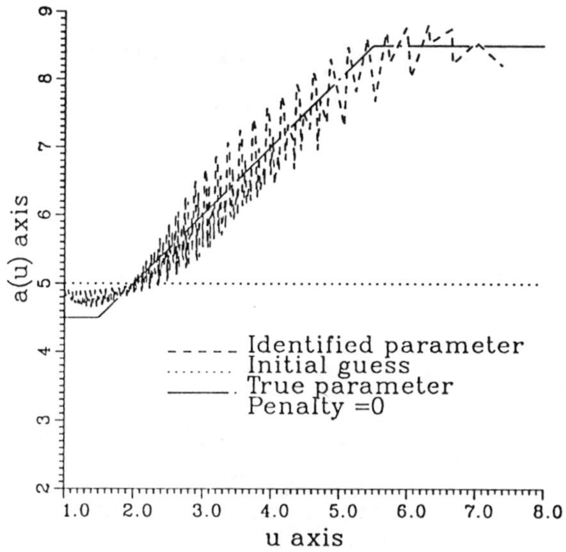

Figure 4.1.

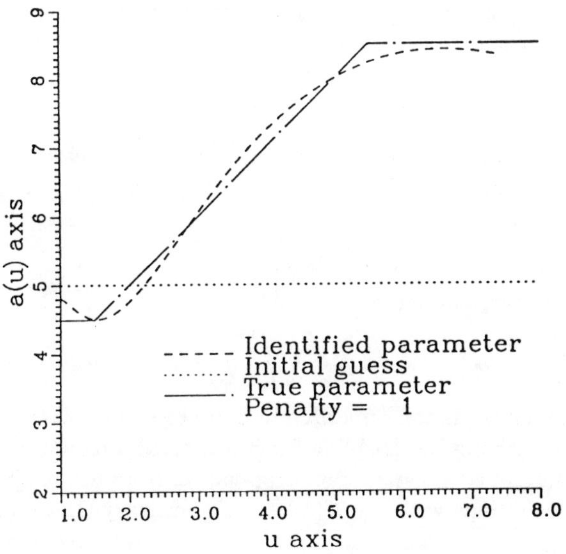

Figure 4.2.

$a(u)$ from the observed temperature. We first test with known functions $u = 6e^t x(1-x)$, $a(u) = e^{-u}$ and the corresponding f, u_0 are obtained from (4.3). We assume that we have

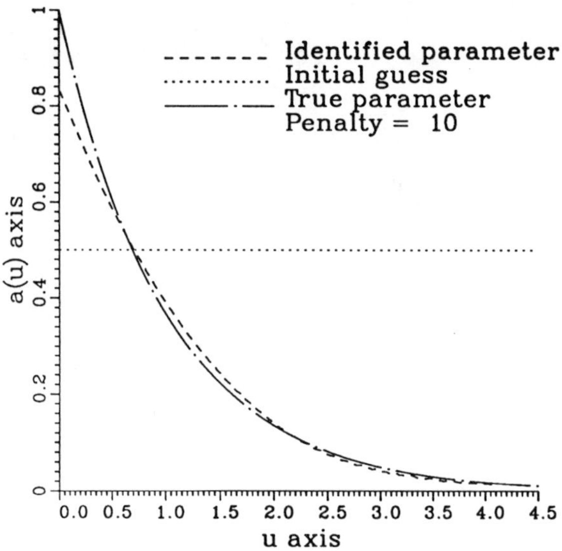

Figure 4.3.

a distributed observation for the u, i.e. $z = u$, and we try to recover the parameter $a(u)$.

When using the method proposed here, instead of identifying $a(u)$ from (4.3), we should identify $b(x,t) = a(u(x,t))$ from the following equation:

$$u_t = (b(x,t)u_t)_x + f(x,t) \tag{4.4}$$

with the corresponding initial and boundary conditions. This means we are going to identify a time dependent parameter. By Lemma 2.1 this parameter should also satisfy the relation:

$$b_t u_x = b_x u_t \ . \tag{4.5}$$

Therefore we compute the cost function as

$$J_{h,\mu}(\tilde{b}_h) = \int_0^1 \int_0^1 |u_h(\tilde{b}_h) - z|^2 \, dx \, dt + \mu \int_0^1 \int_0^1 |\tilde{b}_{h,x} u_t - \tilde{b}_{h,t} u_x|^2 \, dx \, dt \ .$$

Here μ is the penalty and $u_h(b_h)$ is the semidiscrete finite element solution of (4.4).

In the computing we use the cubic B-spline functions to approximate u in space and the Crank- Nicolson scheme plus one step of exptrapolation in time to solve the equation (4.4). So this solves the equations with the $\mathcal{O}(h^4 + \Delta t^4)$-accurary. Here h is the uniform mesh for the x-variable, Δt is step size.

In the computing of the cost function we take the penalty term $\mu = 1/10$. We use the Levenberg-Marquart method (subroutine DBCLSF of the IMSL subroutine library) to perform the minimization of the cost function. Figure 4.3 shows the computed parameter and the true parameter. The mesh size and step size used for u are $h = 1/10$ and $\Delta t = 1/10$. The mesh sizes used for the identified parameter for space and time variables are $h^* = 1/4$.

REFERENCES

[1] O.M. Alifanov and E.A. Artyukhin, *Identification of mathematical models of transient heat transfer processes*, R.W. Lewis and K. Morgan eds., Proceedings of the 4th international conference on "Numerical methods in thermal problems", Swansea U.K. on 15th–18th July, 1985, Part I, 771–779.

[2] H.T. Banks, P.M. Kareiva and K.A. Murphy, *Parameter estimation techniques for interaction and redistribution models: A predator–prey example*, Oecologia 74 (1987), 356–362.

[3] H.T. Banks and K. Kunisch, "Estimation techniques for distributed parameter system," Birkhäuser, Basel, 1989.

[4] H.T. Banks and K.A. Murphy, *Estimation of nonlinearity in parabolic models for growth, predation and dispersal of population*, J. Math. Anal. Appl. **141** (1989), 580–602.

[5] G. Chavent and G. Cohen, *Numerical approximation and identification in a 1–D parabolic degenerated nonlinear diffusion and transport equation*, In Proc. 8th IFIP Conf. on Optimization Techniques, Springer–Verlag, New York (1978), 282–293.

[6] R.S. Falk, *Error estimates for numerical identification of a variable coefficient*, Math. Comp. **40** (1983), 537–546.

[7] M. Křížek and P. Neittaanmäki, "Introduction to finite element method for variational problems," Pitman, Monographs and Surveys in Pure and Applied Mathematics 50, Longman Scientific & Technical, Harlow, 1990.

[8] K. Kunisch, *Rate of convergence for the estimation coefficient in a two point boundary value problem*, in "Proc. of Inverse and Illposed Problems", (H.W. Engl and C.M. Groesch, eds.) Academic Press, London (1988).

[9] A.E. Taylor, "Advanced calculus," Blaisdell publishing Company, 1965.

[10] P. Tervola, *A method to determine the thermal conductivity from mesured temperature profiles*, Int. J. Heat. Mass. Transfer **32** (1989), 1425–1430.

[11] V. Thomée, *Galerkin finite element methods for parabolic problems*, Springer–Verlag, Lecture Notes in Mathematics **1054** (1984).

[12] X.–C. Tai and P. Neittaanmäki, *Error estimates for numerical identification of distributed parameters*, J. Comput. Math., No.4, (1991) to appear.

[13] X.–C. Tai and P. Neittaanmäki, *Pointwise error estimate for distributed parameter identification*, Reports on Applied Mathematics and Computing, No. 3, Department of Math., University of Jyväskylä (1990).

International Series of Numerical Mathematics, Vol. 99, © 1991 Birkhäuser Verlag Basel

Long wave approximation for vortex free boundary flows

V. M. TESHUKOV

Lavrentyev Institute of Hydrodynamics
Siberian Division of the USSR Academy of Sciences
Novosibirsk 630090, USSR

Abstract. Long wave approximation [1] of free boundary problem, describing water waves is considered. In the case of vortical flow corresponding problem may be reduced to Cauchy problem to system of integrodifferential equations [2]. Notion of hyperbolicity is introduced and hyperbolicity conditions for system of long waves are found. Discretization of the problem, based on the characteristic properties of equations is proposed.

Keywords. Vortex flow, hyperbolicity, integrodifferential equations, discretization.

1980 Mathematics subject classifications: 76C05, 65M25, 35R35, 35L40

1. Hyperbolicity of a system of long wave equations

The problem of plane-parallel unsteady wave motion of ideal incompressible free boundary fluid

$$
\begin{aligned}
u_t + uu_x + vu_y + \rho^{-1}p_x &= 0, \\
v_t + uv_x + vv_y + \rho^{-1}p_y &= -g, \quad (0 \le y \le h(x,t)) \\
u_x + v_y &= 0, \\
h_t + u(x,h,t)h_x &= v(x,h,t), \quad p(x,h,t) = 0, \\
v(x,0,t) = 0, \quad u(x,y,0) &= u_0(x,y), \quad h(x,0) = h_0(x)
\end{aligned}
\tag{1}
$$

is considered. Here x, y are the Cartesian coodrinates on a plane; t is the time; u, v are the velocity vector components; p, ρ are the pressure and density (ρ =const), respectively; g is the gravitational acceleration; u_0, h_0 are the prescribed functions; the free surface equation has the form $y = h(x,t)$; $y = 0$ corresponds to an even bottom. For studying large-scale processes, the approximation of the long-wave theory is often used. This approximation is formally obtained by introduction of new variables

$$t' = \epsilon^{\frac{1}{2}}t, \quad x' = x, \quad y' = \epsilon^{-1}y, \quad u' = \epsilon^{-\frac{1}{2}}u, \quad v' = \epsilon^{-\frac{3}{2}}v, \quad p' = \epsilon^{-1}p$$

where ϵ is the small parameter, and by transition to the limit in transformed equations (1), when $\epsilon \to 0$. In this case all equations, except the second one, are unchanged. In the limit the second equation gives the hydrostatic pressure distribution law

$$p'_{y'} = -\rho g \tag{2}$$

Thus, the problem of long-wave approximation is formulated analogously to (1), differing in that the second equation in (1) is replaced by (2).

A second replacement of the independent variables

$$x' = X, \quad t' = T, \quad y' = \Phi(X,T,\lambda)$$

where $\Phi(X,T,\lambda)$ is the solution of the problem

$$\Phi_T + \left(\int_0^{\Phi} u(X,y,T)\,dy\right)_X = 0, \quad \Phi(X,0,\lambda) = \lambda h_0(X)$$

reduces the problem (1)–(2) in the region with unknown boundary to the Cauchy problem in the strip $0 \le \lambda \le 1$ for a system of integro–differential equations

$$u_t + uu_x + g\int_0^1 H_x\,d\lambda' = 0, \quad u(x,0,\lambda) = u_0(x,\lambda h_0(x)), \tag{3}$$
$$H_t + (uH)_x = 0, \quad H(x,0,\lambda) = h_0(x)$$

Here $H = \Phi_\lambda(x,t,\lambda)$ is the derivative of Φ with respect to λ, and $u = u(x,t,\lambda)$, $(x = X, t = T)$. If the flow is vortex-free, then $u_y \equiv 0$ $(u_\lambda = 0,\ H_\lambda = 0)$ and equations (3) are reduced to the classical shallow water theory equations of hyperbolic type. The vortex flows $(u_\lambda \not\equiv 0,\quad H_\lambda \not\equiv 0)$ are described by integro-differential equations (3). For numerical analysis of equations (3), it is important to know their type.

In this study it is shown that under certain conditions for the velocity profile equations (3) represent the ∞-dimensional hyberbolic system. Let us consider systems of the form

$$\vec{U}_t + A\vec{U}_x = 0, \quad \vec{U} = \begin{pmatrix} U_1(x,t,\lambda) \\ \vdots \\ U_m(x,t,\lambda) \end{pmatrix}, \quad (\lambda \in [0,1]) \tag{4}$$

where A is the linear bounded operator in $L_2^m[0,1]$ with any fixed values of x, t (A operates in the variable λ). The functional $\vec{F}$ is called eigenfunctional for A^* if for any smooth function $\vec{f}$

$$(\vec{F},\, A\vec{f}) = k\,(\vec{F},\vec{f}). \tag{5}$$

We consider not only functionals, which are represented with the help of elements of $L_2^m[0,1]$, but also generalized eigenfunctions. Generalized eigenfunctions arise by restricting A to a Banach space $B \subset L_2^m[0,1]$, $(A(B) \subseteq B)$ and are the elements of B^* $(B \subset L_2^m[0,1] \subset B^*)$. Applying the functional $\vec{F}$ to (4) gives the equality

$$(\vec{F},\vec{U}_t + k\vec{U}_x) = 0, \tag{6}$$

called the relation on characteristics $dx/dt = k$. The system of equations (4) is called hyperbolic if the numbers k defined by equation (5) are real and if the system of relations (6) on the characteristics is equivalent to equations (4). The system of equations (3) has the form (4) with

$$A = \begin{pmatrix} u, & g\int_0^1 \ldots d\lambda' \\ H, & u \end{pmatrix}$$

Let the velocity profile be monotone: $u_\lambda \ne 0$, $u \in C^{2+\alpha}[0,1]$, $H \in C^{1+\alpha}[0,1]$, $0 < \alpha < 1$, (x, t are fixed, dependence on λ is considered).

LEMMA 1. *The eigenvalues k_i of a discrete spectrum of the operator A^* are determined by the characteristic equation*

$$g\int_0^1 \frac{H\,d\nu}{(u-k_i)^2} = 1 \tag{7}$$

The values of $k^\lambda = u(x,t,\lambda)$ belong to the continuous spectrum of the operator A^*.

To prove the lemma, it is sufficient to know that the functionals $\vec{F}_i$, operating by the rule

$$(\vec{F}_i,\vec{f}) = \int_0^1 \frac{Hf_1\,d\nu}{(u-k_i)^2} - \int_0^1 \frac{f_2\,d\nu}{u-k_i} \tag{8}$$

satisfy (5) when $k = k_i$ if equation (7) is fulfilled.

It is easily shown that equation (7) always has two real roots:

$$k_1 < \min_\lambda u(x,t,\lambda), \quad k_2 > \max_\lambda u(x,t,\lambda)$$

Generally speaking, equations (7) can also have complex roots.

The generalized eigenfunctions $\vec{F}_1^\lambda$, $\vec{F}_2^\lambda$, operating on $\vec{f}$ by the rule ($f_1 \in C^{1+\alpha}[0,1]$, $f_2 \in C^\alpha[0,1]$, $0<\alpha<1$)

$$\begin{gathered}(\vec{F}_1^\lambda,\vec{f}) = (H(\lambda))^{-1}(\partial f_1/\partial\lambda) - (H(\lambda))^{-2} f_2(\lambda),\\ (\vec{F}_2^\lambda,\vec{f}) = f_1(\lambda) + \int_0^1 \frac{H(\nu)(f_1(\nu)-f_1(\lambda))}{(u(\nu)-u(\lambda))^2}\,d\nu - \int_0^1 \frac{f_2(\nu)\,d\nu}{u(\nu)-u(\lambda)}\end{gathered} \tag{9}$$

correspond to the eigenvalues of the continuous spectrum (the arguments x, t in notations are omitted). Let us define the hyperbolicity conditions of the systems of equations (3), i.e. conditions under which the equality $\vec{f} = 0$ follows from

$$(\vec{F}_1,\vec{f}) = 0, \quad (\vec{F}_2,\vec{f}) = 0, \quad (\vec{F}_1^\lambda,\vec{f}) = 0, \quad (\vec{F}_2^\lambda,\vec{f}) = 0 \tag{10}$$

Introduce now the function of complex variable z

$$\chi(z) = 1 - g\int_0^1 \frac{H\,d\nu}{(u-z)^2}.$$

Let $\overset{+}{\underset{-}{\chi}}(u(\lambda))$ be the limiting values of $\chi(z)$ when $z \to u(\lambda)$ from the upper of lower half-plane

$$\begin{gathered}\overset{+}{\underset{-}{\chi}}(u) = 1 + g(\omega(1)(u(1)-u))^{-1} - g(\omega(0)(u(0)-u))^{-1} - \\ -g\int_0^1 \left(\frac{1}{\omega(\nu)}\right)_\nu \frac{d\nu}{(u(\nu)-u)} \overset{-}{+} g\pi i \left(\frac{1}{\omega}\right)_\lambda \cdot \frac{1}{u_\lambda}\end{gathered}$$

(the notation $\omega = u_\lambda H^{-1}$ is introduced).

LEMMA 2. *Conditions* $u_\lambda \neq 0$, $\overset{+}{\chi}^{-}(u(\lambda)) \neq 0$ *and*

$$\Delta \arg(\chi^{+}(u(\lambda))/\chi^{-}(u(\lambda))) = 0 \tag{11}$$

provide the hyperbolicity of equations (3) (Δ *denotes the function increase on* $\lambda \in [0,1]$*).*

To prove the lemma, it is sufficient to note that equalities (10) with the allowance for (9) result in a singular integral equation for determinig the function $f_1(\lambda)$. Conditions of the lemma provide univalent solvability of the mentioned singular intergral equation.

In Lemma 2, in particular, conditions, providing the absence of the complex roots of equations (7) have been formulated. Note that the presence of the complex roots, as is easily shown, corresponds to flow instability in accordance with the linear approximation.

If conditions of Lemma 2 are fulfilled, relations (6) (and equations (3), respectively) are reduced to the Riemann invariants' conservation equations

$$\begin{aligned} R_t + uR_x = 0, &\quad \omega_t + u\omega_x = 0 \\ r_{it} + k_i r_{ix} = 0, &\quad (i = 1, 2) \end{aligned} \tag{12}$$

where

$$R = u(\lambda) - g\int_0^1 \frac{H(\nu)\,d\nu}{u(\nu) - u(\lambda)}, \quad r_i = k_i - g\int_0^1 \frac{H(\nu)\,d\nu}{u(\nu) - k_i}.$$

Hyperbolicity of equations (3) allows a series of important qualitative properties of solution of the Cauchy problem and mixed ones to be established. These properties are the finiteness of disturbance propagation velocity, the presence of domains of dependence and domains of influence of initial and boundary data. The domains of determinacy of the Cauchy problem solution can also be described. The existence of solution to the Cauchy problem for small time has been proved if the functions $u(x,0,\lambda)$, $u_\lambda(x,0,\lambda)$, $H(x,0,\lambda)$ are continuously differentiable and their first derivatives satisfy the Hölder condition.

Knowledge of characteristic properties is also important when we study the stability of numerical algorithms. The characteristic form of equations (6) (or (12)) is fundamental for the application of the numerical method of characteristics. This analysis posses natural generalization to multidimensional case.

2. SIMPLE WAVES

Let us consider the analogies of the classical simple waves, i.e. solutions of equations (3) of the form $u = u(\alpha(x,t),\lambda)$, $H = H(\alpha(x,t),\lambda)$. Solutions of this form exist if

$$\alpha_t + k\alpha_x = 0$$

where k is the eigenvalue of the operator A^*. Let us consider

$$\alpha = \int_0^1 H\,d\nu = h, \quad k = k_2.$$

The functions $u(h,\lambda)$, $H(h,\lambda)$, $k(h)$ are found as the solution of a system of equations, for $h \le h_m$

$$\frac{\partial u}{\partial h} = -\frac{g}{u-k}, \quad \frac{\partial H}{\partial h} = \frac{gH}{(u-k)^2}, \tag{13}$$
$$\frac{\partial k}{\partial h} = \frac{3}{2} g \left(\int_0^1 \frac{H\, d\nu}{(u-k)^4} \right) \Big/ \left(\int_0^1 \frac{H\, d\nu}{(u-k)^3} \right)$$

with the prescribed values $u(h_m,\lambda)$, $H(h_m,\lambda)$ and $k(h_m)$, when $h = h_m$. From (12) it follows that system (13) has the integrals $R = R(h_m,\lambda)$, $\omega = \omega(h_m,\lambda)$, $r_1 = r_1(h_m)$. The presence of these integrals allows the existence of the smooth solution of equations (13) on the interval $h \in (0, h_m]$. The solutions of equations (13) and equation

$$h_t + k(h)h_x = 0$$

determine completely the simple wave. The self-similar simple wave ($k = x/t$) describes the spreading of the shear flow over a dry channel.

3. Discretization of equations in the variable λ

For numerical calculations, discretization of equations in the variable λ was performed, i.e. the layer occupied with fluid was divided into the sublayers $\lambda_j \le \lambda \le \lambda_{j+1}$. In each layer the dependence of the horizontal velocity vector component u on y was considered to be linear. Let us denote $u_j = u(\lambda_j)$, $(0 \le j \le N,\ \lambda_{j+1} - \lambda_j = N^{-1})$,

$$\eta_j = \int_{\lambda_{j-1}}^{\lambda_j} H\, d\lambda,$$
$$r_j = k_j - g \sum_{i=1}^{N} \frac{\eta_i}{u_i - u_{i-1}} \ln \left| \frac{u_i - k_j}{u_{i-1} - k_j} \right| \tag{14}$$
$$\omega_l = (u_l - u_{l-1})\eta_l^{-1}$$

where k_j $(j = 0, \dots, N)$ are the roots of the characteristic equation

$$1 + g \sum_{i=1}^{N} \omega_i^{-1}((u_i - k_j)^{-1} - (u_{i-1} - k_j)^{-1}) = 0 \tag{15}$$

Quantities r_j, ω_l satisfy the equations

$$r_{jt} + k_j r_{jx} = 0, \tag{16}$$
$$\omega_{lt} + 2^{-1}(u_l + u_{l-1})\omega_{lx} = 0.$$

approximating equation (12). The functions u_j, η_j are found with help of formulas (14), (15) if r, ω_l are known. The approximating system (16) is the hyperbolic one if equation (15) has $N+1$ real roots. The sufficient conditions for hyperbolicity of this system are the monotonicity and convexity of the velocity profile ($\omega_1 \cdot \omega_N > 0$; $\omega_j^{-1} - \omega_{j+1}^{-1} < 0$ or $\omega_j^{-1} - \omega_{j+1}^{-1} > 0$). The initial data $r_j(x,0)$, $\omega_l(x,0)$ are obtained by above-described method of discretization of the initial data for system (3). In the case when the initial data satisfies the hyperbolicity conditions and $N \to \infty$, the convergence of approximate solutions to the exact ones can be established.

The results of numerical calculations of simple waves on the basis of discretization proposed are presented below. In the figures the dependence of u_j, η_j on the characteristic number k is presented. The simple wave adjoints to shear flow with parabolic velocity profile (it is shown by arrows). The fluid layer has been divided into 10 sublayers, different types of simple waves, corresponding to different characteristic numbers defined by equation (15) ($k = k_j$) were considered.

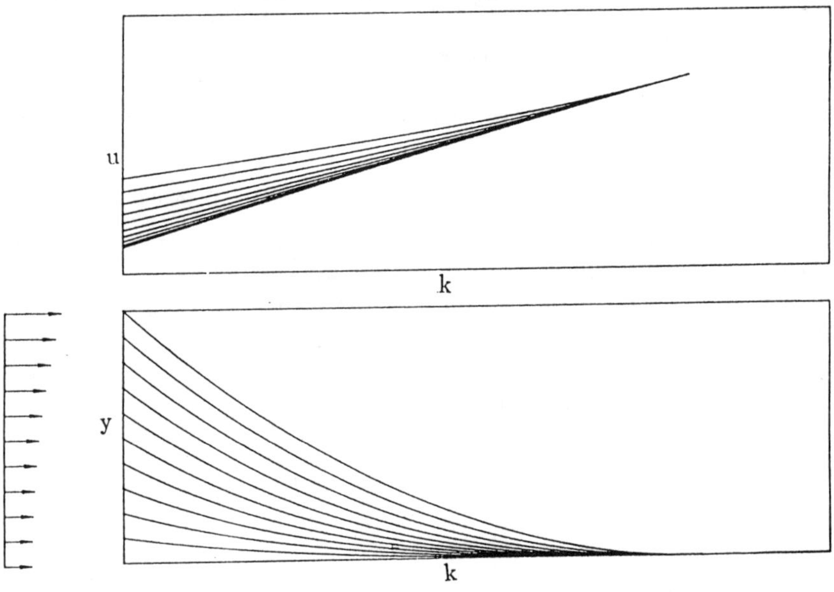

Figure 1

Figure 1 shows the dependence of u_j, η_j on k, in the case, when the characteristic number k satisfies inequality $k < u_j$, ($j = 0, ..., N$). The thickness of every layer tends to zero, and the velocity in every layer tends to a constant.

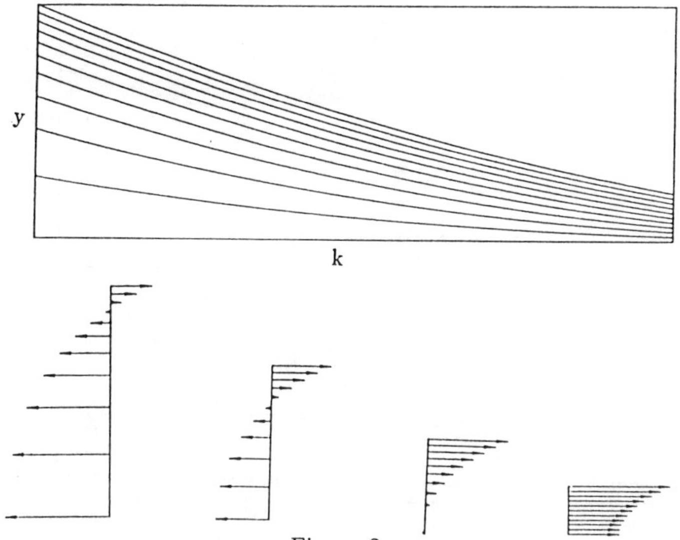

Figure 2

Figure 2 with the same data as in Figure 1 the change of the velocity profile across the a simple wave is presented.

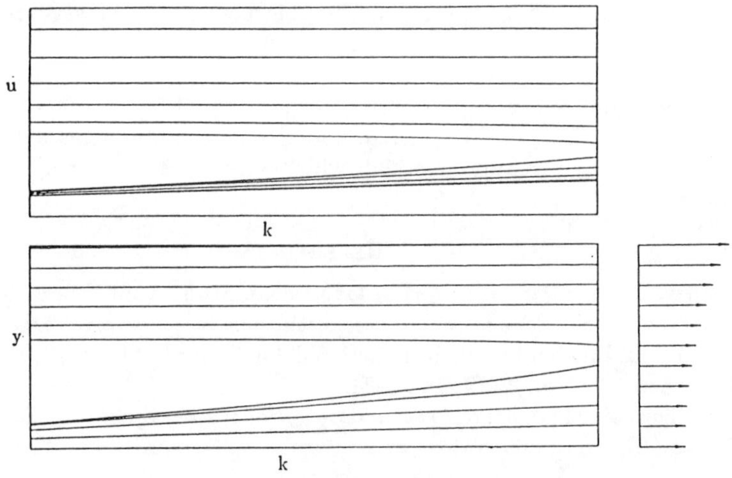

Figure 3

In Figure 3 we consider the case that the characteristic number k satisfies the inequality $u_4 < k < u_5$. The whole depth of the fluid almost does not change, but the thickness of the layer $\lambda_4 < \lambda < \lambda_5$ changes rapidly across the wave. The thicknesses of some lower layers tend to zero.

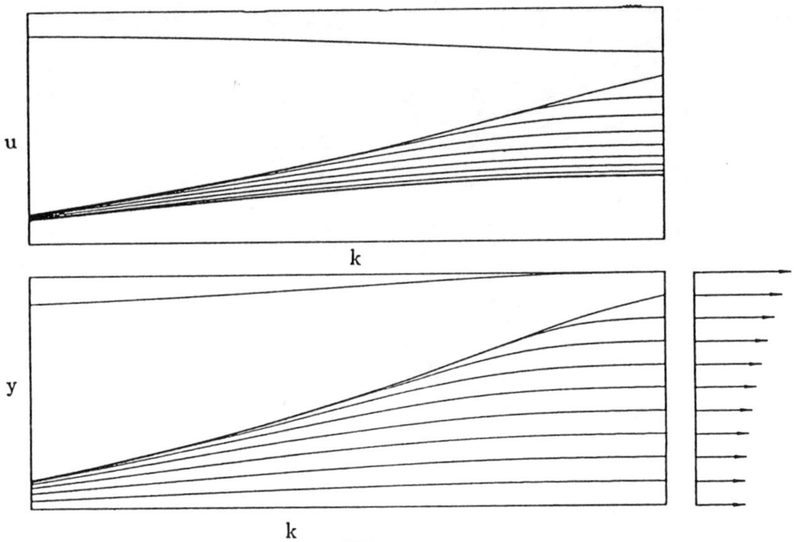

Figure 4

Figure 4 corresponds to the case when k satisfies inequality $u_9 < k < u_{10}$. The most rapid growth of the layer $\lambda_9 < \lambda < \lambda_{10}$. The thickness of lower layers tends to zero.

Conlusions

Integrodifferential equations, appearing in the study of free boundary problems in long wave approximation may be considered, under some conditions, as hyberbolic system of equations. This allows to apply methods which were developed for hyperbolic systems to these equations.

References

[1] Benney, D. J., *Some properties of long waves*, Stud. Appl. Math. **52** (1973), 45–69.

[2] Zakharov, V. E., *Benney equations and quasiclassical approximation in inverse problem method*, English transl. in Functional Anal. Appl. 14 (1980), Funktsional. Anal. i Prilozhen **14, No. 2** (1980), 15–24.

[3] Teshukov, V. M., *On the hyberbolicity of long wave equations*, Soviet Math. Dokl. **32, No. 2** (1985), 469–673.

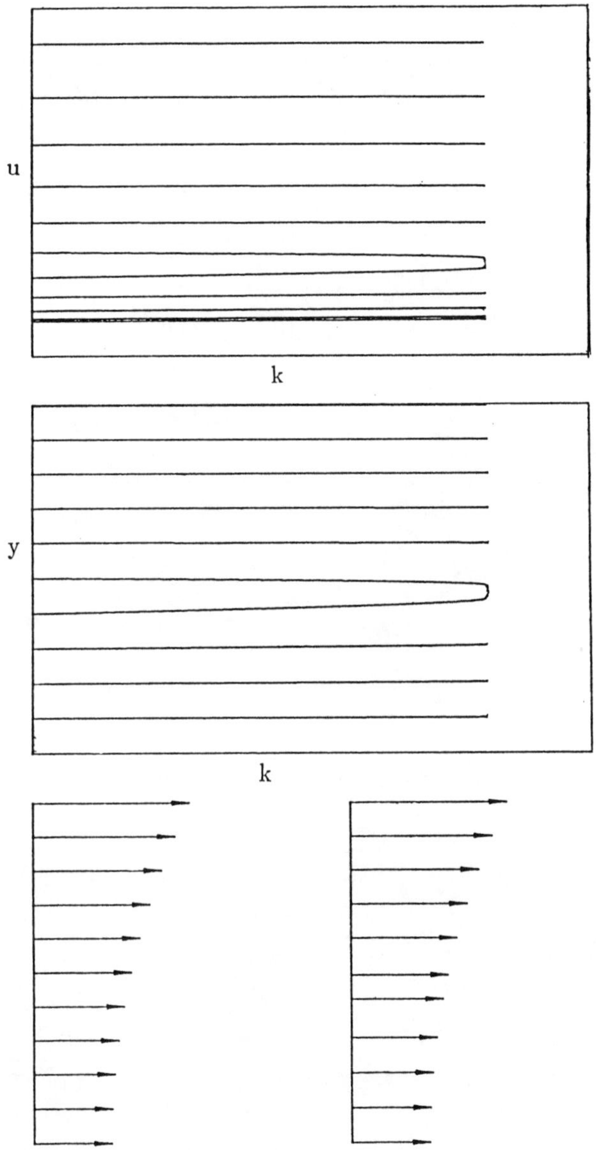

Figure 5

Figure 5 corresponds to the case when k satisfies inequality $u_5 < k < u_6$. The solution cannot be prolonged throw the point $k = k_1$, where the solution has an infinite derivative. At this point system (14) degenerates.

Numerical solution of free boundary problem in optimal control of nonlinear systems

M.V.Trigub

Kharkov Engineering Pedagogics Institute
Electromechanical Department, USSR

Abstract. The problem of design of an approximately optimal action which satisfies a specified criterion in a nonlinear control system with a minimal integral performance estimate is investigated. The problem under study is to approximate the solution of Bellman's equation. The proposed approach combines analytical expansions of nonlinear functions with error evaluation by Krotov's formula.

Keywords. Optimal control problem, Bellman's equation.

1. Formulation of the suboptimal control problem

The dynamics of systems under study is described by ordinary differential equations with a control u

$$\dot{x}_i = \varphi_i(t,x) + \sum_{s=1}^{m} \psi_{is}(t,x)u_s. \tag{1.1}$$

The state vector of the systems $x = (x_1, ..., x_n)$ and the control vector $u = (u_1, ..., u_m)$ are elements of real vector spaces R^n and R^m respectively. The components of the vector-function $x(t)$ are absolutely continuous for $t \in [t_0, \infty[$ and the components of the vector-function $u(t)$ are measurable for $t \in [t_0, \infty[$ and satisfy restrictions of the form

$$|u_s| \leq u_s^*. \tag{1.2}$$

A closed domain of initial conditions $G_0 \subset R^{n+1}$ and cost functional

$$I(x,u) = \int_{t_0}^{\infty} \left[\omega(t,x) + \sum_{s=1}^{m} P_s(u_s) \right] dt \tag{1.3}$$

are given where the pair (x,u) (the trajectory $x(t) \in R^n$ together with the control $u(t) \in R^m$) is the solution of the equations (1.1) for $t \in [t_0, \infty[$ and for the initial condition $(t_0, x_0) \in G_0$. Functions $\varphi_i(t,x), \psi_{is}(t,x), \omega(t,x)$ are analytic in a domain $G_1(t) \subset R^n$

containing coordinate origin $x = 0$, and they are expanded in a power series by degrees of x_i with coefficients continuously dependent on time in the interval $[t_0, \infty[$

$$\varphi_i(t,x) = \sum_{r=1}^{\infty} \varphi_i^{(r)}(t,x),$$

$$\psi_{is}(t,x) = \sum_{r=0}^{\infty} \psi_{is}^{(r)}(t,x), \tag{1.4}$$

$$\omega(t,x) = \sum_{r=2}^{\infty} \omega^{(r)}(t,x), \tag{1.5}$$

where symbol (r) designates the order of form. Functions $P_s(u_s)$ can have one of the following forms: a) $P_s(u_s) = 0$; b) $P_s(u_s) = \delta_s(u_s)^2$; c) $P_s(u_s) = \delta_s|u_s|$. The integrand is a definitely positive function.

The problem is to find a pair $(\overline{x}, \overline{u})$ satisfying the condition

$$|I(t_0, x_0, \overline{u}(t, \overline{x})) - \inf_{\{u\}} I(t_0, x_0, u)| \leq \epsilon \tag{1.6}$$

along each trajectory $\overline{x}(t)$ springing from the domain G_0 of initial conditions for any positive number $\epsilon > 0$ which can be chosen arbitrarily small [**1**].

2. Method of solving the problem under study

In effect, our problem is to approximate the solution of the nonlinear partial differential equation [**1**]

$$B(t,x,V(t,x)) = \omega(t,x) + \frac{\partial V(t,x)}{\partial t} + \sum_{i=1}^{n} \frac{\partial V(t,x)}{\partial x_i} \varphi_i(t,x) + \sum_{s=1}^{m} F_s^*(\xi_s) = 0, \tag{2.1}$$

where

$$F_s^*(\xi_s) = \inf_{|u_s| \leq u_s^*} F_s(\xi_s, u_s), \tag{2.2}$$

$$F_s(\xi_s, u_s) = P_s(u_s) + \xi_s u_s \ , \xi_s = \sum_{i=1}^{n} \frac{\partial V(t,x)}{\partial x_i} \psi_{is}(t,x). \tag{2.3}$$

The idea of the approximate method is the following.

The polynomial approximation of the functions $F_s^*(\xi_s)$ (2.2) on the intervals $[-\beta_s, \beta_s]$, corresponding to any domain $G_2(t) \subseteq G_1(t)$, is proposed:

$$F_s^*(\xi_s) = \lambda_{s2}(\xi_s)^2 + ... + \lambda_{sr}(\xi_s)^r + R_s^r(\xi_s), \tag{2.4}$$

where $R_s^r(\xi_s)$ are errors of approximation.

The Bellman-Krotov's function $V(t, x)$ is defined as a series

$$V(t,x) = V^{(2)}(t,x) + ... + V^{(r)}(t,x) + ... \tag{2.5}$$

Let us substitute the series (1.4),(1.5), (2.5) and the polynomials (2.4) for functions $\varphi_i(t,x)$, $\psi_{is}(t,x)$, $\omega(t,x)$, $V(t,x)$, $F_s^*(\xi_s)$ respectively in the equation (2.1), and set equal to zero the terms having equal degrees of x.

As a result, we obtain an infinite set of equations, the first of them,

$$\begin{gathered} \frac{\partial V^{(2)}(t,x)}{\partial t} + \omega^{(2)}(t,x) + \\ \sum_{i=1}^{n} \frac{\partial V^{(2)}(t,x)}{\partial x_i} \varphi_i^{(1)}(t,x) + \sum_{s=1}^{n} \lambda_{s2}(\xi_s)^2 = 0, \end{gathered} \tag{2.6}$$

where

$$\xi_s = \sum_{i=1}^{n} \frac{\partial V^{(2)}(t,x)}{\partial x_i} \psi_{is}^{(0)}(t,x), \tag{2.7}$$

being Bellman's equation for the linear problem

$$\begin{gathered} \dot{x}_i = \varphi_i^{(1)}(t,x) + \sum_{s=1}^{m} \psi_{is}^{(0)}(t,x) u_s \\ (\dot{x}_i = A(t)x + \Psi(t)u), \end{gathered} \tag{2.8}$$

$$\int_{t_0}^{\infty} \left[\omega^{(2)}(t,x) + \sum_{s=1}^{m} (-4\lambda_{s2})^{-1} (u_s)^2 \right] dt \to \min. \tag{2.9}$$

Here $\varphi^{(1)}(t,x) = A(t)x$ ($A(t)$ is a matrix); $\psi_{is}^{(0)}(t,x) = \psi_{is}^{(0)}(t)$ are elements of a matrix $\Psi(t)$.

The problem (2.8), (2.9) has a unique solution if rank of a matrix

$$Q(t) = \{L_1(t), ..., L_n(t)\},$$

where

$$L_1(t) = \Psi(t), ..., L_{k+1}(t) = \frac{dL_k(t)}{dt} - A(t)L_k(t)$$
$$(k = 1, ..., n-1),$$

equals n.

Let us substitute the solution of the linear problem (2.8), (2.9) for the control in the system (2.8) which takes the form

$$\dot{x}_i = \varphi_i^{(1)}(t,x) + \sum_{s=1}^{m} 2\lambda_{s2}\psi_{is}^{(0)}(t,x)\xi_s, \tag{2.10}$$

where ξ_s is the expression (2.7) .

The equation

$$-\left[\frac{dV^{(r)}(t,x)}{dt}\right]_{(2.10)} = \sum_{i=1}^{n}\left[\varphi_i^{(2)}(t,x)\frac{\partial V^{(r-1)}(t,x)}{\partial x_i} + ... + \varphi_i^{(r-1)}(t,x)\frac{\partial V^{(2)}(t,x)}{\partial x_i}\right] + \omega^{(r)}(t,x)$$
$$+\sum_{s=1}^{m}\sum_{l=2}^{r}\lambda_{sl}\sum_{\substack{k_1+...+k_r=l\\ k_1+...+rk_r=r}} C_l(k_1,...,k_r)\times$$
$$\left[\sum_{i=1}^{n}\frac{\partial V^{(2)}(t,x)}{\partial x_i}\psi_{is}^{(0)}(t,x)\right]^{k_1} \times ... \times$$
$$\left[\sum_{i=1}^{n}\frac{\partial V^{(2)}(t,x)}{\partial x_i}\psi_{is}^{(r-1)}(t,x) + ... + \sum_{i=1}^{n}\frac{\partial V^{(r-1)}(t,x)}{\partial x_i}\psi_{is}^{(2)}(t,x)\right]^{k_r} \tag{2.11}$$

is satisfied by each form $V^{(r)}(t,x)$ of any order $r \geq 3$.

The symbol $\left[\frac{dV^{(r)}(t,x)}{dt}\right]_{(2.10)}$ designates the time derivative of the form $V^{(r)}(t,x)$ in virtue of the equations (2.10) .

Each of the equations (2.11) is reduced to a set of linear ordinary differential equations which is governed by the cofficients of each of the forms $V^{(r)}(t,x)$ correspondingly.

Having solved the equations (2.2) we obtain the vector elements $\overline{u}_s(t,x(t))$ of the sub-optimal control $\overline{u}(t,x(t))$ and the vector elements $F_s^*(\xi_s)$ of the function $F^*(\xi_s)$, which are shown in Fig. 1 for all cases, a), b) and c) respectively.

3. Estimation of Accuracy of the Proposed Method

Using the non-equalities [2, 3]

$$\left|\varphi_i^{(r)}(t,x)\right| \leq \overline{\varphi}_r^i z^r, \quad \left|\psi_{is}^{(r)}(t,x)\right| \leq \overline{\psi}_r^{is} z^r, \quad \left|V^{(r)}(t,x)\right| \leq \overline{V}_r z^r,$$

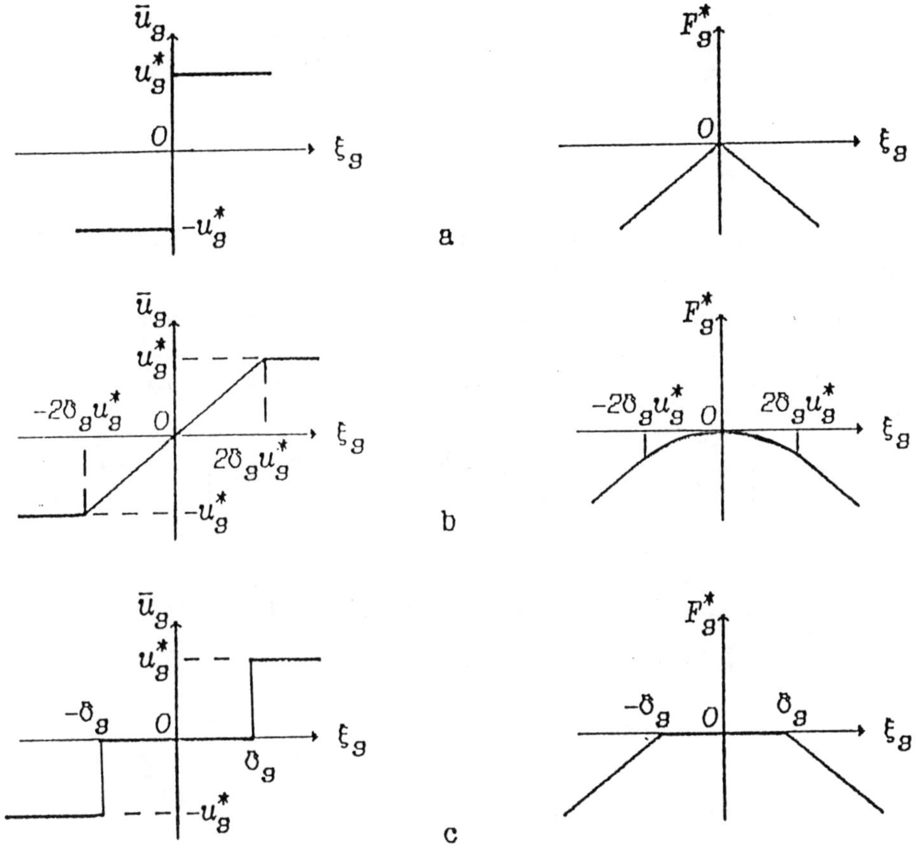

Fig. 1

$$\left|\omega^{(r)}(t,x)+\frac{\partial V^{(r)}(t,x)}{\partial t}\right|\le\overline{\omega}_r z^r,\ \left|\frac{\partial V^{(r)}(t,x)}{\partial x_i}\right|\le rC_r^i\overline{V}_r z^{r-1},\ \frac{dz^2}{dt}\le-\alpha z^2,$$

where $z=\sum_{i=1}^{n}x_i^2$; $\overline{\varphi}_r^i$, $\overline{\psi}_r^{is}$, $\overline{V}_r$, $\overline{\omega}_r$, C_r^i, α are positive constants, we can construct the convergent series [3]

$$V(z)=\sum_{r=2}^{\infty}\overline{V}_r z^r$$

with coefficients

$$\overline{V}_r=\frac{1}{r\alpha}\left\{\sum_{i=1}^{n}\left[(r-1)\,C_{r-1}^i\overline{V}_{r-1}\overline{\varphi}_2^i+\cdots+2C_2^i\overline{V}_2\overline{\varphi}_{r-1}^i\right]+\overline{\omega}_r+\right.$$

$$+\sum_{s=1}^{m}\sum_{l=2}^{r}|\lambda_{sl}| \sum_{\substack{k_1+\dots+k_r=l\\ k_1+2k_2+\dots+rk_r=r}} C_l(k_1,\dots,k_r)\times\left(\sum_{i=1}^{n}2C_2^i\overline{V}_2\overline{\psi}_0^{is}\right)^{k_1}\times\dots\times$$

$$\times\left[\sum_{i=1}^{n}\left(2C_2^i\overline{V}_2\overline{\psi}_{r-1}^{is}+\dots+(r-1)\,C_{r-1}^i\overline{V}_{r-1}\overline{\psi}_2^{is}\right)\right]^{k_r}\Bigg\}.$$

THEOREM 1. *The series of functions $V(t,x)$, $\frac{\partial V(t,x)}{\partial x_t}$, $\frac{\partial V(t,x)}{\partial t}$ converge uniformly in x in any closed domain $G\subset G_2$ for a chosen finite number $r\geq 2$.*

The proof of the Theorem 1 is somewhat lengthy and will not be presented here.

Following Krotov's idea of the global estimations [1] we propose an analytic formula for estimation of proximity of the obtained suboptimal control to the optimal one:

$$\Delta(t_0,V)\leq\Delta_r=\int_{t_0}^{\infty}\left\{2\left[\overline{\omega}_{r+1}+\sum_{i=1}^{n}\sum_{k=2}^{r+1}kC_k^i\overline{V}_k\overline{\varphi}_{r-k+2}^i\right]z^{r+1}(t)+\right.$$

$$\left.+\sum_{s=1}^{m}N_s^r\sum_{i=1}^{n}\sum_{p=2}^{r}pC_p^i\overline{V}_pz^{p-1}\sum_{q=0}^{r}\overline{\psi}_q^{is}z^q\right\}dt,$$

where coefficients N_s^r satisfy the conditions [3]

$$2|R_s^r(\max_{|\xi_s|\leq\beta_s}\xi_s)-R_s^r(\min_{|\xi_s|\leq\beta_s}\xi_s)|=N_s^r\beta_s.$$

Using Weierstrass Theorem about approximation we have

$$\lim_{r\to\infty}N_s^r=0.$$

COROLLARY 1. *The inequality $\Delta_r\leq\epsilon$ for the domain $G\subset G_2$, containing all the suboptimal trajectories which spring from the domain G_0, is true.*

The algorithm of the solution of the problem under study is shown in Fig. 2.

4. SUBOPTIMAL CONTROL OF QUASI-LINEAR SYSTEMS

In case of the problem with a small parameter μ

$$\dot{x}_i=\varphi_i^{(1)}(t,x)+\sum_{s=1}^{m}\psi_{is}(t,x)\,u_s+\mu\sum_{k=2}^{\infty}\varphi_i^{(k)}(t,x),$$

$$\int_{t_0}^{\infty}\left[\omega^{(2)}(t,x)+\sum_{s=1}^{m}P_s(u_s)\right]dt\longrightarrow\min$$

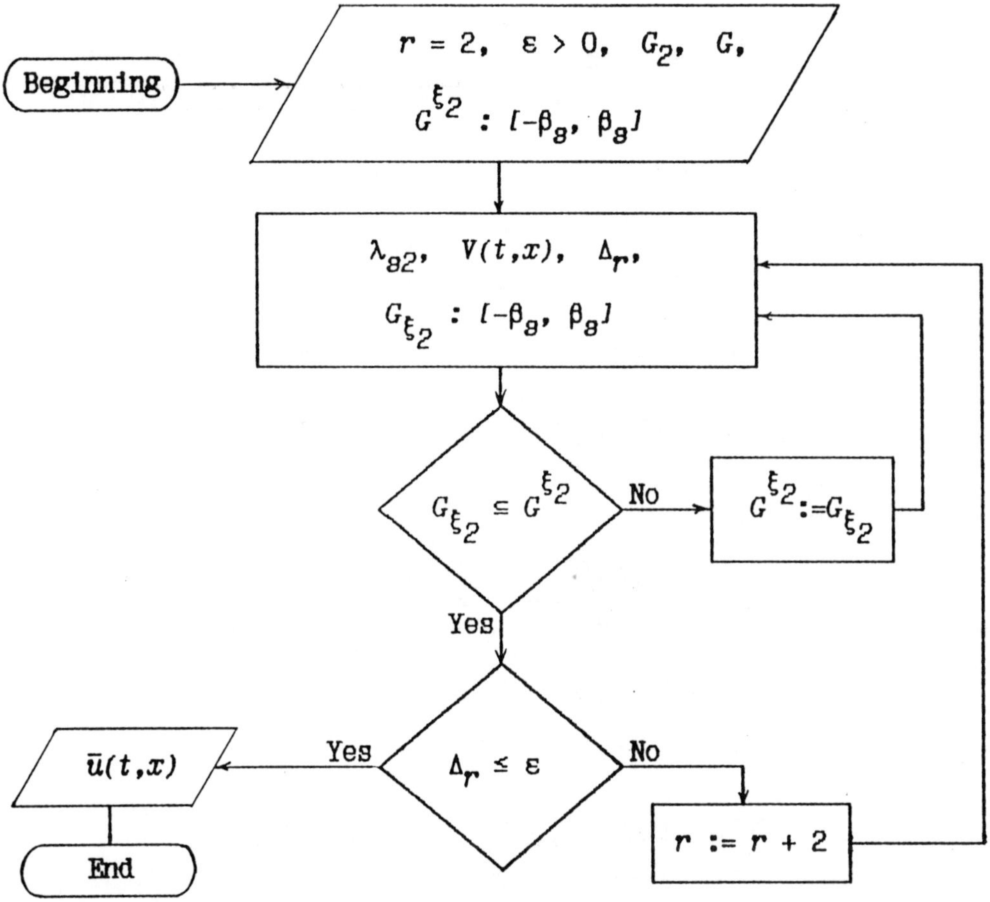

Fig. 2

the Bellman-Krotov's function is defined as a series

$$V(t,x,\mu)=\sum_{r=0}^{\infty}\mu^r W_r(t,x),$$

where

$$W_r(t,x)=\sum_{k=r+2}^{\infty}V_r^{(k)}(t,x).$$

The equations

$$-\left(\frac{dW_0\,(t,x)}{dt}\right)_{(2.10)}=\omega^{(2)}\,(t,x)+\sum_{s=1}^{m}\sum_{lqc=2}^{r+2}\lambda_{sl}\left[\sum_{i=1}^{n}\frac{\partial W_0\,(t,x)}{\partial x_i}\psi_{is}\,(t,x)\right]^l,$$

$$-\left(\frac{dW_r(t,x)}{dt}\right)_{(2.10)} = \sum_{i=1}^{n} \varphi_i(t,x)\frac{\partial W_{r-1}(t,x)}{\partial x_i} +$$

$$+\sum_{s=1}^{m}\sum_{l=2}^{r}\lambda_{sl} \sum_{\substack{k_2+\cdots+k_r=l \\ k_2+\cdots+(r-1)k_r=r \\ 2k_2+\cdots+rk_r\geq r+2}} C_l(k_2,\dots,k_r)\times\left[\sum_{i=1}^{n}\frac{\partial W_1(t,x)}{\partial x_i}\psi_{is}(t,x)\right]^{k_2}\times$$

$$\times\cdots\times\left[\sum_{i=1}^{n}\frac{\partial W_{r-1}(t,x)}{\partial x_i}\psi_{is}(t,x)\right]^{k_r}, \quad r=1,2,\dots$$

are governed by the functions $W_r(t,x)$ for any $r \geq 0$. Coefficients of the convergent series

$$V(x,\mu) = \sum_{r=0}^{\infty}\mu^r\overline{W}_r(z) \qquad \left(\overline{W}_r(z) = \sum_{k=r+2}^{\infty}\overline{V}_k^r z^k\right)$$

are defined in the forms

$$\overline{V}_{r+2}^0 = \frac{1}{(r+2)\alpha}\left\{\sum_{s=1}^{m}\sum_{l=2}^{r+2}|\lambda_{sl}| \sum_{\substack{k_1+\cdots+k_{r+2}=l \\ k_1+2k_2+\cdots+(r+2)k_{r+2}=r+2}} C_l(k_1,\dots,k_{r+2})\times\right.$$

$$\times\left(\sum_{i=1}^{n}2C_2^{0i}\overline{V}_2^0\overline{\psi}_0^{is}\right)^{k_1}\times\cdots\times\left[\sum_{i=1}^{n}2C_2^{0i}\overline{V}_2^0\overline{\psi}_{r+1}^{is}+\cdots+\right.$$

$$\left.\left.+\sum_{i=1}^{n}(r+1)C_{r+1}^{0i}\overline{V}_{r+1}^0\overline{\psi}_2^{is}\right]^{k_{r+2}}\right\}, \qquad r=0,1,2,\dots$$

$$\dots$$

$$\overline{V}_{r+p+2}^r = \frac{1}{(r+p+2)\alpha}\left\{(r+p+1)\sum_{i=1}^{n}C_{r+p+1}^{(r-1)i}\overline{V}_{r+p+1}^{r-1}\overline{\varphi}_2^i+\right.$$

$$+\sum_{s=1}^{m}\sum_{l=2}^{r+p+2}|\lambda_{sl}| \sum_{\substack{k_2^1+\cdots+k_{r+2}^1+k_3^2+\cdots+k_{r+p+2}^{r-1}=l \\ k_2^1+\cdots+k_{r+2}^1+2k_3^2+\cdots+(r-1)k_{r+p+2}^{r-1}=r \\ 2k_2^1+\cdots+(r+2)k_{r+2}^1+3k_3^2+\cdots+(r+p+2)k_{r+p+2}^{r-1}=r+p+2}} C_l\left(k_2^1,\dots,k_{r+2}^1,k_3^2,\dots,k_{r+p+2}^{r-1}\right)\times$$

$$\times\left(\sum_{i=1}^{n}3C_3^{1i}\overline{V}_3^1\overline{\psi}_0^{is}\right)^{k_2^1}\times\cdots\times\left(\sum_{i=1}^{n}3C_3^{1i}\overline{V}_3^1\overline{\psi}_r^{is}\right)^{k_{r+2}^1}\times\left(\sum_{i=1}^{n}4C_4^{2i}\overline{V}_4^2\overline{\psi}_{r-1}^{is}\right)^{k_3^2}\times$$

$$\left.\times\cdots\times\left[\sum_{i=1}^{n}(r+p+1)C_{r+p+1}^{(r-1)i}\overline{V}_{r+p+1}^{r-1}\overline{\psi}_2^{is}\right]^{k_{r+p+2}^{r-1}}\right\}, \quad \begin{array}{l} r=1,2,3,\dots, \\ p=0,1,2,\dots. \end{array}$$

THEOREM 2. *The parameter μ may be chosen so small that functions $V(t,x,\mu)$, $\frac{\partial V(t,x,\mu)}{\partial x_i}$, $\frac{\partial V(t,x,\mu)}{\partial t}$ will be presented by a power series of degrees of x_i which converge uniformly in any closed domain $G \subset G_2$ for any finite number $r \geq 2$.*

The formula for estimating the proximity of the obtained suboptimal control to the optimal one takes the form

$$\Delta(t_0, V) \leq \Delta_{r+2} = \int_{t_0}^{\infty} \left\{ 2 \sum_{i=1}^{n} \sum_{k=0}^{r+1} \sum_{j=k+2}^{r+3} \mu^k C_j^{ki} \overline{V}_j^k \overline{\varphi}_{r-j+4}^i z^{r+3} + \right.$$

$$\left. + \sum_{s=1}^{m} N_s^{r+2} \sum_{i=1}^{n} \sum_{k=0}^{r} \sum_{p=k+2}^{r+2} \mu^k p C_p^{k_i} \overline{V}_p^k z^{p-1} \sum_{q=0}^{r+1} \overline{\psi}_q^{is} z^q \right\} dt.$$

COROLLARY 2. *The inequality $\Delta_{r+2} \leq \epsilon$ for any closed domain $G \subset G_2$, containing all the suboptimal trajectories which spring from any closed domain $G_0 \subset G$ of initial conditions and for any finite number $r \geq 2$, is true.*

The method proposed in this paper has been applied for power plants optimum regulators synthesis.

REFERENCES

[1] V. F. Krotov, V. I. Gurman, "Methods and Problems of Optimal Control," [in Russian], Nauka, Moscow, 1973.

[2] E.G. Albrekht, *To the Theory of Analytic Construction of the Regulators*, Proc. of the Conf. on Applied Theory of Stability [in Russian], Kazan.

[3] M. V. Trigub, *Approximate Optimal Stabilization of a Range of Nonlinear Systems*, [in Russian], Avtomat. i Telemekh **1** (1987), 34-37.

International Series of Numerical Mathematics, Vol. 99, © 1991 Birkhäuser Verlag Basel

Control problem of nonlinear dynamical systems with phase constraints

VU NGOC PHAT

Institute of Mathematics
P.O. Box 631, Bo Ho, 10 000 Hanoi
Vietnam

Abstract. The paper studies control problem of nonlinear dynamical systems discribed by difference equation $x_{k+1} = f_k(x_k, u_k), k = 0, 1, ..., N-1$ with phase constraints $x_k \in M_k$. Basing on new results in multivalued Lipschitzian analysis we obtain local controllability and reachability conditions for linear control systems of this kind. Some corollaries of controllability criteria for linear and nonlinear nondifferentiable discrete-time systems are also given.

Keywords: Discrete-time systems, controllability, nonsmooth analysis.

1. INTRODUCTION

The control problem to be considered in this paper is that of studying controllability properties of the following nonlinear system

$$(1) \qquad x_{k+1} = f_k(x_k, u_k) \quad , k = 0, 1, ..., N-1$$

where $u_k \in \Omega \subset U, x_k \in M_k \subset X; X, U$ are two real finite-dimensional Euclidean spaces; Ω, M_k are nonempty subsets; $f_k(x, u)$ is a given nonlinear function.

A point x is said to be null-controllable (reachable, resp.) if there is a control $u = (u_0, u_1, ..., u_{N-1})$, $u_k \in \Omega$ such that the trajectory $x_0, x_1, ..., x_N$ of (1) satisfies the condition $x_0 = x$, $x_k \in M_k$ $k = 1, ..., N-1$, $x_N = 0(x_0 = 0, x_k \in M_k, k = 1, ..., N-1, x_N = x$, resp.)

Let C, R be the sets of all null-controllable and reachable points via (1). We shall say that the system (1) is locally null-controllable (locally reachable, resp.) iff $0 \in \text{int } C$ $(0 \in \text{int } R$, resp.)

It is well known that controllability properties play an important role in many problems in optimal control and optimal estimation theory such as the existence of optimal solutions, the stability of optimal solution, the convergence of numerical algorithm in discrete-time control problems, etc. The first steps to formalize these matters as a separate area of research were undertaken by Kalman [**1**] who proved some controllability and reachability conditions, known in the literature as the Kalman rang conditions for finite-dimensional linear stationary systems with no constraints on control and state. Since then, much attention in the literature has been devoted to the study of this topic (see surveys [**2,3**] for details). To our knowledge, the controllability properties for nonlinear discrete-time systems are much poorer. Several results exist in the literature concerning the controllability, reachability of nonlinear discrete-time systems, see for example [**4,5,6,7**]. We note that all of these works concerned with only nonlinear discrete systems with unconstrained states, i.e. $M_k = X$, and the methodology used in these works does not apply to the case of nonlinear systems with constrained states.[**12**]

In our paper two types of controllability; null-controllability and reachability are studied and developed for the system (1) with constraints on both control and state $u_k \in \Omega, x_k \in M_k$. Basing on new results in multivalued convex and Lipschitzian analysis obtained in [**8,9,10**], we shall obtain various generalized versions of controllability tests. A controllability support principle for some boundary problem involving locally Lipschitzian multivalued functions forms the basic of necessary conditions for local controllability and reachability. Some corollaries including controllability and reachability conditions for linear discrete-time systems are also obtained.

2. Preliminaries

Instead of studying controllability of (1) we shall consider the following discrete inclusion

$$\begin{cases} x_{k+1} \in F_k(x_k) & , k = 0, 1, ..., N-1, \\ x_k \in M_k & , k = 1, ..., N-1, \end{cases} \tag{2}$$

where

$$F_k(x) = \{f_k(x,u) : u \in \Omega\}.$$

We first list some notation and definition needed later. The interior, the convex hull, the linear hull, the boundary and the closure of a set M are denoted by int M, co M, sp M, bd M and cl M, respectively. Let $X = \mathbf{R}^n, U = \mathbf{R}^m$, and let $F : X \to 2^X$ be a multivalued function with a nonempty convex, closed image-set at every $x \in X$. We shall use the following notations

$$\begin{aligned}
&C^F(y^*,x) && = \sup\{\langle y^*, y\rangle : y \in F(x)\} \quad , y^* \in X^*,\\
&d(x,M) && - \text{the distance from } x \text{ to } M,\\
&d_F(x) && = d(0,F(x)) - \text{ the distance function of } F(x),\\
&B(x,\varepsilon) && - \text{the open ball with radius } \varepsilon \text{ centered at } x,\\
&\partial f(x_0) && - \text{the Clarke generalized gradient of } f \text{ at } x_0 \text{ [8]},\\
&N(x_0,M) && - \text{the Clarke's normal cone to a closed set } M\\
& && \quad \text{at } x_0 \in M \text{ defined as}\\
& && \quad N(x_0,M) = \text{ cl } \{\lambda x^* : \lambda > 0, x^* \in \partial d(x_0,M)\}.
\end{aligned}$$

Definition 2.1. *A set-valued function $F(x)$ is said to be locally Lipschitz at x_0 if there is $B(x_0,\varepsilon)$ and a number $L > 0$ such that for every $x_1, x_2 \in B(x_0,\varepsilon)$ we have*

$$F(x_1) \subset F(x_2) + L\|x_1 - x_2\|B(0,1).$$

$F(x)$ is said to be locally Lipschitz if it is locally Lipschitz at every $x \in X$.

It is known that for a locally Lipschitzian multivalued function the cone

$$X_F = \{y^* \in X^* : C^F(y^*,x) < \infty\}$$

is convex and does not depend on x. Throughout the paper we shall assume that the cone X_F is closed. Note that $C^F(y^*, x)$ is locally Lipschitz with respect to x for every $x^* \in X_F$ if $F(x)$ is locally Lipschitz [**10**]. Therefore we can consider the generalized gradient $\partial C^F(y^*, x)$.

We shall assume that the multivalued function $(y^*, x) \to \partial C^F(y^*, x)$ is upper semicontinuos (u.s.c) in $(y^*, x) \in X_F \times X$ in the sense that if $x_n^* \in \partial C^F(y_n^*, x_n), x_n^* \to x^*, x_n \to x$ in $X, y_n^* \to y^*$ in X_F imply $x^* \in \partial C^F(y^*, x)$. Note that in many special cases the assumption of u.s.c of $\partial C^F(y^*, x)$ can be established without difficulty, for example, if M is a closed set, $g : X \to X$ is a locally Lipschitz single-valued function and $F(x) = g(x) + M$, then $\partial C^F(y^*, x)$ is u.s.c in $(y^*, x) \in X_F \times X$.

LEMMA 2.1[**10**]. *Let $F(x)$ be a locally Lipschitz set-valued map and $\partial C^F(y^*, x)$ is u.s.c in (y^*, x). Then*

$$\partial d_F(x) \subset \text{ co } \{-\partial C^F(y^*, x), y^* \in I(x)\},$$

where

$$I(x) = \{y^* \in X_F : \|y^*\| = 1, d_F(x) = -C^F(y^*, x)\}.$$

In addition, if $d_F(x) > 0$ then $I(x)$ consists of one single element $y^*, \|y^*\| = 1$ and the symbol 'co' can be deleted.

DEFINITION 2.2. *The system (2) satisfies the support principle at the solution $(x_0, \ldots, x_N)$, if there are elements $x_0^*, \ldots, x_{N-1}^*, x_k^* \in X_{F_k}$, not all zero, such that*

$$\text{(3)} \qquad (i) \quad x_{k-1}^* \in \partial C^{F_k}(x_k^*, x_k) - N(x_k, M_k), \quad k = 1, \ldots, N-1,$$

$$\text{(4)} \qquad (ii) \quad C^{F_k}(x_k^*, x_k) = \langle x_k^*, x_{k+1} \rangle, \quad k = 0, 1, \ldots, N-1.$$

LEMMA 2.2 (CONTROLLABILITY SUPPORT PRINCIPLE). *Let M_k be closed subsets containing zero and $0 \in F_k(0)$. Assume that $0 \bar{\in} int\ R$ or $0 \bar{\in} int\ C$. Then the system (2) satisfies the support principle at $(0, \ldots, 0)$.*

PROOF: Let us denote

$$\begin{aligned}
Z &= \mathbf{R}^{(N-1)n}, \\
F(z) &= X \times F_0(x_0) \times \cdots \times F_{N-1}(x_{N-1}), \\
T(z) &= -z + F(z), \\
P_0 &= \mathbf{R}^{Nn} \times \{0\}, \quad P_N = \{0\} \times \mathbf{R}^{Nn}, \\
Q_0 &= \{z \in Z, z \in P_0, 0 \in T(z)\}, \\
Q_N &= \{z \in Z, z \in P_N, 0 \in T(z)\}, \\
\Pi_0 &= \ z \in Z \to \{x_0\}, \\
\Pi_N &= \ z \in Z \to \{x_N\}.
\end{aligned}$$

From definition we have

$$R = \Pi_N(Q_N), \quad C = \Pi_0(Q_0).$$

Let $0\bar{\in}\text{int } R$. Since $0 \in R$, there is a sequence $\{y_n\}$, $y_n \to 0$ and $y_n \bar{\in} R$, setting $\bar{z}_n = (0, \dots, 0, y_n) \in Z$, we can easily show that

$$0\bar{\in}T(\bar{z}_n + z) \quad \text{for all } z \in M, \text{ where}$$
$$M = \{0\} \times M_1 \times \cdots \times M_{N-1} \times \{0\} \subset Z$$

Since $T(z)$ is locally Lipschitz at $\bar{z} = (0, \dots, 0) \in Z$, there is a constant $L > 0$ and for n so large we obtain

$$T(0) \subset T(\bar{z}_n) + L\alpha_n B(0,1),$$

where $\alpha_n = \|\bar{z}_n\| \to 0$ as $n \to \infty$.

Then, obviously, $0 \in T(0)$ and $0 \in T(\bar{z}_n)$ one can find a decreasing sequence of numbers $\varepsilon_n = L\alpha_n$ such that

$$d_T(\bar{z}_n) = d(0, T(\bar{z}_n)) \leq \varepsilon_n.$$

Hence, setting $\varphi_n(z) = d_T(\bar{z}_n + z)$, $z \in M$, we have

$$\varphi_n(0) \leq \inf\{\varphi_n(z),\ z \in M\} + \varepsilon_n.$$

By the variational principle of Ekeland [**9**], there exists elements $v_n \in M$ with $\|v_n\| \leq \sqrt{\varepsilon_n}$ such that

$$\varphi_n(v_n) \leq \varphi_n(z) + \sqrt{\varepsilon_n}\|v_n - z\|, \quad z \in M. \tag{5}$$

In view of Lemma 2 in [**10**], it follows from (5) that

$$0 \in \partial\varphi_n(v_n) + \sqrt{\varepsilon_n} B_z(0,1) + (\mu + 1)\partial d(v_n, M), \tag{6}$$

where μ denotes a Lipschitz constant for $T(z)$ and $B_z(0,1)$ denotes the unit open ball in Z.

Since $0\bar{\in}T(\bar{z}_n + v_n)$, i.e., $\varphi_n(v_n) > 0$, so by Lemma 2.1 and (6) there is $y_n^* \in Z_T$, $\|y_n^*\| = 1$ such that

$$0 \in -\partial C^T(y_n^*, \bar{z}_n + v_n) + \sqrt{\varepsilon_n} B_z(0,1) + (\mu + 1)\partial d(v_n, M) \tag{7}$$
$$C^T(y_n^*, \bar{z}_n + v_n) = -d_T(\bar{z}_n + v_n). \tag{8}$$

On the other hand, since $\|y_n^*\| = 1$, we can assume that the sequence y_n^* converges to the element $y^* \in Z_T$, $\|y^*\| = 1$, and letting $n \to \infty$ in (7) we have

$$0 \in -\partial C^T(y^*, 0) + (\mu + 1)\partial d(0, M). \tag{9}$$

Thus, the inclusion (9) implies the first assertion (3) of the support principle. To prove the second one, notice that $C^T(\cdot)$ is lower semicontinuous in y^* and for some $\alpha > 0$ we have

$$C^T(y^*, z) \leq C^T(y_n^*, \bar{z}_n + v_n) + \alpha\|y_n^*\|\|v_n + z_n\|. \tag{10}$$

From (8) and (10) and by an argument analoguos to that used in the proof of Theorem 3.1 in [**10**], letting $n \to \infty$ we have

$$C^T(y^*, z) \le \lim_{n\to\infty}(-d_T(\bar{z}_n + v_n)) = 0.$$

The converse inequality is obvious as $0 \in T(\bar{z})$; so we have (4).

The case when $0\bar{\in}\text{int } C$ is proved by the same way if we replace z_n by $(y_n, 0, \dots, 0)$.

EXAMPLE 2.1. Let us consider system (2) where $k = 0, 1, 2$, and

$$F(x) = |x| + [0, \infty),$$
$$M_1 = \{x_1 \ge 0\}, \quad M_2 = \{x_2 \ge 0\}.$$

It is obvious that $0\bar{\in}\text{int } R$ and $N(0, M_1) = N(0, M_2) = [0, \infty)$. Then taking $x_0^* = 0$, $x_1^* = 0$, $x_2^* = 1$ we see that this system satisfies conditions (3), (4) at zero-solution.

REMARK 2.1. If R or C is closed and if the solution $(x_0, \dots, x_N)$ of (2) satisfies $x_N \in \text{bd } R$ (or $x_0 \in \text{bd } C$), then we also claim that the system (2) satisfies the support principle at $(x_0, \dots, x_N)$.

EXAMPLE 2.2. Let $X = \mathbf{R}^1$ and let $F(x) = |x| + [-1, 1]$. It is clear that the reachable set R of the system

$$x_{k+1} \in |x_k| + [-1, 1]$$

is $[-1, 3]$. This system satisfies the support principle at the solution $(0, 1, 2, 3)$ for $N = 3$. We see $x_3 \in\text{bd } R$, where $x_0^* = x_1^* = x_2^* = 1$.

EXAMPLE 2.3. Now we consider system (2), where $F(x) = |x| + [-\frac{1}{3}, \frac{1}{3}]$. We have $C = [-1, 1]$ and this system satisfies the support principle at the solution $(1, \frac{2}{3}, \frac{1}{3}, 0)$, where $x_0^* = x_1^* = x_2^* = -1$. We see $x_0 = 1 \in\text{bd } C$.

Examples 2.2, 2.3 show one of the most essential differences between the continuous and discrete-time case, which is that in the continuous case if x_N belongs to the boundary of R (or C) then there is a trajectory leading to x_N lying whole time on bd R(or bd C) satisfying the support principle. In the discrete-time case it is not so.

3. CONTROLLABILITY AND REACHABILITY RESULTS

The following theorems are followed immediately from the above controllability support principle.

THEOREM 3.1. *Assume that $f_k(0, 0) = 0$, $f_k(x, \Omega)$ is a convex, closed subset at every point $x \in X$ for $k = 0, 1, \dots, N-1$. Let $F_k(x) = f_k(x, \Omega)$ be a multivalued function satisfying the assumption stated above. Then the system (1) with constrained states $x_k \in M_k$ is locally reachable (or locally null-controllable) if there are no elements $x_k^* \in X_{F_k}$, $k = 0, 1, \dots, N-1$, not all zero, such that the conditions (3), (4) hold for $x_k = 0$, $k = 0, 1, \dots, N$.*

Now we present some corollaries for linear discrete-time systems. Let us consider linear discrete-time system of the form

$$(11) \qquad \begin{cases} x_{k+1} = A_k x_k + B_k u_k, & k = 0, 1, \dots, N-1, \\ u_k \in \Omega, \quad x_k \in M_k. \end{cases}$$

We note that the conditions (3), (4) in linear case can be written as

(12) $$x^*_{k-1} = A^*_k x^*_k - N(0, M_k), \quad k = 1, 2, \ldots, N-1,$$
(13) $$\langle x^*_k, x\rangle \le 0 \quad \text{for all } x \in B_k\Omega, \quad k = 0, 1, \ldots, N-1.$$

COROLLARY 3.1. *Let Ω, M_k, $k = 1, ..., N-1$ be convex, closed subsets containing zero. For the system (11) to be locally reachable, if $0 \in \operatorname{int} M_k$, a necessary and sufficient condition is that there are no elements $x^*_k \in X_{F_k}$, $k = 0, 1, ..., N-1$, not all zero, such that the conditions (12), (13) hold.*

REMARK 3.1. *If $A_k = A$, $B_k = B$, $M_k = \mathbf{R}^n$, $\Omega = \mathbf{R}^m$ then the above controllability criterion is that*

$$\operatorname{rang}[B, AB, ..., A^{n-1}B] = n.$$

REMARK 3.2. *If the condition 'there are no elements x^*_k, $k = 0, 1, ..., N-1$, not all zero ...' is replaced by 'there are no elements x^*_k, $k = 0, 1, ..., N-1$, where $x^*_N \neq 0$ ...', then in Corollary 3.1 the assumption $0 \in \operatorname{int} M_k$ in necessary condition can be deleted.*

EXAMPLE 3.1. *Let us consider the system (11) where*

$$\begin{aligned} &A_k = (0 \quad 1/k \quad 0),\\ &B_0 = (1/-1), \quad B_1 = (-1/-1), \quad B_2 = (-1/1),\\ &u_k \in \Omega = \{u \in \mathbf{R}^1 : u \ge 0\},\\ &x_k \in M_k = \{(x_1, x_2) \in \mathbf{R}^2,\ x_{i\neq k} \le 0,\ i = 1, 2\}.\end{aligned}$$

It can be verified that there are no elements x^*_0, x^*_1, x^*_2; $x^*_3 \neq 0$ such that the condition (12), (13) hold. Therefore, this system is globally reachable, i.e., $\mathbf{R} = \mathbf{R}^2$ for $N = 3$.

Let us now consider system (1), where

$$\begin{aligned} &f_k(x, u) = f_k(x) + \varphi(u),\\ &f_k(x) = (f^1_k(x), ..., f^n_k(x)),\\ &\varphi(u) : \mathbf{R}^m \to \mathbf{R}^n,\\ &f^i_k(x) \text{ is a Lipschitzian at zero function.}\end{aligned}$$

Denoting $\partial f^i_k(0)$ the generalized subdifferential of $f^i_k(x)$ at zero, we set

$$\partial f_k(0) = (\partial f^i_k(0), ..., \partial f^n_k(0)).$$

Note that every element of $\partial f_k(0)$, which is denoted by $A_k(0)$, is some real $(n \times n)$-matrix. Then for every $A_k(0) \in \partial f_k(0)$ we consider the following system

(14) $$\begin{cases} x_{k+1} = A_k(0)x_k + \varphi(u_k),\\ u_k \in \Omega, \quad x_k \in M_k.\end{cases}$$

THEOREM 3.2. *Let* $f_k^i(0) = 0$, $k = 0, 1, ..., N-1$, $i = 1, ..., n$ *and let* $\varphi(\Omega)$ *be a convex, closed subset. Assume* $0 \in \varphi(\Omega)$ *and* $0 \in int\ M_k$. *If for every* $A_k(0) \in \partial f_k(0)$ *the linear system (14) is locally reachable, then the nonlinear system (1) is locally reachable.*

THEOREM 3.3. *Let* $f_k^i(x)$, $\varphi(u)$ *be given functions satisfying assumptions stated in Theorem 3.2. If for every* $A_k(0) \in \partial f_k(0)$ *there are no elements* $x_k^* \in X_{F_k}$, $k = 0, 1, ..., N-1$, *not all zero, such that*

$$\langle x_k^*, x\rangle \geq 0 \quad \text{for all } x \in \varphi(\Omega),$$
$$\text{and } x_{k-1}^* = A_k^*(0)x_x^* - N(0, M_k), \quad k = 1, 2, ...N-1,$$

then the nonlinear system (1) is locally null-controllable.

The proofs of Theorem 3.2 and 3.3 are based on Theorem 3.1 and Corollary 3.1 and will be omitted.

REMARK 3.3. *If* $f_k(x)$ *is continuous differentiable at* $x = 0$, *then* $\partial f_k(0)$ *consists of one single element,* $f_k'(0)$, *and we obtain controllability condition of* [5, 11] *for nonlinear differentiable systems.*

REFERENCES

[1] Kalman R., *On the general theory of control systems*, Proc. IFAC, London, (1960), 481–492.

[2] Faradzev R.G., Phat V.N. and Shapiro A., *Controllability theory of discretetime dynamical systems (survey)*, [in Russian], Avtomatika i Telemekhanika **1** (1986), 5–25.

[3] Conti R., *Linear controllability in finite-dimension*, Mathematishe (Catania) **1** (1986), p. 36.

[4] Vu Ngoc Phat, *Controllability of nonlinear discrete-time delay systems*, Acta Math. Vietnamica **2** (1980), 63–72.

[5] Vu Ngoc Phat, *Controllability of discrete-time systems with nonconvex constrained controls*, Optimization **3** (1983), 371–375.

[6] Faradzev R.G. and Vu Ngoc Phat, *On the controllability of nonlinear two-parametric discrete-time systems with restrained controls*, Optimization **6** (1985), 869–876.

[7] Yen N.D., *Local controllability for Lipschitzian discrete-time systems*, Acta Math. Vietnamica **2** (1986), 172–179.

[8] Clarke F.H., *A new approach to Lagrange multipliers*, Math. Oper. Reas. **2** (1976), 247–262.

[9] Ekeland I.E., *On the variational principle*, J. Math. Anal. Appl. **47** (1974), 324–362.

[10] Dien F.H., *Locally Lipschitzian set-valued maps and generalized extremal problems with inclusion constraints*, Acta Math. Vietnamica **2** (1983), 102–122.

[11] Sach F.H., *Les point reguliers des applications multivoques et la commadabilite dans les systems discretes*, Universite de Bordeaux, Analyse Appl. et Inf. **8022** (1980), 1–47.

[12] Vu Ngoc Phat, *Controllability of discrete-time systems with multiple delays on control and states*, Int.I. of Control **5** (1989), 1645-1654.